THE ENGLISH
LEGAL SYSTEM

THE ENGLISH LEGAL SYSTEM

by

R. J. WALKER, LL.B. (Lond.)

of Gray's Inn, and the South-Eastern Circuit, Barrister

and

M. G. WALKER, M.A., LL.B. (Cantab.)

of the Inner Temple, Barrister; Lecturer in Laws,
University College London

THIRD EDITION

LONDON
BUTTERWORTHS
1972

ENGLAND:	BUTTERWORTH & CO. (PUBLISHERS) LTD.
	LONDON: 88 Kingsway, WC2B 6AB
AUSTRALIA:	BUTTERWORTHS PTY. LTD.
	SYDNEY: 586 Pacific Highway, Chatswood, NSW 2067
	MELBOURNE: 343 Little Collins Street, 3000
	BRISBANE: 240 Queen Street, 4000
CANADA:	BUTTERWORTH & CO. (CANADA) LTD.
	TORONTO: 14 Curity Avenue, 374
NEW ZEALAND:	BUTTERWORTHS OF NEW ZEALAND LTD.
	WELLINGTON: 26–28 Waring Taylor Street, 1
SOUTH AFRICA:	BUTTERWORTH & CO. (SOUTH AFRICA) (PTY.) LTD.
	DURBAN: 152–154 Gale Street

ISBN—Casebound: 0 406 67754 9
Limp: 0 406 67755 7

PRINTED IN GREAT BRITAIN BY OFFSET LITHOGRAPHY BY
BILLING AND SONS LTD., GUILDFORD AND LONDON

Preface

Widespread changes in the areas of law and procedure covered by this work have necessitated the production of a new edition although scarcely more than two years have elapsed since the last edition. Of these changes the most important have been the abolition of assizes and quarter sessions and the creation of the Crown Court by the Courts Act 1971, the creation of the Family Division of the High Court by the Administration of Justice Act 1969 and of the National Industrial Relations Court by the Industrial Relations Act 1971, the new Rules of the Supreme Court dealing with discovery, inspection and related procedures and interim payment of damages, attachment of earnings and the new County Court Rules. In addition there has been extensive rewriting to take account of other recent statutes and rules and some 70 new cases. This, together with a rather fuller treatment of certain topics, notably Civil Procedure, has resulted in an increase of some 34 pages in the length of the work.

We have endeavoured to state the law as at April 1, 1972, though brief reference is made in the footnotes to prospective legislation including the momentous European Communities Bill.

R. J. Walker
M. G. Walker

April 1972

Table of Contents

PART III—THE ADMINISTRATION OF JUSTICE

PART IV—CIVIL PROCEDURE

PART V—CRIMINAL PROCEDURE

PART VI—OUTLINE OF THE LAW OF EVIDENCE

Table of Statutes

In the following Table references to "*Statutes*" are to Halsbury's Statutes (Third Edition) showing the volume and page at which the annotated text of the Act will be found

Table of Cases

The Historical Sources and Divisions of English Law

SUMMARY

CHAPTER 1

Common Law

A ORIGINS OF THE COMMON LAW

It is normal to regard common law as the primary historical source of English law, with equity and legislation, the two other principal historical sources, each evolving later as a "gloss" on the common law.[1] This view is only tenable if English law is regarded as originating in 1066 with the Norman Conquest. In fact, although modern lawyers hardly ever look beyond the common law to ascertain the existence of a legal rule, the common law has in itself a number of historical sources which were, prior to the Conquest, embodied in local custom. The unique contribution of the Norman Conquest was to unify these local customs into one system of law common to all men, for this reason termed the "common law".

It would be a mistake to suppose that William I by one legislative act created a central system of courts to which was transferred all the jurisdiction of the various local courts and in which was administered a code of law created by the King. This would have been impossible, not only because of the administrative difficulty involved, but because the local courts constituted an important source of revenue to the barons and landowners who consequently resisted attempts to diminish their jurisdiction. What did in fact happen was that the King, over a period of time, assumed control of the administration of justice throughout the land through his judges and justices and created a central system of courts. The jurisdiction of the local courts was never formally abolished but, for various reasons, declined as the jurisdiction of the King's courts grew. This was, however, a slow process and between 1066 and about 1154 the jurisdiction of the King's courts was confined to Pleas of the Crown, disputes between tenants-in-chief over title to land and supervision of the inferior courts.

---

[1] A completely new source of law, when the European Communities Act 1972 comes into operation, will be European Community Law. Clause 2 (1) of the European Communities Bill currently before Parliament provides that:

> "All such rights, powers, liabilities, obligations and restrictions from time to time created or arising by or under the Treaties, and all such remedies and procedures from time to time provided for by or under the Treaties, as in accordance with the Treaties are without further enactment to be given legal effect or used in the United Kingdom shall be recognised and available in law, and be enforced, allowed and followed accordingly."

The ascendancy of the King's courts over the local courts[1] was achieved only over a period of three centuries and may be accounted for by the following factors:—

1   The decline in the judicial powers of the sheriff

The sheriff exercised both a civil jurisdiction, in the shire or county court, and a criminal jurisdiction on his "tourn". The civil jurisdiction declined after the Conquest since pleas relating to land were transferred to the feudal courts and later the royal courts, and pleas not relating to land were generally tried either by the King's justices or by the sheriff himself, sitting by Royal Commission. In addition the interpretation put on the Statute of Gloucester 1278 limited the sheriff's jurisdiction to 40s. The sheriff's criminal jurisdiction was assumed by the King's judges in Assizes and the itinerant justices in Quarter Sessions. Clause 24 of Magna Carta prohibited the sheriff from hearing Pleas of the Crown and by the end of the twelfth century the King's justices exercised an exclusive jurisdiction over all serious crime. However, the sheriff continued to supervise the system of "frankpledge"[2] until this became obsolete in the fourteenth century.

2   The evolution of the writ system[3]

The King, as fountain of justice, would grant a writ to a suitor to enable him to petition the King for a remedy where there was a denial of justice in the local courts. These writs became formalised and a Register of Writs kept with the result that an increasing number of rights arose which were enforceable in the King's courts. This increase resulted in a gradual decline of the civil jurisdiction of the feudal courts, particularly since the early writs were concerned with protecting title to land, disputes concerning which were the principal business transacted in the feudal courts.

3   The introduction by Henry II of the system of Grand and Petty Assizes[4]

The Grand Assize enabled the defendant to a suit concerning land held by freehold tenure (Writ of Right) to claim trial by jury in the royal courts as an alternative to battle. Petty (or possessory) Assizes enabled a person who had

---

[1] The principal courts existing prior to the creation of royal courts were the communal courts of the shire and hundred and the feudal courts held by landowners. See Potter, *Outlines of English Legal History*, Chap. 3.

[2] This system was introduced by William I as a result of the large numbers of Normans slain who had no relatives to bring the criminal to justice. It imposed communal responsibility by making every person without substantial property a member of a group of ten called a "tithing". If one committed a crime the other nine would be responsible for bringing him to trial, failing which they would be liable to pay a fine. A special fine was payable by a hundred in which a murderer was located unless it could be shown that his victim was not a Norman but an Anglo-Saxon ("presentment of Englishry").

[3] See p. 18, *post.*

[4] The word "Assizes" is not here used in its primary sense of a sitting of a court, but as a procedure established by an ordinance passed at such a sitting (bearing in mind that "court" included, at this time, legislative assemblies).

been disseised of land[1] to regain possession summarily without having to undergo the cumbersome procedure attendant upon a writ of right.

4 The ownership of land becoming centralised in the King

Thus originated the modern concept that landowners own not the land itself but an estate in the land, for example, a freehold estate. Consequently all disputes concerning estates in land affected the King's interest. By the reign of Henry II it was established that any suit concerning free tenure had to be commenced by a writ of right issuing from the Chancery. Although the issue raised by the writ was at first tried in the feudal courts, later, proceedings were removable to the royal courts[2] by writ of Pone which alleged a defect in proceedings in the feudal court on which ground the action was removed from its jurisdiction. This allegation was fictitious but the parties were not able to deny its truth. This constitutes an early example of the use of legal fictions to acquire jurisdiction.[3]

5 The increase in the scope of Pleas of the Crown

Such a Plea was based upon a breach of the King's peace[4] and redressible by punishment which usually involved fine or forfeiture. Consequently these pleas were a source of royal revenue and their scope increased with the power of the monarchy. The pleas were principally criminal in modern terms although from them probably developed the great writ of trespass, the basis of the modern law of torts.[5]

6 The Statute of Gloucester 1278

This Statute was passed as an attempt to curb the jurisdiction of the common law courts over personal actions which was growing principally through the recently created writ of trespass. It expressly provided that no action involving less than 40s. could be commenced in the royal courts. In fact the measure backfired because the common law judges interpreted this to mean that no personal actions involving more than 40s. could be tried in the local courts. With the decline in the value of money in the Middle Ages the jurisdiction of the local courts over personal actions correspondingly diminished. To this Statute may be attributed the gradual disappearance of the local courts which eventually necessitated the statutory creation of the modern county courts in 1846.

Thus the common law courts grew and gradually superseded the local courts. Almost all of the latter have ceased to function (although not formally abolished).[6] As part of the reform of the system of courts effected by the Courts Act 1971 those local courts which did function actively were abolished. These were the Bristol Tolzey and Pie Poudre Courts, the Liverpool Court of Passage, the Norwich Guildhall Court and the Salford Hundred Court.[7] These courts,

---

[1] See p. 18, *post*.
[2] To the Court of Common Pleas.
[3] See p. 28, *post*.
[4] As opposed to a Common Plea which was a pure dispute between subjects.
[5] See p. 21, *post*.
[6] Formal abolition is, however, imminent, under the provisions of the Local Government Bill now before Parliament.
[7] Courts Act 1971, s. 43.

prior to their abolition, exercised a civil jurisdiction roughly equivalent to that of county courts. The only other inferior local court functioning prior to the Courts Act 1971 was the Mayor's and City of London Court. This court was formally abolished also; however it has effectively been retained since the Courts Act makes the City of London a county court district and provides that the county court for that district shall be known as the Mayor's and City of London Court.[1]

B   COURTS OF THE COMMON LAW

1   The Curia Regis

The fountain of justice at common law is the King himself. Consequently all common law courts derive their jurisdiction from the King. Modern society accepts the desirability of a separation of the powers of the executive, the legislature and the judiciary. However in medieval times all three functions were exercised by the King in Council. The King's Council is thus the predecessor not only of Parliament but of the courts.

The medieval pattern was for courts to separate from the Council and eventually acquire a jurisdiction independent of it. However the King at all times retained a residual judicial power deriving from his prerogative powers. Thus the three main common law courts, the Court of Exchequer, the Court of Common Pleas and the Court of King's Bench, split off from the Council and their judges exercised jurisdiction to decide civil disputes and major criminal cases in London and on assize. The King's justices assumed jurisdiction over criminal offences. Nevertheless the undefined residual jurisdiction of the King led to other courts deriving their jurisdiction from the Curia Regis, notably the Court of Chancery and the Star Chamber. Indeed it was not until the seventeenth century that the Council itself discontinued its judicial function. The functions of these courts were to remedy the procedural defects and restrictions of the common law courts and to dispense justice where the common law courts were for some reason unable to do so. The obvious results of this *ad hoc* method of creating courts were clashes between them and the common law courts over the extent of their respective jurisdiction.

2   The Court of Exchequer

This was the first of the three central common law courts to split off from the Curia Regis. In the reign of Henry I the Exchequer became a separate department of the Council dealing with the collection and distribution of royal revenue. By the reign of Henry II it had become a court, the judges of which were Exchequer Barons presided over by the Chief Baron who was, after the fourteenth century, always a lawyer, frequently of great distinction.

Originally the jurisdiction of the court was confined to disputes between subjects and the Crown concerning revenue. Later the court acquired jurisdiction over disputes between subjects, such as writs of debt and covenant,[2] through the fiction of "Quominus". This depended upon a fictitious allegation of a debt owed by the plaintiff to the Crown which the plaintiff was the less able (*quominus*) to pay because of the debt owing to him by the defendant.

---

[1] Courts Act 1971, s. 42.
[2] See p. 20, *post*.

This fictitious allegation enabled the court to determine the substantive issue between the parties.

In addition the court appears, at least in its early days, to have exercised an equity jurisdiction, though its procedure was that of the common law courts rather than of the Court of Chancery.

When the court was finally abolished in 1875 its jurisdiction was transferred to the newly-formed High Court, its common law jurisdiction being exercised by the Queen's Bench Division after 1880, and its revenue jurisdiction by the Chancery Division. Its equity jurisdiction had been transferred by statute to the Chancery in 1841.[1]

3 The Court of Common Pleas

While the King was determining civil disputes in Council suitors were obliged to follow the court wherever it travelled. Because of the inconvenience this caused it became the practice for judges to remain permanently in Westminster Hall to try Common Pleas[2] and Magna Carta, c. 17, provided that the common pleas should be held in a "certain place" which was fixed at Westminster.

The judges of the court were full time lawyers appointed from the ranks of the serjeants-at-law, the senior advocates who had an exclusive right of audience in the court. The serjeants were the leaders of the legal profession and consequently the most highly paid. This fact, coupled with the excessive formality of pleading attendant upon the real actions[3] (over which the court had a monopoly), made proceedings in the Common Pleas dilatory and expensive.

The jurisdiction of the court existed over disputes between subjects where the King's interest was not involved. Hence it tried all the real actions and the personal actions of debt, covenant and detinue. It also tried actions of trespass where the title to land was involved. It must be remembered that only wealthy landowners could afford to litigate in the royal courts so that most civil actions in the early Middle Ages in fact involved disputes over title to land. Thus the Common Pleas exercised a far wider jurisdiction than the Exchequer or the King's Bench.

The court was abolished in 1875 and its jurisdiction transferred to the High Court, being exercised by the Queen's Bench Division after 1880.

4 The Court of King's Bench

This was the last of the three central courts to break away from the Council. Consequently it has always remained closer to the King than the Exchequer and the Common Pleas. This is not to say that the King's Bench was not separate from the Curia Regis. Although they were closely associated there is ample evidence that the judges of the King's Bench acted independently of the King[4] by the reign of Edward I and attempts by James I to sit in the court were defeated by Coke. However, because of its association with the King, it acquired jurisdiction to issue the prerogative writs (now "orders") of mandamus, prohibition and certiorari, restraining excesses and abuses of jurisdiction by inferior

---

[1] 5 Vict., c. 5.
[2] As opposed to Pleas of the Crown; see p. 5, *ante*.
[3] See p. 18, *post*.
[4] See Plucknett, *A Concise History of the Common Law*, (5th Edn.), p. 151.

courts and public officials.[1]   In addition the writ of habeas corpus, which it had power to issue, was later of great constitutional importance in curbing the personal exercise by the King of his prerogative powers.   Its wide appellate jurisdiction may also be traced to the exercise of the royal duty to correct deficiencies in cases tried in other courts.

The judicial function was exercised by the judges of the court presided over by the Chief Justice of England, an office ranking above that of Chief Justice of the Common Pleas.[2]   This function was both original and appellate and both civil and criminal.

The original jurisdiction of the King's Bench was exercised principally in civil matters, although the judges of the court exercised original criminal jurisdiction in courts of assize.   The civil jurisdiction, which derived from the Pleas of the Crown and in particular from the writ of trespass, developed in about 1250.[3]   This operated to confer upon the court jurisdiction over most actions in tort since nearly all torts are offshoots of Trespass.   It did not acquire jurisdiction over contract until the writ of assumpsit in the late sixteenth century evolved to replace the writ of debt.[4]   However it filched jurisdiction from the Common Pleas over writs of debt by means of the fictitious Bill of Middlesex procedure.   The King's Bench had jurisdiction over all cases[5] where the defendant was in the custody of the warden of the King's Bench prison.   Consequently the Sheriff of Middlesex was directed by bill to arrest the defendant for a trespass *vi et armis* and take him into custody.   Since the court had jurisdiction over trespass actions it was able to try the real cause of action ancillary to the fictitious trespass suit which was in fact dropped.   If the defendant was in a county other than Middlesex the Sheriff would mark the bill *non est inventus* and a writ of *Latitat* would then direct him to arrest the defendant wherever he "lurks and runs" (*latitat et discurrit*).   The defendant was, in fact, usually happy to acquiesce in the fiction in that it avoided the expense of proceedings by writ in the Common Pleas.

The appellate jurisdiction of the King's Bench existed in both civil and criminal cases.   However the right of appeal was based on an error in procedure in the court below.[6]

5   The Courts of Exchequer Chamber

There were, at different periods of history, no less than four courts bearing the title "Exchequer Chamber".   The jurisdiction of all of them was appellate.

(1)   The oldest was established by statute in 1357[7] as a result of the refusal of the Exchequer to submit to the appellate jurisdiction of the King's Bench.   The court was created to sit in "any council room nigh the exchequer" (hence the name "Exchequer Chamber") and to consist of the Chancellor and the Treasurer

---

[1] This jurisdiction is now exercised by the divisional court of the Queen's Bench Division; see p. 164, *post*.
[2] Coke, for example, was promoted from the latter office to the former.
[3] See p. 21, *post*.
[4] See p. 23, *post*.
[5] Excluding the real actions which remained in the exclusive jurisdiction of the Court of Common Pleas.
[6] See p. 28, *post*.
[7] 31 Edw. 3, St. 1, c. 12.

with assistance from judges of the common law courts as assessors. Its jurisdiction was solely as a court of error from the Exchequer. Hence the business of the court was limited as it was also by the difficulty of getting the Chancellor and the Treasurer together, particularly when the latter office was vacant.

(2)   There existed, even before 1357, a practice of judges reserving difficult points of law for consideration by a bench of judges drawn from all three common law courts and, later, the Chancery. These meetings were no doubt informal at first and the authority of the opinions delivered purely persuasive. They remained informal in the sense that no litigant had a right to require a judge to refer any point of law for consideration. However, the judgments were by the fifteenth century regarded as binding[1] and the informal meetings, by now usually held in the Exchequer Chamber, constituted the sitting of a court. Hence such a court was also termed a Court of Exchequer Chamber. Many of the leading cases of the common law were decided in this court before twelve judges[2] and the court sat until the seventeenth century to determine civil cases and until the nineteenth century in criminal cases.

(3)   A third Court of Exchequer Chamber was set up during the existence of the two already described by statute in 1585.[3] It was set up as a court of error from the King's Bench in cases of debt, detinue, covenant, account, action upon the case, ejectment or trespass commenced[4] in the King's Bench. It consisted of any six judges drawn from the Exchequer Barons and the justices of the Common Pleas. Thus there were at this time three courts of error; *viz.* the Court of Exchequer Chamber (1357) from the Court of Exchequer, the King's Bench from the Common Pleas and the Court of Exchequer Chamber (1585) from the King's Bench. In addition error still lay direct from the King's Bench to the House of Lords. This somewhat complex hierarchy prevailed until the creation of the last Court of Exchequer Chamber in 1830.

(4)   The court created in 1830[5] was the court of error from all three common law courts and was composed of judges of the two courts other than the one in which the trial at first instance took place. Appeal lay from the court to the House of Lords. The court existed until 1875 when its jurisdiction was transferred to the Court of Appeal.

6   Assizes

It was, during the Middle Ages, and indeed always has been, impossible to administer the criminal law on the basis of all trials taking place in London. Consequently, Norman and Plantagenet monarchs adopted the system, which appears to have existed even before the Conquest, of sending out royal justices throughout the kingdom to hold "assizes" (or sittings) of the royal courts. The jurisdiction of these assize courts, at first purely criminal, was later extended to civil proceedings.

---

[1] In 1483 the Chief Justice of the Common Pleas followed a decision of the Exchequer Chamber even though he thought it wrong (Y.B. 1 Ric. 3, Michs. no. 2).
[2] Examples are *Slade* v. *Morley* (1602), Yelv. 2; *Hampden's Case* (1637), 3 State Tr. 825; *Godden* v. *Hales* (1686), 11 State Tr. 1254.
[3] 31 Eliz. 1, c. 1.
[4] This had the effect of confining it to proceedings commenced by bill since action by writ were "commenced" in the Chancery.
[5] 11 Geo. 4 & 1 Will. 4, c. 70.

The assize judges were generally the judges of the common law courts, but could also be serjeants-at-law or even prominent laymen. Consequently they exercised no jurisdiction *virtute officii* but only by reason of commissions issued by the Sovereign. The commissions conferring criminal jurisdiction were the commission of *Oyer and Terminer* and the commission of *Gaol Delivery*. The first directed the persons named in the commission to hear and determine all offences in respect of which the accused had been "presented" by the grand jury of the county.[1] The second directed them to deliver from the gaols of the county, and to try, all persons there awaiting trial.[2]

So successful and popular was the assize system that Edward I organised the circuits on the modern basis with each circuit consisting of a group of counties visited regularly three or four times a year by royal judges. In addition the Statute of Nisi Prius 1285 extended the system to certain civil actions. The basic reason for this extension was the difficulty of transporting local juries to Westminster. Consequently in those personal actions, such as trespass, triable in the King's Bench and Common Pleas with a jury, the sheriff was directed to secure the attendance of a jury at Westminster "unless before" (*nisi prius*) that day the justices of assize should visit that county. The system was extended in the fourteenth and fifteenth centuries to all types of civil action. It would, however, be incorrect to suppose that a trial at *nisi prius* was at this time a trial of the whole action. In fact only the issues of fact were tried at *nisi prius*. The pleading took place *in banc* (in Westminster) and the jury verdict was added to the record of the case to be sent back to Westminster for judgment to be entered since the commissioner of assize had no power to enter judgment. Later, when the commissioners were always lawyers and advocates went on circuit, the whole trial took place at the assize so that the trial of actions might take place in London or at an assize.[3]

7   Justices of the Peace

Originally the office of justice of the peace was an administrative rather than a judicial office but a judicial function was given to it in the fourteenth century as a direct result of the declining criminal jurisdiction of the local courts and the inability of the assizes to deal with the growing number of offenders.

The origin of the justices of the peace is to be found in a royal proclamation of 1195[4] creating the knights of the peace to assist the sheriff in enforcing the law. This function was of an administrative and police character rather than of a judicial character. With the decline of the office of sheriff in the fourteenth century the "keepers of the peace" (*custodes pacis*) as they were by now known,[5] were given a judicial function in addition to their administrative tasks. The

---

[1] See p. 14, *post*.

[2] These commissions were created by the Assizes of Clarendon 1166, and Northampton 1176 and continued to issue until their effective abolition under the provisions of the Courts Act 1971.

[3] The assize system survived until the 1st January 1972—the date on which the Courts Act 1971 came into operation; section 1 (2) provides that "All courts of assize are hereby abolished, and Commissions, whether ordinary or special, to hold any court of assize shall not be issued."

[4] Stubbs, *Select Charters*, pp. 257–258.

[5] The nomenclature "justice of the peace" appears to date from about 1327, and to be an official title after 1361; Plucknett, *A Concise History of the Common Law*, (5th Edn.), p. 168.

former function has increased as the latter has diminished. In 1330 the holders of this new office had become so powerful locally that they were given statutory power to punish the sheriff, if he abused his powers of granting bail to prisoners.

As a result of the effects of the Black Death on the labour market Statutes of Labourers were passed from 1351 in an attempt to regulate prices and wages and to reorganise labour generally. The enforcement of these statutes was placed in the hands of "justices of labourers" who were, in 1361, included in the same commissions as the keepers of the peace. It is from this date that the office of J.P. in its modern sense originates. The new justices of the peace were laymen and not usually legally qualified, a tradition which exists at the present day.[1] Their criminal jurisdiction was at first exercised solely in the sessions which they were, by statute,[2] compelled to hold in each county four times a year. These were the "quarter sessions" and in 1590 the justices in quarter sessions were given jurisdiction over all criminal offences not excluding capital felonies. It was, indeed, not until the Quarter Sessions Act 1842 that the jurisdiction of quarter sessions was limited to exclude treason, murder and felonies punishable with life imprisonment.

Later, in Tudor times, a number of statutes conferred jurisdiction on justices to try offences out of sessions. From these statutes, the first of which was passed in 1496,[3] stems the summary jurisdiction of the justices of the peace in "petty sessions". This summary jurisdiction, which is entirely statutory, is exercised without a jury and justices exercising this jurisdiction are now termed a "magistrates' court".[4]

As indicated earlier, the administrative jurisdiction of justices of the peace declined through the years as the criminal jurisdiction grew. Most of the administrative jurisdiction formerly exercised by justices is now in the hands of local authorities. However certain important functions remain. The common law power to issue warrants of arrest and summonses still exists. The important task of conducting preliminary investigations into indictable offences[5] was conferred on justices of the peace by statutes of 1554[6] and 1555.[7] This procedure eventually superseded the procedure of presentment by a grand jury.[8]

8 The General Eyre

In addition to the royal commissions issued to the justices of assize and to the justices of the peace, described above, there was a far wider commission which existed only until about 1340. This was the commission *ad omnia placita* and the justices to whom this commission was issued constituted the "general eyre". The eyre was in a sense the forerunner of the whole system of itinerant justices. The justices in eyre were concerned to safeguard royal interests of all kinds. For example they supervised the collection of royal revenue due from fines and forfeitures. Also the eyre, once in every seven years, held an inquisition in each

---

[1] See p. 173, *post.*
[2] 36 Edw. 3, st. 1, c. 12.
[3] 11 Hen. 7, c. 3; see Plucknett, *op. cit.,* p. 169.
[4] See p. 173, *post.*
[5] See p. 380, *post.*
[6] 1 & 2 P. & M., c. 13.
[7] 2 & 3 P. & M., c. 10.
[8] See p. 14, *post.*

county into the whole system of the local administration of justice including frankpledge, police duties and the conduct of the sheriff. The procedure involved a series of questions known as the "articles of the eyre" (*capitula itineris*) being put to a special session of the local county court. During the session of the eyre local sessions of the assizes were suspended and the cases heard by the eyre. Thus the general eyre undoubtedly exercised a judicial function superior to that of the assizes, though inferior to the Court of King's Bench.

It is hardly surprising that the visits of the eyre were extremely unpopular and there is on record an incident in which the men of Cornwall fled to the woods. rather than face the eyre. The final extinction of the eyre in about 1340 may be attributed to the growth of Parliament. An unfortunate feature of its extinction was that a useful means of reform of the legal system was lost.

9   The Star Chamber

It is strictly erroneous to classify the Star Chamber as a common law court. It derived its jurisdiction from the King in the same way as the common law courts but it did not administer the common law and, more particularly, adopted a criminal and civil procedure repugnant to that obtaining in the common law courts. In addition, whereas the common law courts quite early in their existence became independent of the Council, the Star Chamber appears always to have retained the closest link with the Council. Hence it administered the royal prerogative rather than the common law although, by doing so, it added considerably to the scope of the criminal law. It has been described as a court of "criminal equity",[1] though the description "equity" is misleading.

Opinions differ as to the origins of the court. It seems to have originated from sittings of the Council in a chamber in Westminster known as the Star Chamber, possibly on account simply of its interior décor. The ancient theory that the court was created by a statute of 1487 (*pro camera stellata*) is now discounted, although this Act did confer jurisdiction upon the court to try certain offences such as riot and rout. The court of Star Chamber consisted of members of the Council, the Chancellor, Treasurer and Privy Seal and common law judges.

The court had a miscellaneous civil jurisdiction over matters outside the common law such as mercantile and ecclesiastical disputes. It also assumed jurisdiction over matters within the scope of the common law courts and for this reason it fell into disfavour with common law judges. The growth of the Court of Chancery during the same period[2] effectively restricted the civil jurisdiction of the Star Chamber since both were at this time conciliar courts.

It is the criminal jurisdiction of the Star Chamber which is of far greater interest and importance since, while the court did not try felonies, it recognised and tried many new offences which were, in modern terms, "misdemeanours". Many of these were offences of a public nature such as riot, unlawful assembly, conspiracy, criminal libel, perjury, forgery and criminal attempts. All these crimes were created to fill gaps in the existing criminal law as administered in the assizes and quarter sessions.

Procedure in the Star Chamber differed radically from procedure in the common law courts. The civil procedure resembled more closely Chancery

---

[1] Radcliffe and Cross, *The English Legal System* (5th Edn.), p. 134.
[2] See p. 30, *post*.

procedure than the dilatory formality of the common law. Criminal procedure was even more fundamentally different. Proceedings were commenced, not by presentment by the grand jury, but by information filed by the Attorney-General. An inquisitorial procedure followed whereby the defendant was examined on oath, sometimes under torture. Witnesses' evidence was frequently given by affidavit thus denying the accused any opportunity of cross-examination. Finally, there was no jury, guilt being determined by the members of the court. In a modern situation such a procedure would be unthinkable and condemned as a total denial of justice. Nevertheless, it was at that time justifiable in the light of the influence on juries which certain persons exercised, the bitterness of the state trials for treason (which took place before juries) and, following the Wars of the Roses, the anarchic situation throughout the realm which the existing criminal law and courts could not remedy. Even Coke, that most noted champion of the common law, described the court as "the most honourable Court (our Parliament excepted) that is in the Christian world".[1]

Nevertheless, in spite of its popularity in Tudor times, the accession of the Stuarts and, in particular, the Civil War resulted in the court becoming a symbol of prerogative power in the eyes of the Puritans and Parliamentarians and one of the first legislative acts of the Long Parliament was the abolition of the Star Chamber in 1641.

C   CRIMINAL PROCEDURE IN THE COMMON LAW COURTS

There have, at different times, been three principal methods of prosecuting accused persons in the royal courts. These methods each involved a different method of trial. The two principal methods of trial, trial on indictment and summary trial, still exist. The third, appeal of felony, existed until the fifteenth century. Each of these procedures must be examined briefly.

1   Appeal of felony

The striking feature of ancient criminal procedure prior to the Norman Conquest was that the responsibility for bringing a person to justice lay not with the Crown but with the individual against whom the crime had been committed. Although most of the ancient procedure became obsolete under the Normans, the appeal of felony created by them perpetuated the ancient concept of private prosecution. The appellant was the victim or his representative and his appeal, originally brought in the local courts, could eventually be brought in the King's Bench. The distinguishing feature of procedure by appeal was that the defendant had a right to call for trial by battle, a method of trial introduced by the Normans.

With the rise of the jury, appeal of felony fell into disfavour with the common law judges who introduced excessive technicalities with which the appellor had to comply. Consequently the procedure became rare although appeals of murder were apparently common until the fifteenth century. An appeal of

---

[1]   4 Inst., p. 65.

murder could not be brought for a year and a day after death whereas an indictment could, in the fifteenth century, be brought at once. Consequently the latter procedure had precedence although an acquittal on indictment was no bar to a subsequent appeal of felony. The procedure died out from the fifteenth century onwards but was not finally abolished until 1819[1] following a case which reminded the legislature that the right to claim battle still existed.[2]

2   Trial on indictment

This is the most important method of trial conceived by the common law. Its importance stems from the fact that it is the only one of the three methods which involved the use of the jury. The conduct of the prosecution of a person accused on indictment may be conveniently divided into four stages: arrest, presentation for trial, trial and sentence.

a   Arrest

Prior to the Conquest there appears to have been very little public responsibility for the apprehension of criminals. The Normans' interest in their apprehension was at least partly financial since the new public crimes known as "felonies" involved the prisoner, if convicted, in forfeiture of his property and escheat of his lands to the Crown. The earliest procedure which evolved to secure the apprehension of criminals was the system of "frankpledge" described above.[3] Later, the Assize of Clarendon 1166 provided that juries of each hundred should present to the royal commissioners when they came on circuit all persons suspected of felony on any ground including information supplied by the sheriff.[4] The creation of these juries illustrates the lack of royal trust in the sheriffs.

After the frankpledge system died out in the fourteenth century the practice grew of every parish appointing a "constable" upon whom were conferred wider powers of arrest than those available to the general public. Also, as the control over the administration of justice passed from the sheriff to the justices of the peace, the latter acquired the right to issue warrants of arrest to the constables.

b   Presentation for trial

This stage of the proceedings has involved, at different periods of history, two bodies; the grand jury and justices of the peace.

The grand jury was the earliest type of jury used at assizes and quarter sessions. Consisting of twenty-four freeholders of the county, it originated in the fourteenth century and was the successor of the jury of presentment of the hundred created by the Assize of Clarendon 1166. The early function of the grand jury was to present persons for trial before the royal justices, frequently on the basis of the jurors' personal knowledge. Hence the members of the grand jury would often be witnesses or at least persons with local knowledge. Later, with the growth of the constabulary, the grand jury exercised the function, which was subsequently assumed by justices of the peace, of inquiring

---

[1] 59 Geo. 3, c. 46.
[2] *Ashford* v. *Thornton* (1818), 1 B. & Ald. 405.
[3] See p. 4, *ante.*
[4] The sheriff still supervised the system of frankpledge.

into allegations of crime in order to decide whether to present a bill of indictment against the prisoner. This function of presenting the bill of indictment was taken over by justices of the peace with the creation of the modern preliminary investigation by statutes of 1554 and 1555. Thereafter the sole function of the grand jury was to certify a bill of indictment preferred at quarter sessions or assizes as a "true bill". Thus it had become redundant and was virtually abolished (save for a few exceptional cases) by the Administration of Justice (Miscellaneous Provisions) Act 1933 and finally abolished by the Criminal Justice Act 1948.

Finally, whatever jurisdiction the grand jury had to act as a trial jury was abolished by a statute of 1352[1] which allowed a member of the trial jury to be challenged on the ground of his having been a member of the jury of presentment. From this date the petty (or trial) jury is seen as completely distinct from the grand jury.

c Trial

The earliest method of trial in the royal courts was trial by ordeal. This method of trial had, of course, existed long before the common law and indeed long before Christianity. Trial by ordeal was regarded as an appeal to God to decide the guilt or innocence of the accused and might take various forms. Ordeal by fire or boiling water was common.[2] This involved burning or scalding the prisoner's hands and bandaging them. The bandages were removed after three days, when guilt would be established if the hands had not healed. A more subtle appeal to the supernatural was "wager of law". This involved the prisoner finding a special number (generally twelve) of oath-swearers to swear to his innocence. If he could not do so, or his oath-swearers faltered in their oath, he was immediately presumed guilty. In an age when the oath would not be sworn lightly it was no doubt difficult to secure oath-swearers if the prisoner was patently guilty. Indeed the ecclesiastical courts retained compurgation until well after the Restoration. Compurgation also existed as a means whereby a defendant could evade liability in certain civil actions.[3]

All these forms of ordeal were attended with elaborate religious ceremony which accounts for the credence placed in their efficacy. Thus when Pope Innocent III in the Lateran Council in 1215 forbade members of the clergy from performing ceremonial at ordeals, the ordeal was effectively abolished as a means of trial.[4] This raised the need for a new method of trial to be found and led to the establishment of trial by jury.

The petty (or trial) jury was created not by statute, but by prerogative exercised through the King's judges. At first, no person could be compelled to submit to trial by jury without his consent. If he remained silent when asked to plead to treason or misdemeanour, this was treated as a plea of guilty. However this was not so in cases of felony. In such cases he had to submit to jury trial and was pressed by heavy weights of iron upon his chest until he did consent or died. This barbaric procedure (known as *peine forte et dure*) usually resulted in acquiescence but many died rather than submit to jury trial. The

---

[1] 25 Edw. 3, st. 5, c. 3.
[2] See Plucknett, *op. cit.*, p. 114.
[3] See p. 30, *post*.
[4] Except for ordeal by battle which continued to exist to determine appeals of felony.

result was that they did not die convicted felons and so did not forfeit their property to the Crown. There is record of a prisoner being pressed to death as late as 1658. In 1772[1] this procedure was abolished and a provision introduced that silence be treated as a plea of guilty in all cases. In 1827 statute[2] altered the position by providing that standing mute be treated as a plea of not guilty.

Trial by jury in the fifteenth century was similar to a modern jury trial. The most notable differences were: that in cases of treason or felony the accused could only have counsel to speak for him on matters of law, not on issues of fact; that he had no right to call any witnesses of his own in cases of felony; that he could not give evidence on his own behalf[3] and, perhaps most significant of all, that the jury which tried him could be fined or imprisoned if the judge considered their verdict perverse. This practice was held to be illegal by VAUGHAN, C.J. in *Bushell's Case*[4] in 1670 after which date no juror could be punished for his decision.

d   Sentence

If found guilty, the prisoner's punishment depended upon whether he stood convicted of felony or misdemeanour. Conviction for felony was punishable by death or maiming and forfeiture of the felon's land and chattels to the Crown. Conviction for misdemeanour, on the other hand, was punishable by fine or imprisonment. Various means were adopted to mitigate the severity of the punishment on a conviction for felony. Indeed, by the end of the eighteenth century only about one condemned prisoner in eight was actually executed. In many cases the death sentence would be remitted through the exercise of the royal prerogative of mercy. This would often take the form of a pardon conditional upon transportation for life of the prisoner to the American or Australian Colonies. In other cases juries fictitiously assessed the value of stolen property at less than one shilling since this reduced the offence from larceny to petty larceny, which was not a capital offence. This is another example of the use of fictions at common law. However a far more important fiction which was used to mitigate the severity of the criminal law was the fiction of "benefit of clergy."

Following the murder of Becket, Henry II was prompted by remorse to concede to the clergy[5] the privilege of exemption from trial in the King's courts. The "criminous clerk" would instead be tried in the ecclesiastical courts where the punishments were far less severe than in the common law courts. In addition there was no jury trial in the ecclesiastical courts but only trial by compurgation (wager of law)[6] which made convictions rare.

As a direct result of the excessive severity of punishment for felony in the common law courts, benefit of clergy was made available[7] to secular as well as religious clerks. The test to determine whether an accused person was a clerk was whether or not he could read. To show ability to read the accused had

---

[1] 12 Geo. 3, c. 20.
[2] 7 & 8 Geo. 4, c. 28.
[3] This impediment was not removed until the Criminal Evidence Act 1898.
[4] (1670), Vaugh., 135.
[5] See Plucknett, *op. cit.*, p. 439.
[6] See p. 15, *ante.*
[7] By the statute 25 Edw. 3, st. 3, c. 4 (1352).

only to recite a verse of Latin commonly supposed to have been Psalm 51, v. 1 and known, for obvious reasons, as the "neck verse". The privilege could, by the fourteenth century, be claimed after conviction and before sentence. If a plea after conviction succeeded the accused could not be subjected to any corporal punishment although he was not exempt from forfeiture of property, the other incident of conviction for felony.

Originally, the plea could be made on any trial for treason or felony (but not for misdemeanour). However a series of statutes beginning in the fifteenth century effectively limited the availability of the privilege. A statute of 1490[1] ensured that the privilege could only be claimed by a first offender by providing that he be branded upon successfully pleading his clergy. In 1576 statute[2] provided that criminous clerks should not be handed over to the church but should be released completely, thus severing the plea from any connection with the ecclesiastical courts. However the same Act conferred a discretionary power on the court to imprison the offender for up to one year. A series of post-Reformation statutes which codified the common law as to felonies such as murder, rape, piracy, robbery and burglary expressly made these offences non-clergyable so that benefit of clergy became available only in the case of certain common law felonies. It was finally abolished by the Criminal Law Act 1827.

3 Summary trial

The third, and latest, method of trial created by the common law was summary trial; trial without a jury. This method of trial was entirely created by statute and was only available where statute so provided. The trial was before justices of the peace holding "petty sessions". A statute of 1848[3] (Sir John Jervis's Act) for the first time created a uniform procedure for summary trials. In modern times the vast bulk of criminal offences are tried in this way.[4]

D CIVIL PROCEDURE AT COMMON LAW

It is not proposed to examine procedure in the local or feudal courts although there is no doubt that most common law actions were triable in these courts until the fourteenth century. These courts each had different methods of securing the defendant's presence, different rules of pleading and different modes of trial. The earliest forms of action tried in the common law courts concerned disputes over title to land. Between 1250 and 1400 the common law provided for the trial of personal actions in the royal courts and by 1400 very few of such actions were not triable at common law.

There is one basic principle underlying the growth of the common law. This is that a common law right only existed if there was a procedure for enforcing it (*ubi remedium ibi ius*). Consequently, substantive law is inextricably bound up with procedure. Maine expressed the situation thus:

> "So great is the ascendancy of the Law of Actions in the infancy of Courts of Justice, that substantive law has at first the look of being gradually secreted in the interstices of procedure".[5]

---

[1] 4 Hen. 7, c. 13.
[2] 18 Eliz. 1, c. 7.
[3] Summary Jurisdiction Act 1848.
[4] Summary procedure is dealt with at length, at pp. 432 *et seq, post.*
[5] Maine, *Early Law and Custom*, p. 389.

With this principle in mind it is possible to examine the history of civil procedure. The course of a civil action in the common law courts may be broadly divided into three stages: (a) the issue of the appropriate writ; (b) pleadings; and (c) trial.

1 Issue of the writ

An action at common law was commenced by the plaintiff purchasing from the Chancery a writ.[1] This writ, when issued, had the same effect as a modern writ in that it constituted a royal command to the defendant to enter an appearance to it. However, until the procedural reforms of the nineteenth century, it differed from the modern writ in that it was not in a standard form. There was a different form of writ for each cause of action. Indeed a cause of action existed only if the facts alleged to disclose that cause of action were within the scope of an existing writ. Since the decision as to whether or not to issue a writ was in the hands of the Chancellor it is at first difficult to see why he did not simply issue a writ whenever he thought that a remedy ought to be available to the plaintiff. Had this been done the common law would have developed extremely rapidly. That this was not in fact done and that the common law developed only gradually over many centuries may be attributed to several factors. First, the Chancellor would not issue a writ which the royal judges were unlikely to enforce. English judges have always regarded the creation of new causes of action with extreme reserve,[2] attaching a peculiar reverence to the achievement of legal certainty. Secondly, since litigation was an important source of local as well as royal revenue, feudal barons were extremely reluctant to agree to any development which would operate to deprive their courts of business and indeed the history of the early period of the common law is marked by the struggle between the local courts and the common law courts with the latter prevailing only gradually. Consequently the various forms of action developed over some six centuries. The precise content and nature of the individual forms of action is clearly a matter of substantive law but it is convenient at this point to outline the historical evolution of the forms of action.[3]

2 The forms of action

a Real Actions

The earliest civil matters over which the common law courts were anxious to assume jurisdiction were those concerning land. Therefore, not unnaturally, the earliest forms of action were actions for the recovery of land. These are termed real actions. Personal actions are actions for damages. Actions in which both land and damages are sought are described as mixed actions. The growth of the real actions is extremely complex. The earliest form of real action was the writ of right. This was not a means of commencing an action in the royal courts but a direction from the King commanding the

---

[1] Other methods, such as proceedings by bill, were superseded by the writ system.
[2] See, for example, *Best* v. *Samuel Fox & Co., Ltd.,* [1952] A.C. 716; [1952] 2 All E.R. 394; *Chapman* v. *Honig,* [1963] 2 Q.B. 502; [1963] 2 All E.R. 513. Maitland describes this force as the *vis inertiae.*
[3] For a simple and lucid guide to this complex historical development see Maitland, *The Forms of Action at Common Law.*

feudal lord to try a dispute concerning title to freehold land between the "demandant" (plaintiff) and the "tenant" (defendant). The action would be tried in the feudal court by battle. Where the tenant in chief of the two claimants was the King himself the issue on the writ would be triable by the King. Thus the earliest jurisdiction of the King derives from his position as a feudal lord. Henry II attempted to extend this form of writ of right so as to by-pass the court of the feudal overlord and make any writ of right triable in the royal courts. His attempt was premature and clause 34 of Magna Carta provided that this writ (*praecipe quod reddat*) should not be issued in future so as to deprive any free man of his court. This did not, however, affect the form of writ of right appropriate where the King was tenant in chief (*praecipe in capite*). Thus there were after 1215 two forms of writ of right, only one of which was properly within the jurisdiction of the common law courts. Nevertheless, even where the issue on the writ was triable in the feudal rather than the royal court, the royal writ had first to be obtained.

The writ of right was effectively brought within the jurisdiction of the royal judges by the introduction, under Henry II, of the Grand Assize. This gave the tenant (defendant) the option of submitting to trial before twelve knights[1] as an alternative to battle. This concept of "jury" trial was further developed by Henry II with the creation of the Possessory (or Petty) Assizes, the method of trial of which was similar to that obtaining at the Grand Assize.[2] The two[3] principal possessory assizes were *Novel Disseisin* and *Mort d'Ancestor*. The first lay at the suit of a plaintiff who had been recently dispossessed (disseised) of his rightful freehold tenement. The latter was available to the heir of a person[4] who died seised as of fee against a person who had obtained seisin before the heir. The actions are often described as mixed actions since damages could be awarded as well as recovery of land. The feature of the Possessory Assizes was that they did not involve declarations as to absolute title but only as to comparative rights to possession (seisin) of freehold land. From these actions stems the modern concept of title to land as being comparative (rather than absolute) and being based upon possession (rather than ownership). Because the Possessory Assizes did not involve the complex ceremonial and procedure attendant upon writs of right, they largely replaced the latter. Nevertheless they were, by their terms, limited in scope and, even at this stage, the common law judges were reluctant to extend the scope of the existing forms of action. This led to the creation of a new type of action—the writ of entry.

Writs of entry were originally created as variations on the Possessory Assizes. However, due to the relative speed of procedure, they became popular and were extended by the Statute of Marlborough 1267, to any suit in which the

---

[1] This was not a jury in the modern sense since the knights were witnesses rather than judges of fact.

[2] Although the recognitors need not be knights but only good and lawful men of the neighbourhood.

[3] There were two other possessory assizes; *darrein presentment* and *utrum*.

[4] Seisin did not pass automatically on the death of the tenant; it only arose when the heir physically entered into possession of the land. Hence the need to provide the heir with a right of action against a person who entered the land before the heir could do so. The degrees of ancestry within the assizes of mort d'ancestor were extended by the later actions of *Aiel* (grandfather), *Besaiel* (great-grandfather) and *Cosinage* (cousin). The original writ extended only to father, mother, brother, sister, uncle and aunt.

demandant alleged a flaw in the tenant's title even though the demandant had not been disseised. The result was that writs of entry became available to determine almost any dispute over title and they were used widely until the fifteenth century when they were in turn superseded by the mixed action of ejectment.[1] The real actions were almost entirely abolished by the Real Property Limitation Act 1833. The few remaining after this date were abolished by the Common Law Procedure Acts 1852–1860.

b   Personal actions prior to 1285

The earliest forms of personal actions were virtually indistinguishable from the real actions. They were commenced by *praecipe quod reddat* commanding the defendant to return personal property (money or chattels) to the plaintiff and ordering the sheriff to bring the defendant before the royal court[2] if he failed to do so. In fact the actions were only distinguishable from the real actions by the relief sought. In Maitland's own words:

> "We are tempted to say that Debt is a 'real' action, that the vast gulf which to our minds divides the 'Give me what I own' and 'Give me what I am owed' has not yet become apparent."[3]

The earliest personal actions at common law were *debt, detinue, covenant* and *account*.[4] *Debt* was an action for a fixed sum of money in return for an executed consideration. Although it was, in modern terms, contractual in nature, it was very far removed from the modern action in contract because of its inherent limitations. The action only lay for a liquidated sum[5] due in full. It was not an action for damages. Also the plaintiff had no right of action until he had fully performed his obligation.[6] Finally the writ became subject to an elaborate and artificial system of pleading and was subject to wager of law.[7]

The writ of *detinue* was similar to debt and certainly the two actions had a similar origin. The praecipe directed the defendant to return a specific chattel which he was wrongfully refusing to return. However, if unsuccessful the defendant always had the option of paying damages rather than returning the chattel. Thus the action was not an action for a specific *res* but and action for damages. Detinue, like debt, was triable by wager of law.

The writ of *account* is one of the few writs which has contributed to modern procedure rather than to substantive law.[8] It was used, as it is today, to compel an "accounting party" such as a manorial bailiff or a business partner to account to the plaintiff for money received on the latter's behalf. The writ was later superseded by the equitable jurisdiction of the Chancellor to take accounts since accounts by bill in the Court of Chancery did not involve the elaborate and expensive procedure of the Court of Common Pleas.

---

[1] See p. 22, *post.*
[2] Usually the Court of Common Pleas.
[3] Maitland, *The Forms of Action at Common Law* (1936 Edn.), p. 38.
[4] *Replevin* was an additional form but of lesser importance being confined to wrongful distress and triable generally in the local courts rather than in the Court of Common Pleas.
[5] It is possible that the action was originally for the return of specific coin.
[6] Alternatively the acknowledgement of a debt by a deed under seal was sufficient to found an action of debt.
[7] See p. 15, *ante.*
[8] For details of this procedure, see p. 255, *post.*

The last of these important early forms of action was the writ of *covenant*. This form of action bears testimony to the peculiar sanctity with which the common law has always regarded the seal. The writ lay for breach of any obligation under the defendant's seal. It was wider than debt in that it lay for the recovery of unliquidated damages and lay for the failure to perform virtually any obligation. However it was restrictive in that there was no action unless the obligation were contained in writing under seal. It appears that the writ was widely used to enforce leases since the obligations between lessor and lessee were originally purely personal It should be noted that covenant could not be brought for the recovery of a debt, even under seal. The action in such a case would have to be in debt.

By the thirteenth century the Register of Original Writs contained some fifty writs, though these were all factual variations upon the basic writs described above. The immediate result of this proliferation of actions, especially the advent of the great writ of trespass during this period, was a decline in the revenue of the local courts. The barons, ever anxious to halt the centralisation of litigation, consequently forced Henry III to agree that no new writs of course (*de cursu*) should be sealed by the Chancellor without the consent of the whole Council. This concession was contained in the Provisions of Oxford 1258. It is questionable how far these Provisions had the force of law but they were undoubtedly instrumental in stunting the growth of the common law and providing for the very narrow course which the subsequent development of the forms of action was to take.

c The Writ of Trespass

The great writ of trespass, "that fertile mother of actions",[1] may be seen as the link between the early forms of action already described and the later writs which are the historical source of most of the modern law of contract and torts. There are conflicting theories about the origins of trespass. A common theory, advanced notably by Maitland, is that the writ had its roots in the old appeal of felony. Though a criminal proceeding this had much in common with a civil action since it was instituted by an individual on his own behalf rather than by the Crown. A second theory regards trespass as an offshoot of the assize of novel disseisin.[2] This is supported by the fact that damages could be awarded in that action. Other scholars attribute the origins of the writ to local procedure and Roman law.

The nature of trespass was that it was a breach of the King's peace by a positive wrongful act. All writs of trespass contained the words *vi et armis et contra pacem domini regis* (by force and arms and against the King's peace). This wrongful act might be directed at the plaintiff's person (*vi et armis*), goods (*de bonis asportatis*) or land (*quare clausum fregit*), but in all cases the act had to be direct. Trespass did not extend to damage indirectly caused. Further limits to the scope of the writ were that it did not protect intangible rights, such as reputation, and that it was a wrong against possession, providing no remedy where the interference was with rights to possession or title to goods or land rather than with actual possession. Trespasses were regarded so seriously that they were (and, of

---

[1] Maitland, *op. cit.*, p. 48.
[2] See Woodbine, *Origins of the Action of Trespass*, 33 Yale Law Journal, pp. 799–816; 34 *ibid.*, pp. 343–370.

course, still are) actionable *per se* (without proof of damage) and were, for a long time, wrongs of strict liability.   Trespass actions were never subject to wager of law, but were triable before a jury, usually in the Court of King's Bench.

d   Actions on the Case

Since a writ corresponded rather to a factual situation than to a legal right the limitation on the creation of new writs imposed by the Provisions of Oxford 1258 brought obvious injustice.   The facts of the plaintiff's case might not be precisely covered by an existing writ, in which event he would have no remedy.   To remedy this injustice the Statute of Westminster II, 1285, c. 24, provided:

> "And whensoever from henceforth it shall fortune in the Chancery, that in one case a writ is found, and in like case (*in consimili casu*) falling under like law, and requiring like remedy, is found none, the clerks of the Chancery shall agree in making the writ. . . ."[1]

The immediate result of this provision was a rapid growth in the number of original writs.   By 1300 there were some 300 writs on the Register but it must be stressed that all the new writs were factual variations upon the existing writs and did not have the effect of recognising new rights.   However, as more and more factual variations on the writ of trespass were allowed, the effect was eventually that new forms of action were created protecting hitherto unprotected rights and enforcing new types of duty.   These actions were the actions on the case.   The name "case" suggests that these actions have their origin firmly in the statute *in consimili casu*.   This view was expressed by Coke[2] and was also favoured by the older legal historians such as Maitland.   The more modern view is that the Statute of Westminster II is not the source of actions on the case but the position is not free from doubt.

The new actions on the case filled the obvious gaps in the writ of trespass. For example, trespass did not extend to damage indirectly caused.   Trespass on the case remedied this by providing a remedy where the defendant caused physical damage to the plaintiff indirectly, for example by leaving a log in the road over which the plaintiff's horse stumbled.[3]   In addition, there grew from trespass on the case three important new forms of action which were to go far toward shaping the growth of contract and tort.   These were the actions of *ejectment, trover* and *assumpsit*.

The important action of *ejectment* filled the gap between the real actions and the writ of trespass.   Originally a purely personal action (remediable only by damages) it became, by the end of the fifteenth century, a mixed action in that the plaintiff could claim both damages and the recovery of land.   It will be recalled that the plaintiff had no remedy in trespass unless he was in possession of the land in question at the time of the alleged wrong. Hence trespass was not available to a landlord or reversioner.   A person out of possession of land had two remedies for its recovery.   He could exercise his common law privilege of self-help and re-enter the land.   However this was not really satisfactory particularly after the Forcible Entry Act 1381,

---

[1] This translation is taken from Maitland, *op. cit.*, p. 51.
[2] 2 Inst., f. 407.
[3] These facts are those of one of the earliest recorded actions of trespass on the case.

which made forcible re-entry a criminal offence. Alternatively the real actions were available to him. These, however, had by this time become unpopular with litigants because of the cumbersome and expensive procedure attendant upon them. It was in order to avoid the cumbersome real actions that the action of ejectment was developed.

Ejectment was originally an action by a lessee to recover leasehold land from which he had been wrongly ejected. It was only extended to freehold land by the use of an incredibly elaborate fiction. The freeholder would allege a fictitious demise (lease) of his land to a fictitious character invariably named John Doe. John Doe would in turn allege that he had been ejected by a second fictitious character named Richard Roe.[1] The plaintiff would then write a letter to the substantive defendant asking him to defend the action and signing it "your loving friend Richard Roe". The action, in form an action by an ejected lessee, would then enable the substantial dispute as to title to freehold land to be tried. Such actions may be recognised in law reports by the title *Doe d.*[2] *A. v. B.*

This action almost entirely superseded the real actions and became the universal form of action for the recovery of land. The famous John Doe in fact existed until his own demise was finally effected by the Common Law Procedure Act 1852. The modern "possession" action, available to any person entitled to possession of land, was created in 1875.

Just as ejectment used a legal fiction to extend a narrow form of action to a very wide set of facts so *trover*, strictly an action depending upon loss and finding, was extended to fill the gap between detinue and trespass to goods. Trover (conversion) went beyond the scope of these two writs since it extended the plaintiff's protection to all acts which constituted an unjustifiable denial of his title to chattels. In the sixteenth century trover largely superseded detinue[3] because of the relatively streamlined procedure attaching to actions on the case. In addition detinue, like debt, was subject to the anachronistic wager of law.

Assumpsit is perhaps the most important of all the actions on the case since from this single writ derive the basic principles of the modern law of contract. Until this time the only "contractual" actions at common law were debt and covenant; thus parties could create a relationship enforceable in the common law courts only by fixing the amount of remuneration in advance (which could only create a cause of action for one of the parties) or by incorporating their agreement in a deed under seal. There was no action on an executory agreement not under seal. In such cases the parties would be compelled to pursue their remedies in the inferior courts with the result that much of the profitable litigation arising out of England's growing mercantile power was outside the scope of the King's courts. In addition the common lawyers were conscious that, unless they took action, the new courts of equity[4] would assume jurisdiction over contract litigation. It was against this background that the common lawyers developed the writ of assumpsit. Assumpsit grew to supersede debt but grew, not out of the writ of debt, but as an offshoot of trespass. Thus it might be said

---

[1] Or William Styles.
[2] "d." means "on the demise of".
[3] Until 1854 when s. 78 of the Common Law Procedure Act gave the court power to order specific restitution of chattels in actions of detinue.
[4] See p. 30, *post.*

that the law of contract and the law of torts have the same origin—trespass. In fact assumpsit in its early history was tortious in nature. The basis of liability was that the defendant was in breach of an obligation which he had assumed (assumpsit). In the fourteenth and fifteenth centuries the defendant's failure could not be mere non-performance. He was at first only liable if he undertook a task, for example, to cure a horse or look after goods as a bailee, and performed it badly (misfeasance).[1] He might also be liable for malfeasance if he gave an oral undertaking which proved to be false. Assumpsit for malfeasance is virtually equivalent to deceit. Finally, in the sixteenth century, assumpsit was extended to non-feasance and at this point of time contract and tort separated. At this time assumpsit could only replace the unpopular writ of debt if the defendant had assumed an obligation to pay the debt, for example by acknowledgement. However in *Slade's Case*[2] in 1602 all the common law judges decided that "every contract executory imports in itself an assumpsit" at which stage assumpsit superseded debt.

Subsequent actions on the case protected intangible rights; *libel, slander, deceit* and *nuisance* are examples.

The history of *libel* and *slander* is complex. Until the late fifteenth century defamation was regarded as a wrong of an essentially spiritual nature and was thus dealt with by the ecclesiastical courts.[3] With the invention of printing the dissemination of libel presented a threat to national security and was recognised as a crime by the Court of Star Chamber, though damages might also be awarded. Slander, however, was not punishable in the Star Chamber, which accounts for the fact that slander, unlike libel, is not a criminal offence at the present day; it may also account for the fact that libel is actionable *per se* whereas slander is not. In the sixteenth century the common law courts recognised a new action on the case for words, though this action was at first confined to allegations of crime. With the abolition of the Star Chamber, the action on the case for words was extended to include libel.

Although the tort of *deceit* was recognised, in its modern form, only in the late eighteenth century,[4] there was, as early as the fourteenth century, a right of action against one who by fraudulent representation induced another to enter into a contract. This form of action was closely associated with assumpsit[5] and was contractual rather than tortious in nature. As stated above, deceit outside the context of a contractual relationship, became actionable in the eighteenth century and the modern definition of fraud, as including recklessness, was laid down a century later.[6]

An assize of *nuisance* appears to have existed prior to the evolution of trespass. This was, however, a real rather than a personal action. The modern tort of

---

[1] In *Waldon* v. *Marshall* (1370), Y.B. Mich. 43 Ed. 3, f. 33, pl. 38, one of the earliest actions of its type, the defendant was held liable when a horse which the defendant had undertaken to cure died through his negligence.

[2] 4 Rep. 92b.

[3] Although the common law courts had jurisdiction to hear actions in relation to the slander of magnates under the *Scandalum Magnatum* provision of the Statute of Westminster I 1275. Although falling into disuse this provision was not in fact repealed until the Statute Law Revision Act 1888.

[4] *Pasley* v. *Freeman* (1789), 3 Term Rep. 51.

[5] See p. 23, *ante.*

[6] *Derry* v. *Peek* (1889), 14 App. Cas. 337.

nuisance, an action for damages for wrongful interference with another's use or enjoyment of land (or, in the case of public nuisance, with another's exercise of a public right) derives from an action on the case developed in the sixteenth century. This action on the case supplanted the old assize of nuisance and extended the action, which had formerly been confined to instances of disseisin, to a wide variety of forms of interference.[1]

In addition to these named actions there existed the innominate action on the case. This special action on the case has been used, albeit cautiously, to provide a remedy where none of the known actions exactly covered the situation. As WILLES, C.J. explained (somewhat optimistically) in 1745:

> "A special action on the case was introduced for this reason, that the law will never suffer an injury and a damage without a remedy."[2]

In fact common law judges have usually been reluctant to recognise a new cause of action. The torts of malicious falsehood,[3] inducing a breach of contract,[4] intentionally causing physical harm[5] and even the modern tort of negligence have their origin in the special action on the case.

The nineteenth century is universally recognised as being the great era of law reform and among the first topics for reform was the existence of the constricting writ system outlined above. The reform was piecemeal. The Real Property Limitation Act 1833 almost entirely abolished the real actions. The Common Law Procedure Act 1852 removed the necessity for specifying a form of action in a writ of summons. This abolished the writ system insofar as the plaintiff no longer had to settle on a choice of writ. However the pleader would, even after this date, still have to follow the precedents of pleading applicable to one of the forms of action. The final abolition of the forms of action was not completed until the passing of the Judicature Acts 1873–1875.[6] These Acts introduced the modern system of pleading whereby the plaintiff merely has to plead facts leaving the court to determine their legal effect.

Nevertheless the common law forms of action are still of great significance. Maitland's famous dictum "The forms of action we have buried but they still rule us from their graves",[7] is an overstatement. However it is important to bear in mind that the forms of action were both procedural and substantive. All that the nineteenth century legislation did was to abolish the procedure. Thus the modern significance of the forms of action is purely substantive. If the plaintiff's case could not have been prosecuted under the terms of a

---

[1] Many of these are enumerated in *Aldred's Case* (1610), 9 Co. Rep. 57b; see also *Walter v. Selfe* (1851), 4 De G. & Sm. 315.

[2] *Winsmore* v. *Greenbank* (1745), Willes 578.

[3] *Shepherd* v. *Wakeman* (1662), Sid. 79.

[4] *Lumley* v. *Gye* (1853), 2 E. & B. 216.

[5] *Wilkinson* v. *Downton*, [1897] 2 Q.B. 57.

[6] Not all countries administering common law systems have introduced similar reforms. In Australia, for example, a system of pleading similar to that existing in this country prior to 1875 still exists so that actions may still fail on purely technical points of pleading; this is well illustrated by the decision of the Judicial Committee of the Privy Council, on appeal from the High Court of Australia, in *Mutual Life and Citizens' Assurance Co., Ltd.* v. *Evatt*, [1971] A. C. 793; [1971] 1 All E. R. 150.

[7] Maitland, *Equity* (1916 Edn.), p. 296.

writ prior to 1852, then, generally, he has no cause of action.[1]   Similarly if he fails to plead facts essential to a cause of action he cannot succeed in that action.[2] However, if he pleads facts which give rise to a cause of action, then he will not fail simply because he has specified the wrong cause of action or been guilty of some other procedural irregularity, as he would have done prior to 1875.[3]

3   Pleadings at common law

Having been issued with a writ the plaintiff was very far from obtaining his remedy in the common law courts.   He had first to satisfy the rigorous formality of pleading attendant upon each writ.   An action could easily be won or lost in the pleading.   This fact prompted Littleton to advise his son:[4]

> "It is one of the most honourable, laudable and profitable things in our law to have the science of well pleading in actions real and personal, and therefore I counsel thee especially to employ thy courage and care to learn this."

Originally pleadings were delivered orally in open court and entered on the court record by the clerk.   This, no doubt, placed a heavy burden on the pleader to be precise.   At this stage pleadings appear to have constituted evidence of the truth of the facts pleaded, so that oral pleadings were at once allegations of fact and evidence in support of those facts.   These oral pleadings were in Norman French.[5]   By the fifteenth century the pleadings had become separate from the trial and were in writing.   Thus the parties were able to fix the issue between them and then argue in support of that issue at the trial.   However there could only be one issue in each action.   The plaintiff could not plead causes of action in the alternative.[6]   The defendant could not raise alternative defences but had to rely upon one defence either of law or of fact.

A defence based on a point of law was termed a "demurrer" and necessarily involved the defendant admitting all the facts alleged by the plaintiff.   A defence on the facts might take the form of a special plea, such as self-defence in assault, or limitation, or a plea of the "general issue".[7]   This amounted to a straight denial of the facts alleged in the issue against the defendant.   There was a special form of general issue in each form of action.   In covenant the general issue was *non est factum*, in debt *nil debet*, in assumpsit *non assumpsit*.   Each plea had to be set out according to the hallowed formula or the plea would founder. Choice of the wrong plea would lose the action as surely as choice of the wrong writ.   It might appear that this system of pleading would ensure a speedy trial if nothing else.   In fact the reverse was true because the defendant's plea of the general issue told the plaintiff nothing about the defence to be raised against him.   Thus by pleading *non assumpsit* the defendant could raise at the trial

---

[1] See, for example, *Bradford Corporation* v. *Pickles*, [1895] A.C. 587; *Best* v. *Samuel Fox & Co.*, [1952] A.C. 716; [1952] 2 All E.R. 394; *Chapman* v. *Honig*, [1963] 2 Q.B. 502; [1963] 2 All E.R. 513.

[2] As to the importance of pleadings, see p. 262, *post*.

[3] *Fouldes* v. *Willoughby* (1841), 8 M. & W. 540; *cf. Letang* v. *Cooper*, [1965] 1 Q.B. 197; [1964] 2 All E.R. 929.   See R.S.C. (Revision) 1965, O. 2, r. 1.

[4] Littleton, *Of Tenures*, s. 534.

[5] They were in English, in fact, after 1362.   The plea rolls, however, were in Latin until 1731 after which date they too were in English.

[6] This inconvenient rule against duplicity was removed by 4 & 5 Anne, c. 3 in 1705.

[7] A plea of "not guilty" in a criminal case is equivalent to pleading the old "general issue".

matters relating, for example, to capacity, lack of consideration, discharge, release or the Statute of Frauds. Consequently, the pleadings were extremely general and the plaintiff would have to be prepared to meet any possible defence at the trial. The need for pleadings to be more specific was introduced eventually by statute. The Civil Procedure Act 1833 conferred power upon the judges to make rules of procedure; this led to the famous Hilary Rules of 1834 which required the defendant to plead his defences specifically. These Rules remedied the abuse of parties concealing their hands until the trial but they created more, rather than less, formality and complexity of pleading. The process of breaking this down began soon afterwards with the passing of the Common Law Procedure Acts 1852–1860, and was perfected by the Judicature Acts 1873–1875, which created the modern system of pleading.[1]

4 Trial

The mode of trial depended upon the form of action. Writs of right were triable by battle, debt and detinue by the archaic wager of law. However all other actions were triable by judge and jury, the method which has survived to the present day, though the jury is rapidly disappearing in favour of trial by a judge alone.

Where an issue of law was raised on a demurrer no jury was involved since juries never decided points of law. The parties would simply appear at one of the three superior common law courts at Westminster and argue the point before the judges of that court. Thus the whole trial would take place *in banc.*

Where, on the other hand, the issue raised was one of fact, for example by the defendant pleading the general issue, this issue had to be decided by a jury. It is noteworthy that the jury in civil cases has a different origin from the criminal jury. While the latter derives from the jury of presentment of the hundred, the civil jury has its origin in the Assizes of Clarendon 1166, and Northampton 1176, which created the Grand and Petty Assizes. Thus the only jury which ever existed in civil actions was the petty jury, twelve in number. However, just as in criminal cases, the civil jury was originally a body of local witnesses and only later came to act as judges of fact. Since all writs of trespass and actions on the case were triable by jury, the effect was that, at common law, virtually all actions in contract and tort were tried by a jury. As the jurors were, at least until the fifteenth century, witnesses, other witnesses were rarely required at the trial and the jurors *qua* witnesses could be punished for a perverse verdict. *Bushell's Case* in 1670[2] established that jurors could no longer be punished for their verdicts from which, one deduces, the concept of jurors as witnesses had completely disappeared.

Jury trials at assizes took place in two stages. The issue of fact was tried at *nisi prius* by the jury and their verdict sent back to the trial court at Westminster since judgment could not be entered at *nisi prius* but only *in banc.* The central court at Westminster then entered judgment on the record in accordance with the jury verdict. Later the whole action became triable on assize or in London although judgments at *nisi prius* were still entered at Westminster as a formality.

There was no appeal by way of rehearing at common law. This was not

---

[1] See p. 58, *post.*
[2] (1670), Vaugh. 135.

introduced until 1875.[1] The first method of appeal from the decision of a common law court was by writ of error alleging an error on the record. This would not extend to any question of fact and could only extend to such points of law as would appear on the record; for example, defects in pleadings or failure to summon all parties to the proceedings. Proceedings in error were also apparently extended to appeals against the decision of a judge on the trial of a demurrer. Where a point of law was not contained in the court record the trial judge might be asked to seal a "Bill of Exceptions" which was annexed to the record and was deemed, by the Statute of Westminster II 1285, c. 31, to be part of the record for the purpose of proceedings in error. The Bill of Exceptions contained points of law not otherwise enrolled such as rulings on the admissibility of evidence or the burden of proof.[2]

Finally in the seventeenth century it became possible for a litigant to "move for a new trial", a procedure which is still an alternative to appeal by way of rehearing in civil actions.

It may be apparent from this chapter that substantive common law and procedure were hidebound by formality and restrictions. The common law partly avoided its own rigidity by the extensive use of fictions. Fictions were used for three basic purposes. First, they were employed to avoid the severity of the criminal law, benefit of clergy being the most notable example.[3] Secondly, fictions were used to extend the scope of the original writs in order to expand substantive law; trover and ejectment were both extended far beyond their literal scope to this end.[4] Finally, fictions were used to assume jurisdiction. Early fictions, such as the writ of pone, were used to acquire jurisdiction from the local courts in matters concerning title to land. Subsequently the common law courts used fictions to acquire jurisdiction from one another. Quominus and Bill of Middlesex[5] are notable examples of this trend which can be explained by the fact that judicial salaries depended upon the volume of litigation conducted.

However fictions were not capable in themselves of remedying all the defects of common law. These included the strictness of the application of common law doctrines and the inadequacy of the remedies available at common law. The overriding defect was, of course, the way in which substantive law was entirely bound up with procedure. Legislation, the principal modern agency of law reform, was not widely used in the Middle Ages.

Consequently an alternative means of providing a gloss on the common law was required. This led to the evolution of the second major historical source of English law—equity.

---

[1] Judicature Acts 1873–1875.
[2] Bills of exceptions were apparently unpopular with common law judges and there is evidence that many of them flatly refused to seal bills. See, for example, *Bridgman* v. *Holt* (1693), Show. Parl. Cas. 111.
[3] See p. 16, *ante*.
[4] See pp. 22–23, *ante*.
[5] See pp. 6–8, *ante*.

CHAPTER 2

Equity

A ORIGINS OF EQUITY

Equity is not peculiar to the English legal system. Continental systems of law recognise the existence of equity. However, in continental systems equity is purely conceptual. It is almost a synonym for "natural justice". In England this is not so. Natural justice is not a concept which forms the basis of English decisions although it no doubt affects the interpretation which judges put on the law. Hence equity in the English legal system does not mean natural justice although its rules are in part based on the concept of justice, particularly where these rules were created to remedy injustice in the common law. Equity, in English law, has been defined by Maitland as—

> "that body of rules administered by our English Courts which were it not for the operation of the Judicature Acts, would be administered by those Courts which would be known as Courts of Equity".

This definition may appear to beg the question but it serves to illustrate that the nature of modern equity can be understood only by reference to its historical origins and development.

Equity, in its original sense of natural justice, was administered in the common law courts until the fourteenth century. Common law judges, particularly the judges of the Court of Exchequer, could exercise some discretion in their application of the law particularly in the question of whether or not to recognise the validity of writs issued out of the Chancery. This discretion was, no doubt, exercised on the basis of doing justice in individual cases and thus amounted to what the continental lawyer would describe as equity. Unfortunately during the fourteenth century the common law became hidebound by formality and so became rigid and inflexible. Provided a litigant could find a writ to fit his case and could surmount the intricacies of pleading attendant upon the writ he had a right to a remedy. No discretion was involved. It has always been a feature of the common law that common law remedies are available as of right. The plaintiff who can show the infringement of his legal right must be granted a remedy irrespective of his conduct or personality.

During this period, also, common law judges ceased to be drawn from the ranks of clerics and were recruited from the ranks of a legal profession whose inclination was toward learning and mastering the intricacies of pleading rather than attempting to reform the law.

Furthermore the political climate of the Middle Ages resulted in measures such as the Provisions of Oxford 1258, the tendency of which was to restrict the expansion of the writ system and to force it to develop along very narrow lines.

Finally the General Eyre, probably the last organ through which equity could be applied in the common law courts, declined in the same period as a result of local unpopularity

Consequently the common law became, quite early in its existence, incapable of providing a means of remedying its own inherent restrictions. This meant that injustices were bound to occur. For example a litigant who had suffered damage might not be able to find an existing form of action into which he could fit his case. Even if he found a form of action he might falter in pleading or might, in debt or detinue, be met by the defendant waging his law. Alternatively if he were a defendant it might be that a remedy would be granted against him contrary to the justice of the case.

A practice grew, in such cases, of dissatisfied litigants petitioning the King to exercise his prerogative in their favour. For a time the King in Council determined these petitions himself. Later they became so numerous that the King delegated this task to his principal minister, the Chancellor. The Chancellor was, it will be recalled, an officer of the common law since he had custody of the Great Seal and controlled the issue of original writs out of the Chancery to litigants at common law. In addition he sat, from time to time, as a judge in the Council and the Court of Exchequer Chamber. He was, until the fall of Wolsey (1515–1529), an ecclesiastic.

In 1474 there is the first recorded instance of the Chancellor issuing a decree in his own name rather than in the name of the King. At this point of time the Court of Chancery was created and became, as the common law courts had become, independent of the King and of the Council.

B   COURTS OF EQUITY

1   The Court of Chancery

This was the principal court of equity and, as stated above, modern equity is the system of law administered in this court. The earliest jurisdiction of the Chancellor, often termed the "Latin" jurisdiction because the proceedings were recorded in Latin,[1] consisted of hearing petitions by litigants to whom a remedy had been denied or against whom an order had been unjustly made at common law. If there had been injustice the Chancellor would remit the case to the King's Bench for investigation. If that court found that a party had been guilty of corruption he would be punished summarily in the name of the King. This is, historically, the less important aspect of the Chancellor's jurisdiction and was extinguished with the abolition of the Court of Star Chamber to which it was

---

[1] The equitable jurisdiction of the Chancellor is generally described as the "English" jurisdiction since proceedings were recorded in English.

transferred when Conciliar jurisdiction was transferred from the Chancellor to that court.

By far the most important aspect of the Chancellor's jurisdiction consisted of the recognition and enforcement of a diverse set of principles now identifiable as the rules of equity.

It is debatable whether equity grew out of the jurisdiction of the Chancellor or whether the Chancellor's jurisdiction developed out of the principles of equity. In any event the growth of equity is inextricably tied up with the office of Chancellor. This was, at different times, both a good and a bad feature of the system. It was a good feature in that brilliant lawyers such as Sir Thomas More (1529–1532), Lord Ellesmere (1596–1617), Sir Francis Bacon (1618–1621), Lord Nottingham (1673–1682) and Lord Hardwicke (1737–1756) were each able to create and mould principles of equity without which it is difficult to imagine how English law could today continue to function. On the other hand, since the Court of Chancery habitually bore the characteristics of the Chancellor, any personal shortcomings which he might possess would become ingrained in procedure in the court. Thus the court was brought into disrepute in the seventeenth century by the sale of offices in the court. All offices, including that of Master of the Rolls, were sold by the Chancellor.[1] Indeed so great was corruption in the court during this period that on the bursting of the South Sea Bubble in 1725 a deficiency of some £100,000 in court funds was discovered as a result of which Lord Macclesfield was impeached and fined £30,000.

A further defect in the Court of Chancery was the organisation of the court. There was an excess of court officials who attempted to extend the ambit of their duties so as to increase their revenue. Apart from the abuse which the sale of these clerkships created the proliferation of Chancery clerks naturally made litigation in the court extremely slow and expensive. The excess of court officers was equalled only by the paucity of judges. At first the Chancellor himself was the only judge. In practice he was unable to hear all cases himself and by the sixteenth century was accustomed to delegate his judicial function to the Masters in Chancery although judgment was delivered only by the Chancellor himself. The chief of these Masters was the Master of the Rolls who in 1729[2] effectively became a second judge of the court. However this did little to speed up the conduct of litigation since the parties had a right to apply to the Chancellor for a re-hearing. Arrears of work were handed down through successive Chancellors. Matters reached a head in the nineteenth century with the elevation of Lord Eldon to the office of Chancellor. Lord Eldon (1801–1827) was a distinguished lawyer but unfortunately suffered from an excess of caution. He would not deliver any judgment or make any order without considering every available authority. There are records of judgments being reserved for months and even years. While this stabilised the court it also brought it into discredit with suitors and the backlog of cases pending became enormous. In 1813 Lord Eldon approved the appointment of a Vice-Chancellor as an additional judge of the Court but this brought little improvement since an appeal lay from his decisions to the Chancellor. Apart from this measure Lord Eldon stood fast against any reform and used the power of his office to thwart any

---

[1] The office of Master of the Rolls was apparently worth £6,000 in the eighteenth century. See *Ex parte the Six Clerks* (1798), 3 Ves. 589.

[2] By 3 Geo. 2, c. 30.

attempt at reform of the judicial system. This obdurate conservatism contributed greatly to the welter of reform which in fact began shortly after his resignation from office in 1827. The Court of Chancery was finally abolished by the Judicature Acts 1873–1875 and its jurisdiction substantially transferred to the Chancery Division of the High Court.

In addition to its equitable jurisdiction the Court, because of its close association with the Crown, acquired jurisdiction over other miscellaneous matters. For example the Crown, as *parens patriae*, had protective custody of all infants within the realm; this jurisdiction, which comprised such matters as the power to appoint guardians, was assigned to the Court of Chancery but is now exercised by the Family Division.[1]

A similar concept existed in relation to persons of unsound mind; since they too were in need of protection the Sovereign assumed responsibility for the care of lunatics and their property. This responsibility was, as with infants, delegated to the Chancellor and is today exercised, for the most part, by the Court of Protection, the judges of which are judges of the Chancery Division.[2]

Procedure in the Court of Chancery

Since proceedings in the Court of Chancery were not commenced by writ the court was never a slave of procedure in the same way as were the common law courts. Consequently, Chancellors were able to create rights and remedies *de novo* as justice required. There was never any pretence that equitable rules dated from time immemorial.[3] It was this that prompted John Selden's immortal aphorism that "Equity varies as the length of the Chancellor's foot".[4]

A Chancery suit was commenced by a petition or bill filed by the plaintiff in the court. This petition originally had not to comply with any particular formality so that its potential scope was unlimited. Later, through the intervention of lawyers, uniformity and complexity came to be required in the drafting of Chancery bills and petitions which became as tortuous as common law pleadings.

Provided that the petition disclosed some reason for the Chancellor's intervention a writ of subpoena would be issued and served on the defendant compelling him to attend in answer to the petition. The defendant was then required to draft an answer to the allegations in the petition. This answer had to be on oath and is the origin of the modern interrogatories. It was a far longer and more detailed document than a common law defence since it disclosed not only the defence but also other factors to influence the Chancellor to exercise his discretion in favour of the defendant. Issue was thereby joined and the action proceeded to trial.

At the trial the evidence of witnesses was often not required and where testimony was required it was given on affidavit so that proceedings before the Chancellor were confined to legal argument on both sides.[5] Where

---

[1] Wardship proceedings were transferred from the Chancery Division to the Family Division by the Administration of Justice Act 1970, s. 1; Sch. 1.

[2] See p. 184, *post.*

[3] See *Re Hallett* (1880), 13 Ch. D. 696, at p. 710, *per* JESSEL, M.R.

[4] Selden, *Table Talk.*

[5] In modern Chancery Division proceedings the evidence is usually given on affidavit in the first instance followed, in the event of a dispute on the facts, by cross-examination of the deponents.

the case involved the existence of a common law right the Chancellor would call for the assistance of two common law judges to act as assessors. Finally the Chancellor would issue a decree in his own name. However this was not the end of the matter. An account might remain to be taken or an estate administered. Also the unsuccessful party might always apply to the Chancellor for a rehearing which would be granted even if the first hearing had been before the Chancellor himself. Even then the matter was not closed because there might be a further appeal to the House of Lords.[1]

2 The Court of Appeal in Chancery

This court was established in 1851[2] to hear appeals from decisions of the Vice-Chancellors (of whom there were by this time three) and the Master of the Rolls. The Lord Chancellor had almost ceased to act as a first-instance judge. The court consisted of the Chancellor and two Lords Justices (the first time that this nomenclature had been adopted). In addition the Chancellor might require any Vice-Chancellor or the Master of the Rolls to sit as an additional judge. There was a further appeal from the Court of Appeal in Chancery to the House of Lords. The court was abolished by the Judicature Acts 1873–1875 and its jurisdiction effectively transferred to the Court of Appeal.

3 The Court of Requests[3]

This court emerged in the fifteenth century from a committee of the Council established to grant relief to poor litigants who were denied a remedy at common law. Hence its jurisdiction was similar to that of the Chancery although it tended only to try cases of minor importance. In these cases the court could dispense equity more quickly and cheaply than could the Court of Chancery. This made the court popular with litigants but unpopular with common lawyers since it frequently meddled in the conduct of actions proceeding in the common law courts. The court was in 1598[4] declared "illegal" and to have "not any power by commission by statute or by common law". In spite of this rebuke the court continued to hold sittings until these were suspended in 1642 on the outbreak of the civil war. The court was not formally abolished but after the Restoration, although the Court of Chancery continued to thrive, the Court of Requests did not and because of the very close association between the court and the Council Charles II did not dare to attempt to revive its jurisdiction.

C NATURE AND CONTENT OF EQUITY

1 Nature of equity

One of the best definitions of the nature of equity is that of LORD COWPER in *Dudley* v. *Dudley*:[5]

> "Now equity is no part of the law, but a moral virtue, which qualifies, moderates, and reforms the rigour, hardness, and edge of the law, and is an universal truth; it

---

[1] This appeal dates from *Shirley* v. *Fagg* (1675), 6 State Tr. 1146.

[2] 14 & 15 Vict., c. 83.

[3] This court should not be confused with the Courts of Requests which were established in the eighteenth century to hear small claims (usually less than 40s.) and which were the forerunners of the modern county courts.

[4] *Stepney* v. *Flood* (1598), Cro. Eliz. 646.

[5] (1705), Prec. Ch. 241, at p. 244; cited by LORD HODSON in *National Provincial Bank, Ltd.* v. *Ainsworth*, [1965] A.C. 1175, at p. 1224; [1965] 2 All E.R. 472, at p. 480.

does also assist the law where it is defective and weak in the constitution (which is the life of the law) and defends the law from crafty evasions, delusions, and new subtilties, invented and contrived to evade and delude the common law, whereby such as have undoubted right are made remediless; and this is the office of equity, to support and protect the common law from shifts and crafty contrivances against the justice of the law. Equity therefore does not destroy the law, nor create it, but assist it."

The basic nature of equity is expressed in the renowned "maxims of equity". Thus equity provided new remedies where a remedy at common law was deficient on the basis that "equity does not suffer a wrong to be without a remedy". "Equity will not assist a volunteer" embodies the principle that a decree of specific performance will not be granted to a person who has given no consideration in return for the obligation which he seeks to have enforced. Similarly equity does not provide a remedy to a person who has behaved unconscionably (for example, a beneficiary who has acquiesced in a breach of trust) since "he who comes to equity must come with clean hands".

Equity's effect upon English law has been felt mainly in relation to the law of property and the law of contract. It has both a positive and a negative aspect to its operation. Its positive operation is demonstrated by the principle that equity will give effect to parties' intentions notwithstanding the absence of some formality required by the common law ("equity looks on that as done which ought to be done"); thus, an agreement to create a formal lease is equivalent to the lease itself; [1] the doctrine of part performance enables a contract to be enforced even though, by reason of the Statute of Frauds, it could not be proved at common law.[2] The negative aspect of equity centres on the equitable doctrine of fraud[3] and operates to restrain persons from enforcing rights which they could otherwise enforce, where to do so would be a fraud (in the equitable sense) on other parties. Thus, to take a simple example, a trustee, notwithstanding his capacity to dispose of the legal estate, will be restrained from so doing in breach of trust;[4] the doctrine of equitable estoppel[5] is founded on a similar principle.

The negative aspect of equity is, usually, rendered effective by the remedy of injunction.

Finally, an important principle of equity is that equity acts *in personam* rather than *in rem*; thus the right of a beneficiary is essentially a personal right against the trustee rather than a right in the trust property itself. This fact is often obscured because the right is both assignable and enforceable against a transferee of the legal estate; however, the fact that it is not enforceable against a *bona fide* purchaser for value of the legal estate without notice of the trust demonstrates the personal nature of an equitable interest. An interesting illustration of the maxim that equity acts *in personam* is that specific performance may be ordered of an agreement relating to land abroad, notwithstanding that an English court would have no jurisdiction to make an order in relation to the land itself.[6]

---

[1] *Walsh* v. *Lonsdale* (1882), 21 Ch. D. 9.
[2] *Maddison* v. *Alderson* (1883), 8 App. Cas. 467.
[3] See p. 39, *post.*
[4] For a recent illustration, see *Waller* v. *Waller*, [1967] 1 All E.R. 305; [1967] 1 W.L.R. 451.
[5] *Central London Property Trust, Ltd.* v. *High Trees House, Ltd.*, [1947] K.B. 130; [1956] 1 All E.R. 256n.
[6] *Penn* v. *Lord Baltimore* (1750), 1 Ves. Sen. 444.

2 Content of equity

Although equitable rules were created on the basis of conscience, they soon became uniform and certain in extent. This development was essential because most equitable rights were rights in land capable of devolution and transfer. For this reason the rules of equity affecting land law soon became quite as rigid and certain as the corresponding common law rules.

The rules of equity were nearly all created between the end of Wolsey's term of office in 1529 and the end of Lord Eldon's Chancellorship in 1827.[1] The most important of these rules are considered below. They resulted sometimes in the recognition of new rights wholly unrecognised in the common law courts (the "exclusive" jurisdiction) and sometimes in the granting of new remedies which the common law did not provide (the "concurrent" jurisdiction).

a New Rights

The rights of a beneficiary under a use or trust—A use or trust may be defined as a relationship in which one person has property vested in him subject to an obligation to permit another person to have the beneficial enjoyment of the property. The first person is described as a trustee, the second as a beneficiary or *cestui que trust*.

The existence of the use, as it was first known, dates back to the thirteenth century. It had even at this date certain advantages. For example, it enabled the Franciscans to enjoy the use of vast estates even though they were pledged to poverty by their order.[2] It made it possible for crusaders to arrange for their land to be held for them while they were in the Holy Land. Until the passing of the Statute of Wills 1540, freehold land could not be devised by will, so that to achieve the devolution of his land in accordance with his wishes the freeholder created uses in his lifetime. None of these methods of employing the use was particularly objectionable to the Crown. However in the fourteenth and fifteenth centuries it was appreciated that the use could be a device for defrauding creditors and in particular for depriving the feudal overlord of the revenue from the incidents of feudal tenure. This loss of revenue eventually meant a loss to the Crown and it was this factor which prompted Henry VIII, never indifferent to a possible loss of revenue, to "force upon an extremely unwilling Parliament"[3] the Statute of Uses 1535. This statute attempted to abolish uses of land by providing that where a person was seised to the use, confidence or trust of another that other was to be treated as seised. Thus if land were granted "to X to the use of Y" the legal estate would vest immediately in Y and X would take no interest whatsoever. The intended effect of this statute was to abolish the use. It did not however extinguish uses altogether

---

[1] Equity after this date became rigidly defined and there have been very few equitable rights or doctrines formulated since then. Notable exceptions are the enforcement of restrictive covenants (*Tulk* v. *Moxhay* (1848), 2 Ph. 774) and the doctrine of quasi-estoppel (*Central London Property Trust, Ltd.* v. *High Trees House, Ltd.*, [1947] K.B. 130; [1956] 1 All E.R. 256n.). For the difficulties involved in the recognition of a new equitable interest in land see *National Provincial Bank, Ltd.* v. *Ainsworth*, [1965] A.C. 1175; [1965] 2 All E.R. 472.

[2] The papacy declared in 1279 that it was lawful for friars to be beneficiaries under uses.

[3] Maitland, *Equity*, (1916 Edn.) p. 35. For an enlightening account of the Parliamentary progress of the Statute of Uses see Plucknett, *A Concise History of the Common Law*, (5th Edn.) pp. 584–587.

since there were many loopholes in the statute. For example the statute did not extend to uses of copyholds, leaseholds or pure personalty since seisin could never exist in these types of property. In addition the statute was held not to apply to "active uses", that is to say uses which imposed a positive duty on the trustee. Finally the common law judges held in 1558[1] that where there was a use upon a use (i.e. "to A to the use of B to the use of C") the Statute of Uses did not execute the second use but only the first (i.e. B, not C, took the legal estate). This was of small significance at common law since the common law judges would not recognise that the second *cestui que use* (C) had any interest. However the Court of Chancery would recognise and enforce the second use because it appeared unconscionable to defeat the donor's intention by giving the first *cestui que use* an unfettered interest. In *Sambach* v. *Dalston*[2] the Chancellor established that the second use was enforceable in equity. Thus the use or trust, as it was becoming known, had become an equitable interest. It may appear illogical that the common law courts would not recognise trusts which were a considerable source of revenue to the Court of Chancery. The reason is that the constricting writ system could not be adapted to encompass the growing law of trusts. Had it been possible to reorganise common law procedure at this stage rather than two centuries later it is probable that equity in the modern sense would never have existed.

Nevertheless trusts were enforceable only in the courts of equity. They were at no time enforceable at common law. It soon became established that the beneficiary could enforce his right not only against the trustee personally but against any transferee of the legal estate (except a bona fide purchaser without notice). Consequently the trust in equity created an interest in property as well as personal rights against the trustee.

The incidents of feudal tenure were abolished in 1660[3] but by this date the trust was being used to serve other purposes. For example the trust could be used to bequeath property for charitable purposes. In the seventeenth and eighteenth centuries the trust was used in the creation of strict settlements of large estates so as to keep family estates from being broken up and sold. Another way in which the trust was employed to meet social conditions was in the creation of marriage settlements by which a father could create a trust in favour of his daughter on marriage thus giving her a beneficial interest which did not pass to the husband on marriage with the rest of her property.

Indeed, to combat the social evil of fortune hunting husbands, wives could be restrained by the terms of the trust from disposing of future income from the trust. This was the "restraint upon anticipation" which was not abolished until 1935 when the legal position of a married woman as regards property was finally equated to that of her husband.[4] In more modern times the trust has proved an invaluable device in the avoidance of the incidence of estate duty.

The equity of redemption—There is a maxim of equity to the effect that "equity looks to the intent and not to the form". This maxim embodies that aspect of the Chancellor's "conscience" which led equity to intervene in the common law relating to mortgages. In the sixteenth century the classical form

---

[1] *Tyrrel's Case* (1558), Dyer 155.
[2] (1634), Toth. 188.
[3] 12 Car. 2, c. 24.
[4] Law Reform (Married Women and Tortfeasors) Act 1935.

of common law mortgage was a conveyance of the land to the mortgagee subject to a covenant to reconvey to the mortgagor on payment of the loan and interest on or before a specified date. This was construed strictly by the common law judges so that the right to a reconveyance was lost after the due date for redemption had passed. This strict view caused injustice and there are records of persons amassing vast fortunes by the simple expedient of advancing money on mortgage and absenting themselves until after the due date for redemption. This practice was the very type of occurrence calculated to prompt the intervention of the Chancellor and so it did. The Court of Chancery recognised a right to redeem after the due date for redemption had passed at law. This right was termed the "equity of redemption" and was an equitable interest in land which the mortgagor could deal with in the same way as a beneficiary under a trust could deal with his beneficial interest. Thus any person who took the legal estate in the land took it subject to the equity of redemption (unless he took it for value without notice). The only way in which the mortgagee could free himself of the fetter of the equity of redemption was to apply to the Court of Chancery to foreclose the mortgage.[1]

The effect of equity recognising these new rights in land was that the Court of Chancery acquired a vast quantity of litigation since by the nineteenth century most estates were the subject of settlements or mortgages.

b New Remedies

Injunction—An injunction is an order of the court compelling or restraining the performance of some act. An injunction which orders the defendant to perform some act is termed "mandatory", as opposed to a "prohibitory" injunction which restrains the defendant from committing some wrong, usually a tort.

The injunction is an equitable remedy but it had its counterpart in the common law writ of prohibition. This writ could be directed at inferior courts to prevent them from exceeding their jurisdiction[2] or at the sheriff to prevent the defendant infringing the plaintiff's right. However the injunction went beyond this writ since it could be directed at the defendant personally ("equity acts *in personam*") and failure to comply resulted in the imprisonment of the defendant for contempt of court.

Injunctions could be issued by the Chancellor not only in respect of equitable interests but also as a remedy for the infringement of common law rights. Thus equity contributed to the growth of the law of torts by providing a remedy where damages were inadequate redress, for example to restrain the commission of a nuisance or the publication of a libel. Unfortunately, the Court of Chancery could not, until 1858, award damages so that the plaintiff who sought damages and an injunction would have to bring two separate actions. The Chancery Amendment Act 1858 (Lord Cairns' Act) eventually remedied this by enabling the Court of Chancery to award damages as well as an injunction.

One particular form of injunction was the bone of contention between the

---

[1] Mortgage by conveyance of the fee simple was abolished by the Law of Property Act 1925 which substituted mortgage by grant of a term of years and created also the charge by way of legal mortage. Any attempt at mortgage by conveyance now takes effect as a lease for a term of 3,000 years.

[2] This is the scope of the present day order of prohibition.

common law courts and the Court of Chancery. This was the "common injunction" by which the Chancellor could restrain a litigant from proceeding to enforce his common law right in the common law courts or from enforcing a judgment obtained at common law, where this would violate principles of equity.[1]

Injunctions, like all equitable remedies, are discretionary. Even where the plaintiff can show that he has an equitable right he will not be awarded an injunction unless he has acted with conscience. In addition an injunction will not be granted where damages would be an adequate remedy. However this discretion can only limit rather than extend the scope of injunctions. Thus there is no discretion to grant an injunction to restrain an act which does not constitute an infringement of any right legal or equitable.[2] To this rule there is a minor exception in that the court can grant an injunction to restrain an act which would constitute an abuse of its own process for example by impeding the conduct of a pending action. Nevertheless the scope of injunctions is wider than the scope of common law remedies in that, while the latter could only be granted after the wrongful act had been performed, an injunction can issue to restrain an apprehended wrong, such an injunction being termed a *quia timet* injunction.[3]

Specific Performance—A decree of specific performance is an order of the court compelling a person to perform an obligation existing under either a contract or a trust. The remedy is particularly appropriate to actions in contract. It shares the characteristics of injunction and other equitable remedies in that its grant is discretionary and it will not be awarded either where the plaintiff has not behaved equitably (for example has given inadequate consideration) or where damages would be an adequate remedy. For this reason specific performance is only available to redress breaches of certain contracts, for example where the subject matter of a contract of sale is a chattel of a rare or personal nature[4] or, more usually, land.[5]

The Chancery Amendment Act 1858 enabled the Court of Chancery to award damages in lieu of, or in addition to, specific performance.

Rectification—The common law has always attached a peculiar sanctity to obligations under seal. It would enforce an obligation merely because it was under seal even though there was no consideration. Equity would not. Un-

---

[1] The common injunction was abolished by the Judicature Act 1873 but there is still power to restrain litigants from proceeding in inferior or foreign courts: see *Ellerman Lines, Ltd.* v. *Read*, [1928] 2 K.B. 144.

[2] *Day* v. *Brownrigg* (1878), 10 Ch.D. 294.

[3] The effect of Lord Cairns' Act in this respect is that a plaintiff may be awarded damages for proprietary loss even though no common law or proprietary right has been infringed: *Leeds Industrial Co-operative Society, Ltd.* v. *Slack*, [1924] A.C. 851. In *Seager* v. *Copydex, Ltd.*, [1967] 2 All E.R. 415; [1967] 1 W.L.R. 923 the plaintiff, an inventor, was awarded damages against a company that made use of confidential information supplied to them by the plaintiff, on the basis of the equitable doctrine of breach of confidence. Virtually the only distinction between the plaintiff's cause of action and an action in tort seems to be that the damages were not recoverable as a matter of right, but only as a matter of discretion.

[4] *Pusey* v. *Pusey* (1684), 1 Vern. 273.

[5] Specific performance may be ordered of an obligation to pay money where the payee is not the plaintiff so that damages would not be an adequate remedy: *Beswick* v. *Beswick*, [1968] A.C. 58; [1967] 2 All E.R. 1197.

fortunately the common law provided very few defences to an action on the defendant's seal. It was no defence at common law that the instrument did not accurately reflect the true intention of the parties. However equity did provide a defence. Where the instrument did not reflect the true intention of the parties, through a mistake in transcribing, the Court of Chancery claimed jurisdiction to rectify the document. Rectification lay only for mistake and did not allow contracts to be rectified but only documents. Nevertheless rectification was (and, in general, still is) only possible where the mistake was mutual. Rectification was apparently first used in respect of marriage settlements but was later extended to voluntary settlements and to written contracts.

Rescission—This remedy, like rectification, grew out of the inability of the common law to prevent a party from suing on a contract or covenant where it was obviously unjust for him to do so because of some collateral matter. In certain circumstances the Court of Chancery would rescind a contract where it was possible to restore the *status quo* between the parties. There were several grounds for applying for rescission, the most important being fraud and innocent misrepresentation.

Fraud in equity is a much wider concept than common law fraud. Fraud only gave rise to an action at common law in the action for deceit, in which case the fraud had to be a false representation of existing fact.[1] The equitable doctrine of fraud certainly encompassed this and went much further. It extended to virtually all circumstances which the layman would describe as instances of fraudulent conduct, such as taking unfair advantage of the weakness or ignorance of another, abusing a fiduciary relationship or disposing of property to defraud creditors. In all such cases the offended party might do nothing and resist a suit for specific performance. However if he had already parted with property this would be inadequate. In such a case he could apply to the court to rescind the contract.

A second ground for ordering rescission was innocent misrepresentation. Innocent misrepresentation at common law was confined to terms of the contract and gave rise only to an action for damages. Misrepresentation in equity extended to representations which did not form part of the contract. Such a representation gave no right to damages but did give a right in equity to rescind, thus filling a gap in the common law.[2]

D RELATIONSHIP BETWEEN COMMON LAW AND EQUITY

1 Prior to 1875

By the very nature of the jurisdiction it exercised the Court of Chancery was bound to come into conflict with the courts of the common law. Equity both supplemented the common law and corrected its deficiencies. Where equity supplemented the common law, as by the recognition of uses and the grant of equitable remedies for the infringement of legal rights, it was not particularly repugnant to common lawyers because it did not countermand their authority. However this was not the case where equity corrected the common law. In these instances there was a direct conflict between the common law courts and

---

[1] *Derry* v. *Peek* (1889), 14 App. Cas. 337.
[2] See now the Misrepresentation Act 1967.

the Chancellor. Thus the Chancellor would rescind a contract or rectify a deed where the common law courts would enforce it in accordance with its original terms. Equity would allow a mortgagor to redeem where the common law would recognise no fetter on the mortgagee's legal estate. In such a case equity would have to prevail or be of no effect. Consequently, in order to assert its prevalence, the Court of Chancery began to issue common injunctions which, although directed at the litigant personally rather than at the common law courts, had the effect of limiting common law jurisdiction. This practice became particularly prevalent during Wolsey's term of office, so much so that the practice was incorporated in the articles of his impeachment. To smooth over the conflict a common lawyer, Sir Thomas More, was appointed as Chancellor. This had no lasting effect and by the end of the sixteenth century the common injunction was once again a well established weapon in the Chancellor's armoury. In 1598 the common lawyers denounced the Court of Requests as an illegal court as a protest against the use of prerogative powers. The conflict with the Chancery itself came soon afterwards with the appointment of Coke as Chief Justice of the Common Pleas in 1606. Coke, a bitter opponent of prerogative power, attacked vigorously the jurisdiction of all the courts exercising this jurisdiction. In 1613 he was transferred to the King's Bench in which court he held in a case in 1615[1] that where a common law court had decided a case the Court of Chancery had no power to intervene between the parties, and that any parties who appealed from a common law decision to the Chancellor would be imprisoned under the Statute of Praemunire. Lord Ellesmere, the Lord Chancellor, brought the dispute to a head in the same year by declaring, in the *Earl of Oxford's Case*,[2] the power of the Chancery to set aside common law judgments "not for any error or defect in the judgment, but for the hard conscience of the party". The dispute was referred to the King, James I. James I, after consulting his Attorney-General, Sir Francis Bacon (Coke's bitterest opponent and destined to be Ellesmere's successor as Chancellor), decided in favour of the Court of Chancery and upheld the validity of the common injunction. Thus the supremacy of equity was established though in the next eighty years this supremacy was by no means unchallenged. As late as 1690 a bill was introduced into Parliament to give the common law courts power to issue writs of prohibition to prohibit the Chancery from encroaching upon their jurisdiction. The bill never became law and the efforts of the common lawyers to evade the consequences of the *Earl of Oxford's Case* thereafter petered out. Nonetheless, by this time most of the rules and principles of equity had become as firmly established as those of the common law and equity had virtually ceased to evolve as a corrective to the common law. The evolution of the doctrine of binding precedent must be blamed for this, though the conservatism of the judges doubtless played a part. LORD ELDON's attitude is epitomised in the following famous extract from one of his judgments:[3]

> "The doctrines of this court ought to be as well settled, and made as uniform, almost, as those of the Common Law. . . . Nothing would inflict on me greater pain, in quitting this place, than the recollection that I had done anything to justify the reproach that the equity of this court varies like the Chancellor's foot."

[1] *Courtney v. Glanvil* (1615), Cro. Jac. 343.
[2] (1615), 1 Rep. Ch. 1.
[3] *Gee v. Pritchard* (1818), 2 Swan. 402, at p. 414.

By the time of the Judicature Acts even as imaginative a lawyer as Sir George Jessel, M.R. could observe:[1]

"This Court is not, as I have often said, a Court of Conscience, but a Court of Law."

2 Equity after the Judicature Acts 1873-1875

The major reforms effected by these Acts are considered in detail below.[2] The Acts abolished the conflict between the common law courts and the Court of Chancery by abolishing these courts themselves and transferring their jurisdiction to the new Supreme Court of Judicature. Consequently the common injunction was abolished and an injunction cannot now issue out of one Division of the High Court to restrain proceedings in any other Division.

However the Judicature Acts fused only the administration of common law and equity. They did not fuse the substantive rules. Thus an award of damages is still a legal remedy and available as of right for infringement of a legal right whereas equitable remedies are still discretionary. There is no longer any duality of jurisdiction since the Supreme Court must give effect to both legal and equitable rights and remedies. Where there is conflict between the rules of common law and equity with reference to the same matter, the rules of equity prevail.[3] The effect of this provision is that certain rules of common law have been extinguished. With respect to interests in land most possible sources of conflict were removed by the property legislation of 1925.

---

[1] *Re National Funds Assurance Co.* (1878), 10 Ch.D. 118, at p. 128.
[2] See p. 58, *post.*
[3] Judicature Act 1873, s. 25; see p. 62, *post.*

CHAPTER 3

Other Historical Sources

A LEGISLATION

Legislation is, after common law and equity, the third major historical source of English law. At the present day legislation is the principal agency of law reform and, with the tendency toward codification, is becoming the most important source of English law. In addition practically all the rules relating to the composition and jurisdiction of the modern courts and procedure applicable therein are statutory. It perhaps presents an accurate picture to say that, while most principles of English law have their origins in common law and equity, most of the detail is now contained in statute.

Early legislation was scarcely distinguishable from common law. Norman and early Angevin monarchs promulgated charters,[1] ordinances[2] and assizes[3] but these are hardly legislation in the modern sense since the concept of a separate legislature had not yet evolved. It is uncertain how far these governmental acts were regarded as authoritative. No doubt many were accepted as having the force of statutes but it was not until the end of the Middle Ages that legislative acts of less authority than statutes ceased to appear. Even statutes did not enjoy the absolute authority accorded to them at the present day. There are many instances in the Year Books of judges refusing to apply statutes because they conflicted with the common law, which was still regarded as sovereign.

The fifteenth century saw the recognition of statutes as being of absolute, literal authority. This corresponded to the emergence of Parliament as the legislature and, in Tudor times, to the printing and publication of statutes which allayed earlier doubts as to authenticity. By the early seventeenth century Coke could state of Parliament's legislative power:

"it is so transcendent and absolute as it cannot be confined either for causes or persons within any bounds".[4]

The nineteenth century heralded the era of codification and statutory definition of the jurisdiction of the courts. In this era legislation passed from being a fairly

---

[1] E.g., Magna Carta 1215.
[2] E.g., Ordinance of Labourers 1349.
[3] E.g., Assize of Northampton 1176.
[4] 2 Inst., Proem.

minor source of law, used mainly to guide the development of the common law, to being a major source of law transcending common law and equity.

Legislation as a source of law differs from common law and equity in several respects. Common law and equity, because of the doctrine of precedent, are inherently limited and can only develop new principles by varying and extending the application of existing principles. Legislation, on the other hand, can embody wholly new principles of law formulated without reference to any existing principles and, more important, can categorically repeal existing law which common law and equity cannot do. These are the principal advantages of legislation as an agency of law reform.

Finally legislation differs from other historical sources of law in another important respect. In the case of common law, equity and other historical sources the rules can only be ascertained by reference to other legal sources, notably precedents. Legislation is its own legal source. For this reason interpretation of statutes is a most important technique since it is only by interpreting the words of a statute that the law which it contains can be deduced from it. This important topic is dealt with fully below.[1]

B CUSTOM

The word "custom" may be used in several different senses. In one sense custom is the principal source of the whole of English law since it is the original source of common law. The early common law was not an entirely new set of rules imported into England by the Normans but rather that body of rules resulting from the welding of the law and custom of England into one system of law. In 1350 counsel declared that "common usage is common law".[2] These customs, such as monogamy, parental rights, the right to use the seashore for navigation and fishing[3] and most of the early criminal law, are no longer regarded as a separate source of law since they have either become part of the common law or been incorporated in statute.

A second use of the word "custom" is to describe conventional trade or business usage. This is really a misuse of the word since trade usage is usually relevant only to imply terms into contracts, so that the court can ascertain what unexpressed terms the parties intended to apply. These are questions of fact rather than questions of law so that custom, in this context, is not a source of law at all. Trade customs need not be ancient[4] provided that they can be proved to be certain. However they must not be illegal or unreasonable and they may always be expressly excluded. Many trade customs were originally an elaborate method of granting discount to purchasers; hence the "baker's dozen" and the fact that 1,000 rabbits mean 1,200 rabbits to rabbit-dealers.[5] Ancient mercantile custom fulfilled a wider function than modern commercial usage since it was the basis of a set of rules of law collectively described as the law merchant. The law merchant, unlike trade usage, is a source of law and is considered below.[6]

---

[1] See p. 102, *post.*
[2] Y.B. 30 Edw. 3, ff. 25, 26.
[3] Though not for bathing or beachcombing; see *Alfred F. Beckett, Ltd.* v. *Lyons,* [1967] Ch. 449; [1967] 1 All E.R. 833.
[4] See *Noble* v. *Kennoway* (1780), 2 Doug. 510, at p. 513, *per* LORD MANSFIELD.
[5] *Smith* v. *Wilson* (1832), 3 B. & Ad. 728.
[6] See p. 46, *post.*

The third common use of the word "custom" is to describe local custom: rules of law which apply only in a definite locality. Custom, in this sense of the word, is a separate source of law.

Local custom

Local custom as a source of law, distinct from common law, has two elementary and unvarying characteristics; first, it must be an exception to the common law and, second, it must be confined in its application to a particular locality such as a county, borough or parish. It may be further limited to a class of persons within that locality, for example fishermen, but it cannot apply to a class of persons generally throughout the kingdom, for if it did it would be part of the common law and not an exception to it.

The modern tendency is to standardise the law by statute and this has resulted in the statutory abolition of many local customs. Customary forms of land tenure and succession[1] were all abolished by the Law of Property Acts 1922 and 1925. The type of local customary right still existing is in the nature of a right of way, right of common or a right to dry fishing-nets[2] on land within the parish. However, a customary profit-à-prendre cannot exist in favour of an indefinite number of persons, such as the inhabitants of a locality, since this would be liable to destroy entirely the subject-matter of the profit.[3]

Customary rules of law, unlike rules of common law, are not judicially noticed until settled by judicial decision. Thus any person who alleges a customary right must plead it and prove its existence. This involves showing that the alleged custom satisfies certain tests. Blackstone's classification of these tests is the generally accepted arrangement and is as follows.

a Antiquity

Local custom must have existed from "time whereof the memory of man runneth not to the contrary" (time immemorial). This has been fixed by statute[4] at 1189, the first year of the reign of Richard I. In practice positive proof of existence in 1189 is rarely available so that the courts are willing to accept as proof evidence that the custom has existed for a long time. This is often done by calling the oldest available local inhabitant as a witness. The burden is then on the party denying the existence of the custom to prove either that it did not exist in 1189 or that it could not have existed in 1189. Thus in *Simpson* v. *Wells*[5] the appellant, who had been charged with obstructing a public foot-way by setting up a refreshment stall, alleged that he had a customary right to do so deriving from "statute sessions".[6] It was shown that statute sessions were first authorised by the Statutes of Labourers in the fourteenth century so that the right could not have existed in 1189.

---

[1] Examples were "Gavelkind" (a customary method of descent applicable in Kent) and "Borough English" (a customary method of descent applicable in Nottingham, Bristol and certain other boroughs whereby freeholds passed on intestacy to the youngest son or brother).
[2] *Mercer* v. *Denne*, [1905] 2 Ch. 538.
[3] *Alfred F. Beckett, Ltd.* v. *Lyons*, [1967] Ch. 449; [1967] 1 All E.R. 833.
[4] Statute of Westminster I 1275.
[5] (1872), L.R. 7 Q.B. 214.
[6] These were ancient fairs held for the purpose of hiring servants.

b Continuance

This is Blackstone's second test for proving custom. The right must have existed uninterrupted. Any interruption of the custom since 1189 defeats its existence.

c Peaceable enjoyment

A custom can only exist by common consent. It must not have been exercised by the use of force, nor secretly, nor under a revocable licence (since this would make the custom dependent upon the will of one individual rather than on public observance): *nec per vim nec clam nec precario*. Thus, where the right to fish depended upon the grant of a licence by the owners of an oyster fishery, it was held that there was no customary right to fish since enjoyment had never been as of right, but only by licence.[1]

d Obligatory force

Where the custom imposes a specific duty that duty must be obligatory. This is true of all rules of law. Indeed it is this which distinguishes a rule of law from a social convention or a moral obligation. Thus, notes Blackstone:

> "a custom that all the inhabitants shall be rated towards the maintenance of a bridge, will be good; but a custom that every man is to contribute thereto at his own pleasure, is idle and absurd, and indeed no custom at all".

e Certainty

A custom must be certain for, as JESSEL, M.R. observed, "the notion of law means a certain rule of some kind".[2] For this reason a usage was held bad which provided that a man in Hereford had capacity to sell land when he could measure an ell[3] and count up to twelve since "one person is twenty years old before he knows how to measure an ell, and another knows how when he is seven years old".[4] Similarly an alleged manorial custom enabling tenants to take away turf "in such quantity as occasion may require" has been held void for uncertainty.[5]

f Consistency

Customs must be consistent with one another. They are, by their nature, inconsistent with the common law but they cannot, in a defined locality, be inconsistent with one another, for as Blackstone observed:

> "if one man prescribes that by custom he has a right to have windows looking into another's garden, the other cannot claim a right by custom to stop up or obstruct those windows: for these contradictory customs cannot both be good, nor both stand together".[6]

The appropriate course of procedure is to deny the existence of a custom inconsistent with one's own customary right. This is not, however, possible if

---

[1] *Mills* v. *Mayor of Colchester* (1867), L.R. 2 C.P. 476; see also *Alfred F. Beckett, Ltd.* v. *Lyons*, [1967] Ch. 449; [1967] 1 All E.R. 833.
[2] *Hammerton* v. *Honey* (1876), 24 W.R. 603.
[3] 45 inches.
[4] Y.B. 12, f. 13 Edw. 3 (R.S.) 236.
[5] *Wilson* v. *Willes* (1806), 7 East 121.
[6] Bl. Comm. 78.

that custom has been settled by judicial decision for then it will be judicially noticed.

g Reasonableness

The last and most important test that custom must satisfy is that of reasonableness. It is for the party refuting the custom to show that it is unreasonable. A custom which is repugnant to a fundamental principle of common law cannot be reasonable. For this reason the House of Lords rejected a custom which enabled a manorial lord to undermine his tenant's land without paying compensation for damage to buildings thereby caused.[1] Equally a customary right to commit a crime could not be reasonable.

Furthermore, if a custom must obviously have been unreasonable in 1189 (though not necessarily unreasonable at the present day) this will tend to show that the custom could not have existed in 1189 and it will be rejected on this ground rather than on the basis of it being unreasonable. In *Bryant* v. *Foot*[2] the rector of a parish claimed thirteen shillings as a customary fee for the celebration of a marriage in the parish. It was held that, having regard to the value of money in 1189, the amount was totally unreasonable so that the custom could not have existed at that date.

C LAW MERCHANT

The law of contract as administered in the common law courts in the thirteenth and fourteenth centuries was extremely rudimentary. Broadly speaking an action could only be brought within the narrow terms of the writ of debt or in respect of the breach of an obligation under seal (writ of covenant). In addition the local courts had only a limited jurisdiction in contract since the Statute of Gloucester 1278, had effectively reduced their jurisdiction to claims involving less than forty shillings.[3]

Thus the existing courts were ill-equipped to deal with the increasing volume of litigation arising from England's growth as a trading centre. The result was that a new set of courts sprang up to deal solely with disputes between merchants. Since these courts were not common law courts they were in no way tied to the common law, and a new set of rules originating partly in custom and partly in international law evolved as the basis of the jurisdiction of these courts.

1 Courts administering the Law Merchant

a Courts of fairs and boroughs

Most mercantile transactions in the Middle Ages were conducted at fairs and markets which were held in fixed places on fixed days. The most important and permanent fairs were held in boroughs which were communities granted a franchise by the King in return for payment of royal dues known as "tolls". The charter granted by the King usually conferred the right to hold a court in the borough. Officers of the borough were also given power to hold courts

---

[1] *Wolstanton, Ltd. and Duchy of Lancaster* v. *Newcastle-under-Lyme Corporation*, [1940] A.C. 860; [1940] 3 All E.R. 101.
[2] (1868), L.R. 3 Q.B. 497.
[3] See p. 5, *ante*.

at the fairs and markets so that the courts of the fairs were generally special sessions of the borough court. These courts were known as "Piepowder" courts,[1] and naturally attracted merchants because of the speed and simplicity of procedure and because the law administered in the courts gave effect to their own customs which formed the basis of their dealings.

The thirteenth and fourteenth centuries were the heyday of the piepowder courts. Thereafter various factors contributed to their obsolescence. In 1466[2] the Court of Common Pleas held that an appeal lay by writ of error to the common law courts. This intervention by the common lawyers was the very thing the merchants wished to avoid. The nature of commerce changed and merchants became less peripatetic. The courts themselves began to acquire a cumbersome and technical procedure while the common law courts, with the evolution of assumpsit, broadened their jurisdiction. By the eighteenth century almost all the piepowder courts had ceased to function.[3]

b Staple courts

In order to facilitate the collection of customs duties from foreign merchants, statutes were passed[4] confining dealing in certain basic commodities such as wool and tin to certain towns. In each of these "staple" towns there was a court which had exclusive jurisdiction over merchants, save in matters involving title to land or felony. These Courts of Staple thus exercised both a civil and criminal jurisdiction and applied a pot-pourri of the common law and mercantile custom.

These courts later assumed jurisdiction over persons who were not merchants but they soon became obsolete with the decline of the staple system.

c High Court of Admiralty

It has at all times been difficult to separate mercantile and maritime law. Both had their origins in foreign legal systems and mercantile custom. The High Court of Admiralty, created in the fourteenth century, had both a civil and a criminal jurisdiction over matters arising on the high seas. The court also assumed jurisdiction over contracts made on land, in the fifteenth century, by the fictitious assumption that the contract was in fact made "on the high seas". The court was closely associated with the Council and the Tudors, particularly Henry VIII, extended its jurisdiction to a wide range of civil and criminal[5] matters having little or no connection with admiralty. The combined effect of this upsurge in the fortunes of the High Court of Admiralty and the corresponding decline of the courts of piepowder and staple was that the former acquired most of the jurisdiction of the latter.

Unfortunately for the Admiralty this euphoric state of affairs was to be of

---

[1] Possibly deriving from the French *"pieds poudrés"* (dusty feet).

[2] Y.B. 6 Edw. 4, M., pl. 9.

[3] The last of these courts, the Bristol Tolzey and Pie Poudre Courts, were abolished by s. 43 of the Courts Act 1971.

[4] Notably 27 Edw. 3, st. 2 (1353).

[5] A statute of 1536, 28 Hen. 8, c. 15, confirmed the court's jurisdiction over crimes committed on the high seas and provided for trial by jury before commissioners. Later, when the court became unpopular with the common lawyers, these commissioners were invariably common lawyers so that the common law in fact controlled the criminal jurisdiction of the court.

limited duration. The same close association with the Council which had helped the rise in the court's fortunes later contributed to their decline. The court, in common with the other conciliar courts, the Court of Chancery, the Court of Star Chamber and the Court of Requests, met the full force of Coke's attack on prerogative powers on his accession to the bench in 1606. He denied that the court was a court of record and regarded it as an inferior court having no power to fine or imprison and being subject to the royal writ of prohibition. The effect of these attacks was not sufficiently strong to overthrow the court but it was sufficient to limit its jurisdiction, in civil cases, to matters actually arising on the high seas. It lost all its jurisdiction over such matters as contracts made abroad. Indeed the common law encroached further upon admiralty jurisdiction and assumed jurisdiction over contracts made either abroad or on the high seas by the fiction (yet another example of the use of fictions to acquire jurisdiction) that the contract was made "in the parish of St. Mary-le-Bow in the Ward of Cheap". Thus all that remained of admiralty jurisdiction were cases involving collisions at sea, salvage and, in the eighteenth and nineteenth centuries, prize. All this jurisdiction was transferred to the new Probate, Divorce and Admiralty Division of the High Court in 1875.[1] The criminal jurisdiction of the Admiralty commissioners, which derived from the statute of 1536, was given to the Central Criminal Court in 1834 and to courts of assize in 1844.[2] Since this date no admiralty sessions have been held.

Appeal lay from the High Court of Admiralty to the Council originally, later to the High Court of Delegates and finally, after 1832, to the Privy Council.

Thus by the seventeenth century the law merchant had passed largely into the jurisdiction of the common law courts.

2 The content of the Law Merchant

Although the law merchant was, by the seventeenth century, administered in the common law courts, the common law judges did not regard it as part of the common law. They were ever aware that it was based on usage. In the leading case of *Goodwin* v. *Robarts*[3] COCKBURN, C.J. described the *lex mercatoria* in the following words:

> "It is neither more nor less than the usages of merchants and traders in the different departments of trade, ratified by the decisions of courts of law."

The effect of the law merchant being derived from custom was that since the common lawyers required proof of the existence of a custom they would not recognise a rule of the law merchant which was unreasonable or repugnant to the common law. On the other hand mercantile customs, unlike local customs, were not required to date from time immemorial so that recent customs could be accepted into the law. Thus, just as equity grew as a gloss on the common law, the law merchant was a gloss on the law of contract which was, even after the evolution of assumpsit, scarcely adequate to meet mercantile needs.

Perhaps the greatest contribution of the law merchant to the common law

---

[1] It is now administered in the "Admiralty Court" of the Queen's Bench Division; Administration of Justice Act 1970, ss. 1 (3), 2; see p. 163, *post*.

[2] The criminal jurisdiction of the Admiralty is now exercised by the Crown Court; Courts Act 1971, s. 6 (2).

[3] (1875). L.R. 10 Ex. 337.

was the concept of negotiability. This was introduced in the seventeenth century by means of a special action on the case on the custom of merchants to fill the gap left by the refusal of the common law to recognise the assignability of choses in action. Eventually the necessity for pleading this special action on the case disappeared and, largely due to the pioneering of Holt, C.J., bills of exchange were accepted at common law. Holt, C.J. (Chief Justice of the King's Bench 1689–1710) formulated the principles of transfer by endorsement, presumption of consideration and the rule that a *bona fide* holder's title was not invalidated by defects in the title of the transferor. Holt's work was perfected by the great Scots lawyer Lord Mansfield who was Chief Justice of the King's Bench between 1756 and 1788. The negotiable instrument is by no means the sole contribution of the law merchant to English law. Partnership, the law of agency and insurance are three major branches of the law which have the custom of merchants as their primary source. The nineteenth century, the age of codification, saw the incorporation of much of the law merchant into statute. The Bills of Exchange Act 1882, the Partnership Act 1890 and the Sale of Goods Act 1893 are examples of such statutes.

D CANON LAW

The canon law, the law of the Western or Catholic Church, has influenced the growth of English law in two ways. First it was the basis of many concepts which were formulated in the lay courts and as such is a primary source of other sources of law. Examples of common law concepts which originated in the canon law are: the nature of criminal law and its close association with moral fault, imprisonment as a punishment for crime (the purpose of which the canonists conceived to be the possibility of repentance through solitary contemplation). wager of law as a method of trial and, of course, the nature of Christian marriage and family rights. In addition the common law trial by ordeal relied for its efficacy on the participation of the clergy. Canon law also influenced the nature of equity, the strong moral content of which is attributable to the fact of the early Chancellors being clerics. Specific concepts of equity, such as the recognition of marriage as good consideration for a marriage settlement, are undoubtedly identifiable with a canon law origin.

The second, and more important, way in which canon law became a source of English law was by its application in the ecclesiastical courts. In this context canon law was a system of law wholly independent of the common law since the ecclesiastical courts were, during the Middle Ages, completely outside the control of the King.

I Ecclesiastical courts
It would be impossible in a general outline of the historical sources of English law to deal fully with the myriad of ecclesiastical courts which have existed at different times in history. Only a broad outline is possible.

a Hierarchy
The lowest ecclesiastical court was the court of the archdeacon. Above the archdeaconry courts were the diocesan courts of the bishops, the consistory courts. These were the courts of first instance in all matters not concerning

members of the clergy. The consistory courts also exercised appellate jurisdiction over clergy discipline as administered in the archdeaconry courts.
Appeal lay from the consistory courts to the provincial courts of the two archbishops (York Chancery and Court of Arches).[1]

Until the Reformation the Papal Curia was at the summit of the hierarchy.
The Pope possessed both legislative and judicial power over the English clergy;
his judicial function was both original and appellate but was, obviously, confined to cases of major importance. The result of the Reformation was the
abolition of all Papal jurisdiction. The legislative power of the Pope passed to
Parliament and Convocations of the clergy. The jurisdiction to hear appeals
from the provincial courts was assumed by the Court of Delegates established
by statute[2] in 1533. The commissioners, appointed by the Crown, might be
bishops, common law judges or "civilian" lawyers. The unsatisfactory composition of the court prevented it from enjoying any great respect. In addition
it followed no system of precedent and did not record its decisions. Its jurisdiction in both ecclesiastical and admiralty matters was transferred to the Privy
Council in 1832.

b   Procedure

Procedure in the ecclesiastical courts resembled procedure in the Court of
Chancery rather than common law procedure. Proceedings were instituted by
a document known as a "libel" which was similar in form to a Chancery
petition. The parties were examined in court and could be represented by the
proctors and advocates who composed that part of the legal profession which
practised in the ecclesiastical courts and had been schooled in civil law at the
universities of Oxford and Cambridge.[3] The judges of the consistory and
provincial courts were styled Chancellors and they sat without a jury. Judgment was in the form of a decree.

c   Conflict with the common law

All courts outside the common law system clashed with the common lawyers
at one time or another. The ecclesiastical courts were no exception to this
rule. The conflict between Church and State in the reign of Henry II precipitated the question of the scope of the jurisdiction of the Church courts. In 1164
the English bishops were induced to agree the concessions of jurisdiction contained in the Constitutions of Clarendon. The most important concessions of
jurisdiction were over *advowsons* (the right[4] to nominate clergymen to an
ecclesiastical benefice), disputes over which were conceded to be outside the
jurisdiction of the ecclesiastical courts, disputes over whether land was held
under common law or spiritual tenure (*frankalmoign*)[5] and, finally, the right of

---

[1] For the present hierarchy and jurisdiction of the ecclesiastical courts, see p. 182, *post*.
[2] 25 Hen. 8, c. 19. The Court of Delegates also heard appeals from the High Court of
Admiralty.
[3] Eventually the degree of Doctor of Civil Law, obtainable only at these Universities,
became an essential qualification for practice in the ecclesiastical or admiralty courts.
Those qualified had their chambers in buildings called "Doctors' Commons" in which
the Court of Arches and the High Court of Admiralty sat.
[4] The right, which generally belonged to the person who had endowed the church, was a
valuable right in property and capable of conveyance.
[5] This was decided by an "assize *utrum*". If land were found to be held in *frankalmoign* any
dispute passed into the jurisdiction of the ecclesiastical courts.

the common law courts to try clerics for criminal offences in respect of which they had been convicted in the church court. This last concession of jurisdiction was removed after the murder of Becket which was the origin of the long history of the privilege of "benefit of clergy".[1]

After this the jurisdiction of the ecclesiastical courts became fairly clearly defined and did not cause any serious clash with the common lawyers until the seventeenth century when the whole system of ecclesiastical courts was brought down by the Civil War. The system was reinstated by the Restoration but shortly afterwards lost its jurisdiction over the laity in matters of criminal law and moral offences.

The surviving jurisdiction of the ecclesiastical courts over the laity comprised probate and matrimonial jurisdiction. This in turn became resented by the common lawyers and was removed by the Matrimonial Causes Act 1857 and the Court of Probate Act 1857. Since this date the jurisdiction of the ecclesiastical courts has been confined to matters affecting members of the Church where this jurisdiction does not conflict with the jurisdiction of the ordinary courts.[2]

2 Content of the Canon Law as administered in the Ecclesiastical Courts

That part of the ecclesiastical courts' jurisdiction which concerned the enforcement of doctrine and morals and matters concerning only the clergy has not passed into English law and remains solely the province of the ecclesiastical courts. Thus offences such as incontinence, adultery, usury and slander have not become part of the general criminal law.

The part of canon law which is a source of the general English law is that part which concerns probate and matrimony. By no means the whole of the law of probate was within the control of the church courts. Their jurisdiction was in fact confined to wills of personalty (including leaseholds). This jurisdiction also extended to granting letters of administration on intestacy. However no probate or letters of administration were required in respect of realty. Disputes as to the validity of wills, so far as they disposed of realty, could only be determined in the common law courts.[3] Although matters concerning the validity of wills were within the jurisdiction of the ecclesiastical courts matters concerning their construction and the administration of estates were not. These were dealt with by the Court of Chancery. This unfortunate dichotomy of jurisdiction was perpetuated by the Judicature Acts and existed until the Administration of Justice Act 1970 re-named the Probate, Divorce and Admiralty Division the Family Division and transferred contentious probate business to the Chancery Division.[4] Probate jurisdiction was transferred to the newly-created Court of Probate by the Act of 1857. The Court was given power to hear and determine all questions relating to testamentary matters. This jurisdiction was finally assigned to the Probate, Divorce and Admiralty Division in 1875.

---

[1] See p. 16, *ante.*
[2] See p. 172, *post.*
[3] The procedure was by action of ejectment by the devisee against the heir-at-law.
[4] Administration of Justice Act 1970, s. 1 (4); see p. 162, *post.*

Perhaps the most important aspect of modern law which has its origin in the canon law as administered in the ecclesiastical courts is family law. Although a common law marriage was (and still is) possible in special circumstances most marriages were celebrated in church so that marriage was, and always has been, a relationship with strong religious implications. Although the ecclesiastical courts, accepting marriage as indissoluble, had no power to grant a divorce in the modern sense they did have power to pronounce decrees of nullity, restitution of conjugal rights[1] (calling on a deserting spouse to return to the other) and a "divorce" *a mensa et thoro* (judicial separation, which relieves one spouse of the duty of cohabiting with the other). Divorce *a vinculo* became possible by private Act of Parliament in the latter half of the seventeenth century, though this was exceedingly expensive. Divorce by judicial decree was made possible for the first time by the Matrimonial Causes Act 1857. This Act, passed to give effect to the report of a royal commission set up in 1850 to consider this branch of the law, transferred the matrimonial jurisdiction of the ecclesiastical courts to the new Divorce Court. This jurisdiction was assigned by the Judicature Acts to the Probate, Divorce and Admiralty Division of the High Court.

The ecclesiastical courts conflicted in certain respects with the common law courts. Thus, although the ecclesiastical courts recognised legitimation by subsequent marriage of the parents, the common law did not and excluded such children from succession under a disposition to "children". The ecclesiastical concept of legitimation was not, in fact, recognised in English law until the passing of the Legitimacy Act 1926.

E ROMAN LAW

Roman law, the basis of most continental systems of law, is, surprisingly, of very minor importance as a source of English law. It is not a direct source at all in the sense that there was never a system of English courts applying solely Roman law. Any influence that Roman law has had on the growth of English law has been indirect. The source of law which owes most to Roman law is canon law. The reason is that the Chancellors and advocates in the ecclesiastical courts were indoctrinated with the civil law through their studies at Oxford and Cambridge. Thus the formal requirements of wills in many cases have their counterpart in Roman law as have many of the rules relating to parental authority.

Roman law also undoubtedly influenced maritime and mercantile law since the Venetian and Genoese mercantile customs which these branches of the law utilised had a civilian basis.

The common law itself has from time to time borrowed from Roman law. The principal link between Roman law and common law is Bracton's treatise *De Legibus et Consuetudinibus Angliae* written in Latin in about the year 1250. Bracton was well versed in Roman law and the civilian principles he incorporated into his treatise owed much to the writings of the Roman jurist Justinian. Thus common law judges, faced with a case of first impression with

---

[1] The sanction for failure to comply with the decree could be excommunication until the Ecclesiastical Courts Act 1813 which replaced this with power to commit for contempt. This was in turn abolished by the Matrimonial Causes Act 1884. The decree was abolished by the Divorce Reform Act 1969.

little or no assistance to be gleaned from English precedents, have looked to Bracton for assistance and in doing so have adopted Romanist principles. The leading example is the judgment of HOLT, C.J. in *Coggs* v. *Bernard*[1] which classifies bailments in accordance with Bracton's classification, itself based on Roman law. Similarly, in *Dalton* v. *Angus*[2] LORD BLACKBURN, one of the greatest of common law judges, considered the Roman doctrine of *usucapio* (prescription) when deciding a difficult question on the subject of easements. Also, in a modern case,[3] the question of whether the owner of a swarm of bees could follow them on to the land of another was answered by reference to Justinian's Institutes which, as every student of Roman law knows, deals with that precise question.

[1] (1703), 2 Ld. Raym. 969.
[2] (1881), 6 App. Cas. 740.
[3] *Kearry* v. *Pattinson*, [1939] 1 K.B. 471; [1939] 1 All E.R. 65.

CHAPTER 4

Administrative Reforms of the Nineteenth Century

A THE NEED FOR REFORM

English law has been compared to a river which is "first fed by the springs of the common law" and later by "the fountain of equity, and the wells of the law merchant and ecclesiastical law".[1] The chief cause for concern at the beginning of the nineteenth century was not the existence of separate sources of law, for these complemented and supplemented one another to produce one body of English law, but the fact that these sources were being administered in different courts. Thus the common law was administered principally by the three superior common law courts, equity by the Court of Chancery, canon law by the ecclesiastical courts and the law merchant and maritime by the High Court of Admiralty. In addition procedure in the individual courts was generally defective in one or more respects. The restrictive operation of the doctrine of precedent together with the inherent conservatism of judges made it impossible for judicial reform to correct the major deficiencies which existed. Only sweeping legislation could clear the dead wood and the nineteenth century was to be the great era of legislative reform. It must not be supposed that the need for reform was universally accepted. Those who profited by the general corruption of the officials of the Court of Chancery or by the complexity of pleading in the common law courts were by no means anxious to alter their situation. Others could not conceive that so majestic a system as the English Legal System could be in any way improved. Thus Blackstone in his *Commentaries on the Laws of England* published in 1765 painted a rosy picture of the system. Lord Eldon opposed virtually every reformative measure introduced during his Chancellorship (1801–1827). Fortunately there were others such as Jeremy Bentham, Sir Samuel Romilly and Lord Brougham who could detect the fundamental flaws which existed. The principal matters needing reform were as follows:

---

[1] Potter, *op. cit.* (5th Edn.), p. 1.

(1) the duality of jurisdiction between the common law courts and the Court of Chancery whereby a plaintiff might have to commence two separate actions in respect of one set of facts: an action in the common law courts to obtain damages and a separate action in the Chancery for an equitable remedy such as an injunction;

(2) the system whereby the Chancellor could restrain a litigant from enforcing his common law rights by means of a common injunction;

(3) the fact that the ecclesiastical courts exercised exclusive jurisdiction in matters of probate and matrimonial causes over persons who were not members of the Church of England;

(4) the conflict of jurisdiction between the common law courts and the High Court of Admiralty;

(5) the fact that the jurisdiction of the three superior common law courts had become co-extensive in many cases through the widespread use of fictions such as Bill of Middlesex and *Quominus*;

(6) the lack of a system of courts to try small civil claims. Those local courts and borough courts which had fulfilled the useful function of dispensing justice summarily and cheaply had, by the nineteenth century, been almost entirely swallowed up by the superior courts of the common law. The result was the creation of a vacuum since the considerable costs of proceedings in Westminster or at *nisi prius* made litigation impracticable where the sum involved was not large;

(7) the complex and inadequate system of appeals in both civil and criminal cases at common law (the right to appeal against a finding of fact in criminal cases, a long-felt need, was not in fact introduced until 1907);[1]

(8) the formal and artificial procedure existing in the common law courts.[2] The cornerstone of procedural difficulty at common law was, of course, the writ system with its many different forms of action, each subject to a different procedure and a different system of pleading. If the plaintiff was unfortunate enough to choose the wrong writ he would be non-suited and would have to start his action all over again. His error could not be cured by amendment, nor could he plead in the alternative;

(9) the scandalous condition of the Court of Chancery. The complete inadequacy of the judicial staff of the court led to an ever-increasing backlog of cases which became even greater under Lord Eldon due to that Chancellor's excessive caution and dilatory conduct. The inadequacy of the judicial staff was matched only by the welter of court officials whose bribery and corruption have already been noted.[3]

Almost all of these defects were corrected by legislation between 1825 and 1875, culminating in the Judicature Acts 1873–1875. The Judicature Acts were so comprehensive and sweeping as to merit separate consideration, but, before that, the principal steps leading to their passing must be traced.

---

[1] Criminal Appeal Act 1907.
[2] See p. 17, *ante*.
[3] See p. 31, *ante*.

B   REFORMS PRIOR TO 1873

1   Reforms of the Common Law Courts and Procedure

a   Uniformity of Process Act 1832

This Act was the first of the procedural reforms. It abolished the various different forms of commencing proceedings and substituted one form of writ of summons to be used for commencing personal actions in all three common law courts. It did not affect real actions. It must not be supposed that the Act abolished the necessity for selecting a particular form of action. It did not. The plaintiff still had to specify his cause of action by reference to one form of action and if he selected the wrong one he would be non-suited just as before.

b   Real Property Limitation Act 1833

This statute formally abolished almost all the real actions. In fact the statute had but slight effect since it did not affect the action of ejectment which had long superseded the real actions nor did it affect the procedure for bringing those real actions which were not abolished.

c   Civil Procedure Act 1833

This Act extended the procedural reforms commenced by the Uniformity of Process Act 1832. Apart from finally abolishing wager of law and, for the first time, making it possible for the defendant to pay money into court in satisfaction of the plaintiff's claim, the Act created a new system of pleading. Although this system swept away many of the anachronistic rules of pleading it scarcely simplified pleading and eventually had to be repealed because it created a system which proved to be far more complex than the system which it was intended to replace.

d   Common Law Procedure Acts 1852–1860

The three Common Law Procedure Acts of 1852, 1854 and 1860 constituted the first real attempts at comprehensive reform of the common law system. Each was passed following recommendations contained in the reports of the Civil Procedure Commissioners appointed in 1850.

The Common Law Procedure Act 1852 revised completely proceedings at first instance and on appeal and created many of the rules of procedure which were eventually incorporated in the Rules of the Supreme Court annexed to the Judicature Acts. The fundamental reform was the abolition of the forms of action. After 1852 the necessity for naming a specific form of action on the writ of summons was removed. Consequently joinder of causes of action, hitherto impossible, was recognised and one source of duplicity of proceedings removed. The action of ejectment and its two protagonists John Doe and Richard Roe were laid to rest and replaced by the modern action for the recovery of land. Amendment of pleadings became possible, judgment in default of appearance was introduced and service outside the jurisdiction allowed for the first time.

The 1852 Act was concerned principally with reforming the internal structure of common law procedure. The Common Law Procedure Act 1854 was the first major step in fusing the administration of law and equity. This important

Act for the first time enabled a defendant in the common law courts to raise an equitable defence. Such a defence, for example fraud or undue influence, could be raised in any case in which the defendant would be entitled to equitable relief against the common law judgment, that is to say cases where the Chancellor would issue a common injunction. The same Act gave the common law courts power to grant injunctions and to compel discovery of documents and administer interrogatories. A final important innovation of the 1854 Act was the provision that a judge might, with the consent of the parties, try issues of fact without a jury. This was the first step in the rapid decline of the jury in civil cases.

2 Chancery reforms

Compared with the striking reforms of common law procedure in the nineteenth century, Chancery reforms in the corresponding period were somewhat minor. The creation of the Chancery Court of Appeal to relieve the Chancellor of most of his work as a judge at first instance,[1] the appointment of Vice-Chancellors in 1813 and 1841[2] and the authorisation of the Master of the Rolls to sit as a regular Court in 1833[3] were all reforms aimed at clearing the arrears of litigation which had accumulated through the insufficient number of judges in the Court of Chancery.

Procedural reforms along the lines of the Common Law Procedure Acts 1852–1860 tended during the same period to assimilate Chancery procedure and common law procedure. The Court of Chancery Procedure Act 1852 abolished the need for every fact in the plaintiff's bill to be contained in interrogatories appended to the bill, which was henceforth to contain simply numbered paragraphs setting out the material facts on which the plaintiff relied concluding with a prayer for relief. The same Act abolished the need for the Court of Chancery to state a case for the opinion of the common law courts and enabled the Court of Chancery itself to decide all questions of law and fact arising in any case before it.

Finally, the Chancery Amendment Act 1858 (Lord Cairns' Act) empowered the Court of Chancery to award damages either in addition to or in lieu of an injunction or a decree of specific performance in respect of infringement of a common law right. This removed the necessity for bringing separate actions in the common law courts and the Chancery in respect of one cause of action. Lord Cairns' Act also provided for issues of fact and assessment of damages to be determined by a jury, but this revolutionary power was never exercised.

3 Creation of the County Courts

In the nineteenth century, due to the decline of the jurisdiction of the borough courts of record, there was an urgent need for the creation of a system of small claims courts.

One attempt to satisfy this need took the form of the creation, by private Acts of Parliament, of Courts of Requests for actions concerning small debts. These courts were not a great success since the judges were often local people, unqualified in the law with no great respect for evidence or rules of procedure.

---

[1] Court of Chancery Act 1851.
[2] Court of Chancery Act 1841.
[3] 3 & 4 W. 4, c. 94.

In 1749 an Act[1] attempted to revive the jurisdiction of the ancient Middlesex county court by allowing the county clerk (a barrister) and the suitors of the court to sit in the various hundreds in turn to try cases involving not more than 40s. This experiment of a permanent judge touring the county to deal with small claims was successful and upon it was modelled the system of county courts established in 1846.

The County Courts Act 1846 ("An Act for the recovery of small debts and demands") created some 500 county courts divided into sixty circuits each with its own judge who was to be a barrister of at least seven years standing appointed by the Chancellor. The upper limit of the jurisdiction of these courts was fixed at £20 but so popular did they become that it was raised to £50 in 1850. The power to remit cases from the superior courts at Westminster to the county courts was created in 1856 in respect of actions of contract where the sum claimed did not exceed £50. Since their creation the financial limits of the county courts' jurisdiction have risen steadily and the courts can no longer properly be described as small claims courts. Nevertheless the advent of legal aid has brought most county court proceedings within the reach of all.

4   Creation of the Courts of Probate and Divorce

The Court of Probate Act 1857 and the Matrimonial Causes Act 1857 had the combined effect of terminating the jurisdiction of the ecclesiastical courts over persons who were not members of the Church. Henceforth the jurisdiction of the ecclesiastical courts was confined to internal matters. The new Court of Probate was presided over by a judge who was also a judge of the newly formed Divorce Court.[2] These courts, together with the High Court of Admiralty, moved to Westminster Hall so that Doctors' Commons were abolished. The existing doctors and proctors had a right of audience before these courts but, since this right was also shared by all barristers, their office became extinct.

The jurisdiction of the Courts of Probate and Divorce has already been considered.[3]

C   THE JUDICATURE ACTS 1873–1875[4]

1   The Supreme Court of Judicature

The Judicature Acts of 1873 and 1875 came into operation together[5] on November 1, 1875. Their principal effect was to create a new Supreme Court of Judicature to which was transferred the jurisdiction of all the superior courts of law and equity except the Chancery Courts of the Counties Palatine of

---

[1] 23 Geo. 2, c. 33.
[2] Sir Cresswell Cresswell was appointed the first judge of the Probate and Divorce Courts.
[3] See pp. 51–52, *ante*.
[4] These statutes, the full short titles of which are the Supreme Court of Judicature Acts 1873–1875, are now consolidated in the Supreme Court of Judicature (Consolidation) Act 1925, commonly cited as the Judicature Act 1925.
[5] The Judicature Act 1873 was intended to come into operation on November 2, 1874 but this was postponed when it was appreciated that further amendments were necessary.

Lancaster and Durham[1] which were unaffected. The Supreme Court was divided into two parts, the High Court of Justice and the Court of Appeal.[2]

a High Court of Justice

The High Court was given the jurisdiction formerly exercised by the three common law courts,[3] the Court of Chancery, the Courts for Probate and Divorce and Matrimonial Causes, the High Court of Admiralty, the Courts of Common Pleas at Lancaster and Durham, and the courts created by the commissions of oyer and terminer, gaol delivery and assize.[4] The High Court was also given jurisdiction to hear appeals from the county courts, but this jurisdiction was transferred to the Court of Appeal in 1934.[5]

The High Court was formed in five divisions; Chancery Division, Probate, Divorce and Admiralty Division, Queen's Bench Division, Common Pleas Division and Exchequer Division. It was, however, provided that the number of divisions might be altered by Order in Council[6] and, after the deaths of the Chief Justice of the Queen's Bench and Chief Baron of the Exchequer in 1880, the Common Pleas and Exchequer Divisions were merged in the Queen's Bench Division. Since that date, therefore, there have been three divisions of the High Court.[7]

The divisions of the High Court are not separate courts. Thus each division has equal competence and a judge of one division has jurisdiction to sit in any division and may, indeed, be required to do so by the Lord Chancellor.

The principle of equal competence is aptly illustrated by the recent decision of the Court of Appeal in *Re L.*[8] The case turned on the question of whether a judge of the Probate, Divorce and Admiralty Division had power to order a blood test on an infant for the purpose of determining paternity. It was argued that, if jurisdiction to order a blood test existed, it derived from the inherent custodial jurisdiction of the Court of Chancery[9] and could, therefore, be exercised only by a judge of the Chancery Division in wardship proceedings. LORD DENNING, M.R. disposed of this argument as follows:[10]

> "This wide jurisdiction of the old Court of Chancery is now vested in the High Court of Justice and can be exercised by any judge of the High Court. As a matter of convenience, the jurisdiction is exercised by making the child a ward of court and putting it under the care of a judge of the Chancery Division; but that is only

---

[1] See p. 160, *post*.

[2] The Supreme Court now consists of the Court of Appeal, the High Court and the Crown Court; Courts Act 1971, s. 1 (1); as to the Crown Court, see p. 165, *post*.

[3] The Court of Exchequer, Court of Common Pleas and Court of King's Bench.

[4] The jurisdiction of the London Court of Bankruptcy was added by the Bankruptcy Act 1883.

[5] Administration of Justice (Appeals) Act 1934.

[6] Judicature Act 1873, ss. 32–36.

[7] See p. 160, *post*. The Probate, Divorce and Admiralty Division has, however, been re-named the Family Division (Administration of Justice Act 1970, s. 1 (1)).

[8] [1968] P. 119; [1968] 1 All E.R. 20; applying *R. v. Gyngall*, [1893] 2 Q.B. 232.

[9] See p. 32, *ante*.

[10] [1968] P. at pp. 156–157; [1968] 1 All E. R. at pp. 24–25. The substantive point of the case is now of purely historical interest since specific power to order blood tests is now contained in the Family Law Reform Act 1969, s. 20 and, furthermore, wardship jurisdiction is now assigned to the Family Division by the Administration of Justice Act 1970, s. 1 (2); Sch. 1.

machinery. If a question arises as to the welfare of a child before any judge of the High Court, he can make such order as may be appropriate in the circumstances. He need not send the case over to a Chancery judge."

Nevertheless business is distributed between the three divisions in approximately the same way as it was distributed between the courts whose jurisdiction the High Court assumed in 1875.[1] Common law matters are generally dealt with in the Queen's Bench Division, equity suits in the Chancery Division and matrimonial causes and matters affecting children in the Family Division.[2] In many cases there is a choice as to whether to proceed in one division or another and if an action is commenced in one division it may be transferred to another division. Such a transfer is made, however, for convenience rather than for want of jurisdiction.

b   Court of Appeal

The Court of Appeal was established by the Acts rather on the model of the Court of Appeal in Chancery than on the Exchequer Chamber, that is to say, with permanent judges rather than judges of first instance sitting in turn to hear appeals from one another's decisions. To the Court of Appeal was transferred the jurisdiction of the Court of Exchequer Chamber, the Court of Appeal in Chancery, the Court of Appeal from Lancaster, the Court of the Lord Warden of the Stannaries[3] and the admiralty jurisdiction (except in prize cases) of the Judicial Committee of the Privy Council.

The Court of Appeal is composed of a number of ex-officio judges, of whom only the Master of the Rolls and the Lord Chief Justice usually sit, and permanent Lords Justices of Appeal.[4]

The jurisdiction of the Court of Appeal was originally intended to be concerned mainly with appeals from the High Court. Since 1875, however, the appellate jurisdiction of the divisional court of the Queen's Bench Division in civil matters has declined so that the appellate jurisdiction of the Court of Appeal has widened in scope. Thus the power to entertain applications for a new trial was transferred from the divisional court of the Queen's Bench Division to the Court of Appeal in 1890.[5] More important still were the transfer of county court appeals to the Court of Appeal in 1934 and of criminal appeals in 1966.[6]

c   Procedure

Before the nineteenth century each court regulated its own internal procedure with very little intervention by Parliament. The nineteenth century saw a change of attitude and the setting-up of commissions by Parliament to consider procedure in the courts. It was as a result of the reports of these commissions that the Common Law Procedure Acts 1852–1860 and the various Chancery

---

[1] Although a certain amount of redistribution, notably in relation to probate, admiralty and wardship business, was effected by the Administration of Justice Act 1970.

[2] For details of the present jurisdiction of the divisions of the High Court, see pp. 160–165, *post*.

[3] A franchise court of the Stannaries in Cornwall.

[4] See p. 157, *post*.

[5] Judicature Act 1890, s. 1.

[6] Criminal Appeal Act 1966.

Procedure and Chancery Amendment Acts, particularly the Acts of 1852 and 1858,[1] were passed. The purpose of these Acts was to assimilate common law and equity procedure. This process was completed by the Judicature Acts which created a single set of rules of procedure to apply throughout the Supreme Court. The first set of Rules of the Supreme Court was contained in a schedule to the Judicature Act 1875. Section 17 of the 1875 Act also provided power for judges of the Supreme Court to make rules of procedure, a function now carried out by the Rule Committee. These Rules are constantly varied to provide for new causes of action and new statutory provisions.[2] The original rules comprised those features of common law procedure introduced in 1852 which had proved workable together with the most useful rules of procedure hitherto applicable in the Court of Chancery. The result has been a happy one in that the formalism of the old system of pleading has almost entirely disappeared and substantive law and procedure have become completely separate, the former no longer the servant of the latter. The function of modern procedure is to facilitate the enforcement of rights not to create them. Although it is still possible for an action to be won or lost in the pleadings[3] this hardly ever occurs and procedural errors do not have the catastrophic effect they once had.

2 The House of Lords

The House of Lords in the nineteenth century was under constant fire from critics because the judicial strength of the House fell far short of that required of the highest court of appeal in the realm. Lay peers could and did sit and it was not uncommon for only one lawyer, the Lord Chancellor, to sit on the hearing of an important appeal. An attempt was made to strengthen the composition of the House by conferring a life peerage upon the leading Exchequer Baron, Parke, B. However the Committee of Privileges held that, as a life peer, he had no right to sit and vote in the House.[4] The result was that the Judicature Act 1873 contained a provision abolishing the judicial function of the House of Lords. This section never took effect because it was repealed before the Judicature Act 1873 came into force. The eventual solution was to provide for the creation of salaried life peers who were legally qualified to exercise the House's judicial function. This was effected by the Appellate Jurisdiction Act 1876. Since this date lay peers have, by convention, taken no part in the judicial sessions of the House. Nevertheless the House of Lords was not made a part of the Supreme Court of Judicature and is still not a part of the Supreme Court. Consequently the House of Lords retains the right to regulate its own procedure in regard to the hearing of appeals.[5]

3 Fusion of the Administration of Law and Equity

The primary effect of the Judicature Acts on the relationship between law and equity was to fuse their administration. This was done by transferring the jurisdiction of the existing superior courts of law and equity to one court—the

---

[1] See p. 57, *ante*.
[2] See p. 233, *post*.
[3] See, for example, *Esso Petroleum Co., Ltd.* v. *Southport Corporation*, [1956] A.C. 218; [1955] 3 All E.R. 864.
[4] *Wensleydale Peerage Case* (1865), 5 H.L.Cas. 958.
[5] For details of the jurisdiction of the House of Lords, see p. 156, *post*.

Supreme Court of Judicature. The Supreme Court judges were directed by the Acts to give effect to both legal and equitable rights and remedies.[1] Thus the duality of jurisdiction which existed prior to 1875, whereby two actions might have to be brought to enforce one right, was abolished. Also abolished was the common injunction, the need for which stemmed from the pre-existing duality of jurisdiction.

It is an open question how far the Judicature Acts fused the rules of law and equity by fusing their administration. This question cannot be answered categorically because of the differing natures of certain rules of equity. Most rules of equity grew, not in conflict with common law rules, but as a gloss upon them. Thus the equitable rights and duties arising out of the creation of a trust are not inconsistent with the legal rights in the subject matter of the trust. The legal estate of the trustee is not denied by the equitable interest of the bene-ficiary; it is merely subject to the beneficial interest. Maitland himself per-ceived very little direct conflict between the rules of law and equity, seeing equity as a gloss on the common law.[2] Nevertheless, certain rules of equity undoubtedly grew in direct conflict with corresponding common law rules. In such cases the Chancellor would issue a common injunction restraining one party from exercising his common law right. For example the Chancellor would restrain a party from suing to enforce an obligation which had been induced by fraud, duress or undue influence. Since these defences could, after 1875, be pleaded in the Supreme Court of Judicature, it is possible to say that the common law rule has been merged into the corresponding rule of equity. In such a case the Judicature Acts did more than fuse the administration of law and equity; they fused the rules themselves. The framers of the Judicature Acts specified nine particular cases of conflict and provided that in these cases the equitable rule should prevail.[3] In addition section 25 (11) of the Judicature Act 1873 provided:

> "Generally in all matters not hereinbefore particularly mentioned in which there is any conflict or variance between the rules of equity and the rules of the common law with reference to the same matter the rules of equity shall prevail."

There have, in fact, been few cases in which common law and equity have conflicted since 1875 but wherever there has been a conflict the equitable rule has prevailed.[4]

---

[1] Judicature Act 1873, ss. 24, 25.
[2] Maitland, *Equity*, pp. 16-20.
[3] Judicature Act 1873, s. 25.
[4] Examples are *Job* v. *Job* (1877), 6 Ch.D. 562 (liability of executors); *Walsh* v. *Lonsdale* (1882), 21 Ch.D. 9 (enforceability of an agreement for a lease); *Berry* v. *Berry*, [1929] 2 K.B. 316 (variation of a deed by parol evidence). In an amusing exchange between bench and bar at the conclusion of a recent case (*Hill* v. *C. A. Parsons & Co., Ltd.*, [1971] 3 All E.R. 1345; [1971] 3 W.L.R. 995) LORD DENNING, M.R. remarked "It is the common lawyers who now do equity!", the point being that, in a case in which the Court of Appeal had by majority granted an interlocutory injunction, the dissenting member of the Court, STAMP, L.J., was the only judge who had come to the Court of Appeal from the Chancery Division.

CHAPTER 5

The Divisions of English Law

A CRIMINAL LAW

1 Nature and characteristics of a crime

Crimes, together with torts, have the characteristic of defying definition. The reason for this is that, whereas concepts such as a contract or trust are comparatively narrow in scope, the word "crime" covers innumerable forms of conduct. All these forms of conduct have one thing in common; they may all result in prosecution in the criminal courts. However a definition of a crime as conduct which may result in a prosecution in the criminal courts is hardly a definition at all. Nor is it particularly helpful to define a crime as the breach of a public duty redressible by punishment at common law or under a statute. Apart from the objections that punitive damages may be awarded in tort and that the treatment of criminal offenders does not always involve punishment, this definition is really just a way of saying that a crime is an infringement of the criminal law. Other characteristics of crime, such as the fact that only the Crown can remit punishment[1] or that criminal procedure differs from civil procedure or that any member of the public can institute criminal proceedings, are not definitive of a crime because they all presuppose that the conduct in question is a crime. The conduct is not criminal because it has these characteristics; it has these characteristics because it is criminal conduct.

This raises the question whether any definition is possible which identifies conduct as criminal by reference to the nature of the conduct itself. Is there any common feature between murder, treason, incest, taking a conveyance (vehicle) without the consent of the owner[2] and failing to accord precedence to a foot-passenger on a pedestrian crossing?[3] The answer seems to be that all these offences, and indeed all criminal offences, are offences against either public morality or social standards. Thus all criminal conduct contravenes either public morality or standards of conduct which society has considered it expedient to impose upon its members. In most cases offences against public

---

[1] By royal pardon or *nolle prosequi* entered by the Attorney-General.
[2] Theft Act 1968, s. 12 (1).
[3] Pedestrian Crossings Regulations 1954, reg. 4.

morality will be found to be common law offences since basic principles of right and wrong do not substantially alter. Nevertheless public morality is not immune to change. Thus suicide was a crime until the Suicide Act 1961 altered the law. The legalisation of homosexuality between adult males and abortion, in certain circumstances, effected by the Sexual Offences Act 1967 and the Abortion Act 1967 provides further example of law reform reflecting change in public morality. Offences against social standards are usually statutory offences since the rapid growth of social phenomena which the common lawyers never foresaw generally requires Parliamentary intervention. Thus many thousands. of persons are convicted every year of offences under the Road Traffic Acts and Regulations. There is generally nothing immoral in their conduct. They have simply contravened laws which society, through Parliament, has considered it expedient to create to deal with the social problems posed by the modern phenomenon of the motor vehicle. However it would be complacent to define a crime as a contravention of public morality or standards of social behaviour. Many forms of conduct infringe social standards such as cleanliness, or truthfulness, but are not criminal because the infringement of these standards does not disturb the everyday running of society to such an extent as to justify legislative intervention. More important by far is the fact that some forms of conduct which are clearly contrary to public morality and do affect society as a whole are not criminal. The classic example is adultery which is a criminal offence in several sophisticated legal systems but not in England. The usual justification advanced for this is that adultery is a matter of private morality, which is unconvincing, or alternatively that it would pose great difficulties of detection which is, surely, totally irrelevant. The true reason is probably that society would, as a whole, resent what it would consider an autocratic intervention into its private affairs. There is a considerable difference of opinion on the question of whether it is the function of the law to enforce morals. The Wolfenden Committee on Homosexual Offences and Prostitution[1] reported the function of the criminal law as being—

> "to preserve public order and decency, to protect the citizen from what is offensive or injurious. . . . It is not . . . the function of the law to intervene in the private lives of citizens, or to seek to enforce any particular pattern of behaviour, further than is necessary to carry out the purposes we have outlined."

The alternative view is that the function of the criminal law includes the enforcement of public morality. This proposition is supported by the decision of the House of Lords in *Shaw* v. *Director of Public Prosecutions*.[2] In that case the House held that an agreement to publish the "Ladies Directory", containing names, addresses and photographs of persons willing to engage in prostitution and perversion, constituted a "conspiracy to corrupt public morals" which was a criminal offence. VISCOUNT SIMONDS defined the function of the criminal law thus:[3]

> "In the sphere of criminal law I entertain no doubt that there remains in the courts of law a residual power to enforce the supreme and fundamental purpose of the law,

---

[1] Cmnd. 247 of 1957.
[2] [1962] A.C. 220, [1961] 2 All E.R. 446; affirming the decision of the Court of Criminal Appeal *sub. nom. R.* v. *Shaw*, [1961] 1 All E.R. 330.
[3] [1962] A.C. at pp. 267, 268; [1961] 2 All E.R. at p. 452.

to conserve not only the safety and order but also the moral welfare of the State. . . .
The law must be related to the changing standards of life, not yielding to every
shifting impulse of the popular will but having regard to fundamental assessments of
human values and the purposes of society."

The scope of *Shaw's* case is uncertain.   A liberal construction of Viscount
Simonds's speech suggests that there is conduct which, irrespective of precedent or legislation, is intrinsically criminal.   This view is not entirely novel
since there is authority of the Court of Criminal Appeal for the existence of the
offence of "public mischief" which is wide enough to cover conduct such as that
in *Shaw's* case.   The leading earlier case is *R. v. Manley*.[1]   The accused in that
case alleged falsely that she had been attacked and robbed.   The police were put
to considerable trouble and expense in investigating her story and members
of the public were put in suspicion.   She was convicted of public mischief and
her appeal against conviction, on the ground that no such offence was known
to the law, was dismissed.   In *Shaw's* case the Court of Criminal Appeal decision
was similar in that it recognised an offence of committing acts calculated or
intended to corrupt public morals.

The narrower view of *Shaw v. Director of Public Prosecutions* is that it is a
decision solely on the crime of conspiracy.   This narrow conception of the
criminal law also involves regarding *R. v. Manley* as wrongly decided and,
indeed, the decision has been widely criticised.[2]   That decision, and the Court of
Criminal Appeal reasoning in *Shaw's* case, stand alone in modern times[3] in that
they suggest that conduct committed by one person (as opposed to a conspiracy)
may be criminal solely because it contravenes public morality or the public interest.   There are many cases to the contrary in which accused persons have behaved palpably dishonestly and yet have been acquitted because they did not fall
within the scope of any offence known to the criminal law.[4]   In such cases the
courts have generally been willing to leave to Parliament the task of altering the
law.   If this view is correct a crime can only be identified by reference to the
historical sources of the criminal law.

---

[1] [1933] 1 K.B. 529.   The conduct in question would now constitute a summary offence
under s. 5 (2) of the Criminal Law Act 1967.
[2] Notably by the Court of Criminal Appeal in *R. v. Newland*, [1954] 1 Q.B. 158;
[1953] 2 All E.R. 1067;   see also *Joshua v. R.*, [1955] A.C. 121; [1955] 1 All E.R. 22.
[3] Though several old authorities to this effect were cited by the Court of Criminal Appeal
in *Shaw v. Director of Public Prosecutions*, [1962] A.C. 220, at pp. 226 *et seq.*;   affirming
sub. nom. R. v. Shaw, [1961] 1 All E.R. 330; see also *R. v. Grimes*, [1968] 3 All E.R. 179 n.
in which it was held that an act, or an attempt, to pervert the course of justice was criminal
per se.   In *R. v. Knuller (Publishing, Printing and Promotions), Ltd.*, [1971] 3 All E.R. 314;
[1971] 3 W.L.R. 633 the Court of Appeal appears to have favoured the wider view of
Shaw's case though the convictions were, in fact, of conspiracy to corrupt public morals
and conspiracy to outrage public decency.
[4] Examples are *Fisher v. Raven*, [1964] A.C. 210; [1963] 2 All E.R. 389; *Director of Public
Prosecution v. Nieser*, [1959] 1 Q.B. 254; [1958] 3 All E.R. 662.   There have, of course,
been many cases in which prosecutions have failed because the wrong offence has been
charged in the indictment.   This doubtless explains the modern tendency of prosecuting
authorities to charge complicated or difficult cases involving two or more defendants as
conspiracies instead of (or, in some cases, in addition to) charging specific offences.   The
practice has been deprecated (see, for example, *Verrier v. Director of Public Prosecutions*,
[1967] 2 A.C. 195; [1966] 3 All E.R. 568 (H.L.)) but, regrettably, persists.

2 Historical sources of criminal law

As we have seen, the three major historical sources of English law are common law, equity and legislation. Of these equity has had no effect on the development of criminal law. The reason for this is that the courts of equity had no criminal jurisdiction. The phrase "criminal equity" is sometimes used to describe the criminal jurisdiction of the Court of Star Chamber[1] but this terminology is confusing since all crimes created in the Court of Star Chamber and later, after the abolition of that court, enforced in the common law courts, are treated as common law offences.

The twin sources of the criminal law are common law and legislation. The earliest common law offences were felonies which were all punishable with death and forfeiture. Examples of these early offences, which are basic to any civilised legal system, are murder, manslaughter, rape, larceny and robbery. The common law developed, as English law has always developed, pragmatically. Thus when it became clear that the existing criminal law was deficient, new crimes were created. As a result there grew, in the courts of the common law, a practice of extending existing crimes so as to create new crimes, a practice not dissimilar to that which took place in relation to the civil law. These later offences were generally regarded as less serious than the original offences and so were only misdemeanours. A number of misdemeanours, such as perjury, forgery and attempts appear to have originated in the Court of Star Chamber.

In the nineteenth century the legislature replaced the judiciary as the chief organ of law reform, so that legislation is now the source of almost all change in the criminal law. Statutes such as the Debtors Act 1869, the Falsification of Accounts Act 1875 and the Road Traffic Acts were passed to fill gaps in the criminal law. In addition most common law crimes have been codified and are now defined and contained in statutes such as the Offences Against the Person Act 1861, the Sexual Offences Act 1956 and the Theft Act 1968. Thus statutes are now the most important source of the criminal law.

3 Classification of crimes

It is possible to classify crimes in various ways. They may, for example, be classified by subject matter into offences against the person, offences against property and offences against public order. This classification is not, however, significant. Nor, at the present day, is the common law classification into treason, felonies and misdemeanours of any practical significance. There are, in fact, only two forms of classification which are of any importance. The first is that of arrestable and non-arrestable offences, which is a substantive classification introduced by the Criminal Law Act 1967 to replace the division of crimes into felonies and misdemeanours; the second is the procedural classification of offences as indictable or summary. Before considering the effects of these classifications it will be as well to consider briefly the common law division of crimes into treason, felony and misdemeanour, if only as a matter of historical interest.

a Treasons, felonies and misdemeanours

The significance of this classification is now purely historical. The long title of the Criminal Law Act 1967 begins:

---

[1] See p. 11, *ante*.

"An Act to amend the law of England and Wales by abolishing the division of crimes into felonies and misdemeanours and to amend and simplify the law in respect of matters arising from or related to that division or the abolition of it; . . ."[1]

To this end section 1 (1) of the Act provides: "All distinctions between felony and misdemeanour are hereby abolished." Section 1 (2) goes on to provide that

"on all matters on which a distinction has previously been made between felony and misdemeanour, including mode of trial, the law and practice in relation to all offences cognisable under the law of England and Wales (including piracy) shall be the law and practice applicable at the commencement of this Act in relation to misdemeanour."

Section 12 (6) of the Act provides that references in the Act to felony do not include treason. Thus the common law offences of misprision, compounding and being an accessory after the fact still exist in relation to treason. Since the Treason Act 1945 there has been no procedural distinction between treason and felony so that treason is now best regarded as a specific offence rather than as a generic term. Bail in treason cases can be granted only by order of a High Court judge or the Secretary of State[2] but, apart from this provision, there is no procedural distinction between trial for treason and trial for any other offence.

The reason for abolishing the distinction between felony and misdemeanour was that the distinction had become artificial. At common law felonies were the most serious offences and were punishable with forfeiture of the felon's property to the Crown and, in some cases, death. Misdemeanours attracted neither death nor forfeiture. Thus the acid test as to whether an offence was a felony or a misdemeanour was whether it was punishable with death and forfeiture. The death penalty for felony as such was abolished early in the common law by the combined operation of the fiction of benefit of clergy[3] and statute. Forfeiture for felony was abolished by the Forfeiture Act 1870. Consequently the distinction between felony and misdemeanour had become an anachronism, particularly since many serious offences such as obtaining by false pretences and fraudulent conversion were only misdemeanours whereas any larceny, for example, constituted a felony. In addition certain irritating consequences flowed from the distinction. It is no longer necessary to advert to these distinctions since, in so far as special rules applied to felonies, they have all been abolished by section 1 (2) of the 1967 Act.

b Arrestable and non-arrestable offences

The Criminal Law Act 1967 creates a new class of offences to be known as "arrestable offences". The description applies to

"offences for which the sentence is fixed by law or for which a person (not previously convicted) may under or by virtue of any enactment be sentenced to imprisonment for a term of five years, and to attempts to commit any such offence."[4]

All other offences are, *a fortiori*, non-arrestable offences (though this indecorous terminology does not appear in the Act). The new classification is of primary

---

[1] This part of the Act implements recommendations in the Criminal Law Revision Committee's Seventh Report entitled *Felonies and Misdemeanours* (Cmnd. 2659).
[2] Magistrates' Courts Act 1952, s. 8.
[3] See p. 16, *ante*.
[4] Section 2 (1).

significance in relation to powers of arrest. At common law, powers of arrest without warrant existed only in relation to treason, felony or breach of the peace. Under the 1967 Act powers of arrest without warrant exist in relation to arrestable offences, although the power to arrest to stay a breach of the peace, which probably includes any crime, is unaffected by the Act.

The offences of being an accessory after the fact and misprision, which existed at common law only in relation to felonies, were abolished, but, by sections 4 and 5, new, analogous offences, in relation to arrestable offences, of impeding the apprehension of offenders and concealing material information for value (other than the making of reasonable compensation for loss or injury) were created. In addition the words "arrestable offence" were substituted for "felony" in a number of enactments set out in Schedule 2 to the Act.

c Indictable and summary offences

This is the procedural classification of offences. The classification of an offence as indictable or summary primarily determines the mode of trial. Trial on indictment is before a judge and jury at the Crown Court. Summary trial is before magistrates in a magistrates' court. It does not, however, follow that all summary offences are tried summarily or that all indictable offences are tried on indictment. In addition there are certain offences which, by the terms of the statute creating them, are triable either summarily or on indictment.

Details of procedure at trials on indictment and summary trials are contained in Part V of this book.[1]

4 General principles of criminal liability

The elements of every crime are different. There is, however, a general principle of criminal liability which applies (in the absence of an express statutory provision to the contrary) to all crimes. This is that the prosecution must prove (1) that the accused has been a party to an act which is forbidden by the criminal law, and (2) that the accused possessed the state of mind required for that crime. The first of these elements in a crime is termed its *actus reus*, the second, its *mens rea*. As a general principle *actus reus* and *mens rea* must both be present for a crime to be committed, though this principle is not invariable.

a Actus reus

The *actus reus* of a crime includes every element in a particular crime other than the accused's state of mind. Thus the *actus reus* of a crime depends upon the definition of that crime. For example, defining robbery, the Theft Act 1968, s. 8 (1) provides:

> "A person is guilty of robbery if he steals, and immediately before or at the time of doing so, and in order to do so, he uses force on any person or puts or seeks to put any person in fear of being then and there subjected to force."

The *actus reus* of this offence involves (i) stealing, and (ii) using force or putting or seeking to put any person in fear of being subjected to force. Both elements must be present in order for the *actus reus* to be completely constituted. An *actus reus* can consist of an omission to act in circumstances where the accused has a legal duty to act. The crimes of incitement, conspiracy and attempt to commit

---

[1] See p. 349, *post*.

a crime may appear to be exceptions to the principle that there is an *actus reus* in every crime. Although it is difficult, in these crimes, to distinguish the *actus reus* from the *mens rea*, it is not impossible.[1]

b Mens rea

In the formative years of the common law "wrongs" were not specifically describable as crimes or torts because there was no distinct procedure. One trial might result in punishment of the perpetrator of the wrong and compensation of the victim. At this stage a wrong such as trespass could be committed without proof of any intention or blameworthiness on the part of the offender. However, when, in the twelfth century, civil and criminal procedure became distinct criminal liability began to depend upon guilt or blameworthiness on the part of the accused. The criminal law regards conduct rather from the aspect of the offender than from the point of view of the victim (compare the law of torts which is primarily concerned to compensate the plaintiff). Thus it is a maxim of criminal law that a crime depends upon proof of a guilty mind— *actus non facit reum nisi mens sit rea*.

A general definition of *mens rea* is impossible for the *mens rea* of every crime differs. The *mens rea* of murder is an intention to kill or cause grievous bodily harm while the *mens rea* of attempted murder is an intention to kill. In burglary the accused must have an intent to commit one of several offences;[2] in theft, an intent permanently to deprive the owner; in forgery an intent to defraud or deceive. However, not every crime requires a specific intent, and even in crimes which do require proof of a specific intent the *mens rea* does not only comprise that specific intent. The accused must also have a state of mind referable to the whole of his conduct. This general intention may involve proof of intention, negligence, recklessness or even inadvertence. Thus *mens rea* comprises a general mental state and, in certain crimes, a specific intention.[3]

Intention is, itself, an extremely complex concept and it is sufficient to note that it may, depending on the particular crime concerned, be understood to relate either to the performance of an act or to a consequence of that act. An act is regarded as intentional if it is voluntarily performed and the actor is intellectually capable of forming an intention; a consequence is intended if it was foreseen by the actor. Foresight is, of course, a matter of inference and in 1960 the House of Lords alarmed a large proportion of the legal world by holding that the question of foresight of consequences was to be determined objectively, i.e. according not to what consequences the accused himself foresaw but to what consequences he ought to have foreseen.[4] The decision was widely criticised as being inconsistent with general principles of criminal liability and, following a recommendation of the Law Commission, was eventually overruled by section 8 of the Criminal Justice Act 1967 which reintroduced a subjective test of foresight of consequences.

Whereas all crimes require proof of an *actus reus,* not all crimes depend upon proof of *mens rea*. There are many statutory offences of strict liability where the state of mind of the accused is irrelevant and the crime consists solely in the

---

[1] See Smith and Hogan, *Criminal Law* (2nd. edn.), pp. 148–178.
[2] Theft Act 1968, s. 9 (1), (2).
[3] See GlanvilleWilliams, *The Mental Element in Crime.*
[4] *Director of Public Prosecutions* v. *Smith*, [1961] A.C. 290; [1960] 3 All E.R. 161.

performance of the *actus reus*. In such a case the words of the statute must be clear and unequivocal for there is a presumption of statutory interpretation against the imposition of criminal liability without fault.[1]

B   LAW OF TORTS

1   Nature of a tort

A tort may be defined as the infringement of a legal right not arising exclusively out of a contract or trust and giving rise to a cause of action for unliquidated damages. This definition, like most other definitions of torts, is not of much assistance in identifying the nature of a tort. It is only possible to identify a tort by possessing a prior knowledge of the rights which the law of torts protects. The infringement of one of these rights is a tort. The general function of the law of torts is to provide compensation to a person in respect of damage caused by another. However this is not the basis upon which the law of torts has grown. Thus there are many cases in which one person may cause loss or damage to another without committing a tort or indeed any actionable wrong. There is no action for infringement of privacy, nor for loss caused by legitimate business competition. A wife has no action for the loss of her husband's consortium[2] (although a husband has such a right), nor has a tenant any remedy if given notice to quit by a landlord for giving evidence against the latter in judicial proceedings.[3] Every legal right involves a correlative legal duty imposed on another person or persons. A right protected by the law of torts involves a correlative duty owed by every member of the community, unlike a contractual right which only involves a duty on the part of the other contracting party. Nevertheless a tort is no easier to identify looked at from the standpoint of the defendant's duty. It has no general moral character. While certain torts involve conduct on the part of the defendant which would be regarded as immoral or anti-social (for example, battery, deceit, malicious prosecution, enticement), others have no moral content whatsoever (such as trespass to land, nuisance and the concept of vicarious liability). Also by no means all conduct which is immoral or intended to cause damage to another is tortious. Treason, obscenity, contempt of court[3] and perjury[4] are not torts even where their commission causes and is intended to cause damage to another.

Conversely certain conduct is tortious even though it causes the plaintiff no damage or loss whatsoever. "The least touching of another in anger is battery."[5] Any act of trespass, however trivial, is actionable *per se*. Similarly there are some torts which not only do not depend upon the fault of the defendant but do not even require him to have intended to commit the tortious act. The conclusion to be drawn is that there is nothing intrinsic in the nature of conduct which marks it as tortious. Usually a tortious act is an intentional or negligent act on the part of the defendant which causes loss or damage to the plaintiff but, as indicated above, none of these conditions need be present for a

---

[1] The House of Lords has in two recent cases reconsidered this principle: see *Warner* v. *Metropolitan Police Commissioner*, [1969] 2 A.C. 256; [1968] 2 All E.R. 356; *Sweet* v. *Parsley*, [1970] A.C. 132; [1969] 1 All E.R. 347; see p. 111, *post*.
[2] *Best* v. *Samuel Fox & Co., Ltd.*, [1952] A.C. 716; [1952] 2 All E.R. 394.
[3] *Chapman* v. *Honig*, [1963] 2 Q.B. 502; [1963] 2 All E.R. 513.
[4] *Hargreaves* v. *Bretherton*, [1959] 1 Q.B. 45; [1958] 3 All E.R. 122.
[5] *Cole* v. *Turner* (1704), 6 Mod. Rep. 149, *per* HOLT, C.J.

tort to be committed, nor does their presence render any act tortious where it would not otherwise be so.[1]

It is equally fruitless to attempt to identify a tort by reference to the nature of the rights or interests which the law of torts protects for these are diverse. Personal interests such as freedom from physical harm or restraint are protected by such torts as assault, battery, false imprisonment and negligence. The right to one's fair name and reputation is protected by the torts of libel and slander. Property rights are protected by torts such as trespass to goods or land, conversion, detinue and nuisance. The torts of deceit, malicious falsehood, passing-off, conspiracy and inducing a breach of contract protect commercial or business interests. Finally such miscellaneous interests as the right to vote[2] and the right of a traveller to be accommodated at an inn[3] are within the province of the law of torts.

The only way in which it is possible to identify tortious conduct is by reference to the historical development of tort. The plaintiff in an action in tort can succeed only if he can show a right historically protected by the law of torts, can persuade the court to vary an existing right to such an extent as, in fact, to create a new right or if he has a statutory right. This means that new rights of action in tort can be created either judicially or by legislation. In modern times the judiciary is so restricted by the operation of the doctrine of precedent[4] that it is extremely rare for a new right to be created judicially. Examples of new torts which have evolved through the willingness of judges to extend existing causes of action in comparatively recent times are the tort of inducing a breach of contract, which was created in the case of *Lumley* v. *Gye*[5] in 1853 as an extension of the existing tort of enticement of a servant, and liability under the rule in *Rylands* v. *Fletcher*[6] which evolved as an offshoot of nuisance in 1866. In more recent times the tort of intimidation has either been created or has taken on a wholly new form in the case of *Rookes* v. *Barnard*.[7]

Apart from isolated examples, such as those above, judicial development of the law of torts since the abolition of the forms of action in 1852[8] has been limited. Consequently when new social conditions arise with which the common law cannot be adapted to deal the law of torts can only be extended by statute. This has been frequently done to deal with such developments as broadcasting[9] and the mechanisation of industry.[10] In addition any victim of emitted radiation from a nuclear plant can be comforted by the thought that the legislature has ensured that he will not be without a remedy.[11]

In general, however, development of the law of torts has been limited since the nineteenth century and only by referring to the historical sources of this branch of the law can its characteristics be positively identified.

---

[1] *Bradford Corporation* v. *Pickles*, [1895] A.C. 587.
[2] *Ashby* v. *White* (1703), 2 Ld. Raym. 938.
[3] *Constantine* v. *Imperial London Hotels, Ltd.*, [1944] K.B. 693; [1944] 2 All E.R. 171.
[4] See p. 122, *post*.
[5] (1853), 2 E. & B. 216.
[6] (1866), L.R. 1 Exch. 265; affirmed (1868), L.R. 3 H.L. 330.
[7] [1964] A.C. 1129; [1964] 1 All E.R. 367.
[8] See p. 56, *ante*.
[9] Defamation Act 1952, s. 1.
[10] Factories Act 1961.
[11] Nuclear Installations (Licensing and Insurance) Act 1959, s. 4 (1).

2   Historical sources of the law of torts

Of the historical sources of English law equity has had only a very slight influence on the law of torts. The only direct contribution of equity to torts is the equitable remedy of injunction.[1] Legislation is of increasing importance as a source of every branch of the law. It is, however, the common law to which the student must turn as the fundamental source of the law of torts.

The peculiar system of substantive law being ancillary to procedure in the common law courts has already been discussed in detail. It is sufficient to state, in this context, that virtually the whole of the modern law of torts (excluding, of course, breach of statutory duty) derives from the writ of trespass and the actions on the case which evolved from that writ.[2] Until the fourteenth century trespass constituted the whole of the existing law of torts with the exception of detinue, an even older action deriving from the action of debt.[3] One commentator has stated that[4]

> "had there been a medieval *Salmond* or *Winfield* trespass would have been the title, not of a chapter but of the book"

In the nineteenth century two important developments took place. First the writ system was abolished by the Common Law Procedure Act 1852. This dispensed with the necessity for the plaintiff to select one form of action to fit his claim. Thereafter he merely had to plead facts leaving the court to decide whether he had a remedy. The effect of this was to give the law of torts a certain fluidity but not to increase the scope of the existing torts.

The second important development was the acceptance of the binding force of judicial precedent.[5] Consequently the restrictive influence of procedure was replaced by the restrictive influence of precedent. It is this factor which secures the rigidity and restrictive interpretation of the law of torts at the present day. The courts are extremely slow to recognise a new right since the traditional view of the judicial function is the application of the law rather than its creation.

The only real development which the abolition of the forms of action has brought about is that the name given to a tort is purely descriptive. Certain factual situations give rise to a cause of action; others do not. To identify these factual situations as deceit, nuisance or negligence is useful only for the purposes of classification. At the present day no practical consequence can follow from classifying one factual situation as trespass and another as negligence rather than vice-versa. This point is particularly clearly illustrated by the recent case of *Letang* v. *Cooper*.[6] The plaintiff was run over by a car which was allegedly being driven negligently by the defendant. She contended that this gave rise to two causes of action; trespass and negligence. The action for negligence was clearly statute-barred but the plaintiff maintained that, on a true construction of the Limitation Acts, her action for trespass was not. This argument found favour with the judge at first instance, but his decision was reversed by the Court of Appeal. DIPLOCK, L.J. (as he then was) explained the situation thus:[7]

---

1 See p. 37, *ante.*
2 See p. 21, *ante.*
3 See p. 20, *ante.*
4 74 L.Q.R. 407 (Milsom).
5 See p. 122, *post.*
6 [1965] 1 Q.B. 232; [1964] 2 All E.R. 929.
7 [1965] 1 Q.B. at p. 242; [1964] 2 All E.R. at p. 934.

"A cause of action is simply a factual situation the existence of which entitles one person to obtain from the court a remedy against another person. Historically the means by which the remedy was obtained varied with the nature of the factual situation and causes of action were divided into categories according to the 'form of action' by which the remedy was obtained in the particular kind of factual situation which constituted the cause of action; ... But it is essential to realise that when, since 1873, the name of a form of action is used to identify a cause of action, it is used as a convenient and succinct description of a particular category of factual situation which entitles one person to obtain from the court a remedy against another person. To forget this will indeed encourage the old forms of action to rule us from their graves. ... The description 'negligence' was in fact used by the plaintiff's pleader; but this cannot be decisive, for we are concerned not with the description applied by the pleader to the factual situation and the action founded on it, but with the description applied to it by Parliament in the enactment to be construed. It is true that the factual situation also falls within the description of the tort of 'trespass to the person'. But that, as I have endeavoured to show, does not mean that there are two causes of action. It merely means that there are two apt descriptions of the same cause of action. It does not cease to be the tort of 'negligence', because it can also be called by another name. An action founded on it is none the less an 'action for negligence' because it can also be called an 'action for trespass to the person'."

3 The relationship between torts and crimes

a *Distinction between torts and crimes*

It is difficult to distinguish a tort from a crime solely by reference to the nature of the conduct in question. Many forms of conduct are both tortious and criminal. This coincidence occurs when the defendant's conduct infringes both a private right and a public duty. Thus offences against the person such as murder, manslaughter, assault and battery, rape and false imprisonment also give rise to actions in tort. Similarly theft, obtaining property by deception and burglary are crimes against property which will also confer upon the victim a civil right of action. Where the private right does not carry with it a correlative public (as opposed to private) duty the defendant's tort is not a crime. Thus slander, trespass to land and private nuisance are three examples of conduct which is tortious as such but not necessarily criminal. Conversely offences against public order or the administration of justice such as perjury,[1] contempt of court,[2] riot and treason are not torts because there is no private right infringed. The crime of public nuisance is only actionable as a tort if an individual suffers damage over and above the general inconvenience to the public. Thus there is nothing intrinsic in conduct which stamps it as tortious or criminal or both. Nevertheless there are a number of other ways in which torts differ from crimes. The principal distinctions are as follows.

(1) An individual may consent to the commission of conduct against him which would otherwise be tortious. Since a tort infringes only his private right he is always free to waive this right. Consent is often a defence to crime also. Certain crimes such as theft depend upon absence of consent. However, insofar as a crime is an offence involving breach of a public, as opposed merely to a private, duty there are certain crimes to which an individual cannot consent even where the crime is basically an infringement of his private right. Thus it

---

[1] *Hargreaves v. Bretherton*, [1959] 1 Q.B. 45; [1958] 3 All E.R. 122.
[2] *Chapman v. Honig*, [1963] 2 Q.B. 502; [1963] 2 All E.R. 513.

is clear that where the infliction of physical harm is so serious that it is contrary to the public interest to allow it the criminal law will intervene irrespective of the victim's consent.[1]

(2)   A corollary of (1) is that the Crown may pardon a crime but it may not pardon a tort since this would amount to waiving the individual's right to compensation. Nevertheless a similar result may be achieved by retrospective legislation.[2]

(3)   Since criminal law is concerned partially, though not solely, with the enforcement of public morality the courts are more willing to recognise new categories of criminal conduct than new torts.[3]

(4)   The procedure for trying civil and criminal cases is substantially different.   Trial on indictment in the Crown Court and civil proceedings in the High Court or a county court are so radically different that there is little basis for comparison.   In the magistrates' courts, on the other hand, there is little fundamental distinction between civil and criminal proceedings.   Civil proceedings are commenced by complaint, criminal proceedings by information. In *R.* v. *Dunmow Justices, Ex parte Anderson*[4] civil proceedings instituted by information were quashed.   However the Lord Chief Justice did not state categorically that civil and criminal proceedings could not be conducted together where they arose on the same facts although he thought it generally undesirable.

(5) Sanctions and remedies differ. In the mind of the layman possibly the basic distinction between torts and crimes is the nature of the consequences which are likely to flow from their commission. The basic function of the law of torts is to compensate the plaintiff for the infringement of his right. Criminal sanctions, on the other hand, are directed at the offender and usually involve some form of punishment or correction. However this distinction is somewhat blurred in the case of both torts and crimes. In tort the plaintiff may, in certain circumstances, be awarded exemplary damages, which damages are awarded to punish or make an example of the defendant. In *Rookes* v. *Barnard*[5] the House of Lords took the opportunity of acknowledging exemplary damages, although regarding their punitive character as an anomaly. LORD DEVLIN (who delivered the only speech on this topic) justified this anomaly in the following terms:[6]

> "there are certain categories of cases in which an award of exemplary damages can serve a useful purpose in vindicating the strength of the law, and thus affording a practical justification for admitting into the civil law a principle which ought logically to belong to the criminal".

Their lordships, however, limited cases in which exemplary damages could be awarded to cases falling within one of three narrow categories and stated that in other cases exemplary damages should not be awarded for as LORD DEVLIN observed:[7]

---

[1] *R.* v. *Donovan*, [1934] 2 K.B. 498.
[2] A modern illustration is furnished by the War Damage Act 1965.
[3] *R.* v. *Manley*, [1933] 1 K.B. 529;   *Shaw* v. *Director of Public Prosecutions,* [1962] A.C. 230; [1961] 2 All E.R. 446; see p. 64, *ante.*
[4] [1964] 2 All E.R. 943; [1964] 1 W.L.R. 1039.
[5] [1964] A.C. 1129; [1964] 1 All E.R. 367.
[6] [1964] A.C. at p. 1226; [1964] 1 All E.R., at p. 410.
[7] [1964] A.C., at p. 1230; [1964] 1 All E.R., at p. 412.

"I do not care for the idea that in matters criminal an aggrieved party should be given an option to inflict for his own benefit punishment by a method which denies to the offender the protection of the criminal law."

The principles of *Rookes* v. *Barnard* were affirmed, albeit with reservations, by the House of Lords in the much-publicised case of *Cassell & Co. Ltd.* v. *Broome*[1] in which the Court of Appeals' bold assertion that the decision of the House of Lords on exemplary damages in *Rookes* v. *Barnard* was *per incuriam*[2] and wrong was roundly condemned. In the instant case, an award of exemplary damages of £25,000 was justified because of the conduct of both defendants in publishing a libel which in effect blamed the plaintiff for the loss of many ships from a merchant convoy in an incident during the second world war despite the most explicit warning against publication.

This limited power of punishment which civil courts have in tort actions may be compared with the powers which criminal courts have, under certain statutes, to compensate the victim. For example where a person is convicted of any offence with reference to a theft, the court has power to make an order for restitution of the stolen property under section 28 of the Theft Act 1968. A person convicted of an offence of destroying or damaging property belonging to another may be ordered to pay such sum by way of compensation (not exceeding £400 in the case of a magistrates' court) as the court thinks just.[3]

b The coincidence of civil and criminal proceedings

It will be appreciated that where conduct infringes both a private right and a public duty it may give rise to both civil and criminal proceedings. These proceedings are not, as a rule, interdependent. They will take place in different courts. The civil action will generally be tried in the county court or the Queen's Bench Division of the High Court; the criminal proceedings in the magistrates' court or the Crown Court. By way of exception it appears that both civil and criminal proceedings may be tried together in the magistrates' court although this is not in practice done and was discouraged by LORD PARKER, C.J. in *R.* v. *Dunmow Justices, Ex parte Anderson*.[4] The reason for discouraging the practice of trying civil and criminal proceedings together given in that case was that the rules concerning the relevance and admissibility of evidence would generally differ. Many rules of evidence are common to both civil and criminal proceedings, but not all. The burden and standard of proof differ considerably in civil and criminal proceedings.[5] Evidence of the character of the accused may sometimes be relevant in criminal proceedings

---

[1] [1972] 1 All E.R. 801; [1972] 2 W.L.R. 645 (the "Destruction of Convoy PQ17" libel case).

[2] See pp. 130–135, *post*, on the points arising out of the case in relation to the doctrine of judicial precedent.

[3] Criminal Damage Act 1971, s. 8. Although forfeiture for felony was abolished in 1870 and felony itself was abolished in 1967, the Forfeiture Act 1970, s. 4 (as amended) allows a court, on the application of a person aggrieved, on a person's conviction of any offence tried on indictment to award compensation not exceeding £400 for loss of or damage to property. Magistrates' Courts have similar powers under the Magistrates' Courts Act 1952, s. 34.

[4] [1964] 2 All E.R. 943; [1964] 1 W.L.R. 1039.

[5] See p. 482, *post*.

whereas the character of the parties is hardly ever relevant in civil proceedings, although it may be relevant in exceptional cases such as defamation.[1]

Where separate civil and criminal proceedings do take place in respect of the same conduct the rule at common law was that the outcome of one set of proceedings did not affect the outcome of the other proceedings.   Thus the fact that a person had been convicted of a crime did not prevent him from suing in defamation a person who alleged that he was guilty of that crime, and that person could not justify his allegation by relying on the conviction.   This occasionally produced absurd situations[2] and the rule was eventually abrogated by the Civil Evidence Act 1968.[3]

To this rule that the coincidence of civil and criminal proceedings is irrelevant there is now only one exception.   Where a person has been prosecuted summarily for an assault by or on behalf of the person aggrieved, and has been either convicted and punished or acquitted following a hearing on the merits, no civil proceedings may subsequently be taken against him in respect of that assault.[4]   This, in fact, forces the victim of such an assault to decide whether he wishes to institute civil or criminal proceedings, and avoids an unnecessary duplication of proceedings in respect of a fairly minor wrong.[5]

C LAW OF CONTRACT

1 Nature of a contract

Legal rights and duties between individuals may come into existence in two ways.   The first is by operation of the law itself.   Common law obligations owed by one person to another are enforced by the law of torts.   Obligations may also arise in equity, for example obligations under a trust, or by statute. The second way in which an obligation may arise between parties is by the agreement of those parties to be bound.   This is the nature of a contract.   A contract may be defined as an agreement which creates obligations enforceable by law.   Although every contract depends upon an agreement to assume a legal obligation not every agreement is a contract.   The question of whether or not an agreement constitutes a contract (meaning a legally enforceable contract) is a question which depends upon an examination of the law relating to contracts. Thus the law of contract is merely a branch of English law as a whole.   Just as is the case with torts and crimes, a contract cannot be defined or characterised except by reference to the law itself.   A legal obligation arises not merely because the parties agree that it shall arise.   The agreement is just one of several circumstances which must be present before the law will recognise an obligation.   For this reason, therefore, it is not strictly accurate to say (as is stated at the beginning of this paragraph) that obligations may arise between parties by the agreement of those parties to be bound.   It would be more accurate to say

---

[1] See p. 462, post.
[2] Hinds v. Sparks, [1964] Crim.L.R. 717;   Goody v. Odhams Press Ltd., [1967] 1 Q.B. 333; [1966] 3 All E.R. 369;   Barclays Bank, Ltd. v. Cole, [1967] 2 Q.B. 738;   [1966] 3 All E.R. 948.
[3] Sections 11 and 13;   see p. 465, post.
[4] Offences Against the Person Act 1861, ss. 44, 45.
[5] The Rule in Smith v. Selwyn, whereby an action in tort was postponed to a criminal prosecution of the felon where the tortious act was a felony, was abolished by the Criminal Law Act 1967, s. 1.

that an agreement to create an obligation creates an obligation enforceable by law provided that certain other conditions are fulfilled. Before considering these other conditions it is necessary to note that there are other legal relationships which depend upon the phenomenon of agreement but which are not classified as contracts. Thus a conveyance of land or a transfer of property involve agreement but are not contracts in the sense of being subject to the law of contract. It may be argued that whether or not a legal relationship is described as a contract is merely a matter of terminology. This is not so because, although certain rules relating to contracts generally are applicable to other legal transactions such as conveyances or even marriages, most rules applicable to contracts do not apply by analogy to these transactions. Also, statutory provisions which expressly apply to contracts are clearly not intended to apply to every legal relationship created consensually. Once again the scope of the relationship referred to by the word "contract" is ascertainable only by reference to the historical sources of English law. An agreement is classifiable as a contract if it would have been enforceable in the common law courts by use of one of the three writs of debt, covenant or assumpsit. Although many of the rules applicable to contracts have changed and are continuing to change, and although many of these rules are equitable or statutory the nature of a contract remains as it was at common law prior to the abolition of the writ system.[1] It would be beyond the scope of this work to investigate the principles of the law of contract. Suffice it to mention that the essential elements of a valid contract are as follows:

(1)   there must be an agreement consisting of an offer by one party and an acceptance by the other;

(2)   either the contract must be contained in a deed under seal or there must be valuable consideration given by each party;

(3)   the agreement must have been reached with the intention of creating a legal relationship and must, by its character, be capable of doing so;[2]

(4)   the parties must have the legal capacity to contract; and

(5)   In some cases the parties must comply with certain formalities imposed by law.

Case law has created exceptions to these principles and, in some cases, has almost succeeded in distorting them. Judicial inroads into the doctrine of consideration are an example of this. Nevertheless each remains essential to the creation of a valid enforceable contract.

2   Historical sources of the law of contract

All three major historical sources of English law have influenced the law of contract. The nature of a contract and the basic rules were formulated in the

---

[1] See p. 18, *ante*.

[2] This is the most important element in a contract and where it is present the court will strive to give effect to the parties' intention. Where the agreement is merely a friendly or domestic arrangement not intended to give rise to legally enforceable obligations the court will interpret it accordingly: *Balfour* v. *Balfour*, [1919] 2 K.B. 571; see also *Ford Motor Co., Ltd.* v. *Amalgamated Union of Engineering and Foundry Workers*, [1969] 2 All E.R. 481; [1969] 1 W.L.R. 339. However where a party has acted on the faith of the agreement the courts are very reluctant to allow the other party to say that he did not intend to create a legal relationship: *Carlill* v. *Carbolic Smoke Ball Co.*, [1893] 1 Q.B. 256; *Simpkins* v. *Pays*, [1955] 3 All E.R. 10; [1955] 1 W.L.R. 975.

courts of the common law. However equity and legislation have also made substantial contributions to this branch of the law.

a   Common law

The three forms of action which primarily effected the growth of the law of contract were debt, covenant and assumpsit. The nature and scope of these writs has already been described in the context of the development of the forms of action at common law.[1] It will be recalled that assumpsit replaced debt and provided a general means of enforcing bargains. It should, however, be noted that assumpsit did not supersede the writ of covenant, the result being that obligations under seal are, to this day, enforceable without proof of consideration whereas, in contracts not under seal, consideration is essential.

A particularly interesting result of the merger of the whole of the writ of debt into assumpsit was that assumpsit became available for the recovery of monies such as judgment debts, statutory fines and customary dues hitherto within the province of debt on a record. This was anomalous since these debts did not arise, in many cases, by agreement and are thus not properly describable as contractual. This branch of the law of contract is now termed "quasi-contract" and is a striking illustration of the fact that the nature of a contractual obligation is ascertainable by reference to the history of contract rather than to the conduct of the parties.

Since debt had already assimilated the ancient writ of account, there were many other forms of quasi-contract where the defendant had received money to the plaintiff's use and had failed to account to him for it. The courts have since used the concept of quasi-contract to enforce restitution wherever one person is unjustly enriched at the expense of another. For example, money paid under a mistake of fact, money paid in pursuance of a void contract or an illegal contract may all be recovered in quasi-contract.

b   Equity

The growth and nature of the source of law known as equity has already been described.[2] It is sufficient to note at this point that one aspect of the jurisdiction of the Court of Chancery (the principal court administering equity prior to 1875) was to mitigate the hardship of the common law and lessen the rigidity of common law rules. This aspect of equity affected contract rather than tort. Equity would relieve oppressed suitors. For example, at common law an obligation under seal was enforceable against the defendant even if the plaintiff had been guilty of fraud or undue influence. In such a case the Court of Chancery would intervene and rescind the obligation. Equity has, in more recent times, enabled the courts, in certain circumstances, to avoid the harsher effects of the common law doctrines of consideration[3] and privity of contract.[4] Similarly many of the rules relating to misrepresentation are rules of equity.

Equity also intervened to avoid the operation of statutory rules of contract where this would cause injustice. On the basis that "equity looks to the intent,

---

[1] See p. 20, *ante.*
[2] See p. 29, *ante.*
[3] *Central London Property Trust, Ltd.* v. *High Trees House, Ltd.*, [1947] K.B. 130; [1956] 1 All E.R. 256 n.; *D. and C. Builders, Ltd.* v. *Rees*, [1966] 2 Q.B. 617; [1965] 3 All E.R. 837.
[4] *Beswick* v. *Beswick*, [1968] A.C. 58; [1967] 2 All E.R. 1197.

not to the form" the Court of Chancery introduced the doctrine of part performance to avoid the need for a memorandum under the Statute of Frauds 1677 or the Law of Property Act 1925, s. 40.

A third way in which the Court of Chancery supplemented the common law was by the grant of remedies in cases where the common law provided no remedy or an inadequate remedy. The two main remedies available in equity are injunction and specific performance. The latter is a remedy which applies to contract rather than tort and is the means whereby the court can compel the performance of a contract according to its terms.[1]

c Statute

Legislation is the chief modern agency of law reform. The law intervenes as little as possible in the freedom of parties to enter into contracts. For this reason legislation has had rather less effect on the law of contract than on other branches of the law such as criminal law, torts and the law of property. Nevertheless *laissez faire* is a concept which has diminished in operation in the modern industrial society. Consequently legislation has in the present century grown in importance as a source of the law of contract. Statutes such as the Restrictive Trade Practices Act 1956, and the Resale Prices Act 1964 were passed to safeguard the public interest by preventing individuals from entering into contracts which were detrimental to the interests of society as a whole. On the other hand Parliament also intervenes, as equity once did, to protect individual members of society from their own weakness or susceptibility. Thus statutes such as the Gaming Acts, Moneylenders Acts and Hire Purchase Acts have all served to protect certain sections of society against others by restricting their freedom of contract. In addition, as in all branches of the law, where the doctrine of judicial precedent has perpetuated an artificial or unjust situation, statute has been the means of rationalising the law; the Misrepresentation Act 1967 is an example of this.

3 Relationship between contract and tort

The nature of contractual obligations differs fundamentally from the nature of tortious obligations in that the former are primarily fixed by the parties themselves while rights and duties in tort are primarily fixed by law.[2] However this fundamental distinction is blurred in certain respects. Thus certain contractual obligations are fixed by law. For example statutes such as the Moneylenders Act 1927, the Law of Property Act 1925 and the Hire-Purchase Act 1965 impose certain obligations which must be complied with in contracts to which these statutes apply; the Sale of Goods Act 1893 operates to imply terms into contracts thus imposing obligations on the parties unless they agree otherwise; the Road Traffic Act 1960 compels persons to enter into contracts of insurance against third party risks. Similarly, rights and duties in tort may sometimes be varied contractually. For example a contractual licence to enter land permits what would otherwise be the tort of trespass to land;[3] an occupier of land may contractually exclude his duty of care to lawful visitors.[4]

---

[1] See p. 38, *ante*.
[2] See Winfield, *Province of the Law of Tort* (1931 Edn.), p. 100.
[3] *Hurst* v. *Picture Theatres, Ltd.*, [1915] 1 K.B. 1.
[4] Occupiers' Liability Act 1957, s. 2 (1).

In certain cases, due to the tortious nature of assumpsit for misfeasance and malfeasance, the same act may constitute both a tort and a breach of contract, generally where the defendant's conduct is alleged to be negligent or fraudulent. Thus, for example, a dentist who negligently extracts a private patient's tooth is liable for breach of his contractual obligation to exercise proper care in the plaintiff's treatment and is also liable in the tort of negligence.[1]   Similarly a negligent act may constitute both a breach of contract to one person, an employer for instance, and a tort to another.   This occurred in *Lister* v. *Romford Ice and Cold Storage Co., Ltd.*,[2] where the negligence of a driver towards his passenger was held to be a breach of contract towards his employer.   VISCOUNT SIMONDS, in that case, observed that:[3]

> "It is trite law that a single act of negligence may give rise to a claim either in tort or for breach of a term express or implied in a contract.   Of this the negligence of a servant in performance of his duty is a clear example."

Often the coincidence of contractual and tortious liability will be of no importance.   The plaintiff's success will not depend upon whether he chooses to describe his action as an action in contract or an action in tort.   However there are certain rules of English law which are expressed to apply only to "contract" or only to "tort".   Consequently there are several cases where the course of an action will be affected according to whether it is termed an action in contract or an action in tort.   Generally the plaintiff will plead both causes of action in the alternative.   The question then arises as to the approach the court will adopt in classifying the nature of the action.   It seems clear that if the plaintiff can derive any advantage from framing his action in contract rather than tort he will be allowed to do so.   For instance in *Matthews* v. *Kuwait Bechtel Corporation*[4] the plaintiff suffered injury while working in Kuwait for the defendant corporation under a contract to be governed, according to its terms, by English law.   He sought leave[5] to serve a writ out of the jurisdiction which he could in an action in contract but not in an action in tort.   He was granted leave on the basis that he had a cause of action in contract irrespective of the fact that he also had an action in tort.[6]   The recent case of *Chesworth* v. *Farrar*[7] provides an illustration of the importance of characterisation.   This case involved an action brought against the estate of a deceased person for the proceeds of sale of certain antiques owned by the plaintiff, the action being brought more than six months after the grant of representation to the estate.   It followed (from the Law Reform (Miscellaneous Provisions) Act 1934, s. 1 (3)) that, insofar as the action lay in tort, it was statute-barred.[8]   However EDMUND DAVIES, J. (as he then was) held that

---

[1] *Edwards* v. *Mallan*, [1908] 1 K.B. 1002.   There would, probably, be no contract with a National Health Service patient.

[2] [1957] A.C. 555; [1957] 1 All E.R. 125.

[3] [1955] A.C., at p. 573; [1957] 1 All E.R., at p. 131.   See also M'*Alister* (or *Donoghue*) v. *Stevenson*, [1932] A.C. 562 which serves to illustrate this point.

[4] [1959] 2 Q.B. 57; [1959] 2 All E.R. 345.

[5] Under (what is now) R.S.C. (Revision) 1965, O. 11, r. 1.

[6] See also *Sellars* v. *Best*, [1954] 2 All E.R. 389; [1954] 1 W.L.R. 913 (measure of damages under the Fatal Accidents Acts wider in contract than in tort).

[7] [1967] 1 Q.B. 407; [1966] 2 All E.R. 107.

[8] This would no longer be so, there being now no special period of limitation for proceedings in tort against the estates of deceased persons: Proceedings Against Estates Act 1970, s. 1.

the plaintiff's right to the proceeds of sale of his goods sounded in quasi-contract rather than in tort, so that the cause of action was not an "action in tort" within the 1934 Act and was, therefore, not statute-barred.[1]

However it more frequently happens that the plaintiff might derive an advantage from framing his action in tort rather than in contract. This is all the more likely now that an action in negligence may be maintained in respect of financial loss.[2] For example, the measure of damages in tort is somewhat wider than in contract; aggravated damages are recoverable in tort but not usually in contract;[3] limitation periods differ since a cause of action in contract accrues upon breach whereas in most torts it accrues only when damage is suffered. The approach which the courts adopt in this sort of case may be described as unpredictable. In several actions against solicitors in respect of professional negligence, plaintiffs have failed to recover for certain heads of damage on the basis that they were too remote in an action in contract, notwithstanding that they might not have been too remote in tort.[4] Nor can these cases be explained solely by reference to the history of the solicitor-client relationship, which has always been entirely contractual. In *Bagot* v. *Stevens Scanlan & Co.*,[5] DIPLOCK, L.J. (sitting at first instance) stated a wider principle, namely that all professional relationships in contract give rise to a contractual duty alone and not to any duty independent of contract. The question in that case arose in a neat form. The defendant architects had supervised the construction and installation of a drainage system in pursuance of a contract with the plaintiff. This supervision ended in February, 1957. The drains were alleged to have been constructed negligently in that the pipes began to crack and cause flooding in or about the end of 1961. The writ was issued in April, 1963, by which time it was admitted that an action in contract would be statute-barred, the six year period of limitation having commenced in February, 1957, and thus expired before the issue of the writ. DIPLOCK, L.J. (as he then was) held, on the trial of a preliminary point of law, that no action would lie in tort even though such an action might not be statute-barred, expressly adopting the following statement of law set out in the judgment of GREER, L.J. in *Jarvis* v. *Moy, Davies, Smith, Vandervell & Co.*:[6]

> "The distinction in the modern view, for this purpose, between contract and tort may be put thus: where the breach of duty alleged arises out of a liability independently of the personal obligation undertaken by contract, it is tort, and it may be tort even though there may happen to be a contract between the parties, if the duty in fact arises independently of that contract. Breach of contract occurs where that which is complained of is a breach of duty arising out of the obligations undertaken by the contract."

---

[1] Though the action for breach of bailment, being based upon the infringement of a right of possession, was tortious in nature (although the bailment was contractual) and therefore barred.

[2] *Hedley Byrne & Co., Ltd.* v. *Heller & Partners, Ltd.*, [1964] A.C. 465; [1963] 2 All E.R. 575.

[3] *Addis* v. *Gramophone Co., Ltd.*, [1909] A.C. 488. The rules of remoteness also differ; see *The Heron II*, [1969] 1 A.C. 350; [1967] 3 All E.R. 686; *Doyle* v. *Olby (Ironmongers), Ltd.*, [1969] 2 Q.B. 158; [1969] 2 All E.R. 119.

[4] *Groom* v. *Crocker*, [1939] 1 K.B. 194; [1938] 2 All E.R. 394; *Hall* v. *Meyrick*, [1957] 2 Q.B. 455; [1957] 2 All E.R. 722; *Clark* v. *Kirby-Smith*, [1964] Ch. 506; [1964] 2 All E.R. 835.

[5] [1966] 1 Q.B. 197; [1964] 3 All E.R. 577.

[6] [1936] 1 K.B. 399, at p. 405.

DIPLOCK, L.J., having stated this wide principle, went on to acknowledge that there were exceptional relationships where a duty was owed in tort as well as in contract:

> "I think that on examination all those will turn out to be cases where the law in the old days recognised either something in the nature of a status like a public calling (such as common carrier, common innkeeper, or a bailor and bailee) or the status of master and servant. There it can be properly said, as it was in such cases as *Lister* v. *Romford Ice and Cold Storage Co., Ltd.*[1] that, independently of contract, there existed from the mere status a relationship which gave rise to a duty of care not dependent on the existence of a contract between the parties."[2]

Thus the position can be summarised by stating that where the duty alleged to have been broken arises out of a contract the plaintiff's right of action lies only in contract even though the defendant's conduct is also tortious, except where the relationship arises out of the defendant's public calling or is a master-servant relationship. It follows from this that the plaintiff can never enforce an unenforceable contract by framing his action in tort, and there are many authorities to support this proposition.[3] However there is nothing to prevent an action in tort where the breach of duty alleged arises independently of contract, merely because the plaintiff and defendant stand in a contractual relationship.[4]

The "pigeonhole" approach owes its existence in English law to the medieval writ system. It can, occasionally, cause injustice. This is well illustrated by the anomalous doctrine of privity of contract. X enters into a contract with Y for the benefit of Z. There is no logical reason why Z should not be able to sue upon that contract for to allow him to do so would impose upon Y no greater obligation than he had agreed to undertake. Nevertheless Z has no right of action.[5]

D   LAW OF PROPERTY

1   The nature of property

The word "property" is used in two distinct senses. The layman's concept of property is of a thing in which rights exist. This meaning of the word property is also adopted occasionally by lawyers when speaking of movable and immovable property.[6] However the usual legal meaning of the word property signifies not the thing itself but that interest in the thing which the law recognises. Thus

---

[1] [1957] A.C. 555; [1957] 1 All E.R. 125.
[2] [1964] 3 All E.R. 577, at p. 580. It seems that if, in this type of case, the action in tort is, for some reason, barred no action will lie in contract: *Turner* v. *Stallibrass*, [1898] 1 Q.B. 56; *Ballet* v. *Mingay*, [1943] K.B. 281; [1943] 1 All E.R. 143.
[3] Examples are *Jennings* v. *Rundall* (1799), 8 Term Rep. 335; *R. Leslie, Ltd.* v. *Sheill*, [1914] 3 K.B. 607.
[4] *Burnard* v. *Haggis* (1863), 14 C.B. N.S. 45; *Bowmakers, Ltd.* v. *Barnet Instruments, Ltd.*, [1945] K.B. 65; [1944] 2 All E.R. 579.
[5] *Tweddle* v. *Atkinson* (1861), 1 B. & S. 393; cf. *Beswick* v. *Beswick*, [1968] A.C. 58; [1967] 2 All E.R. 1197.
[6] The Theft Act 1968 uses the word property in this sense, viz. "A person is guilty of theft if he dishonestly appropriates property belonging to another" (s. 1 (1)); "'Property' includes money and all other property, real and personal, including things in action and other intangible property" (s. 4 (1)).

one speaks of "property in land" or of "property passing" by disposition even though there has been no physical dealing with the thing itself.

Property may be defined as a right *in rem* which the law recognises and protects in any commercial asset. All proprietary rights are rights *in rem* which means that they exist in the thing itself and are enforceable against the whole world, as opposed to rights *in personam* which exist only against another person, such as contractual rights. However, although all proprietary rights are rights *in rem*, it does not follow that all rights *in rem* are proprietary rights. Thus a person's right to his reputation, a husband's right to his wife's consortium and a father's right to his daughter's services are all rights *in rem* in the sense that they are enforceable against the whole world; they are nevertheless not property. The reason is that they are not transferable or assignable. They are not commercial assets.

There is, inevitably, an overlap between the law of property and the law of contract and tort. The law of property is that body of rules which determines the scope of proprietary rights and the means by which they may be created, transferred and extinguished. However, if a proprietary right is infringed the remedy usually lies in an action in tort. For example, an interference with a person's possession of land is the tort of trespass to land; interference with his use or enjoyment of land is a nuisance; an act which amounts to a denial of his title to chattels is conversion. The overlap may be accounted for by the fact that the law of torts has its origins in procedure and an action in tort was and is a procedural means of enforcing a proprietary right.

Given that the word "property" signifies a proprietary interest which the law recognises it cannot be defined further in general terms. This is because there are varying degrees of interest which may exist in the same subject-matter, particularly in land. Thus a freeholder, a lessee and a mortgagee all have an interest in land describable as property though the actual rights which each possesses are obviously different. The nature and extent of property in land is an extremely complex study and depends upon an examination of the historical origins and development of the various legal and equitable interests which may exist in land. The law of property in goods is somewhat less complex.

a Property in goods

There are two types of property in goods: "general property" and "special property". General property in goods is the highest interest recognised by law which may exist in goods and is virtually synonymous with "ownership" or "title". The use of the word "property" in relation to goods is generally accepted as meaning general property. Thus section 1 (1) of the Sale of Goods Act 1893 provides:

> "A contract of sale of goods is a contract whereby the seller transfers or agrees to transfer the property in goods to the buyer for a money consideration, called the price."

Section 62 (1) of the same Act defines "property":

> " 'Property' means the general property in goods, and not merely a special property".

Although "property" is virtually synonymous with "ownership" the words are not freely interchangeable because ownership is used in several statutes in a far wider sense.[1]

Any legal interest in chattels short of general property is termed a "special property". Special property in goods may arise under a trust but, since trusts of movables are rarely encountered, usually arises by virtue of a bailment. Bailment is a transaction whereby one person (the bailor) transfers to another (the bailee) possession of goods, the former retaining the general property in them, with a condition that they will, when the purpose of the bailment has been fulfilled, be returned to the bailor or otherwise dealt with in accordance with the conditions of the bailment. A hirer, a pledgee and the holder of a lien are all bailees. The bailee has, put simply, possession without title. Thus virtually all forms of special property are founded on possession.

"Possession" is a somewhat different concept in law than it is in common parlance. To the layman, possession connotes control by physical contact with the thing possessed. However this, in law, is not possession. A servant who is holding goods on behalf of his master has only "custody" and no property in the goods whatsoever. Conversely legal possession does not depend upon physical contact. A person is in possession of all the goods in his house even when he is not present in the house. Similarly a landowner is presumed to possess chattels on his land even though he is unaware of their existence.[2] The law of torts protects possession and rights to possession in goods rather than ownership. Thus even a thief may maintain an action for trespass to goods against a subsequent wrongdoer. The plaintiff in an action for conversion need show only a right to possession which enables him to sue anyone other than the true owner.[3]

b Property in land

Property in land is less easy to define. The terms general and special property do not apply in relation to land. Land, in English law, cannot be owned in the absolute sense in which there may be ownership of chattels. This is because of the feudal concept of landholding which originated in the Middle Ages and is still the basis of English land law. This concept is that the Sovereign is the absolute owner of all the land in the realm. Individuals may only hold estates in the land by a form of tenure.

Tenures.—Thus all landowners are, in theory, tenants of the Sovereign. In the Middle Ages there were several forms of tenure, the obligations which were imposed on the tenant in return for his tenure being termed the "incidents" of that form of tenure. Tenures differed according to whether the holder was a freeman or a villein.

The tenures held by freemen were known as "freehold" tenures. The two principal forms of freehold tenure in the Middle Ages were tenure by "knight

---

[1] For examples, see Public Health Act 1936, s. 343 (1); Town and Country Planning Act 1947, s. 119 (1); Factories Act 1961, s. 176. The Theft Act 1968 is expressed in terms of property "belonging to another" (s. 5).

[2] *South Staffordshire Water Co.* v. *Sharman*, [1896] 2 Q.B. 44.

[3] *Armory* v. *Delamirie* (1722), 1 Stra. 505.

service" and "socage" tenure.[1] Knight service involved the tenant providing a certain number of knights to fight in the lord's army. In time of peace this provision was replaced by the obligation to pay a sum of money known as *scutagium* (shield-money). Military tenure was abolished in 1660[2] and converted into the second form of freehold tenure—"socage" tenure. The incidents of socage tenure varied considerably. They might involve the provision of weapons for the lord's army or of agricultural services. One standard incident of socage tenure was escheat, whereby the land was forfeited to the superior lord if the tenant died without an heir. It was in order to avoid the burdensome incidents of feudal tenure that the device of the trust was employed.[3]

Villeins could also hold land. The incidents attaching to unfree tenure varied but generally involved the payment of money, the rendering of agricultural services, escheat and the payment of fines on alienation (transfer) of the land. Unfree tenure was evidenced by an entry on the roll of the manorial court. It thus became known as tenure by copy of the roll—"copyhold" tenure. Copyhold tenure might be converted into freehold tenure by enfranchisement. Those copyholds which were not so converted were converted into socage tenure by the Law of Property Act 1922 (which came into force on January 1, 1926).[4] Thus, since 1926, the only form of tenure which still exists is socage tenure.[5] It is arguable, therefore, that the history of tenures is of purely academic interest. Nevertheless it does illustrate the nature of the modern system of landholding and it is the basis of the doctrine of estates. Before examining briefly the nature of an estate in land it should be noted that leasehold was not a feudal tenure, so that a leasehold estate in land does not arise from tenure in the same way as a freehold estate.

Estates.—While tenure concerns the relationship between the lord and his tenant, the interest which the latter has in the land itself is termed an "estate". Just as the highest interest which a person may have in goods is a general property, so the highest interest which he may own in land is an estate. At common law there were several different types of estate which a person might hold in land. Estates might be in possession or reversion; they might be absolute or conditional; they might be of indefinite duration or limited in point of time. Above all several estates could exist simultaneously in the same parcel of land. It is sufficient to state that, since 1926, there are now only two legal estates in land: (i) an estate in fee simple absolute in possession (freehold), and (ii) a term of years absolute (leasehold).[6] The freehold estate is held by socage tenure, though tenure is no longer of practical importance. Although it must be an estate "in possession" this does not mean actual occupation since possession is defined so

---

[1] Other forms of freehold tenure were *frankalmoign* (whereby religious houses undertook to say prayers for the soul of the superior feudal lord) and *serjeanty* (whereby the tenant had to provide various honorary services).

[2] Tenures Abolition Act.

[3] See p. 35, *ante*.

[4] Section 128, Sched. 12.

[5] "Crownhold" which might be classified as a form of tenure, was created by the Land Commission Act 1967 but abolished by the Land Commission (Dissolution) Act 1971.

[6] Law of Property Act 1925, s. 1 (1).

as to include the receipt of rents and profits.[1]   Thus a freehold landlord has a legal estate in the land in spite of the physical possession of the leasehold tenant. The second legal estate, the leasehold estate, is not based on tenure according to the feudal concept.   Leases in the Middle Ages were regarded only as creating purely personal obligations between the parties, not as creating any estate in the land itself.   It was only when the same form of action[2] became appropriate for both the freeholder and the leaseholder to recover the land in the common law courts, in the fifteenth century, that the leaseholder was recognised as having an estate in the land.

Apart from the two legal estates in land which may exist since 1926 there are many other interests in land which may still exist.   Although these interests were, in some cases, describable as "estates" at common law and in equity they are now termed "interests" in land rather than estates.   These interests may be further classified as "legal", for example easements and charges by way of legal mortgage, or "equitable", such as interests under a trust and life interests.   The importance of the classification lies in the formalities of conveyancing.

2   Classification of property

The foregoing examination of the nature of "property" demonstrates that the word may be used in several different contexts where it may be understood to bear different meanings.   The logical method of classifying these various types of property is by reference to the subject matter in which the property exists— land or chattels.   Nevertheless English law has not generally chosen to adopt this classification.   The historical division of property is into real property and personal property.

a   Real and personal property

Real property.—In the infancy of the common law the only matters in which the royal courts were interested in assuming jurisdiction were, broadly speaking, crimes and disputes over title to land.   The earliest forms of action available at common law were actions for the recovery of land.   These were termed "real" actions[3] and the subject matter of such an action consequently described as "real" property (or realty).   Thus any interest in land held under feudal tenure was classed as real property.   This description includes not only the basic interest of the tenant, his *feudum* or fee, but also any other interest in the land such as a right of way.   The real actions were not available for the recovery of chattels. Disputes over property in chattels could be pursued by one of the "personal" actions[4] such as debt or detinue.   Thus property in chattels is termed "personal" property.   More significant is the fact that personal property comprises lease-holds since a lease, until the fifteenth century, was regarded as creating only personal obligations and not any interest in land.   There thus arose the ano-malous situation whereby freehold interests in land are classified as real property

---

[1] Laws of Property Act 1925, s. 205 (1) (xix).
[2] The action of ejectment; see p. 22, *ante.*
[3] See p. 18, *ante.*
[4] See p. 19, *ante.*

whereas leasehold interests in the same land are classified as personal property. This is of lesser significance now but was vital prior to 1926. Until this date the rules of intestate succession differed radically in relation to real and personal property respectively. Real property passed to the heir at law, to the exclusion of other sons and daughters; personal property, with which the feudal system was little concerned, devolved upon the next of kin. Consequently there is, in the law reports, a considerable volume of litigation concerned with determining whether specific property is real or personal. The equitable doctrine of conversion depends almost entirely upon this type of dispute between the heir at law and the next of kin. The general purport of the 1925 legislation was to assimilate real and personal property. Indeed, "An Act to assimilate and amend the law of real and personal estate" are the opening words of the long title of the Law of Property Act 1922.

Virtually all the distinctions between the old rules relating to real and personal property were abolished by the 1925 legislation, particularly the intestate succession rules. Nevertheless the distinction between real and personal property is still drawn. For example a testator who makes a bequest of "all my realty" to a named beneficiary will not succeed in passing to him any leasehold interests he may have. Similarly, since personal property may be seized in execution of a judgment, a leasehold interest may theoretically be taken in execution whereas a freehold interest cannot be seized.[1]

Personal property.—Personal property, sometimes called "personalty" or "chattels", comprises that property which was protected at common law by the personal actions. There are three classes of personal property: (i) leaseholds, sometimes described as "chattels real", (ii) "choses in possession" and (iii) "choses in action".

A chose in possession is a right in something which is capable of physical possession, such as a car, furniture or a domestic animal. It is distinguishable from a chose in action which is a right in something which has no physical existence and can thus be enforced only by action. The latter is sometimes described as incorporeal property though this is scarcely an accurate classification since all legal property is incorporeal. Examples of choses in action are debts, rights under a negotiable instrument, stock and shares, trade mark copyrights, patents and business goodwill. All these things are commerci[ ] assets and therefore property although they have no physical existence. Generally the same legal rules apply to choses in possession as to choses in action although, by their nature, choses in action must attract special legal rules regarding their creation and transfer. They cannot, obviously, be transferred by physical delivery and thus there are a number of rules, generally embodied in statutes, regulating the formalities for transferring this type of property.

b Movable and immovable property

A more logical classification of property is by reference to the thing in which it exists. Most continental legal systems have adopted this classification and English law is, in turn, leaning towards this classification and away from the archaic distinction between realty and personalty. It will be appreciated that

---

[1] See p. 303, *post.*

"property" as applied to movable and immovable property connotes the thing in which the right exists rather than the right itself. It would, indeed, be strictly accurate to speak of "property in a movable object" rather than "movable property". However the expression "movable property" is commonly understood to bear this meaning.

Immovable property.—The expression "immovable property" means land. However this definition requires clarification because the legal concept of land is somewhat wider than that implied in common usage. This fact manifests itself in two maxims of English land law, expressed, characteristically, in Latin. The first is *cuius est solum, eius est usque ad caelum et ad inferos* (he who owns the soil owns everything above and beneath it). Thus, in theory, the owner of land has a right to all minerals beneath the surface and to all the airspace above his land. In fact his rights are somewhat more limited both by common law and statute. His rights in airspace are, in practice, confined to that part of his airspace essential to the enjoyment of the land,[1] and there is, by statute, no right of action in trespass or nuisance merely by reason of the flight of a civil aircraft over another's land.[2] In addition certain rights over minerals are vested in the Crown. Gold and silver belong to the Crown at common law; petroleum and coal have been vested in the Crown by statute.[3]

A second extension which the law makes to the ordinary conception of land is embodied in the maxim, *quicquid plantatur solo, solo cedit* (whatever is joined to the soil becomes part of the soil). This affixation may be natural or artificial. Natural adjuncts such as trees and crops are part of the land; so also are fixtures regarded as part of the realty. There is much learning attached to the question of what are fixtures. The degree of annexation of the chattel to the land is important but not decisive since the purpose for which it was annexed must also be taken into account.[4] It is often important to decide whether or not an article is a fixture and thus immovable property. For example, no fixtures can be seized in execution or by way of distress since they cease to be chattels. Because of this maxim the sale of a house is always completed by a conveyance of the estate in the land upon which the house stands, the purchaser acquiring all that is affixed to the land in question.[5]

Movable property.—Movable property comprises all things which are not within the definition of immovable property. The nomenclature is here rather open to question since choses in action are classified as movable property although they are not, in the literal sense, capable of being moved.

The fact that English law is tending to discard the distinction between real and personal property in favour of the distinction between movable and immovable property is evident in the English conflict of laws rules. When classifying a legal problem involving property, as the judge must do in order to decide which legal system shall be invoked to determine the problem, the property will be defined as movable or immovable, never as real or personal.

---

[1] *Kelsen v. Imperial Tobacco Co. (of Great Britain and Ireland) Ltd.,* [1957] 2 Q.B. 334; [1957] 2 All E.R. 343.
[2] Civil Aviation Act 1949, s. 40 (1) (a).
[3] Petroleum (Production) Act 1934; Coal Industry Nationalisation Act 1946.
[4] *Leigh v. Taylor,* [1902] A.C. 157.
[5] See Law of Property Act 1925, s. 62.

3 Sources of the law of property

All three major historical sources of English law have combined to mould the English law of property.

The common law is the basis of the law of property. The fundamental distinction between real and personal property is a common law distinction which derived from the procedural methods of enforcing property rights in the common law courts. The early common law was almost entirely land law and the doctrines of tenures and estates are based on feudalism which was, in itself, the cornerstone of the common law. The introduction of much of the law relating to pure personalty (personal property excluding leaseholds) into English law was more devious. Many of the rules relating to the acquisition of personal property stem from Roman law, then were incorporated into the law merchant and finally into the common law when the common law assimilated the English law merchant.[1]

Equity has also been a major source of land law. The principal contribution of equity to English law as a whole has been the trust, which originated as a device for avoiding the incidents of feudal tenure and the impossibility, at common law, of devising land by will.[2] The interest of a beneficiary under a trust and the equity of redemption of mortgages are the two main classes of equitable property in land.

Finally statute is an important source of the law of both real and personal property. Medieval statutes such as *Quia Emptores* 1290, the Statute of Uses 1535 and the Tenures Abolition Act 1660 shaped the feudal land law. The modern "property legislation", embodying the Law of Property Acts 1922–1925, the Settled Land Act 1925, the Land Charges Act 1925, the Land Registration Act 1925, the Trustee Act 1925 and the Administration of Estates Act 1925 have simplified and standardised the system of transferring interests in land known as conveyancing, although they have not altered the basic principles of land law.

Most of the law relating to choses in action is now statutory. Indeed many choses in action such as patents, stock and shares, copyrights and trade marks are entirely the creation of statute.

Finally the rights which an individual may exercise over his own property have been severely curtailed by legislation in the public interest. The need for planning has resulted in Town and Country Planning Acts, Housing Acts and the creation of the radical power of compulsory purchase of land. The desire to control land speculation led to the controversial Land Commission Act 1967 which (*inter alia*) created a new public authority, the Land Commission, with extensive powers to acquire, manage and dispose of land. The scheme was not, however, a success and the Commission was dissolved by the Land Commission (Dissolution) Act 1971. In addition the legislature has found it necessary to protect tenants and confer upon them additional rights by Rent Acts, Housing Acts, Landlord and Tenant Acts and, most recently, by the Leasehold Reform Act 1967 which enables leaseholders, in certain circumstances, to enlarge their leasehold interest into a freehold.

---

[1] See p. 48, *ante.*
[2] See p. 35, *ante.*

PART II

The Legal and Literary Sources of English Law

SUMMARY

The word "source" is used in various senses in relation to law. A *formal* source of law is that from which a system of law derives its validity, whether that be, for example, the general will or the will of a dictator; consideration of formal sources is a matter of jurisprudence rather than of the legal system and is thus outside the scope of the present work. The *historical* sources of English law have been examined. It remains to consider the *legal* and *literary* sources. The authority for any proposition of law is the legal source of that proposition; the legal sources have been defined as the gates through which new principles can find entrance into the law. Literary sources are simply the materials in which the legal sources are recorded; every legal source has its corresponding literary source. The principal legal sources of English law are legislation and judicial precedents (though custom, which is treated in the present work as a purely historical source, is regarded by some as a legal source). The corresponding literary sources are, with respect to legislation, the various publications of statutes, notably the Queen's Printer's Copy, and, with respect to precedents, law reports. Text books are an indirect literary source of all legal sources, though the old "books of authority" are a legal source in themselves.

CHAPTER 6

Legislation

A THE FUNCTIONS OF LEGISLATION

The broad function of all legislation is to create, alter or revoke law to give effect to the intention of the legislative body. Subordinate legislation fulfils various specific functions, scarcely capable of classification. The functions of Acts of Parliament, by far the most important form of legislation, may be classified as follows.

1 Revision of substantive rules of law

Although all statutes are concerned with law revision in the broadest sense relatively few statutes are concerned with altering or revising substantive rules of law or "lawyers' law" as it is sometimes called. Such statutes are frequently passed when the law, through the restrictive operation of the doctrine of judicial precedent, has become stale and incapable of adaptation. The need for reform often manifests itself in a House of Lords decision. Where a decision of the House of Lords is unpopular the law is usually altered by statute. There are many examples on the statute book of Acts passed with the apparent intention of overruling the effect of a House of Lords decision.[1] When a more general reform of the law is required the initiative frequently comes from lawyers. Until 1965 the machinery for generating law reform was conspicuously erratic in its operation, consisting mainly of the Law Revision Committee and, subsequently, the Law Reform Committee which considered, on their own initiative or at the invitation of the Lord Chancellor, branches of the law requiring reform and then published reports containing recommendations. The Committees consisted of practising lawyers who met from time to time, when pressure of other work permitted. Their recommendations often, but by no means always, were subsequently taken up by Parliament. Where the question was of wider public importance, heads of government departments might

---

[1] Examples are: Parliamentary Papers Act 1840; Limitation Act 1963; Trade Disputes Act 1965; War Damage Act 1965. The apparent intention of these Acts is to reverse House of Lords decisions immediately preceeding them though Acts of Parliament do not expressly name cases which they are obviously intended to overrule.

refer the question to a special committee for report or the Crown might set up a Royal Commission. A recent example of law reform based on the recommendations of a Royal Commission is the Courts Act 1971 which follows basically the recommendations of the so-called "Beeching Commission".[1]

However a major addition to the machinery of law reform was made by the Law Commissions Act 1965 which established the Law Commissions. Section 3 (1) of the Act defines the duty of the Commissions (there is a separate Commission for Scotland) thus:

> "It shall be the duty of each of the Commissions to take and keep under review all the law with which they are respectively concerned with a view to its systematic development and reform, including in particular the codification of such law, the elimination of anomalies, the repeal of obsolete and unnecessary enactments, the reduction of the number of separate enactments and generally the simplification and modernisation of the law."

The creation of the Law Commission has been universally acknowledged as an important step forward in law reform, for which the former Lord Chancellor, Lord Gardiner, must take most of the credit. The Commissions, by reason of the appointment of full-time Commissioners of the highest calibre and of full-time administrative staff, have been able to produce a steady flow of reports, recommendations and draft Bills, most of which have been implemented by Act of Parliament within a relatively short time. Thus, for example, out of 76 Public Acts which received the Royal Assent in 1971, no fewer than 11 were based wholly or in part on recommendations of the Law Commission.[2]

2   Consolidation of enactments

Where a branch of the law has evolved piecemeal, a consolidating statute may be passed, for the purpose of clarification, containing substantially the existing law in a consolidated form. There is a special procedure whereby such statutes may be passed without Parliamentary debate. This procedure was introduced by the Consolidation of Enactments (Procedure) Act 1949 and numerous Acts have been passed under it, examples being the Marriage Act 1949, the Magistrates' Courts Act 1952, the Matrimonial Causes Act 1965 and the Attachment of Earnings Act 1971.

3   Codification

Codification differs from consolidation in that an Act may only be said to consolidate statute law, whereas it may codify both case law and statute law. Nevertheless codification is similar in function to consolidation in that in both cases the object of the statute is to simplify and clarify the existing law rather than to effect substantial alterations to it. Notable examples of codifying statutes are the Offences Against the Person Act 1861 and the Sale of Goods Act 1893.

---

[1] *Report of the Royal Commission on Assizes and Quarter Sessions*: Cmnd. 4153 (1969).

[2] These were the Vehicles (Excise) Act, the Animals Act, the Coinage Act, the Administration of Estates Act, the National Savings Bank Act, the Law Reform (Miscellaneous Provisions) Act, the Nullity of Marriage Act, the Criminal Damage Act, the Statute Law Repeals Act, the Recognition of Divorces and Legal Separations Act and the Law Reform (Jurisdiction in Delict) (Scotland) Act.

4 Collection of revenue

The annual Finance Act implementing the Budget proposals is concerned primarily with the collection of revenue by the Crown. Other Acts, notably the Income Tax Act 1952, fulfil the same function. Possibly on account of the considerable energies expended on the task of tax avoidance these statutes tend to promote rather more litigation than the average statute, including numerous "test cases" in which the Inland Revenue is concerned to discover whether the drafting of a measure has achieved the desired effect.

5 Social legislation

The law student, faced with a list of the Acts of Parliament passed in any single year, will probably feel that most of them do not concern him at all and will regard them as of secondary importance. These Acts are varied in their scope and functions but may be classified together as social legislation. Such Acts are concerned with regulating the day to day running of the social system rather than with creating criminal offences or rights and duties between individuals. There is an increasing tendency for Parliament to delegate to subordinate bodies the power to make regulations of this nature. It is, of course, wrong to suppose that social legislation is of no interest to the lawyer. When legislation attempts to strike a balance between competing social priorities there is an inevitable tendency towards dispute and, as a result, litigation. An obvious modern example is legislation concerning landlord and tenant. Population increases, immigration and the centralisation of industry have resulted in housing becoming a major social problem. Acts passed as a result, such as the Landlord and Tenant Acts and the Rent Acts have become the subject of a huge volume of litigation over their interpretation.

B FORMS OF LEGISLATION

Early legislation in England took several different forms, such as charters, provisions, ordinances and statutes. At the present day, however, there are only three different forms which legislation may take: Acts of Parliament, delegated legislation and autonomic legislation.

1 Acts of Parliament

Parliament is recognised as sovereign and as possessing unlimited legislative power. This has not always been so[1] but in modern times it has not been seriously contended that the courts have any power to override the intention of the legislature. The procedure[2] is, briefly, that a Bill is drafted by Parliamentary draftsmen under the supervision, generally, of a minister of the Crown. The Bill is then introduced in either the House of Commons or the House of Lords by a member of Parliament. If it passes through all its stages within the Parliamentary session it receives the Royal Assent and becomes an Act of Parliament. The contents of the Act are set out in various publications, though references to present day Acts are to the Queen's Printer's Copy published by

---

[1] See, for example, dicta of COKE, C.J. in *Bonham's Case* (1609), 8 Co. Rep. 113b and of HOLT, C.J. in *City of London* v. *Wood* (1701), 12 Mod. Rep. 669.
[2] Details of Parliamentary procedure will be found in works on constitutional law.

Her Majesty's Stationery Office and on sale there to the general public. The Stationery Office publishes these copies in annual volumes and also publishes annually an Index to the Statutes in Force, for reference purposes. In addition the Incorporated Council of Law Reporting publishes annually the texts of Acts taken from the Queen's Printer's Copies.

The mode of citation of statutes has undergone change. Early statutes were cited by the name of the place where Parliament met.[1] Subsequently statutes were cited by reference to their regnal year and chapter. Thus, for example, the Criminal Justice Act 1948 would be cited as 11 & 12 *Geo.* 6, *c.* 58 indicating that the Act was the twenty-seventh passed in the Parliamentary session extending over the eleventh and twelfth years of the reign of George VI. This exceedingly cumbersome method of citation was not abolished until 1962.[2] Although Acts still have chapter numbers (a legacy of the fiction that only one Act was passed in a Parliamentary session), reference is now to the calendar year rather than to the regnal year. In practice Acts are commonly cited by reference to their short title, and this is permissible by section 2 of the Short Titles Act 1896. Many Acts passed prior to 1896 have been endowed with short titles retrospectively and Acts passed since that date contain a section conferring upon themselves a short title.

2   Delegated legislation

"Delegated legislation" is the description given to the vast body of rules, orders, regulations and bye-laws created by subordinate bodies under specific powers delegated to those bodies by Parliament. The advantage of delegated legislation is that it enables regulations to be made and altered quickly without the need, usually, for placing them before Parliament. The vital feature which distinguishes Parliament from any other person or body having legislative power is that the latter is not sovereign. Delegated legislation is valid only if it is within the legislative powers conferred by Parliament (*intra vires*). If it is not it is said to be *ultra vires* and is, in that event, inoperative. Thus, for example, the Rules of the Supreme Court are delegated legislation, being passed by a Rule Committee under powers conferred by the Judicature Acts.[3] The power conferred upon the Committee is limited to creating rules of procedure. Consequently, if any Rule of the Supreme Court has the characteristic of a rule of substantive law rather than a rule of procedure it is ineffective.[4] Delegated legislation which is concerned solely with implementing the detail of a general policy contained in an Act of Parliament is useful and unexceptionable. However, the powers delegated are frequently defined in the widest terms with the effect of conferring a legislative function on some body almost equivalent to that of Parliament itself.[5] This power is always, of course, subject to control by

---

[1] E. g., Statute of Gloucester 1278; Provisions of Oxford 1258.
[2] Acts of Parliament Numbering and Citation Act 1962 (10 & 11 Eliz. 2, c. 34).
[3] At present, the Judicature Act 1925, s. 99.
[4] See *Re Grosvenor Hotel (No. 2)*, [1965] Ch. 1210; [1964] 3 All E.R. 354; *Ward* v. *James*, [1966] 1 Q.B. 273; [1965] 1 All E.R. 563.
[5] The powers tend to be very widely defined in time of war. See, for example, the extraordinarily wide powers to make Defence Regulations conferred by the Supplies and Services (Transitional Powers) Act 1945 and the Supplies and Services (Extended Powers) Act 1947, cited in *Law in the Making*, by C.K. Allen (7th Edn.), pp. 540 *et seq.*

Parliament but, where the legislative power is conferred upon a Minister of the Crown, this may not be an effective control.[1]

The highest form of delegated legislation is Order in Council which is nominally an order of the Privy Council consisting of the Sovereign and Privy Councillors. Many Acts are brought into operation by Order in Council, the power to make the Order being contained in the Act itself.[2] In fact, though not in theory, an Order in Council is generally made by the Government and merely sanctioned by the Privy Council. The effect, therefore, is to confer wide legislative power upon Government departments.[3]

Orders in Council and certain other Regulations are published in Statutory Instruments[4] (formerly Statutory Rules and Orders) by the Queen's Printer and available at Her Majesty's Stationery Office. They are cited by calendar year and number (for example: *S.I.* 1959, *No.* 64) and, often, by a short title.

3 Autonomic legislation

This differs from delegated legislation in that an autonomous body has an independent power to legislate for its own members and, in some cases, for members of the general public. Though this power is usually conferred by Parliament

---

[1] *Liversidge* v. *Anderson*, [1942] A.C. 206; [1941] 3 All E.R. 338; see also *Kruse* v. *Johnson*, [1898] 2 Q.B. 91; *Buck* v. *Attorney-General*, [1965] Ch. 745; [1964] 2 All E.R. 663.

[2] An Act may be brought into force by Order in Council even though the power to make the Order derives from the Act itself: Interpretation Act 1889, s. 37.

[3] In this context attention may be drawn to clause 2 (2) of the European Communities Bill currently before Parliament which provides that:

"Subject to Schedule 2 to this Act, at any time after its passing Her Majesty may by Order in Council, and any designated Minister or department may by regulations, make provision—

(*a*) for the purpose of implementing any community obligation of the United Kingdom, or enabling any such obligation to be implemented, or of enabling any rights enjoyed or to be enjoyed by the United Kingdom under or by virtue of the Treaties to be exercised; or

(*b*) for the purpose of dealing with matters arising our of or related to any such obligation or rights or the coming into force, or the operation from time to time, of subsection (1) above [see, p. 3, *ante*];

and in the exercise of any statutory power or duty, including any power to give directions or to legislate by means of orders, rules, regulations or other subordinate instrument, the person entrusted with the power or duty may have regard to the objects of the Communities and to any such obligation or rights as aforesaid."

The above provision has been widely criticised on the ground that it confers legislative power which is so extensive that it ought properly to be exercised only by Parliament directly. Schedule 2 of the Bill does, in fact, limit the powers somewhat in that it excludes power to make any provision imposing or increasing taxation, to make any retrospective provision or to create any new criminal offence punishable with imprisonment for more than two years or punishable on summary conviction with imprisonment for more than three months or with a fine of more than £400 (or £5 a day if calculated on a daily basis).

[4] Statutory Instruments Act 1946. Statutes conferring subordinate legislative powers frequently, though not always, provide that the Statutory Instrument made thereunder shall be laid before Parliament. In this event a copy of the Instrument must be so laid before it comes into operation: Statutory Instruments Act 1946, s. 4. The effect of laying the Instrument before Parliament varies. In some cases the Instrument does not take effect until expressly approved by resolution while in others it takes effect immediately subject to cancellation by negative resolution within forty "sitting" days.

this is not always so. The power is in all cases, however, sanctioned by Parliament. Examples of autonomous legislative bodies are public undertakings such as transport and gas authorities whose bye-laws affect the public at large. The Church of England, the General Medical Council, The Law Society, trade unions and even limited companies are autonomous in the sense that they have power to control their own internal structure and to legislate for their members. It is arguable that such legislation does not affect the public but it does in a negative sense in that any individual who causes a breach of the regulations created by an autonomous body may commit a civil wrong.

In almost all cases autonomic legislation is confined in its extent by an Act of Parliament in which event it is subject to the doctrine of *ultra vires*. An important exception, however, is constituted by the prerogative jurisdiction of the Privy Council. This jurisdiction is principally concerned with legislating by Order in Council for Crown Colonies. The power is subject to the ordinary rules of English law though not to the doctrine of *ultra vires*.[1] It will thus be apparent that Orders in Council may be passed either under powers conferred by individual Acts or under a general prerogative power independent of statute. Both of these are subject to the law, although only the first is subject to the doctrine of *ultra vires*.[2]

C THE OPERATION OF STATUTES

In defining the scope of a statute it is necessary to advert both to its geographical area of operation and to the time during which it is operative.

1 Geographical operation

There is a presumption that an Act of Parliament is operative throughout the United Kingdom[3] but not elsewhere unless in either case a contrary intention appears in the Act itself. The contrary intention may either limit or extend the geographical operation of the Act. Thus Acts frequently contain a section restricting their operation to exclude Scotland or Northern Ireland. The Limitation Act 1963, for example, is in three parts: Part I applying to England and Wales, Part II to Scotland and Part III to Northern Ireland. A similar reduction in the geographical operation of legislation occurs in the case of Acts which are expressed to apply only to a limited locality; such Acts are described as "local Acts". An Act may be partly local and partly general. For example, sections 83 and 86 of the Fires Prevention (Metropolis) Act 1774 were held to be applicable throughout the United Kingdom although the operation of the Act as a whole was confined to the London area.

Conversely an Act may expressly or by necessary implication extend outside the United Kingdom, though there is a presumption against this. For example,

---

[1] *The Zamora*, [1916] 2 A.C. 77 (P.C.).
[2] See *Buck* v. *Attorney-General*, [1965] Ch. 745; [1964] 2 All E.R. 663.
[3] Since it lies within the prerogative power of the Crown to extend its sovereignty and jurisdiction to areas of land or sea over which it has not previously asserted sovereignty or jurisdiction, the words "United Kingdom" incorporate such area of land or sea as may from time to time be formally declared by the Crown to be subject to its sovereignty and jurisdiction as part of the United Kingdom: see *Post Office* v. *Estuary Radio, Ltd.*, [1968] 2 Q.B. 740, at p. 748; [1967] 3 All E.R. 663, at p. 680 *per* DIPLOCK, L.J. (as he then was).

section 57 of the Offences Against the Person Act 1861 provides that the crime of bigamy is committed "whether the second marriage shall have taken place in England or Ireland, *or elsewhere.*" An Act which does have extraterritorial operation is, however, generally limited to apply only to British subjects or persons owing allegiance to the Crown.[1]

2 Temporal operation

a *When a statute begins to be operative*

Until 1793[2] a statute came into force on the first day of the Parliamentary session in which it was passed. Consequently virtually all legislation was retrospective. The present law is that a statute comes into force on the day on which it receives the Royal Assent, unless some other date is specified in the Act itself. Frequently some future date will be specified to enable persons affected by the Act to prepare for its operation. Thus the Highways (Miscellaneous Provisions) Act 1961 came into operation on August 3, 1964, the delay being for the purpose of enabling highway authorities, upon whom a new duty to maintain highways was imposed, to effect such repairs as were necessary to comply with the stringent provisions of the Act. Alternatively an Act may provide that it is to come into force on a "day to be appointed". The day is appointed by Order in Council unless the Act provides for appointment by a Minister. In either case the appointed day is published in a Statutory Instrument. The disadvantage of this practice is that it is slightly more difficult to determine when the Act is coming into force and it is necessary to consult the calendar of appointed days. Different parts of an Act or sections in an Act may be brought into force at different times and it appears that there are portions of Acts in existence which have never been brought into force.[3]

The effect of a statute coming into operation is that, if it is a Public Act, and every Act passed since 1850 is presumed to be a Public Act in the absence of a contrary provision, it immediately becomes effective and the courts take judicial notice of it.[4]

Delegated legislation generally comes into force when it is passed but section 3 (2) of the Statutory Instruments Act 1946 provides that where a person is charged with contravening the provisions of a Statutory Instrument it shall be a defence to prove that the Instrument had not been issued by Her Majesty's Stationery Office at the date of the alleged contravention, unless it is proved that at that date reasonable steps had been taken for the purpose of bringing the purport of the Instrument to the notice of the public, or of persons likely to be affected by it, or of the person charged.[5]

Retrospective operation. As a general rule a statute only affects factual situations which arise during the period of its operation. There is a presumption against the statute being retroactive. This presumption is particularly strong where the statute in question creates criminal penalties or tax obligations or

---

[1] *Joyce* v. *Director of Public Prosecutions,* [1946] A.C. 347; [1946] 1 All E.R. 186.
[2] Acts of Parliament (Commencement) Act.
[3] See *R.* v. *Kynaston* (1927), 19 Cr. App. Rep. 180.
[4] Interpretation Act 1889, s. 9.
[5] See *R.* v. *Sheer Metalcraft, Ltd.,* [1954] 1 Q.B. 586; [1954] 1 All E.R. 542.

would operate to deprive a person of a vested right in property.[1] However, Parliament is sovereign and statutes may be, and occasionally are, expressed to be retroactive even where this operates to deprive a person of a vested right in property. A recent illustration was the controversial War Damage Act 1965 which operated to remove vested rights to compensation from the Crown and which was exceptional in that it was also expressed to apply to proceedings commenced before the Act came into force.[2] Also, statutes aimed at preventing tax avoidance are sometimes expressed to be retroactive and there seems to be no presumption against retroactivity in the case of statutes of this type.[3] An Act of indemnity, the purpose of which is to validate or legalise *ex post facto* that which was initially invalid or illegal, must by its nature be retroactive.[4] It seems that Parliament's intention to make a statute retroactive need not, in exceptional cases, be expressed provided the intention can be clearly implied from the statute read as a whole. Thus in *Williams* v. *Williams*[5] the new financial provisions of the Matrimonial Proceedings and Property Act 1970 were held to apply to a case in which the decree of divorce was granted before the 1970 Act came into force, notwithstanding that the changes in the law effected by the Act were clearly substantive rather than procedural and notwithstanding also the absence of any express provision making the 1970 Act provisions retroactive. A statute which alters rules of evidence or procedure rather than rules of substantive law is always retroactive, in the absence of a contrary intention, since the rules of evidence and procedure which a court is bound to observe are those in existence at the time of the hearing.[6]

Where a statute applies to a situation arising from a continuing state of affairs it is a moot point whether the statute may properly be said to be retrospective. Thus the Road Traffic Act 1962, which enables a court to impose disqualification upon a driver who has had two previous endorsements on his driving licence, was in one case held to apply so as to justify a sentence of disqualification where the first of the accused's previous convictions occurred before the Act came into force.[7] This was not regarded by the court as a retrospective application of the statute in question.

b　When a statute ceases to be operative

No statute becomes obsolete by the passing of time. Nevertheless there are many ancient statutes more honoured in the breach than in the observance. In

---

[1] In R. v. *Fisher* [1969] 1 All E.R. 100; [1969] 1 W.L.R. 8 the rule against retrospective operation operated, for once, against the accused in that he was convicted of an offence which had, at the time of his trial, been abolished by statute since the conduct in question had been, at the time of commission, an offence.

[2] Section 1 (2). The action affected was *Burmah Oil Co., Ltd.* v. *Lord Advocate*, [1965] A.C. 75; [1964] 2 All E.R. 348.

[3] See, for example, Finance Act 1936, s. 18; *Lord Howard de Walden* v. *Inland Revenue Commissioners*, [1942] 1 K.B. 389; [1942] 1 All E.R. 287.

[4] Examples of Acts of indemnity are: Indemnity Act 1920; Indian Divorces (Validity) Act 1921; Charitable Trusts (Validation) Act 1954.

[5] [1971] P. 271; [1971] 2 All E.R. 764.

[6] See *Barber* v. *Pigden*, [1937] 1 K.B. 664; [1937] 1 All E.R. 115; *Blyth* v. *Blyth*, [1966] A.C. 643; [1966] 1 All E.R. 524; cf. *Carson* v. *Carson*, [1964] 1 All E.R. 681; [1964] 1 W.L.R. 511; R. v. *Reah* [1968] 3 All E.R. 269; [1968] 1 W.L.R. 1508.

[7] *Carter-Fea* v. *Graham* (1964), 62 L.G.R. 279. A similar approach is adopted where the statute imposes increased penalties for offences committed before it came into force: *Director of Public Prosecutions* v. *Lamb*, [1941] 2 K.B. 89; [1941] 2 All E.R. 499.

the past the approach of the legislature has generally been to do nothing until the need for repeal manifested itself. Thus the plaintiff in a nineteenth century case was no doubt disturbed to discover that his opponent had a right to claim trial by battle;[1] two cases in recent years have involved statutes of 1351 and 1381 respectively[2] while recent cases concerning the rights of "squatters" on other persons' premises have involved consideration of the 1429 Statute of Forcible Entry.[3] As a final example of ancient legislation which is still utilitarian may be cited the Justices of the Peace Act 1361 under the provisions of which prosecutions are sometimes brought and persons bound over to keep the peace.[4]

There are indications at last, however, that the pragmatic approach to statute revision is gradually yielding to a systematic reform of legislation. The Law Commissions are expressly required to review "obsolete and unnecessary enactments" with a view to repeal.[5] Steps in this direction have been taken by the passing of the Criminal Law Act 1967, Part II of which is devoted to the repeal of unnecessary and obsolete enactments, listed in Schedules 3 and 4 of the Act, the Statute Law (Repeals) Act 1969 which repealed numerous obsolete enactments, including the Sunday Observance Acts, the Law Reform (Miscellaneous Provisions) Act 1970 which abolished the anachronistic actions for breach of promise of marriage, damages for adultery, enticement and harbouring of a spouse and enticement, harbouring and seduction of a child, and the Statute Law (Repeals) Act 1971 which repealed more than one hundred and seventy separate Statutes in whole or in part. All of these recent Acts were passed following recommendations by the Law Commissions.

To the above rule that statutes do not become obsolete with the passing of time there is an exception. Certain statutes are expressed to be operative only for a limited period, usually because they are experimental or transitional though the best known statutes of this type, the Army Act and the Air Force Act are re-enacted periodically so as to avoid the prohibition on keeping a standing army in time of peace.[6] There have been notable recent examples of statutes containing the seeds of their own desuetude. Thus the Protection from Eviction Act 1964 was a transitional measure aimed at preserving security of tenure for tenants pending the passing of the Rent Act 1965; the Murder (Abolition of Death Penalty) Act 1965 was expressed to expire on the 31st July 1970 unless Parliament by affirmative resolution of both Houses otherwise determined (which it did in 1969). These temporary statutes may acquire a new lease of life by the passing of an Expiring Laws Continuance Act 1970 which is effected solely for the purpose of renewing statutes which would otherwise expire. Thus Part I of the Commonwealth Immigrants Act 1962, an experimental measure

---

[1] *Ashford* v. *Thornton* (1818), 1 B. & Ald. 405.
[2] *Hemmings* v. *Stoke Poges Golf Club, Ltd.*, [1920] 1 K.B. 720; *Joyce* v. *Director of Public Prosecutions*, [1946] A.C. 347; [1946] 1 All E.R. 186.
[3] *R.* v. *Robinson*, [1971] 1 Q.B. 156; [1970] 3 All E.R. 369; *R.* v. *Mountford*, [1971] 2 All E.R. 81; [1971] 2 W.L.R. 1106.
[4] See *R.* v. *Aubrey-Fletcher, Ex parte Thompson*, [1969] 2 All E.R. 846; [1969] 1 W.L.R. 872.
[5] Law Commissions Act 1965, s. 3 (1).
[6] Prior to 1955 this was done by means of annual Acts. However a new procedure was established by the Army Act 1955, s. 226 and the Air Force Act 1955, s. 224. Under this procedure the Acts are renewable annually by Order in Council, a new Act of Parliament being required only every five years.

expressed to last for only one year is at the time of writing, still in force having been renewed annually since 1963.

Unless it is one of those which are expressed to be operative for a limited period a statute ceases to have effect only when repealed by another statute, since only Parliament is competent to repeal its own enactments. Repeal may be express or implied. In modern times almost all repeal is express and it is common for a statute to include a schedule of repeals, expressly incorporated into the body of the Act, where there are several provisions repealed. Implied repeal is possible and occurs where two statutory provisions are inconsistent with one another. In this situation the later provision impliedly repeals the earlier to the extent of the inconsistency.[1] The courts, however, lean against implied repeal and will attempt to reconcile seemingly conflicting provisions wherever possible. In addition there is a rule that a public Act does not impliedly repeal a private or local Act (*generalia specialibus non derogant*).[2] Unless the contrary intention appears repeal does not have the effect of revivifying any earlier repealed rule of law, statutory[3] or otherwise.[4]

D THE INTERPRETATION AND CONSTRUCTION OF STATUTES

1 The need for interpretation and construction

Where the words of a statute are clear and unambiguous persons affected by its provisions will regulate their conduct according to the terms of the statute and the need for judicial interpretation will not arise. However, if the meaning or extent of a statute is uncertain or ambiguous litigation is inevitable and the statute will fall to be interpreted. There is a technical distinction between interpretation and construction. "Interpretation" is simply the process whereby a meaning is assigned to the words in a statute. "Construction", on the other hand, is the process whereby uncertainties or ambiguities in a statute are resolved. It follows that every statute which comes before a court is interpreted whereas only uncertain or ambiguous provisions require construction. The processes are not usually distinguished by judges since, by the nature of things, litigation only arises around the wording of a statute where it is ambiguous or, at least, uncertain.

a Ambiguity

Ambiguity arises through an error in drafting whereby words used in a statute are found to be capable of bearing two or more literal meanings. Language is an imprecise tool and even Parliamentary draftsmen, in using words intended to convey one meaning, occasionally contrive to give rise to an alternative meaning which neither they nor the legislature ever envisaged. Thus the Restriction of Offensive Weapons Act 1959 made it an offence to "offer for sale" certain

---

[1] See, for example, *Smith* v. *Benabo*, [1937] 1 K.B. 518; [1937] 1 All E.R. 523; *Ellen Street Estates* v. *Minister of Health*, [1934] 1 K.B. 590.

[2] Thus it was held in *Bishop of Gloucester* v. *Cunnington*, [1943] K.B. 101; [1943] 1 All E.R. 61, that the restrictions on the recovery of leasehold property imposed by the Rent and Mortgage Interest Restriction Acts 1920–1939 did not affect the right of a bishop to recover possession of a parsonage under the Pluralities Act 1838.

[3] Interpretation Act 1889, s. 11 (1).   [4] *Ibid.*, s. 38 (2).

offensive weapons including "flick knives". A shopkeeper who displayed weapons of this type in his window was held, by a divisional court, to be not guilty of an offence under the Act because, as every student of the law of contract knows, the exhibition of goods in a shop window does not constitute an offer.[1] Where the subject matter of a statute is a branch of the law which is intrinsically complex, such as landlord and tenant or income tax, it seems to be virtually impossible to choose language which is entirely free from ambiguity. Nevertheless the judiciary has on occasion been less than sympathetic to the draftsman's plight.[2]

b   Uncertainty

Uncertainty is far more common than ambiguity. Uncertainty occurs where the words of a statute are intended to apply to various factual situations and the courts are called upon to decide whether or not the set of facts before them amounts to a factual situation envisaged by the Act. For example the words "an accident arising out of and in the course of his employment" in the Workmen's Compensation Acts were the source of innumerable cases, not because they were in any way ambiguous but because their scope was uncertain, being adaptable to endless permutations of facts. The use of general, and ostensibly clearly defined, words such as "road",[3] "park",[4] "premises",[5] "ship"[6] and "loudspeaker"[7] has created problems of construction which the legislature could not have envisaged, while, more recently, the courts have been called upon to resolve such conundrums as whether the cremation of humans is "the subjection of goods or materials to any process"[8] and whether an orange squeezed by hand is a "manufactured beverage".[9] LORD DENNING has expressed the difficulty as follows:[10]

> "It must be remembered that it is not within human powers to foresee the manifold sets of facts which may arise, and, even if it were, it is not possible to provide for them in terms free from all ambiguity."

The primary difficulty in such cases is that the words themselves are almost the only guide which may be used to the meaning which Parliament intended.

---

[1] *Fisher* v. *Bell*, [1961] 1 Q.B. 394; [1960] 3 All E.R. 731; see also *Partridge* v. *Crittenden*, [1968] 2 All E.R. 421; [1968] 1 W.L.R. 1204.
[2] See *Great Western Rail. Co.* v. *Bater*, [1922] 2 A.C. 1, at p. 11; *Barentz* v. *Whiting*, [1965] 1 All E.R. 685; [1965] 1 W.L.R. 433; *London County Council* v. *Lees*, [1939] 1 All E.R. 191; *Davies* v. *Warwick*, [1943] K.B. 329; [1943] 1 All E.R. 309; *R.* v. *Royle*, [1971] 3 All E.R. 1359; [1971] 1 W.L.R. 1764.
[3] *Griffin* v. *Squires*, [1958] 3 All E.R. 468; [1958] 1 W.L.R. 1106.
[4] *Re Ripon (Highfield) Housing Order, 1938*, [1939] 2 K.B. 838; [1939] 3 All E.R. 548.
[5] *Whitley* v. *Stumbles*, [1930] A.C. 544.
[6] *The Gas Float Whitton (No. 2)*, [1896] P. 42.
[7] *Reynolds* v. *John*, [1956] 1 Q.B. 650; [1956] 1 All E.R. 306.
[8] *Bourne (Inspector of Taxes)* v. *Norwich Crematorium, Ltd.*, [1967] 2 All E.R. 576; [1967] 1 W.L.R. 691.
[9] *Customs and Excise Commissioners* v. *Savoy Hotel, Ltd.*, [1966] 2 All E.R. 299; [1966] 1 W.L.R. 948. For a delightfully sardonic exposition of the difficulty of ascertaining the "right" meaning of words, see the judgment of DIPLOCK, L.J. (as he then was) in *Slim* v. *Daily Telegraph, Ltd.*, [1968] 2 Q.B. 157, at pp. 171–172; [1968] 1 All E.R. 497, at p. 504.
[10] *Seaford Court Estates, Ltd.* v. *Asher*, [1949] 2 K.B. 481, at p. 499; [1949] 2 All E.R. 155, at p. 164 (affirmed [1951] A.C. 508; [1950] 1 All E.R. 1018).

The view is often expressed, even by members of the judiciary themselves,[1] that the legislature should publish a statement of its aims in relation to any particular Act.[2] In fact such statements often are published but, in interpreting and construing the Act in question, the judiciary for some reason diligently eschews them.[3]

2 Judicial approaches to interpretation

The basic task of the judge is to ascertain the intention of Parliament. Nevertheless there are three recognised approaches to this task. These approaches, which differ radically, are commonly known as the "literal" rule, the "golden" rule and the "mischief" rule. It is never possible to know in advance which approach any particular court will favour. / Certain decisions have been based on one of these rules, others on the application of another. In the case of *Vacher* v. *The London Society of Compositors*[4] the House of Lords, construing section 4 (1) of the Trade Disputes Act 1906, adverted to all three rules, while in the recent case of *Letang* v. *Cooper*[5] the Court of Appeal applied the literal and golden rules in the alternative in construing provisions of the Limitation Acts.

Each of these approaches to interpretation must be considered individually.

a The literal rule

The basic approach to statutory interpretation, as already stated, is to ascertain the intention of the legislature. The literal rule of interpretation is that this intention must be found in the ordinary and natural literal meaning of the words used. If these words, interpreted literally, are capable of alternative meanings the literal rule clearly cannot be applied. Hence the approach breaks down in the face of an ambiguity. However, if the words are capable of only one literal meaning the literal rule is that this meaning must be applied even if it appears unlikely or absurd. The rule may be expressed as an irrebuttable presumption that Parliament intends the ordinary and natural meaning of the words it employs. The rule will, in most cases, produce a reasonable interpretation of the statute. However, in extreme cases where the statute has been carelessly drafted, the rule may produce a manifest absurdity. Thus in <u>Inland Revenue Commissioners</u> v. <u>Hinchy</u>[6] the House of Lords was called upon to construe section 25 (3) of the Income Tax Act 1952 which provided that any person delivering an incorrect tax return should forfeit ". . . treble the tax which he ought to be charged under this Act". Although Parliament presumably intended[7] a penalty of treble the unpaid tax the House of Lords held that the literal meaning of the words of the subsection was that the respondent was liable to pay treble the whole amount of tax payable by him for the year.

---

[1] See, for example, observations of LORD DU PARCQ in *Cutler* v. *Wandsworth Stadium, Ltd. (in Liquidation)*, [1949] A.C. 398, at p. 410; [1949] 1 All E.R. 544, at p. 549.

[2] The long title frequently does this, but generally too briefly to be of real assistance: see p. 114, *post*.

[3] See *London County Council* v. *Central Land Board*, [1959] Ch. 386; [1958] 3 All E.R. 676.

[4] [1913] A.C. 107.

[5] [1965] 1 Q.B. 232; [1964] 2 All E.R. 929.

[6] [1960] A.C. 748; [1960] 1 All E.R. 505.

[7] The law was in fact changed shortly after this decision by the Finance Act 1960, s. 44.

Fisher v. *Bell*, quoted earlier,[1] is a further example of the application of the literal rule producing a result which appeared contrary to the intention of the legislature.

Although there are numerous cases in which the literal rule has been applied strictly[2] there appears to be a modern judicial tendency to apply the golden rule or the mischief rule in cases where the literal rule would produce a perverse decision. This tendency is exemplified, characteristically, in the following words of LORD DENNING, M.R.:[3]

"... the literal meaning of the words is never allowed to prevail where it would produce manifest absurdity or consequences which can never have been intended by the legislature."

The diversity of judicial approach is well illustrated by the speeches of the House of Lords in *Kammins Ballrooms Co., Ltd.* v. *Zenith Investments (Torquay), Ltd.*[4] The case turned on the interpretation of section 29 (3) of the Landlord and Tenant Act 1954 which provides that "No application [for the grant of a new tenancy] shall be entertained unless it is made not less than two nor more than four months" after (*inter alia*) the tenant's request for a new tenancy. On the question of whether the court had power to consider an application made less than two months after the tenant's request, the House of Lords (VISCOUNT DILHORNE dissenting) held that the court did have such power, thereby appearing to disregard the clear words of the section for as VISCOUNT DILHORNE observed:[5]

"The appellants' contention here is that the words 'no application ... shall be entertained' must be interpreted as meaning that an application shall in certain circumstances be entertained notwithstanding that it is made too early or too late. That seems to me to involve implying something wholly inconsistent with the words expressly used. True it is that English is a flexible language but that does not mean that one can disregard the natural and ordinary meaning of the words used unless it is apparent that some other meaning was intended.

If language is clear and explicit, the court must give effect to it 'for in that case the words of the statute speak the intention of the legislature' (*Warburton* v. *Loveland* (1832), 2 Dow. & Cl. 480, *per* TINDAL, C.J. at p. 489). 'And in so doing it must bear in mind that its function is *jus dicere*, not *jus dare*: the words of a statute must not be overruled by the judges, but reform of the law must be left in the hands of Parliament' (*Maxwell on Interpretation of Statutes*, 12th edn. (1969), p. 1)."

VISCOUNT DILHORNE was, however, a lone voice in support of this traditional approach. LORD REID acknowledged that:[6]

---

[1] [1961] 1 Q.B. 394; [1960] 3 All E.R. 731; see p. 103, *ante*.
[2] See, for example; *Magor and St. Mellons Rural District Council* v. *Newport Corporation*, [1952] A.C. 189; [1951] 2 All E.R. 839; *Prince Ernest of Hanover* v. *A.-G.*, [1957] A.C. 88; [1957] 1 All E.R. 49; *Barclays Bank, Ltd.* v. *Cole*, [1967] 2 Q.B. 738; [1966] 3 All E.R. 948; The Law Commission report, *The Interpretation of Statutes* (1969 Law Com. No. 21) recommended a statutory provision to the effect that "a construction which would promote the general legislative purpose underlying the provision in question is to be preferred to a construction which would not".
[3] *Corocraft* v. *Pan American Airways, Inc.*, [1969] 1 Q.B. 616, at p. 655; [1969] 1 All E.R. 82, at p. 88.
[4] [1971] A.C. 850; [1970] 2 All E.R. 871.
[5] [1971] A.C. 850, at p. 869; [1970] 2 All E.R. 871, at p. 883.
[6] [1971] A.C. 850, at p. 859; [1970] 2 All E.R. 871, at p, 874.

"If the words of an Act are so inflexible that they are incapable in any context of having but one meaning, then the court must apply that meaning, no matter how unreasonable the result—it cannot insert other words. But such cases are rare because the English language is a flexible tool".

LORD REID then went on to find, somewhat ingeniously, that the words were not, in fact, unambiguous, thus enabling him to reject the apparent literal meaning. LORD DIPLOCK, on the other hand, made no pretence of applying the literal rule and his speech typifies the trend away from rigid adherence to literal interpretation:[1]

"Upon the literal approach, semantics and the rules of syntax alone could never justify the conclusion that the words '*No* application . . . *shall be* entertained *unless*' meant that some applications should be entertained notwithstanding that neither of the conditions which follow the word 'unless' was fulfilled . . . It can be justified only upon the assumption that the draftsman of the Act omitted to state in any words he used in the subsection an exception to the absolute prohibition to which Parliament must have intended it to be subject.

A conclusion that an exception was intended by Parliament, and what that exception was can only be reached by using the purposive approach."

b   The golden rule

The golden rule is that words in a statute must be interpreted in such a way as to avoid a manifestly absurd result. Perhaps the best known statement of the rule is to be found in the judgment of PARKE, B. in *Becke* v. *Smith*:[2]

"It is a very useful rule in the construction of a statute to adhere to the ordinary meaning of the words used, and to the grammatical construction, unless that is at variance with the intention of the legislature to be collected from the statute itself, or leads to any manifest absurdity or repugnance, in which case the language may be varied or modified so as to avoid such inconvenience, but no further."

Where the statute permits of two or more literal interpretations the court must adopt that interpretation which produces the least absurd or repugnant result. This application of the golden rule is not, of course, inconsistent with the literal rule since the latter cannot be applied in a case of ambiguity. This is the narrow aspect of the golden rule and has been adopted in several well-known cases. Thus, for example, section 57 of the Offences Against the Person Act 1861 provides that "Whosoever, being married, shall *marry* any other person during the life of the former husband or wife" shall be guilty of bigamy. The word *marry* permits of alternative meanings. It may be construed to mean *contracts a valid marriage* or *goes through a ceremony of marriage*. Since the former meaning would produce an absurd result, the latter must be applied.[3]

However, where the statute is capable of only one literal meaning and the court rejects that meaning in favour of a construction which is obviously more rational the golden rule is, in effect, being applied in preference to the literal rule. There have been relatively few cases in which this wide application of the golden rule has been adopted. Of the few cases in which this has been

---

[1] [1971] A.C. 850, at p. 880; [1970] 2 All E.R. 871, at p. 892.
[2] (1836), 2 M. & W., at p. 195.
[3] *R.* v. *Allen* (1872), L.R. 1 C.C.R. 367; see also *Young* v. *Clarey*, [1948] Ch. 191; [1948] 1 All E.R. 197; *Mills* v. *Cooper*,[1967] 2 Q.B. 459; [1967] 2 All E.R. 100.

done perhaps the best known is *Re Sigsworth*[1] in which the golden rule was applied to prevent a murderer from taking on the intestacy of his victim although he was, as her son, the sole "issue" on a literal interpretation of the Administration of Estates Act 1925. More recently, in interpreting section 47 of the same Act, HARMAN, J. (as he then was) rejected a literal interpretation which he considered absurd in these words:[2]

> "I take this course because I am convinced that Parliament, in laying down rules for ascertaining next-of-kin, cannot have intended to promote those more remote over those nearer in blood."

A major criticism of the wide application of the golden rule in preference to the literal rule is that it is inherently subjective. The judge who decides that a literal interpretation is contrary to the intention of the legislature is, *ipso facto*, ascertaining the intention of the legislature from some source or sources other than the statute itself, and this is, strictly, beyond his judicial function.

c The mischief rule

The last approach to interpretation is generally described as the mischief rule, or the Rule in *Heydon's Case*. The rule is that where a statute was passed to remedy a mischief the court must adopt the interpretation of the statute which will have the effect of correcting the mischief in question. In *Heydon's Case*,[3] itself, the rule was defined thus:

> ". . . four things are to be discussed and considered: (1) what was the common law before the making of the Act; (2) what was the mischief and defect for which the common law did not provide; (3) what remedy the Parliament hath resolved and appointed to cure the disease of the commonwealth; and (4) the true reason of the remedy."

The narrower operation of this rule is to resolve ambiguities in cases in which the literal rule cannot be applied. For example, a "single woman" for the purposes of affiliation proceedings is a woman with no husband to support her, not necessarily an unmarried woman, since the mischief which the Acts[4] were passed to remedy is the possibility of a woman having an illegitimate child with no means of supporting it.[5]

However, just as the golden rule has been applied in preference to the literal rule, so also has the mischief rule been so applied in a few cases.[6] In these cases there exists a clear exception to the general rule that the intention of Parliament is to be ascertained solely from the words of the statute. In order to ascertain the mischief which the statute was passed to correct the judge may legitimately have regard to the preamble of the statute, to headings[7] and to extrinsic sources such as reports of Royal Commissions or Law Reform Committees which may indicate the state of the law before the passing of the Act.

---

[1] [1935] Ch. 89.
[2] *Re Lockwood*, [1958] Ch. 231, at p. 238; [1957] 3 All E.R. 520, at p. 524.
[3] (1584), 3 Co. Rep. 7a.
[4] The present Act is the Affiliation Proceedings Act 1957.
[5] *Kruhlak* v. *Kruhlak*, [1958] 2 Q.B. 32; [1958] 1 All E.R. 154.
[6] See, for example, *Powell Lane Manufacturing Co.* v. *Putnam*, [1931] 2 K.B. 305; *Wiltshire* v. *Barrett*, [1966] 1 Q.B. 312; [1965] 2 All E.R. 271.
[7] *Qualter, Hall & Co., Ltd.* v. *Board of Trade*, [1962] Ch. 273; [1961] 3 All E.R. 389.

Supplying omissions.—An interesting problem of construction arises when the court is faced with a factual situation for which the statute has not provided. Such a situation is termed a *casus omissus*. It can only be remedied by attributing to Parliament an intention which Parliament never had. This amounts to a legislative act on the part of the judiciary and is a function which the more conservative judges are slow to adopt. Thus DENNING, L.J. (as he then was) explained, in the Court of Appeal, the judicial function in respect of omissions as follows:[1]

> "We sit here to find out the intention of Parliament and of Ministers and carry it out, and we do this better by filling in the gaps and making sense of the enactment than by opening it up to destructive analysis."

On appeal LORD SIMONDS roundly condemned this approach and, in a now famous dictum, described it as a "naked usurpation of the legislative function under the thin disguise of interpretation".[2] "If a gap is disclosed," LORD SIMONDS explained, "the remedy lies in an amending Act." Nonetheless it is a truism that hard cases make bad law and the courts have, from time to time, been prepared to assume the authority to supply omissions left by the legislature. The leading illustration is to be found in the majority decision of the House of Lords in *Edwards* v. *Porter*[3] where it was held that, although a husband "need not be joined" in an action against his wife, he could be joined if the plaintiff so wished. The Married Women's Property Act 1882, the Act in question, was silent on this point.[4]

Whichever of the three approaches to interpretation is adopted, the court is still bound to interpret the words of the Act before it. If interpretation discloses an uncertainty or ambiguity the court will then be bound to construe the statute. The judges themselves have formulated a large body of rules for the interpretation and construction of statutes. These rules, which equate approximately to the rules for the construction of documents generally, are exceedingly complex and only those most commonly encountered are discussed below, by way of example.

3 Rules of interpretation and construction

a *The statute must be read as a whole*

Words in isolation may import meanings different from that which they bear in conjunction.[5] A statute must be read as a whole. Every section must be read in the light of every other section, especially in the light of an interpretation section,[6] and schedules, if incorporated into the body of the Act, must be read with the Act.

---

[1] *Magor and St. Mellons Rural District Council* v. *Newport Corporation*, [1950] 2 All E.R. 1226 at p. 1236.

[2] [1952] A.C. 189, at p. 191; [1951] 2 All E.R. 839, at p. 841.

[3] [1925] A.C. 1.

[4] See also: *Astor* v. *Perry*, [1935] A.C. 398; *Re Radio Communications in Canada (Regulation and Control)*, [1932] A.C. 304; *Chandris* v. *Isbrandtsen Moller Co., Inc.*, [1951] 1 K.B. 240; [1950] 1 All E.R. 768; *Wagg* v. *The Law Society*, [1957] Ch. 405; [1957] 2 All E.R. 274; *Williams* v. *Williams*, [1971] P. 271; [1971] 2 All E.R. 764 (see p. 100, *ante*).

[5] See observations on the words "unfair competition" in *Lee* v. *Showmen's Guild of Great Britain*, [1952] 2 Q.B. 329, at p. 338; [1952] 1 All E.R. 1175, at p. 1178.

[6] See p. 116, *post*.

An interesting illustration of this, and other, rules of interpretation is afforded by the decision of the House of Lords in the leading case of *Beswick* v. *Beswick*[1]. The case raised the question of whether Parliament had by section 56 of the Law of Property Act 1925 inadvertently abrogated the common law rule that a person cannot sue on a contract to which he is not a party. Section 56 (1) provides that "A person may take an . . . interest in land or other property, or the benefit of any condition, right of entry, covenant or agreement over or respecting land or other property, although he may not be named as a party to the conveyance or other instrument. . . ." Section 205 (1) of the 1925 Act, the interpretation section, provides that "In this Act *unless the context otherwise requires* . . . (xx) 'Property' includes any thing in action. . . ." It was argued that the combined effect of these provisions was to enable a stranger to a contract to enforce the contract. This argument prevailed in the Court of Appeal[2] but was rejected by the House of Lords. Their lordships pointed out that section 56 is one of 25 sections in the Act grouped under the heading "Conveyances and other instruments" and in those circumstances held that the context did require the word property to be limited in its effect to real property.

The long title and the short title, being part of the enactment, must, strictly, be consulted in interpreting any part of the Act though, in practice, the courts will only refer to the long title to resolve an ambiguity and do not regard the short title as an aid to interpretation at all.[3] Headings, marginal notes, punctuation and schedules which are not expressly incorporated into the text are not part of the enactment and are, accordingly, not aids to interpretation.

b   The eiusdem generis *rule*

This rule is but a particular aspect of the wider rule that the statute must be read as a whole. The rule is that general words which follow two or more particular words in an Act must be confined to a meaning of the same kind (*eiusdem generis*) as the particular words. It is common drafting practice, when the intention is to cover a wide range of similar circumstances, to use two or three particular examples to create a *genus* followed by a general expression, such as "or other place", which has the effect of extending the operation of the enactment to all particular circumstances which are within the *genus* created. The operation of the rule can best be illustrated by two examples.

Section 1 of the Betting Act 1853 prohibited the keeping of a "house, office, room or other place" for betting with persons resorting thereto. In *Powell* v. *Kempton Park Racecourse Co.*[4] the point at issue was whether Tattersalls' ring at a racecourse was an "other place" within the meaning of the Act. The House of Lords held that it was not since the words "house, office, room" created a *genus* of indoor places within which a racecourse, being outdoor, did not fall.

Similarly in *Brownsea Haven Properties, Ltd.* v. *Poole Corporation*[5] it was held

---

[1] [1968] A.C. 58; [1967] 2 All E.R. 1197; see also *Crook* v. *Edmonson*, [1966] 2 Q.B. 81; [1966] 1 All E.R. 833.
[2] [1966] Ch. 538; [1966] 3 All E.R. 1. The Court of Appeal appear to have overlooked the vital words "unless the context otherwise requires" in s. 205 (1). In the event the House of Lords was able to uphold the decision of the Court of Appeal by an ingenious use of the remedy of specific performance; see p. 38, *ante*.
[3] See p. 114, *post*.
[4] [1899] A.C. 143; cf., *Culley* v. *Harrison*, [1956] 2 Q.B. 71; [1956] 2 All E.R. 254.
[5] [1958] Ch. 574; [1958] 1 All E.R. 205.

that regulations enabling a local authority to make orders for the direction of traffic "in all times of public processions, rejoicings, or illuminations, and in any case when the streets are thronged or liable to be obstructed" did not confer power to create a one-way traffic system for the six months of the summer holiday season.

It should be noted that there must be at least two specific words to create a *genus*. Thus where an Act referred to "theatres and other places of amusement" it was held that a funfair was within the Act even though not *eiusdem generis* with the word "theatres".[1]

c Penal provisions are construed narrowly

Where a statute imposes criminal liability or tax obligations (which are treated as penal) and the statute is ambiguous or uncertain, it should be construed in favour of the individual.[2] Thus it has been held that the offence of "knowingly possessing an explosive" requires knowledge on the part of the accused that the substance possessed is explosive, not merely that he possesses the substance.[3] One aspect of this general rule is the presumption against the imposition of liability without fault.[4]

However, this rule of interpretation is not strong enough to displace the literal rule. Consequently, where a statute unambiguously creates a criminal penalty or a tax the court is bound to give effect to it even though it appears unjust.[5]

d Interpretation Act 1889

This Act prescribes definitions of certain words and phrases which are commonly encountered in Acts of Parliament. Thus:

> "... unless the contrary intention appears, (a) words importing the masculine gender shall include females; and (b) words in the singular shall include the plural, and words in the plural shall include the singular".[6]

> "... 'month' shall mean calendar month".[7]

However these, and other, definitions are only presumptive and yield to a contrary intention, express or implied in the Act being interpreted. Thus, although the word "person" is defined in section 2 of the Interpretation Act to include a body corporate, it was held in one case that a corporation which undertook legal work was not guilty of the offence of acting as an unqualified "person" since the enactment in question could only apply to persons who could qualify as solicitors.[8]

---

1 *Allen* v. *Emmerson*, [1944] K.B. 362; [1944] 1 All E.R. 344. For a recent striking illustration of the operation of the rule see *Customs and Excise Commissioners* v. *Savoy Hotel, Ltd.*, [1966] 2 All E.R. 299; [1966] 1 W. L. R. 948.
2 *Dock Co. at Kingston-upon-Hull* v. *Browne* (1831), 2 B. & Ad. 43; *D'Avigdor-Goldsmid* v. *Inland Revenue Commissioners*, [1953] A.C. 347; [1953] 1 All E.R. 403.
3 *R.* v. *Hallam*, [1957] 1 Q.B. 569; [1957] 1 All E.R. 665.
4 See p. 111, *post*.
5 E.g., *R.* v. *Hare*, [1934] 1 K.B. 354; *Inland Revenue Commissioners* v. *Hinchy*, [1960] A.C. 748; [1960] 1 All E.R. 505, see p. 104, *ante*.
6 Section 1 (1).
7 Section 3.
8 *Law Society* v. *United Service Bureau, Ltd.*, [1934] 1 K.B. 343. This *lacuna* was filled by s. 22 of the Solicitors Act 1957; see also *Penn-Texas Corporation* v. *Murat-Anstalt*, [1964] 2 Q.B. 647; [1964] 2 All E.R. 594.

4 Presumptions in construction

It is possible to express almost any rule of statutory interpretation in the form of a presumption. The rules against retrospective operation and against extra-territorial operation are often expressed as presumptions. The reason for rules of statutory interpretation being described as presumptions is that their operation is rebutted by an express provision to the contrary in the Act itself. They thus have the quality of evidentiary presumptions. Nevertheless, although it is probably a mere matter of terminology, the following are always described as presumptions rather than as rules.

a Presumption against alteration of the law

Parliament, like the judiciary, is presumed to know the law. Consequently if an Act does not expressly alter the law it will be presumed that Parliament did not intend it to have that effect. In the words of DEVLIN, J. (as he then was):[1]

> "A statute is not to be taken as effecting a fundamental alteration in the general law unless it uses words which point unmistakably to that conclusion."

Thus, prior to the Criminal Evidence Act 1898 a wife was incompetent to give evidence against her husband. That Act made her competent to do so but, in the absence of an express provision, the House of Lords in *Leach* v. *R.*[2] held that it did not make her compellable.

Nevertheless it is important to remember that Parliament can expressly make fundamental alterations to the common law and, if such a change appears from a literal interpretation of the words used, the use of any presumption to the contrary is out of place. The presumption against fundamental change also applies in relation to statute law, one aspect being the presumption that a consolidating statute does not, simply by verbal alteration in the provision re-enacted, thereby introduce a fundamental change of meaning.[3]

b Presumption against the imposition of liability without fault

This may be regarded as an aspect of the general presumption against fundamental change in the common law by mere implication. At common law *mens rea* is an element in all crimes,[4] though not in all torts. Although the legislature can, and frequently does, create offences of strict or absolute liability the intention so to do must be clear and unambiguous. LORD REID, in the leading case of *Sweet* v. *Parsley*, explained the judicial approach as follows:[5]

> "Our first duty is to consider the words of the Act; if they show a clear intention to create an absolute offence, that is an end of the matter. But such cases are very rare.[6] Sometimes the words of the section which creates a particular offence make

---

[1] *National Assistance Board* v. *Wilkinson*, [1952] 2 Q.B. 648, at p. 661; [1952] 2 All E.R. 255, at p. 260.
[2] [1912] A.C. 305; *Beswick* v. *Beswick*, [1968] A.C. 58; [1967] 2 All E.R. 1197 (p. 109, *ante*) is a paradigm of this presumption.
[3] See *Beswick* v. *Beswick (supra)*; *Woolley* v. *Woolley*, [1968] P. 29; [1966] 3 All E.R. 855.
[4] See *R.* v. *Tolson* (1889), 23 Q.B.D. 168, at p. 181; *Younghusband* v. *Luftig*, [1949] 2 K.B. 354; [1949] 2 All E.R. 72.
[5] [1970] A.C. 132, at p. 148; [1969] 1 All E.R. 347, at p. 349. See also *R.* v. *Gould*, [1968] 2 Q.B. 65; [1968] 1 All E.R. 849.
[6] See, for examples, *R.* v. *Prince* (1875), L.R. 2 C.C.R. 154; *Cundy* v. *Le Coq* (1884), 13 Q.B.D. 207.

it clear that *mens rea* is required in one form or another.   Such cases are quite fre-
quent.¹   But in a very large number of cases there is no clear indication either way.
In such cases there has for centuries been a presumption that Parliament did not
intend to make criminals of persons who were in no way blameworthy in what they
did.   That means that, whenever a section is silent as to *mens rea*, there is a presumption that, in order to give effect to the will of Parliament, we must read in words
appropriate to require *mens rea*."

c   Presumption against depriving a person of a vested right

In the absence of express provision the courts will not construe a statute as
having the effect of depriving a person of a right vested in him before the
statute came into operation.   This is linked with the presumption against
retrospective operation though it is more than an illustration of the latter
presumption.   For example, every person has a right to the use and enjoyment
of his own land.   The remedy for infringement of this right is an action in
trespass or nuisance, depending on the character of the interference.   Consequently where a statute authorises the performance of an act, which constitutes
a nuisance to the plaintiff, the statute will not be construed as having the effect
of removing the plaintiff's right unless it is clearly intended to have that effect.²
Even stronger is the presumption against removing a right to compensation.³
Nevertheless, this can be done expressly as evidenced by the War Damage Act
1965 which removed a right to compensation from the Crown in respect of
damage to or destruction of property caused by the Crown in time of war, or in
contemplation of the outbreak of war.⁴

d   Presumption against ousting the jurisdiction of the courts

Individuals cannot, by contract, exclude the jurisdiction of the courts.   Although
Parliament may exclude an individual's recourse to the courts, the provision
purporting so to do must be absolutely clear and unambiguous since the courts
are extremely wary about permitting legislative or executive interference with
their jurisdiction.   The principle was stated by Viscount Simonds as follows
in *Pyx Granite, Ltd.* v. *Ministry of Housing and Local Government:*⁵

> "... it is a principle not by any means to be whittled down that the subject's
> recourse to Her Majesty's courts for the determination of his rights is not to be
> excluded except by clear words.   That is, as McNair, J. called it in *Francis v. Yiewsley*

---

¹ See, for examples, *R.* v. *Hallam*, [1957] 1 Q.B. 569; [1957] 1 All E.R. 665; *Vane* v.
Yiannopoullos, [1965] A.C. 486; [1964] 3 All E.R. 820.
² *Metropolitan Asylum District* v. *Hill* (1881), 6 App. Cas. 193.
³ *Ministry of Health* v. *Stafford Corporation*, [1952] Ch. 730; [1952] 2 All E.R. 386.   It was
on this basis that the Court of Appeal held in *Allen* v. *Thorn Electrical Industries, Ltd.*, [1967]
1 Q.B. 487; [1967] 2 All E.R. 1137 that the prohibition on pay increases introduced by
the Prices and Incomes Act 1966 did not deprive the plaintiff of his right to an increase
which had been agreed upon before the prohibition came into effect.
⁴ The right had been held to exist in *Burmah Oil Co., Ltd.* v. *Lord Advocate*, [1965] A.C. 75;
[1964] 2 All E.R. 348.
⁵ [1960] A.C. 260, at p. 286; [1959] 3 All E.R. 1, at p. 6, cited with approval by Lord
Donovan in *Ealing London Borough* v. *Race Relations Board*, [1972] 1 All E.R. 105, at p. 108;
[1972] 2 W.L.R. 71, at p. 75; the decision illustrates the application of the presumption
in that the House of Lords held that the machinery established under the Race Relations
Act 1968 for referring disputes to certain nominated county courts did not exclude the
inherent jurisdiction of the High Court to make a declaration as to rights under the Act;
see p. 266, *post*.

and West Drayton Urban District Council[1] a 'fundamental rule' from which I would not for my part sanction any departure."

One application of this rule is the principle that a provision which expressly states that the decision of an inferior court, tribunal or administrative body shall be "final" does not exclude the prerogative jurisdiction of the High Court to review the decision.

" . . . if a tribunal goes wrong in law and the error appears on the face of the record, the High Court will interfere by certiorari to quash the decision. It is not to be deterred by the enactment that the decision is 'final'. The decision may be final on the facts but it is not final on the law."[2]

e   Presumption that a statute does not bind the Crown

One of the few relics of the prerogative of the Crown is the rule that the Crown is not bound by a statute unless expressly named in it. The rule extends to the Crown and to its servants and agents though not to nationalised industries.[3] The Crown Proceedings Act 1947 placed the Crown, with certain exceptions, in the same position as a private person in the law of torts. Consequently, statutes which affect common law rights and duties are usually expressed to bind the Crown. Examples are the Limitation Act 1939 and the Occupiers' Liability Act 1957. The Crown is no longer a preferred creditor in bankruptcy[4] and the general trend of modern legislation is towards the removal of the Crown's privileges and immunities.[5]

5   Material aids to construction

The distinction between interpretation and construction has already been noted. All statutes require interpretation but only statutes whose provisions are ambiguous or uncertain in extent require construction, though the processes of interpretation and construction are inextricably interrelated. Judges frequently make no attempt to distinguish the processes of interpretation and construction. The distinction is, however, material since not all aids to construction are legitimate aids to interpretation. Thus the aids to construction which do not form part of the enactment may only be consulted where the process of interpretation has disclosed an uncertainty or an ambiguity.

There are two classes of aids to construction; internal aids and external aids.

a   Internal aids

An internal (or intrinsic) aid is an aid which is to be found within the Queen's Printer's copy of the statute itself. Those parts of the statute which form part of the enactment must, of course, be consulted as part of the general process of interpretation in applying the general rule that the statute must be read as a

---

[1] [1957] 2 Q.B. 136, at p. 148; the passage referred to does not appear in the report of the case in [1957] 1 All E.R. 825.
[2] *Tehrani* v. *Rostron*, [1972] 1 Q.B. 182, at p. 187; [1971] 3 All E.R. 790, at p. 793, per LORD DENNING, M.R.; see also *R.* v. *Medical Appeal Tribunal, Ex parte Gilmore*, [1957] 1 Q.B. 574; [1957] 1 All E.R. 796, where the earlier authorities are reviewed; *Sagnata Investments, Ltd.* v. *Norwich Corporation*, [1971] 2 Q.B. 614; [1971] 2 All E.R. 1441.
[3] *Tamlin* v. *Hannaford*, [1950] 1 K.B. 18; [1949] 2 All E.R. 327.
[4] Bankruptcy Act 1914, s. 151.
[5] See *Madras Electric Supply Corporation (in liquidation)* v. *Boarland (Inspector of Taxes)*, [1955] A.C. 667; [1955] 1 All E.R. 753.

whole. Other parts of the Queen's Printer's copy are not aids to interpretation though some, but not all, are aids to construction. There has not, however, been a universal judicial adherence to these basic principles and the modern tendency is to regard those parts of the statute which are not strictly part of the enactment, that is to say punctuation, headings and marginal notes, as aids to construction in cases of ambiguity. Thus in *Director of Public Prosecutions* v. *Schildkamp* LORD REID stated:[1]

> " . . . it may be more realistic to accept the Act as printed as being the product of the whole legislative process, and to give due weight to everything found in the printed Act. I say more realistic because in very many cases the provision before the court was never even mentioned in debate in either House, and it may be that its wording was never closely scrutinised by any member of either House. In such a case it is not very meaningful to say that the words of the Act represent the intention of Parliament but that punctuation, cross-headings and sidenotes do not.
>
> So if the authorities are equivocal and one is free to deal with the whole matter I would not object to taking all these matters into account provided that we realise that they cannot have equal weight with the words of the Act. Punctuation can be of some assistance in construction. A cross-heading ought to indicate the scope of the sections which follow it . . . But a sidenote is a poor guide to the scope of the section for it can do no more than indicate the main subject with which the section deals."

It is necessary to identify and distinguish the constituent parts of a statute. *Long title*—The long title of an Act begins with the words "An Act" and goes on to describe the general effect of the Act. Thus the Act whose short title is the "Law of Property Act 1925" has the long title: "An Act to consolidate the enactments relating to Conveyancing and the Law of Property in England and Wales." It might be supposed that the insertion of a long title would afford Parliament the opportunity of stating its general intention in passing the Act, but in fact long titles tend to be succinct rather than explanatory and generally do little more than identify the subject matter of the Act. Their insertion would appear to rest rather on tradition than on utility.

Until the nineteenth century the long title was not part of the Act itself and was therefore not regarded as a legitimate aid to interpretation. The modern long title, however, is part of the enactment and may be the subject of debate and amendment in Parliament. Consequently, it may be regarded as a legitimate aid both to interpretation and construction. A Master of the Rolls observed in 1899:[2]

> "I read the title advisedly because now and for some years past the title of an Act of Parliament has been part of the Act. In the old days it used not to be so, and in the old books we are told not to regard it, but now the title is an important part of the Act and is so treated by both Houses of Parliament".

Although the long title is part of the Act, it is a minor aid to construction. There have been conspicuously few cases in which it has been consulted and it

---

[1] [1969] 3 All E.R. 1640, at p. 1641; [1970] 2 W.L.R. 279, at pp. 281–282; see also *Limb & Co. (Stevedores)* v. *British Transport Docks Board*, [1971] 1 All E.R. 828; [1971] 1 W.L.R. 311.

[2] LINDLEY, M.R. in *Fielding* v. *Morley Corporation*, [1899] 1 Ch. 1, at p. 3; see also *Vacher* v. *London Society of Compositors*, [1913] A.C. 107, at p. 128; *R.* v. *Delmayne*, [1970] 2 Q.B. 170, at p. 175; [1969] 2 All E.R. 980, at p. 983.

certainly cannot prevail over an express provision in the body of the Act. Thus "An Act to amend the law with respect to wills of personal estate made by British subjects" (Wills Act 1861) has been held to apply to the will of an alien.[1] The long title should not be confused with the preamble though, now that preambles are rarely encountered, judges do occasionally describe the long title as the preamble.[2]

Short title—This is the title by which Acts are commonly, and properly, cited. In theory the short title is a valid aid both to interpretation and to construction, but there appears to be no reported case in which the short title has been used to determine a point of construction, though reference has sometimes been made to it. The short title could certainly not be used to introduce ambiguity into the body of the Act and, indeed, the short titles of certain Acts do not reflect the content of the Act accurately. The Criminal Procedure Act 1865, for example, applies to both civil and criminal proceedings.

Preamble—The preamble is that part of the statute which precedes the enacting words and sets out the reason for the statute being passed, for example the mischief which the statute is passed to remedy. In old cases great weight was attached to the preamble as an aid to construction.[3] Important Acts such as the Statute of Uses 1535, the Statute of Frauds 1677 and the Parliament Act 1911 have long and instructive preambles. Probably the best known preamble is that of the Charitable Uses Act 1601 which is still regarded as containing the criteria to be adopted when considering whether a particular object is a "charitable" one.[4] Where a statute has a preamble, it traditionally begins with the word "Whereas". Modern statutes, however, rarely contain a preamble and where one is included it is generally too brief to be of assistance. Consequently the preamble is of declining importance as an aid to construction. Although the preamble is part of the enactment, like the long title, it cannot be introduced to create an ambiguity in the body of the Act. In the words of LORD HALSBURY:[5]

"... If an enactment is itself clear and unambiguous, no preamble can qualify or cut down the enactment".

It might be argued that, since the preamble and the long title form part of the enactment, the enactment cannot be "clear and unambiguous" if the long title or the preamble is inconsistent with the body of the Act. The courts have not generally acceded to this line of argument.[6]

Headings—A section or group of sections in an Act may be preceded by a heading. Such headings are not part of the enactment and for that reason logic would suggest their exclusion. Notwithstanding, headings are often consulted

---

[1] *Re Groos*, [1904] P. 269; see also *R.* v. *Bates*, [1952] 2 All E.R. 842; [1953] 1 W.L.R. 77; *Re Wykes*, [1961] Ch. 229, at p. 242; [1961] 1 All E.R. 470, at p. 475.

[2] E.g. WINN, L.J. in *Crook* v. *Edmondson*, [1966] 2 Q.B. 81, at p. 89; [1966] 1 All E.R. 833, at p. 835; BAKER, J. (as he then was) in *Limb & Co. (Stevedores)* v. *British Transport Docks Board* (*supra*).

[3] *Belasco* v. *Hannant* (1862), 3 B. & S. 13; *Sussex Peerage Claim* (1844), 11 Cl. & F. 85.

[4] See, for example, the consideration of this preamble in *Incorporated Council of Law Reporting for England and Wales* v. *A.-G.*, [1971] Ch. 626; [1971] 3 All E.R. 1029.

[5] *Powell* v. *Kempton Park Racecourse Co.*, [1899] A.C. 143, at p. 157.

[6] *A.-G.* v. *Prince Ernest Augustus of Hanover*, [1957] A.C. 436; [1957] 1 All E.R. 49; *Ward* v. *Holman*, [1964] 2 Q.B. 580; [1964] 2 All E.R. 729; *Powell* v. *Kempton Park Racecourse Co.* (*supra*).

as an aid to construction where the enactment is uncertain or ambiguous.[1]   The modern judicial tendency appears to be to treat a heading as if it were a preamble.[2] In *Director of Public Prosecutions* v. *Schildkamp*[3] Lord Upjohn was in favour of according greater weight to headings than were the other law lords, and accordingly observed:[4]

> "In my opinion, it is wrong to confine their role to the resolution of ambiguities in the body of the Act.   When the court construing the Act is reading it through to understand it, it must read the cross-headings as well as the body of the Act and that will always be a useful pointer as to the intention of Parliament in enacting the immediately following sections.   Whether the cross-heading is no more than a pointer or label or is helpful in assisting to construe or even in some cases to control the meaning or ambit of those sections must necessarily depend on the circumstances of each case."

Marginal notes—Marginal notes are not part of an Act and are inserted by the draftsman purely for facility of reference.   It has happened that a marginal note has borne no relation to the content of a section which had been considerably altered during the passage of the Bill.[5]   For this reason the old rule was that marginal notes were not regarded as a legitimate aid to construction, even in the event of ambiguity.[6]   Nevertheless there have been cases in which the court has clearly adverted to the marginal note in construing a section.[7]   Thus Upjohn, L.J. (as he then was) observed in a recent case:[8]

> "While the marginal note to a section cannot control the language used in the section, it is at least permissible to approach a consideration of its general purpose and the mischief at which it is aimed with the note in mind."

In the light of the speeches of the House of Lords in *Director of Public Prosecutions* v. *Schildkamp* (*supra*), it now appears that the court is entitled to look at marginal notes in cases of ambiguity, though they clearly carry little weight and certainly cannot displace a meaning which appears from the enactment proper.

Interpretation sections—It is a relatively modern drafting technique to include an interpretation section in an Act.   The Law of Property Act 1925, for example, has a long section containing definitions of, and guides to, the interpretation of numerous words and phrases employed in that Act.[9]   Although an interpretation section is as much a part of the Act as any other section, the inter-

---

[1] For an instructive recent case see *Crook* v. *Edmondson*, [1966] 2 Q.B. 81; [1966] 1 All E.R. 833 in which the words "immoral purposes" were construed in the light of the group of sections of the Sexual Offences Act 1956 in which those words occurred; see also *Beswick* v. *Beswick*, [1968] A.C. 58; [1967] 2 All E.R. 1197 (*ante*, p. 109).

[2] *Martins* v. *Fowler*, [1926] A.C. 746; *Re Carlton*, [1945] 1 Ch. 280; [1945] 2 All E.R. 370; *Qualter, Hall & Co., Ltd.* v. *Board of Trade*, [1962] Ch. 273; [1961] 3 All E.R. 389.

[3] [1969] 3 All E.R. 1640; [1970] 2 W.L.R. 279.

[4] [1969] 3 All E.R., at p. 1656; [1970] 2 W.L.R., at p. 298.

[5] Married Women (Maintenance in Case of Desertion) Act 1886, s. 1 (2).

[6] See *R.* v. *Bates*, [1952] 2 All E.R. 842; [1953] 1 W.L.R. 77; *Chandler* v. *Director of Public Prosecutions*, [1964] A.C. 763; [1962] 3 All E.R. 142.

[7] E.g., *Pride of Derby and Derbyshire Angling Association, Ltd.* v. *British Celanese, Ltd.*, [1953] Ch. 149; [1952] 1 All E.R. 179; *R.* v. *Vickers*, [1957] 2 Q.B. 664; [1957] 2 All E.R. 741.

[8] *Stephens* v. *Cuckfield Rural District Council*, [1960] 2 Q.B. 373, at p. 383; *Limb & Co. (Stevedores)* v. *British Transport Docks Board*, [1971] 1 All E.R. 828; [1971] 1 W.L.R. 311 (*supra*).

[9] Section 205; see *Beswick* v. *Beswick* (*supra*).

pretation of a word depends rather on its context than on the interpretation section, and, in any event, if there is an inconsistency between an interpretation section and the body of an Act the latter prevails. This is especially so when the interpretation section uses the word "includes". In this case the interpretation section will be regarded as extending rather than restricting the normal meaning of the words in question. Thus where an interpretation section[1] defined "street" by stating that it "should apply to and include any highway, not being a turnpike road", the Court of Appeal held that the word "street" could include a turnpike road since the interpretation section extended rather than restricted the ordinary and natural meaning of the word.[2]

Schedules—Schedules are part of the enactment if expressly incorporated by a section in the Act itself. They are used (*inter alia*) for prescribing forms, furnishing illustrations, listing repeals effected by the Act and setting out transitional provisions. They cannot be regarded as altering or enlarging the ordinary meaning of words used in the Act. Thus in *Ellerman Lines, Ltd.* v. *Murray*[3] the House of Lords, in interpreting an Act passed to give effect to an International Convention, steadfastly refused to look at a schedule to the Act in which was set out the text of the Convention because the words of the Act were unambiguous. It is to be presumed that the House would have considered the schedule, had the Act been uncertain or ambiguous, in order to apply the mischief rule.[4]

b   External aids

An external (or extrinsic) aid to construction is an aid which is not to be found in the Queen's Printer's copy of the Act. Since the function of the courts is to ascertain the intention of the legislature, it might be thought that they would readily refer to statements made in Parliament as to the intention of the member or party introducing the Bill. In fact the reverse is the case. The reports of debates on the Bill in its passage through Parliament are rigidly excluded[5] as are explanatory memoranda upon the effects of the Act, where these are issued.[6]

---

[1] Public Health Act 1848, s. 2.

[2] *Nutter* v. *Accrington Local Board* (1879), 4 Q.B.D. 375.

[3] [1931] A.C. 126.

[4] See *Salomon* v. *Commissioners of Customs and Excise*, [1967] 2 Q.B. 116; [1966] 3 All E.R. 871. In *Corocraft, Ltd.* v. *Pan American Airways, Inc.*, [1969] 1 Q.B. 616; [1969] 1 All E.R. 82 there was no ambiguity or uncertainty in the English Act but the Court of Appeal nevertheless adopted the text of the Convention (the meaning of which differed from that of the Act, the Carriage by Air Act 1932), distinguishing *Ellerman Lines, Ltd.* v. *Murray* on the basis that in that case the intention of Parliament had been to give effect to the English text of the Convention whereas in the present case the intention was to give effect to the original Convention. There is a presumption that Parliament intended to fulfil, rather than break, its international obligations; cf. *The Andrea Ursula*, [1971] 1 All E.R. 821; [1971] 2 W.L.R. 681.

[5] *Assam Railways and Trading Co., Ltd.* v. *Inland Revenue Commissioners*, [1935] A.C. 445; *R.* v. *Hertford College* (1878), 3 Q.B.D. 693. In *Beswick* v. *Beswick*, [1968] A.C. 58, at p. 74; [1967] 2 All E.R. 1197, at p. 1202 reasons advanced for the rule were that it would add to the time and expense of preparing cases if counsel had to read all the debates in *Hansard* and that reports of debates in select committees are not available to the public.

[6] *London County Council* v. *Central Land Board*, [1959] Ch. 386; [1958] 3 All E.R. 676. However, in *Sagnata Investments, Ltd.* v. *Norwich Corporation*, [1971] 2 Q.B. 614; [1971] 2 All E.R. 1441, LORD DENNING, M.R. did refer to *Hansard, Parliamentary Debates* when considering the mischief intended to be remedied by the Betting, Gaming and Lotteries Act 1963, Sch. 6.

In a case this century[1] LORD HALSBURY, L.C. refused to deliver a speech on the interpretation of a statute which he had helped to draft. This rigid and widely criticised rule appears to have entered English law in the eighteenth century.[2] Perhaps the most striking illustration of the rule excluding extrinsic aids to interpretation is the case of *Ellerman Lines, Ltd.* v. *Murray*, noted above, in which the House of Lords refused to look at the text of an International Convention when interpreting a statute passed to give effect to that Convention. However, in the event of ambiguity, it is now clearly established that, when construing a statute passed to enact matters agreed at an International Convention the court is entitled to look at the Convention to ascertain what Parliament must have intended.[3] Thus it probably makes no difference whether the text of the Convention is scheduled to the Act or not. This principle and the presumption that Parliament intends to fulfil its international obligations will doubtless be of considerable practical importance in the coming years when the courts are called upon to construe the legislation which will be passed to implement the rules of the European Economic Community. It may be observed that most continental countries adopt the opposite approach and encourage consultation of the Parliamentary and political history of the statute. These materials are known as *travaux préparatoires* and are an invaluable aid to the task of discovering the intention of continental legislatures. However, although the general rule in relation to external aids is one of exclusion,[4] there are certain legitimate external aids to construction and these are set out below.

Dictionaries—Words in statutes are presumed to bear their ordinary and natural meaning and it is legitimate to consult a dictionary to ascertain the meaning of words which have no particular legal meaning. Thus in *Re Ripon (Highfield) Housing Confirmation Order* 1938[5] the court adopted the Oxford English Dictionary definition of the word "park". Nevertheless dictionaries bear only slight weight and, in context, the dictionary meaning may not be the one which Parliament presumably intended. Thus in *Mills* v. *Cooper*[6] a divisional court rejected the Shorter Oxford English Dictionary definition of a "gypsy" while in *Thornton* v. *Fisher and Ludlow, Ltd.*[7] the same dictionary's definition of a "passage" was not adopted. Words and phrases which have a particular legal meaning are described as "terms of art" and do not necessarily bear the meaning which laymen would attribute to them.[8]

Reports of Committees—Although the Parliamentary history of an Act is rejected as an aid to construction, reports of the Law Commissions, Law Reform Committees and similar bodies are legitimate aids to discovering the state of the pre-existing law and the mischief which the statute was passed to

---

[1] *Hilder* v. *Dexter*, [1902] A.C. 474.
[2] *Millar* v. *Taylor* (1769), 4 Burr. 2303.
[3] *The Banco*, [1971] P. 137; [1971] 1 All E.R. 524; cf. the cases cited in fn. 4, p. 117, *ante*.
[4] The Law Commission report, *The Interpretation of Statutes* (1969, Law Com. No. 21) recommended the admission of extrinsic material, other than reports of Parliamentary proceedings.
[5] [1939] 2 K.B. 838; [1939] 3 All E.R. 548.
[6] [1967] 2 Q.B. 459; [1967] 2 All E.R. 100.
[7] [1968] 2 All E.R. 241; [1968] 1 W.L.R. 655.
[8] See *Sydall* v. *Castings, Ltd.*, [1967] 1 Q.B. 302; [1966] 3 All E.R. 770, on the construction of the word "descendants" as a term of art; see also *Barclays Bank, Ltd.* v. *Cole*, [1967] 2 Q.B. 738; [1966] 3 All E.R. 948, on the meaning of the word "fraud".

remedy. It is not, however, legitimate to interpret the words of an Act in accordance with the recommendations of a Committee which preceded its passing. Thus in *Letang* v. *Cooper*[1] the Court of Appeal held that the words "negligence, nuisance or breach of duty" in the Law Reform (Limitation of Actions, &c.) Act 1954 were wide enough to embrace the tort of trespass to the person even though the Tucker Committee report,[2] which preceded the 1954 Act, expressed an intention to exclude this form of action from the shorter limitation period recommended in that report.

c *Judicial precedents*

The application of the doctrine of judicial precedent to the interpretation of statutes was recently explained by LORD UPJOHN:[3]

> "It is quite clear that judicial statements as to the construction and intention of an Act must never be allowed to supplant or supersede its proper construction and courts must beware of falling into the error of treating the law to be that laid down by the judge in construing the Act rather than found in the Act itself. No doubt a decision on particular words binds inferior courts on the construction of those words on similar facts, but beyond that the observations of Judges on the construction of statutes may be of the greatest help and guidance but are entitled to no more than respect and cannot absolve the court from its duty of exercising an independent judgment."

Thus where a superior court has interpreted the words of an Act, an inferior court in the hierarchy is bound to adopt that interpretation if faced with the same words in the same Act. The position is less clear if the later court is called upon to interpret the same or similar words in another part of the same Act or in another Act. In this event the earlier decision will be a binding precedent only if the two provisions in the Acts in question are *in pari materia* (deal with the same subject matter). This occurs most commonly when the later Act is a consolidating statute and the earlier Act is one of those repealed and consolidated. In such a case decisions on the interpretation of the words of the earlier Act will be treated as binding upon courts interpreting the corresponding provisions in the later Act.[4] Similarly, if the later Act employs words or phrases which have been the subject of judicial interpretation in an earlier Act dealing with the same subject matter there is a presumption that they are intended to bear the same meaning, on the basis that Parliament is presumed to know the law.[5] For example, the House of Lords, in assigning a meaning to the word "wreck" in the Merchant Shipping Act 1925, adopted the interpretation

---

[1] [1965] 1 Q.B. 232; [1964] 2 All E.R. 929.
[2] Cmnd. 7740. In *Sagnata Investments, Ltd.* v. *Norwich Corporation* (*supra*) LORD DENNING, M.R., in considering the legislative history of the Betting, Gaming and Lotteries Act 1963 took into account the recommendations of the Royal Commission on Betting, Lotteries and Gaming (Cmnd. 8190 of 1951).
[3] *Ogden Industries, Pty., Ltd.* v. *Lucas*, [1970] A.C. 113, at p. 127; [1969] 1 All E.R. 121, at p. 126.
[4] *Mitchell* v. *Simpson* (1890), 25 Q.B.D. 183; *Smith* v. *Baker*, [1891] A.C. 325.
[5] Cf. *Maxwell on Interpretation of Statutes* (11th edn. 1962) p. 303, cited with approval in *R.* v. *Freeman*, [1970] 2 All E.R. 413, [1970] 1 W.L.R. 788 in which the Court of Appeal held that, since there was no relevant distinction between the definition of "firearm" in s. 57 (1) of the Firearms Act 1968 and the definitions in earlier Firearms Acts, Parliament must be taken to have adopted in the 1968 Act the interpretation which had been placed on the definition in the Firearms Act 1920.

of that word which had been given in a case decided on the wording of the Merchant Shipping Act 1894.[1]   However, where the earlier decision is upon similar words in a statute which is not *in pari materia* with the statute requiring interpretation, or where the words are used in a different context, that decision is not a binding precedent.[2]

---

[1] *The Olympic*, [1913] P. 92; *Barras* v. *Aberdeen Steam Trawling and Fishing Co.*, [1933] A.C. 402.
[2] *London Corporation* v. *Cusack-Smith*, [1955] A.C. 337; [1955] 1 All E.R. 302; *Goodrich* v. *Paisner*, [1957] A.C. 65; [1956] 2 All E.R. 176.

CHAPTER 7

Law Reports and Precedents

A THE RELATIONSHIP BETWEEN LAW REPORTS AND THE DOCTRINE OF PRECEDENT

The operation of the doctrine of precedent is inextricably bound up with law reporting. The rule is that any decision may be cited to a court provided that it is vouched for by a member of the Bar who was present when judgment was delivered. In addition, since judges take judicial notice of the whole of English law, an individual judge may rely upon a precedent of which he is aware even though the decision is unreported.[1] There is, thus, no rule that a case may only be cited or relied upon as a precedent if it is reported. Nevertheless personal recollection by judges or counsel is so impermanent and haphazard that it could not possibly form the basis of a workable system. Hence precedents are almost always contained in law reports. The close nexus between law reporting and the doctrine of judicial precedent is evidenced by the fact that the modern doctrine of binding precedent was formulated only when an integrated system of law reporting evolved in the nineteenth century.

It is important to distinguish a law report from a court record. The court record contains, basically, the names of the parties, the form of action (until these were abolished), the pleadings and the decision or order of the court. A law report contains most of these and, in addition, the judgment of the court containing the reasoning upon which the decision has been based. It is this reasoning which is the important element in the decision for the purposes of the doctrine of precedent. For this reason court records, such as the Plea Rolls, copies of which dating from the twelfth century are preserved in the Public Record Office, are of little value as precedents.

One might suppose that, because law reports are fundamental to the doctrine of precedent which is the cornerstone of the English legal system, the courts would have created a methodical system of producing law reports. It is an extraordinary anomaly that this has never been done. Law reporting has been

---

[1] In addition, transcripts of judgments of the House of Lords and Court of Appeal are filed in the Bar Library in London. Until 1951 no record was maintained anywhere of judgments of the Court of Appeal: see *Gibson* v. *South American Stores (Gath & Chaves) Ltd.*, [1950] Ch. 177, at p. 195; [1949] 2 All E.R. 985, at p. 995.

left entirely to private enterprise so that, even at the present day, there is an element of chance and individual preference in the matter of whether or not a case is reported.

The historical evolution of the modern system of law reporting is considered below, but first the operation of the precedent system requires detailed examination.

B THE OPERATION OF THE DOCTRINE OF PRECEDENT

1 The doctrine of binding precedent

The traditional view of the function of an English judge is that it is not to make law but to decide cases in accordance with existing legal rules. This gives rise to the doctrine of binding precedent whereby the judge is not merely referred to earlier decisions for guidance; he is bound to apply the rules of law contained in those decisions. The operation of the doctrine depends upon the hierarchy of the courts. All courts stand in a definite relationship to one another. A court is bound by decisions of a court above itself in the hierarchy and, usually, by a court of equivalent standing.[1] Given that the doctrine of precedent has binding force within this framework, the question naturally arises of how the law may develop if cases are always to be determined according to ageless principles. In practice there are several ways in which the doctrine retains its flexibility. These are dealt with in detail below[2] but it is sufficient to note at this juncture two basic principles: first, that superior courts have power to overrule decisions of inferior courts and, in certain cases, to overrule their own earlier decisions, and, secondly, that any rule of law may be changed by statute. Consequently every rule of law is subject to change, either by the judges themselves or by Parliament. However, the disadvantage of legislation as a source of law is that statutes require interpretation by judges, and these interpretations are in themselves judicial precedents. Therefore it is an oversimplification to regard legislation as superior to precedent as a source of law.

The advantages of the precedent system are said to be certainty, precision and flexibility.[3] Legal certainty is achieved, in theory at least, in that, if the legal problem raised has been solved before, the judge is bound to adopt that solution. Precision is achieved by the sheer volume of reported cases containing solutions to innumerable factual situations arising in any particular branch of the law. No code or statute, no matter how carefully drafted, could anticipate the legal problems which these variations of fact may promote. Consequently, the judge in a continental legal system must generally decide cases on the basis of broad principles. Finally, flexibility is achieved by the possibility of decisions being

---

[1] Under clause 3 (1) of the European Communities Bill currently before Parliament: "For the purposes of all legal proceedings any question as to the meaning or effect of any of the Treaties, or as to the validity, meaning or effect of any Community instrument, shall be treated as a question of law (and if not referred to the European Court, be for determination as such in accordance with the principles laid down by and any relevant decision of the European Court.)"

[2] See p. 127, *post*.

[3] See observations of RUSSELL, L.J. in *Gallie* v. *Lee*, [1969] 2 Ch. 17, at p. 41; [1969] 1 All E.R. 1062, at p. 1076 (affirmed *sub nom. Saunders* v. *Anglia Building Society*, [1971] A.C. 1004; [1970] 3 All E.R. 961).

overruled and by the possibility of distinguishing and confining the operation of decisions which appear unsound, the latter process being of particular importance.

The obvious disadvantages of the system are its inherent rigidity, which may occasionally cause hardship, and the vast and ever-increasing bulk of reported cases to which the court must advert to determine what is the law, since an excess of case law tends to obscure basic principles.[1]

Finally, it is self-evident that there cannot be an infinite regression. Every rule of law must have its origin. If it was not created by statute, then it must have been created by a court. Thus where there is no precedent the doctrine breaks down and the judge is bound to reach a decision in accordance with general principles. Even in modern times cases arise for which there is no precedent. These cases are described as cases of first impression and require the judge to make law rather than to apply it.[2] This he will do by reference to analogous principles but even legal principles must have their origin so that the declaratory theory of the common law is not of universal application.

2 The binding element in precedents

a The ratio decidendi

It is a misstatement to speak of a "decision" as being binding, just as it is not technically correct to regard a "decision" as overruled. It is not the decision which binds, any more than it is the decision which is overruled; it is the rule of law contained in the decision. This element in a decision is termed the *ratio decidendi* of the case. Not every statement of law made by a judge in the course of his judgment is part of the *ratio*. For this reason it is important to be able to analyse a decision and isolate from it the *ratio decidendi*.

Every decision contains the following basic ingredients:

(1) findings of material facts, direct and inferential. An inferential finding of fact is the inference which the judge (or jury if there is one) draws from the direct, or perceptible, facts. For example, from the direct facts of the speed of a vehicle, the length of skid marks and the state of the road the judge or jury may infer negligence. Negligence is an inferential finding of fact. Similarly, cruelty, in matrimonial proceedings, is an inference of fact which may or may not be drawn from the direct facts of the respondent spouse's treatment of the other spouse during the marriage;

(2) statements of the principles of law applicable to the legal problems disclosed by the facts; and

(3) judgment based on the combined effect of (1) and (2).

For the purposes of the parties themselves and their privies, (3) is the material element in the decision for it determines finally their rights and liabilities in relation to the subject matter of the action. It is the judgment that estops the parties from reopening the dispute.[3]

However, for the purpose of the doctrine of precedent, (2) is the vital element

---

[1] Thus, for example, in *Qureshi* v. *Qureshi*, [1971] 1 All E.R. 325; [1971] 2 W.L.R. 518 some 94 authorities (and 8 textbooks) appear to have been cited to the court.

[2] E.g., *Philips* v. *Brooks*, [1919] 2 K.B. 243; *Noble* v. *Harrison*, [1926] 2 K.B. 332; *Lancashire Loans, Ltd.* v. *Black*, [1934] 1 K.B. 380; *British Transport Commission* v. *Gourley*, [1956] A.C. 185; [1955] 3 All E.R. 796.

[3] See p. 471, *post*.

in the decision. This is, indeed, the *ratio decidendi*. Thus the *ratio decidendi* may be defined as the statement of law applied to the legal problems raised by the facts as found upon which the decision is based. The two other elements in the decision are not precedents. The judgment is not binding (except directly on the parties themselves); nor are the findings of fact. This means that, even where the direct facts of an earlier case appear to be identical to those of the case before the court, the judge or jury is not bound to draw the same inference as that drawn in the earlier case. This point is well illustrated by the leading case of *Qualcast (Wolverhampton) Ltd.* v. *Haynes.*[1] In that case an employee sued his employers for damages for negligence in failing to provide a safe system of work. The county court judge, at first instance, held himself bound to find the defendants liable by earlier cases in which employers, having taken similar precautions to those taken by the defendants in the present case, had been held liable. This was wrong for, as the House of Lords explained, these cases, even though decided by a judge sitting alone rather than with a jury, were decisions based upon inferences of fact which were not to be regarded as binding. Otherwise, as Lord Somervell observed:[2] "the precedent system will die from a surfeit of authorities".

Moreover, not every statement of law in a judgment is binding. Only those statements which are based upon the facts as found and upon which the decision is based are binding. Any other statement of law is, strictly, superfluous and is described as an *obiter dictum* (something said "by the way").

b   Obiter dicta

There are two types of *obiter dicta*. First, a statement of law is regarded as *obiter* if it is based upon facts which either were not found to exist or, if found, were not found to be material. For example, the famous statement of equitable estoppel contained in the judgment of Denning, J. (as he then was) in *Central London Property Trust, Ltd.* v. *High Trees House, Ltd.*[3] is clearly *obiter* since it applied to a set of facts which were not found to be present in the case. Similarly, in *Rondel* v. *Worsley*[4] the House of Lords expressed opinions to the effect that a barrister might be held liable in tort when acting outside the province of litigation and that a solicitor, when acting as advocate, might enjoy immunity from action. Since the case concerned only the liability of a barrister when acting as advocate, the opinions in question were necessarily *obiter*.

A second type of *obiter dictum* is a statement of law which, although based on the facts as found, does not form the basis of the decision. An obvious example is a statement of law in support of a dissenting judgment. Similarly, where a court makes statements of law leading to one conclusion and then adopts a contrary decision on the facts for a different reason, those statements are necessarily *obiter* since they do not support the decision. A case in point is the recent decision of the House of Lords in *Hedley Byrne & Co., Ltd.* v. *Heller & Partners, Ltd.*[5] The proposition of law in that case, that the maker of a state-

---

[1] [1959] A.C. 743; [1959] 2 All E.R. 38.
[2] [1959] A.C., at p. 758; [1959] 2 All E.R., at p. 43. It should be remembered that, in the tort of negligence, only the existence of a duty of care is a question of law; whether or not the defendant has broken his duty is a question of fact.
[3] [1947] K.B. 30; [1956] 1 All E.R. 256n.
[4] [1969] 1 A.C. 191; [1967] 3 All E.R. 993; see p. 219, *post*.
[5] [1964] A.C. 465; [1963] 2 All E.R. 575.

ment owes a duty of care, in certain circumstances, to persons whom he may expect to rely upon that statement, is, strictly, *obiter* since the bank which gave the advice was protected by its disclaimer of responsibility. That being so, the further statement as to what rule of law would have been applied but for the disclaimer cannot be regarded as essential to the decision. This was recognised by DANCKWERTS, L.J. in *Rondel* v. *Worsley*[1] where that Lord Justice expressed the view that the wide statement of the law made by the House of Lords in *Hedley Byrne* was no more than a *dictum*. Nevertheless, *Hedley Byrne* does illustrate that the strict rules for isolating the *ratio decidendi* of a case are sometimes of little value since, the reasoning of the House of Lords, having been expressly applied in the Court of Appeal and approved in other cases,[2] almost certainly represents the present English law. It seems that where the House of Lords states a rule of law and expressly overrules earlier contrary decisions, that statement will be treated as binding even though not strictly essential to the decision.[3]

In some cases the court decides a case and goes on to state a principle of law which is of much wider application than the decision requires. In such a case only that part of the statement of law which applies to the actual facts of the case before the court is *ratio*, the wider principle embodied in the statement being *obiter*. A good illustration of this may be found in the line of cases concerning the liability of hospitals for the negligence of surgeons and other hospital staff. In *Hillyer* v. *St. Bartholomew's Hospital*[4] the Court of Appeal, in considering the liability of a hospital for the negligence of a consultant surgeon, stated a broad principle that a hospital was not vicariously liable for the negligence of any doctor, because the hospital could not control the manner in which he performed his work. This statement was clearly wider than was necessary for the decision and the Court of Appeal, in a later case,[5] limited the principle to liability for consultant surgeons and held it not to apply to a resident surgeon, since the basis of vicarious liability is the existence of a contract of service rather than the ability of the employer to control the manner in which the employee performs his work.[6]

---

[1] [1967] 1 Q.B. 443; [1966] 3 All E.R. 657; (affirmed [1969] 1 A.C. 191; [1967] 3 All E.R. 993).

[2] *Clay* v. *A.J. Crump & Sons, Ltd.,* [1964] 1 Q.B. 533; [1963] 3 All E.R. 687; *Bagot* v. *Stevens, Scanlan & Co.,* [1966] 1 Q.B. 197; [1964] 3 All E.R. 577.

[3] A similar example is afforded by the case of *Fairman* v. *Perpetual Investment Building Society,* [1923] A.C. 74, where the statement of law as to whether the plaintiff was an invitee or a licensee was not essential to the decision and, therefore, strictly *obiter*. Nevertheless the House of Lords subsequently regarded this statement as a second *ratio* of the case in *Jacobs* v. *London County Council,* [1950] A.C. 361; [1950] 1 All E.R. 737; the cases are now of purely academic interest since s. 1 of the Occupiers' Liability Act 1957 has abolished the common law distinction between invitees and licensees.

[4] [1909] 2 K.B. 820.

[5] *Cassidy* v. *Ministry of Health,* [1951] 2 K.B. 343; [1951] 1 All E.R. 574. See also *Gold* v. *Essex County Council,* [1942] 2 K.B. 293; [1942] 2 All E.R. 237.

[6] For a recent illustration of a wide principle being subsequently narrowed see *Re Grosvenor Hotel (No. 2),* [1965] Ch. 1210; [1964] 3 All E.R. 354, in which the Court of Appeal treated as *obiter* (and wrong) the wide statement of the law relating to Crown Privilege made by the then Lord Chancellor in *Duncan* v. *Cammell, Laird & Co, Ltd.,* [1942] A.C. 624; [1942] 1 All E.R. 587, notwithstanding that the statement in question had been applied by appellate courts on several occasions; see now *Conway* v. *Rimner,* [1968] A.C. 910; [1968] 1 All E.R. 874.

It is difficult to isolate the *ratio decidendi* of a case which is argued on more than one ground. If the court is willing to decide the case on one ground it will usually refrain from expressing an opinion on any other point of law raised. Such a point is then said to be "left open". There are numerous of important points of law which have been left open and which remain, in fact, undecided.[1] However the court sometimes feels constrained to deal with every point of law raised and then to give its decision. Which of these statements of law is the *ratio decidendi* of the case? The problem often arises when considering the decisions of appellate courts where different members of the court have arrived at the same conclusion, but for different reasons. A reason adopted by a majority of the court is, *prima facie*, *ratio* whereas a reason adopted only by a minority is usually regarded as inessential to the decision and, therefore, not binding. The position is even more complicated where no one reason is favoured by a majority. Clearly every case must have a *ratio decidendi* and the answer seems to be that it depends upon which of the alternative reasons subsequent courts are prepared to accept as *rationes*. It is certainly possible for a case to have two or more *rationes decidendi*. The case of *Fairman* v. *Perpetual Investment Building Society*[2] is an example. The House of Lords in that case gave two reasons for its decision, both of which were accepted as binding by the House itself in *Jacobs* v. *L.C.C.*[3] On the other hand, in *Read* v. *J. Lyons & Co., Ltd.*[4] the House of Lords advanced two reasons for its decision that the defendants were not liable under the rule in *Rylands* v. *Fletcher*:[5] (1) that the rule did not apply in the absence of an escape of the dangerous substance from the defendant's occupation or control; and (2) that the rule did not apply unless the plaintiff had an interest in land affected by the escape. The second reason, which is principally contained in the speech of LORD MACMILLAN, was, in a later case,[6] treated by the Court of Appeal as *obiter*, on the basis that it was not essential to the decision. The position is complicated in that the statement to this effect in the Court of Appeal case was, itself, *obiter* because the plaintiff's action failed for another reason. Consequently it remains undecided whether the second reason in *Read* v. *J. Lyons & Co., Ltd.* is *ratio* or *obiter*.[7]

It would be erroneous to suppose that *obiter dicta* are of no authority. Strictly, they are not of binding authority but have only persuasive authority. Nevertheless, where the statement in question has fallen from a court of high authority and is a deliberate statement of law as opposed to a casual expression of opinion it will usually be followed in the absence of binding authority to the contrary. By way of example may be cited the case of *Adams* v. *Naylor*[8] in which the House of Lords disapproved the practice of Government departments setting

---

[1] See *Minter* v. *Priest*, [1930] A.C. 558; *Dunne* v. *North-Western Gas Board*, [1964] 2 Q.B. 806; [1963] 3 All E.R. 916.

[2] [1923] A.C. 74.

[3] [1950] A.C. 361; [1950] 1 All E.R. 737. The case is particularly notable in that one of the two reasons given in *Fairman*'s case was clearly not essential to the decision. See fn. 3, p. 125, *ante*.

[4] [1947] A.C. 146; [1946] 2 All E.R. 471.

[5] (1868), L.R. 3 H.L. 330.

[6] *Perry* v. *Kendricks Transport, Ltd.*, [1956] 1 All E.R. 154; [1956] 1 W.L.R. 85.

[7] The Court of Appeal in *Dunne* v. *North-Western Gas Board*, [1964] 2 Q.B. 806; [1963] 3 All E.R. 916, expressly left the point open.

[8] [1946] A.C. 443; [1946] 2 All E.R. 241.

up a nominal defendant to avoid the Crown's immunity from actions in tort. Although this disapproval was *obiter*, the Court of Appeal in *Royster* v. *Cavey*[1] adopted it and refused to sanction this long-standing practice. Similarly, the statement of the principle of equitable estoppel made by DENNING, J. (as he then was) in *Central London Property Trust, Ltd.* v. *High Trees House, Ltd.*,[2] although clearly *obiter*, has been adopted by superior courts and is now an accepted rule of equity.[3] There could be no more striking example, finally, than the "neighbour principle" propounded by LORD ATKIN in *M'Alister (or Donoghue)* v. *Stevenson*.[4] This statement of law, though far wider than the decision required, has become the basis of the modern tort of negligence and has been cited and applied on occasions too numerous to mention.

3 Precedents which are not binding

a Persuasive authorities

Only the *ratio decidendi* of a decision is binding. *Obiter dicta* are of persuasive authority. It has already been noted that the *dicta* of an appellate court may carry great weight. However, *dicta*, of whatever weight, may be rejected if a later court wishes to adopt a contrary solution.

Other persuasive precedents are decisions of courts inferior in the hierarchy to the court which is invited to follow their decisions. Thus, for example, Court of Appeal decisions are of persuasive authority in the House of Lords.

A third class of persuasive authorities consists of the decisions of Scottish, Irish, Commonwealth and foreign courts. There is an increasing tendency on the part of English judges to draw analogies from other legal systems but these authorities are accepted as being of persuasive authority only. Special mention must be made of "decisions" of the Judicial Committee of the Privy Council. The advice of the Privy Council to Her Majesty is not strictly binding on any English judge. Thus, even a first instance judge may legitimately decline to follow a decision of the Privy Council.[5] However, Privy Council decisions are of very great persuasive authority for the obvious reason that the Council is in practice composed, for judicial sittings, of those persons who usually sit in the House of Lords. Nevertheless, despite the similarity in composition between the Privy Council and the House of Lords, there had not, until recently, been any suggestion that Privy Council authorities were of equivalent weight to House of Lords cases. However, the Court of Appeal in the case of *Doughty* v. *Turner Manufacturing Co., Ltd.*[6] expressed the view (albeit *obiter*) that the Court of Appeal's own decision in *Re Polemis*[7] was no longer good law in the light of the subsequent Privy Council decision in *The Wagon Mound*.[8] More recently,

---

[1] [1947] K.B. 204; [1946] 2 All E.R. 642. This decision precipitated the passing of the Crown Proceedings Act 1947 which enabled the Crown to be sued in tort.

[2] [1947] K.B. 130; [1956] 1 All E.R. 256n.

[3] See *Tool Metal Manufacturing Co., Ltd.* v. *Tungsten Electric Co., Ltd.*, [1955] 2 All E.R. 657; *D. and C. Builders, Ltd.* v. *Rees*, [1966] 2 Q.B. 617; [1965] 3 All E.R. 837.

[4] [1932] A.C. 562.

[5] DIPLOCK, J. (as he then was) did so in *Port Line, Ltd.* v. *Ben Line Steamers, Ltd.*, [1958] 2 Q.B. 146; [1958] 1 All E.R. 787. See also *Dulieu* v. *White*, [1901] 2 K.B. 669.

[6] [1964] 1 Q.B. 518; [1964] 1 All E.R. 98.

[7] [1921] 3 K.B. 560.

[8] *Overseas Tankship (U.K.), Ltd.* v. *Morts Dock and Engineering Co., Ltd.*, [1961] A.C. 388; [1961] 1 All E.R. 404.

in *Worcester Works Finance, Ltd.* v. *Cooden Engineering Co., Ltd.*,[1] the Court of Appeal, faced with a conflict of authority between previous decisions of the Court of Appeal and, more recently, the Privy Council, had no hesitation in preferring the latter, LORD DENNING, M.R., laying down the principle that when the Privy Council disapproves of a previous decision of the Court of Appeal, the latter is at liberty to depart from its previous decision. In the light of these decisions it now seems that decisions of the Privy Council enjoy a standing as precedents superior to that of precedents of the Court of Appeal.

b   Precedents which have been overruled

A precedent does not lose its authority with the passing of time. Indeed the strength of a precedent increases with age in that courts tend to be reluctant to overrule long-standing authorities, unless they are clearly wrong. Apart from the desirability of attaining certainty, the main reason for the reluctance of judges to overrule old decisions is the fact that, since overruling operates retrospectively, it might have the effect of disturbing financial arrangements, depriving persons of vested proprietary rights and even imposing criminal liability. Thus in *Re Compton*[2] the Court of Appeal would not overrule a long line of old authorities concerning charitable trusts although it considered these cases anomalous. Similarly the rule in *Pinnel's Case*,[3] though plainly anomalous, has never been overruled. In *Foakes* v. *Beer*[4] the House of Lords would not overrule *Pinnel's Case*; LORD FITZGERALD, though doubting that the rule was a good one, did not feel that the House would be justified in overruling it having regard simply to its longevity.[5] On the other hand there is little hesitation felt in overruling decisions which the court considers to be clearly wrong. Thus in *Bourne* v. *Keane*[6] the House, considering an aspect of the law of trusts, overruled by a majority a series of long-standing decisions even though this had the effect of disturbing many existing trusts and settlements. More recently in *Button* v. *Director of Public Prosecutions*[7] the House of Lords, in holding that the common law offence of affray could be committed in a private place, overruled a line of authority to the effect that an affray could take place only in a public place.

The process of overruling must be carefully distinguished from the process of reversing a decision. A decision altered on appeal is said to be "reversed". Reversing differs from overruling in that the former affects the decision in the case whereas the latter only affects the rule of law upon which the decision is based.[8] Strictly, it is not correct to speak of a decision as "overruled" since it is only the rule of law contained in the decision which is affected, not the decision itself.

A decision may be overruled either by statute or by a higher court. If it is

---

[1] [1971] 3 All E.R. 708; [1971] 3 W.L.R. 661.
[2] [1945] Ch. 123; [1945] 1 All E.R. 198.
[3] (1602), 5 Rep. 117a.
[4] (1884), 9 App. Cas. 605.
[5] *Ibid.*, at p. 630. The rule has, of course, been undermined by the doctrine of equitable estoppel: see *D. and C. Builders, Ltd.* v. *Rees*, [1966] 2 Q.B. 617; [1965] 3 All E.R. 837.
[6] [1919] A.C. 815.
[7] [1966] A.C. 591; [1965] 3 All E.R. 587.
[8] See *Metropolitan Police District Receiver* v. *Croydon Corporation*, [1957] 2 Q.B. 154; [1957] 1 All E.R. 478.

overruled by a higher court the earlier decision is deemed to have been based on a misunderstanding of the law. The earlier rule of law is deemed never to have existed. This is the declaratory theory of the common law. The common law is never changed; it is merely restated correctly. Consequently all judicial overruling operates retrospectively. It is this which distinguishes judicial overruling from overruling by statute, since the latter (in the absence of an express provision to the contrary) operates only when the statute becomes operative. Another difference between judicial overruling and overruling by statute is that statutes, unlike judges, do not expressly name the decisions which they overrule. Nevertheless it is not usually difficult to identify the cases which are overruled by a statute, particularly where the statute follows closely upon an unpopular decision of a superior court, often the House of Lords.

It appears that in the Supreme Court of the United States there is power to overrule decisions prospectively, that is to apply the earlier decision to the facts of the instant case but to overrule it in so far as it may affect future cases.[1] In the United States Supreme Court the power is held to be based on the common law, though it has never been recognised in this county. However, in *Jones* v. *Secretary of State for Social Services*,[2] a case in which the House of Lords declined to overrule a previous decision of the House although a majority were of the opinion that the *ratio* of the earlier decision was wrong, LORD SIMON advanced the opinion that the most satisfactory method of dealing with the appeal would have been to allow it on the basis that it was covered by the earlier decision but to have overruled the earlier decision prospectively. In the event, however, he simply concurred in allowing the appeal and went on to say that, although an extension of judicial power to include prospective overruling should be considered (a suggestion with which LORD DIPLOCK agreed), it would preferably be the subject of Parliamentary enactment, adding:[3]

> "In the first place, informed professional opinion is probably to the effect that your Lordships have no power to overrule decisions with prospective effect only; such opinion is itself a source of law; and your Lordships, sitting judicially, are bound by any rule of law arising extra-judicially. Secondly, to proceed by Act of Parliament would obviate any suspicion of endeavouring to upset one-sidedly the constitutional balance between executive, legislature and judiciary. Thirdly, concomitant problems could receive consideration—for example whether other courts supreme within their own jurisdictions should have similar powers as regards the rule of precedent; whether machinery could and should be devised to apprise the courts of the potential repercussions of any particular decision; and whether any court (including the appellate committee of your Lordships' House) should sit in banc when invited to review a previous decision."

The passage above illustrates clearly the reasons why it is preferable for major changes in the law to be made by Parliament, rather than by the judiciary.

c Precedents which can be distinguished

The process of "distinguishing" is probably the major factor in enabling the doctrine of precedent to remain flexible and adaptable. Cases are distinguished on their facts. The *ratio decidendi* of a case is, by definition, based upon the

---

[1] *Linkletter* v. *Walker* (1965), 381 U.S. 618, cited in *Jones* v. *Secretary of State for Social Services* (*infra*).
[2] [1972] 1 All E.R. 145; [1972] 2 W.L.R. 210; see p. 132, *post*.
[3] [1972] 1 All E.R., at p. 198; [1972] 2 W.L.R., at p. 271.

material facts of that case. Consequently if the court is willing to regard as material any fact not common to the case before it and the precedent cited, the two cases can be distinguished. The law reports are full of strained distinctions where the court was evidently anxious not to follow an apparently binding precedent. In theory it is possible to distinguish virtually any precedent since factual situations will almost never precisely duplicate themselves. Nevertheless there are practical limits beyond which the court will be unlikely to go. Cases which are indistinguishable⁶ are described as being "on all fours" with one another. To illustrate how fine a distinction may be drawn between ostensibly parallel factual situations reference may be made to two well known cases concerning the tort of conversion. In *England* v. *Cowley*[1] the defendant refused to allow the plaintiff to remove goods from his, the defendant's, premises. This was held not to be conversion since there was no absolute denial of title. This case was distinguished by the Court of Appeal in *Oakley* v. *Lyster*[2] in which the defendant refused to allow the plaintiff to remove material from his, the defendant's, land and, in addition, asserted his own title to the material. This was held to be an act of conversion, the assertion of title apparently making the denial of title absolute.[3]

d   Statements of law made per incuriam

The Court of Appeal in the leading case of *Young* v. *Bristol Aeroplane Co., Ltd.*[4] established the principle that the Court of Appeal was not bound to follow its own earlier decision if satisfied that the decision in question was reached *per incuriam* (through lack of care). This means that some relevant statutory provision or precedent, which might have affected the decision, was not brought to the attention of the court. Although the principle in *Young*'s case was expressed to apply only to the Court of Appeal, it has been applied in other courts. Thus in *R.* v. *Northumberland Compensation Appeal Tribunal, Ex parte Shaw*[5] a divisional court of the King's Bench Division declined to follow a Court of Appeal decision on the ground that the latter had been reached *per incuriam*, a relevant House of Lords decision not having been cited to the Court of Appeal. In *Cassell & Co., Ltd.* v. *Broome*[6] the House of Lords rejected in condemnatory terms the Court of Appeal's decision to the effect that the decision of the House of Lords in *Rookes* v. *Barnard*[7] on the issue of exemplary damages had been reached *per incuriam* because of two previous decisions of the House. LORD

---

[1] (1873), L.R. 8 Exch. 126.   [2] [1931] 1 K.B. 148.
[3] For a further illustration of artificial distinction in the tort of conversion compare *Hiort* v. *Bott* (1874), L.R. 9 Exch. 86 with *Elvin and Powell* v. *Plummer Roddis, Ltd.* (1933), 50 T.L.R. 158.
[4] [1944] K.B. 718; [1944] 2 All E.R. 293 (affirmed [1946] A.C. 163; [1946] 1 All E.R. 98); see p. 133, *post*.
[5] [1951] 1 K.B. 711; [1951] 1 All E.R. 268.
[6] [1972] 1 All E.R. 801; [1972] 2 W.L.R. 645.
[7] [1964] A.C. 1129; [1964] 1 All E.R. 367. This decision had already been subjected to devastating criticism in the courts of the Commonwealth and had been repudiated by the Privy Council; see *Australian Consolidated Press, Ltd.* v. *Uren*, [1969] 1 A.C. 590; [1967] 3 All E.R. 523. No less devastating was the criticism of LORD DENNING, M.R., culminating in the description of the doctrine laid down by LORD DEVLIN in *Rookes* v. *Barnard* as "hopelessly illogical and inconsistent"; *Broome* v. *Cassell & Co., Ltd.*, [1971] 2 All E.R. 187, at p. 199; [1971] 2 W.L.R. 853, at p. 870, an approach which attracted vehement criticism from the majority of the House of Lords.

HAILSHAM, L.C., in the course of the leading speech for the majority, asserted that[1]

> "it is not open to the Court of Appeal to give gratuitous advice to judges of first instance to ignore decisions of the House of Lords in this way"

while LORD REID[2] took the view that it was "obvious that the Court of Appeal failed to understand LORD DEVLIN's speech". The *per incuriam* principle is of limited application. Very few decisions have subsequently been regarded as having been reached *per incuriam* and in *Morelle* v. *Wakeling*[3] a Master of the Rolls stated that such instances should be "of the rarest occurrence", and should be limited to "decisions given in ignorance or forgetfulness of some inconsistent statutory provision or of some authority binding on the court concerned". Thus the doctrine will not be extended to cases which were merely not fully argued or which appear to take a wrong view of the authorities or to misinterpret a statute.

4 The hierarchy of the courts

It has already been noted that the doctrine of binding precedent depends for its operation upon the underlying principle that English courts form a hierarchy with each court standing in a definite position in relation to every other court. The structure of this hierarchy must now be considered for the purposes of the doctrine of precedent.

a House of Lords

The House of Lords stands at the summit of the English hierarchy of courts. Decisions of the House of Lords are binding upon all other courts trying civil or criminal cases, whether or not appeal lies to the House from those courts.

Until recently the House of Lords regarded itself as strictly bound by its own earlier decisions, which were thus immutable except by legislation. This principle was finally established in the case of *London Street Tramways Co.* v. *L.C.C.*[4] at the end of the last century, although in ensuing years the principle had, on occasion, been doubted.[5]

In 1966 the rule in the *London Street Tramways* case was finally discredited. LORD GARDINER, L.C., on behalf of himself and the Lords of Appeal in Ordinary, made a statement to the effect that their Lordships proposed in future to depart from their own earlier decisions where it appeared right to do so.[6] They would, however, bear in mind the danger of disturbing retrospectively financial arrangements and rights in property and the special need for preserving certainty in the criminal law. The Lord Chancellor made it clear, moreover, that this statement was not intended to apply elsewhere than in the House of Lords.

Although this statement was not made in the context of an actual decision it has been regarded as having the force of law, so that the House will depart from its own earlier decision when the occasion arises to do so.

---

1 [1972] 1 All E.R. 801, at p. 809; [1972] 2 W.L.R. 645, at p. 653.
2 [1972] 1 All E.R., at p. 835; [1972] 2 W.L.R., at p. 681.
3 [1955] 2 Q.B. 379; [1955] 1 All E.R. 708.   4 [1898] A.C. 375.
5 See *Myers* v. *Director of Public Prosecutions*, [1965] A.C. 1001; [1964] 2 All E.R. 881; *Scruttons, Ltd.* v. *Midland Silicones, Ltd.*, [1962] A.C. 446; [1962] 1 All E.R. 1.
6 Reported at [1966] 3 All E.R. 77; [1966] 1 W.L.R. 1234.

Nevertheless the practical consequences of this change in the law have been slight. Prior to 1972 in more than five years since LORD GARDINER's statement the House of Lords did not overrule any of its previous decisions. Their reticence is aptly demonstrated by the recent case of *Jones* v. *Secretary of State for Social Services*.[1] In this important case, involving the construction of the National Insurance (Industrial Injuries) Act 1946, a majority of the House (consisting of seven members) declined to overrule a previous decision of the House[2] although a majority of their lordships were of opinion that the *ratio* of the earlier decision was wrong. Since there was no suggestion that the earlier authority could be distinguished it might appear that, a majority of the House being of the opinion that the decision was wrong, there would be no alternative but to overrule it. Three of the majority of four who believed the earlier authority to be wrong were in favour of overruling it and had the fourth, LORD SIMON, agreed, the House would undoubtedly have overruled its own earlier decision. However LORD SIMON gave several reasons why, in his opinion, it would be wrong to depart from *Dowling*'s case, notably that the power to depart from a previous decision "is one to be most sparingly exercised", and that a variation of view on a matter of statutory construction would rarely provide a suitable occasion.

However, the wait for a suitable occasion was not a long one and in *British Railways Board* v. *Herrington*[3] the House, on the question of the extent of the duty of care owed by an occupier of land to trespassers, restated the law and refused to follow the statement of the law, which had stood for over 40 years, laid down in *Addie (R) and Sons (Collieries), Ltd.* v. *Dumbreck*.[4]

Apart from the possibility of the House of Lords being prepared to depart from its own earlier decisions there are three basic means by which a House of Lords decision may lose its authority. First, and most obviously, it may be overruled by statute. Secondly, it may be distinguished. The process of distinguishing applies in the House of Lords as in other courts. Indeed, in the past it has been applied with more force in the House of Lords than elsewhere because there was no other judicial means of avoiding an undesirable precedent. Thus in *Scruttons, Ltd.* v. *Midland Silicones, Ltd.*[5] the House of Lords distinguished its own earlier decision in *Elder, Dempster & Co., Ltd.* v. *Paterson, Zochonis & Co., Ltd.*[6] on the facts even though the legal problem raised in each case, namely whether a stranger to a contract can take advantage of a contractual exemption clause, appeared very similar. Indeed LORD DENNING,

---

[1] [1972] 1 All E.R. 145; [1972] 2 W.L.R 210. The House also came near to so doing in *Conway* v. *Rimmer*, [1968] A.C. 910; [1968] 1 All E.R. 874 when departing from its previous decision in *Duncan* v. *Cammell, Laird & Co., Ltd.*, [1942] A.C. 624; [1942] 1 All E.R. 587. Nevertheless close examination of the speeches seems to indicate that only two of their lordships (LORD MORRIS and LORD HODSON) based their reasoning on a departure from the *ratio* of the earlier case, the majority being able to distinguish that case.
[2] *R.* v. *Deputy Industrial Injuries Commissioner, Ex parte Amalgamated Engineering Union, In re Dowling*, [1967] 1 A.C. 725; [1967] 1 All E.R. 210.
[3] [1972] 1 All E.R. 749; (1972) 2 W.L.R. 537.
[4] [1929] A.C. 358.
[5] [1962] A.C. 446; [1962] 1 All E.R. 1.
[6] [1924] A.C. 522. See also *Adler* v. *Dickson*, [1955] 1 Q.B. 158; [1954] 3 All E.R. 397.

though describing himself as "not unduly attached to the strict doctrine of precedent" doubted whether the cases were distinguishable.

Finally, it is possible for a House of Lords decision to be rejected if given *per incuriam*. This possibility was expressly mentioned by LORD HALSBURY, L.C. in the *London Street Tramways* case. In modern conditions it would be most unlikely for a case to pass through the House of Lords with an important authority not cited. As stated above, the Court of Appeal in *Broome* v. *Cassell & Co., Ltd.*[1] regarded a House of Lords decision as being given *per incuriam* on the basis that two House of Lords authorities were not cited to the House. Reference has already been made to the manner in which the House of Lords disapproved the Court of Appeal's application of the *per incuriam* doctrine. LORD DIPLOCK was alone, however, in going so far as to state that the Court of Appeal had no power to treat a decision of the House of Lords in this way:[2]

> "The Court of Appeal found themselves able to disregard the decision of this House in *Rookes* v. *Barnard* by applying to it the label *per incuriam*. That label is relevant only to the right of an appellate court to decline to follow one of its own previous decisions, not to its right to disregard a decision of a higher appellate court or to the right of a judge of the High Court to disregard a decision of the Court of Appeal."

b Court of Appeal

The precise authority to be accorded to decisions of the Court of Appeal was to some extent rendered uncertain by the Criminal Appeal Act 1966 which transferred the jurisdiction of the former Court of Criminal Appeal to the Court of Appeal. The problems raised by this merger have not yet fallen to be determined but, for the time being, the respective positions of the civil and criminal divisions of the Court of Appeal appear to be as follows.

Civil division—Decisions of the Court of Appeal are binding on all inferior courts trying civil or criminal cases, including divisional courts.[3] There seems to be no reason to suppose that inferior criminal courts will not be bound by decisions of the civil division of the Court of Appeal. The Court of Appeal is bound by decisions of the House of Lords, and by its own earlier decisions.[4] The latter principle was affirmatively established in the leading case of *Young* v. *Bristol Aeroplane Co., Ltd.*[5] LORD GREENE, M.R., who delivered the judgment of the court, cited three exceptional circumstances in which an earlier decision of the Court of Appeal would not be regarded as binding.

(1) Where there are two conflicting decisions, the Court may choose which it will follow, the decision not followed being deemed to be overruled. Thus, in *Fisher* v. *Ruislip-Northwood U.D.C.*[6] the Court, of which LORD GREENE was again a member, was required to choose between conflicting lines of authorities concerning the liability of local authorities to motorists who collided with unlit air-raid shelters.

---

[1] [1971] 2 All E.R. 187; [1971] 2 W.L.R. 853.
[2] *Cassell & Co., Ltd.* v. *Broome*, [1972] 1 All E.R. 801, at p. 874; [1972] 2 W.L.R. 645, at p. 724.
[3] *Brownsea Haven Properties, Ltd.* v. *Poole Corporation*, [1958] Ch. 574; [1958] 1 All E.R. 205.
[4] *Sed quaere*: is it bound by a decision of the Judicial Committee of the Privy Council? See p. 127, *ante*. The Court of Appeal is also bound by decisions of courts which exercised equivalent jurisdiction prior to 1875: the Court of Exchequer Chamber and the Chancery Court of Appeal; see *Ex parte M'George* (1882), 20 Ch.D. 697.
[5] [1944] K.B. 718; [1944] 2 All E.R. 293 (affirmed [1946] A.C. 163; [1946] 1 All E.R. 98).
[6] [1945] K.B. 584; [1945] 2 All E.R. 458.

(2)   The Court is bound to refuse to follow a decision of its own which, though not expressly overruled, cannot stand with a later House of Lords decision.

(3)   The Court is not bound to follow a decision of its own (nor, apparently, a decision of the House of Lords)[1] if that decision was given *per incuriam*. This principle, explained earlier, is not confined to the Court of Appeal.

Recently, however, the principle of *Young* v. *Bristol Aeroplane Co., Ltd.* has been under fire, principally from LORD DENNING, M.R. In *Boys* v. *Chaplin*[2] the Court of Appeal held that it was not bound by an interlocutory decision of two Lord Justices. In *Gallie* v. *Lee*[3] LORD DENNING evinced a desire to depart from the rule in *Young's* case in the following words:[4]

> "We are, of course, bound by the decisions of the House [of Lords], but I do not think we are bound by prior decisions of our own, or at any rate, not absolutely bound. We are not fettered as it was once thought. It was a self-imposed limitation; and we who imposed it can also remove it. The House of Lords have done it. So why should not we do likewise?"

This was, however, a minority opinion. RUSSELL, L.J. saw the position of the House of Lords in quite a different light, saying of the Master of the Rolls:[5]

> "I think that in one respect he has sought to wield a broom labelled 'For the use of the House of Lords only'.... I do not support the suggestion that this court is free to override its own decisions ... the availability of the House of Lords to correct error in the Court of Appeal makes it in my view unnecessary for this court to depart from its existing discipline."

LORD DENNING reiterated in *Hanning* v. *Maitland (No. 2)*[6] his view that:

> "we are no longer absolutely bound by prior decisions of our own, no more than the House of Lords are."

Again in *Barrington* v. *Lee*,[7] a case concerned with liability as between vendor and purchaser in respect of an estate agent's default over a deposit, LORD DENNING, dealing with the effect of the Court of Appeal's decision in *Burt* v. *Claude Cousins & Co., Ltd.*[8] on similar facts boldly asserted:[9]

> "We are not absolutely bound by *Burt's* case. We no longer look to see if the case can be brought within the exceptions stated in *Young* v. *Bristol Aeroplane Co., Ltd.*"

Once again, however, LORD DENNING was expressing a minority view for EDMUND DAVIES and STEPHENSON, L.JJ., though concurring in the result of the appeal by distinguishing *Burt's* case, both re-affirmed the principles of *Young's*

---

[1] *Broome* v. *Cassell & Co., Ltd. (supra).*
[2] [1968] 2 Q.B. 1; [1968] 1 All E.R. 283 (affirmed [1971] A.C. 356; [1969] 2 All E.R. 1085).
[3] [1969] 2 Ch. 17; [1969] 1 All E.R. 1062 (affirmed *sub nom. Saunders* v. *Anglia Building Society,* [1971] A.C. 1004; [1970] 3 All E.R. 961).
[4] [1969] 2 Ch., at p. 37; [1969] 1 All E.R., at p. 1072.
[5] [1969] 2 Ch., at p. 41; [1969] 1 All E.R., at p. 1076; the third member of the court, SALMON, L.J. (as he then was), took a middle view and stated that a change in policy, though possibly desirable, would require a pronouncement of the whole Court of Appeal.
[6] [1970] 1 Q.B. 580, at p. 587; [1970] 1 All E.R. 812, at p. 815.
[7] [1972] 1 Q.B. 326; [1971] 3 All E.R. 1231.
[8] [1971] 2 Q.B. 426; [1971] 2 All E.R. 611.
[9] [1972] 1 Q.B., at p. 338; [1971] 3 All E.R., at p. 1238.

case and disagreed with the view of LORD DENNING quoted above. STEPHENSON, L.J.'s judgment epitomises the traditional approach:[1]

"what may be thought timorous subservience to judicial precedent is, in my judgment, preferable to the uncertainty which will be introduced into the law in fields not easy to delimit by the bolder work of demolition and restoration proposed by LORD DENNING, M.R., in this case ... We must take care lest in struggling to straighten out the law we bend it until it breaks."

The civil division of the Court of Appeal is certainly not bound by decisions of the now defunct Court of Criminal Appeal. It is uncertain whether the civil division will regard itself as bound by decisions of the criminal division of the Court of Appeal, which now exercises that jurisdiction formerly exercised by the Court of Criminal Appeal. The better view appears to be that the civil division will regard itself as bound by decisions of the criminal division so that the inelegant conflict which has, in the past, existed between the civil and criminal appeal courts[2] is now unlikely to recur.

It may be noted finally that a "full court" of five or more judges of the civil division is sometimes convened to hear cases involving particularly important or difficult points of law. The full court of the civil division has, however, no greater authority than the normal court and its decisions carry no more weight as precedents.[3]

Criminal division—Decisions of the criminal division of the Court of Appeal bind inferior courts trying criminal cases, including the divisional court of the Queen's Bench Division, and will probably be regarded as binding upon inferior courts trying civil cases. The division will probably regard itself as bound by decisions of its predecessor, the Court of Criminal Appeal, and by decisions of the civil division of the Court of Appeal subject to the exceptions contained in *Young* v. *Bristol Aeroplane Co., Ltd.*

The Court of Criminal Appeal formulated the principle that it would not be bound by its own previous decision where this would cause injustice to an appellant, the rationale of this principle being that the desire for attaining justice transcends the desirability of certainty, where it appears right to do so. The rule was stated by LORD GODDARD, C.J. in *R.* v. *Taylor*[4] in the following terms:

"This court, however, has to deal with questions involving the liberty of the subject, and if it finds, on reconsideration, that, in the opinion of a full court assembled for that purpose, the law has been either misapplied or misunderstood in a decision which it has previously given, and that, on the strength of that decision, an accused person has been sentenced and imprisoned, it is the bounden duty of the court to reconsider the earlier decision with a view to seeing whether that person had been

---

[1] [1972] 1 Q.B., at p. 345; [1971] 3 All E.R., at p. 1245.
[2] The historic conflict occurred in the cases of *R.* v. *Denyer*, [1926] 2 K.B. 258 (C.C.A.) and *Hardie and Lane* v. *Chiltern*, [1928] 1 K.B. 306 (C.A.) in which the Court of Appeal, on the subject of the legality of trade stop-lists, declined to follow the earlier decision of the Court of Criminal Appeal and expressly disapproved it. The conflict on this point could thus be solved only by the House of Lords and this was done in *Thorne* v. *Motor Trade Association*, [1937] A.C. 797; [1937] 3 All E.R. 157.
[3] This was established in *Young* v. *Bristol Aeroplane Co., Ltd.*, [1944] K.B. 718; [1944] 2 All E.R. 293.
[4] [1950] 2 K.B. 368; [1950] 2 All E.R. 170; overruling *R.* v. *Treanor* (or *McAvoy*), [1939] 1 All E.R. 330.

properly convicted. The exceptions which apply in civil cases ought not to be the only ones applied in such a case as the present."

This rule was adopted by the criminal division of the Court of Appeal in *R. v. Gould.*[1]

In the past, decisions of the Court of Criminal Appeal have been somewhat less reliable as precedents than the decisions of other appellate courts. This is accounted for by the fact that the court rarely reserved judgment, that only one judgment was usually given and that dissents were not recorded. Although the Criminal Appeal Act 1966, s. 2 (4) expressly provides that separate judgments may be pronounced on a question of law, it is probable that precedents of the criminal division of the Court of Appeal will still be regarded with more circumspection than decisions of the civil division.

c High Court

Divisional courts—In civil matters divisional courts are bound by decisions of the House of Lords and Court of Appeal (including, probably, the criminal division), subject to the exceptions set out in *Young v. Bristol Aeroplane Co., Ltd.*,[2] and also by their own earlier decisions. The latter principle was clearly established in *Police Authority for Huddersfield v. Watson.*[3] Divisional court decisions in civil cases are binding on judges of the same division of the High Court sitting alone, and, possibly,[4] on judges of other divisions.[5]

In criminal cases the position of the divisional court of the Queen's Bench Division is closely analogous to that of the criminal division of the Court of Appeal. Thus, it is bound by its own earlier decisions subject to the *caveat* expressed by LORD GODDARD in *R. v. Taylor.*[6] This was decided by LORD GODDARD himself in *Younghusband v. Luftig,*[7] though it was stated in that case that a "full" divisional court of five or more judges has no more power than the normal court of two or three. In *Nicholas v. Penny*[8] the divisional court of the Queen's Bench Division refused to follow its own earlier decision in which important authorities had not been cited to the court.

Judges at first instance—Decisions of High Court judges sitting alone at first instance are binding on inferior courts but are not binding on other High Court judges. For this reason it is a dangerous practice to rely upon principles of law which are contained only in first instance decisions, since they are not binding in any High Court action. Naturally, they are of persuasive authority

---

[1] [1968] 2 Q.B. 65; [1968] 1 All E.R. 849; the necessity for a "full court" of five or more judges seems to have been tacitly abolished; cf. *R. v. Newsome,* [1970] 2 Q.B. 711; [1970] 3 All E.R. 455 which appears to assert greater power for a court of five to depart from the earlier decision of a court of three than a court of three would possess.

[2] See p. 133, *ante: R. v. Northumberland Compensation Tribunal, Ex parte Shaw,* [1952] 1 K.B. 338; [1952] 1 All E.R. 122.

[3] [1947] K.B. 842; [1947] 2 All E.R. 193.

[4] *Bretherton v. United Kingdom Totalisator Co., Ltd.,* [1945] K.B. 555; [1945] 2 All E.R. 202.

[5] See *Re Seaford, Seaford v. Seifert,* [1967] P. 325; [1967] 2 All E.R. 458 (reversed [1968] P. 53; [1968] 1 All E.R. 482) in which a judge of the Probate, Divorce and Admiralty Division regarded himself as bound by a decision of the divisional court of the Queen's Bench Division; cf. *Elderton v. United Kingdom Totalisator Co., Ltd.* (1945), 61 T.L.R. 529; (affirmed [1945] 2 All E.R. 624).

[6] *Supra.*

[7] [1949] 2 K.B. 354; [1949] 2 All E.R. 72.

[8] [1950] 2 K.B. 466; [1950] 2 All E.R. 89.

and a High Court judge will hesitate before "not following" the decision of one of his brethren, if only for reasons of comity. Nevertheless, where a first instance judge is clearly convinced that an earlier decision at first instance is wrong, he will be free to refuse to follow that decision. There have been several direct clashes between decisions of first instance judges, a notable recent example occurring in relation to the subject of the enforceability of solus agreements between petrol companies and garages.[1]

It is sometimes said that judges of the Chancery Division are less willing to depart from decisions of their brethren than are judges of other divisions. This is only true insofar as to depart from any earlier authority might have the effect of disturbing financial arrangements or depriving a person of a vested proprietary right.

d Inferior courts

The Crown Court, magistrates' courts, county courts and other inferior tribunals are bound by the decisions of all superior courts, not excluding first instance decisions of the High Court. The decisions of one inferior court are not binding upon any other inferior court, chiefly because the decisions of inferior courts are not reported.

In conclusion it would probably be optimistic to state categorically that the doctrine of binding precedent as applied in English courts achieves certainty while retaining flexibility. Its operation depends, as with the interpretation of statutes, on the conception of the particular judge or court trying a case of the judicial function. The rules for determining the *ratio decidendi* of a case and the hierarchy of the courts are sufficiently well defined to achieve legal certainty. On the other hand, the *per incuriam* doctrine, the process of distinguishing, the capacity of superior courts to overrule decisions and the absolute power of Parliament to change the law all serve to keep the doctrine flexible. In the last analysis the doctrine of precedent is usually seen to operate fairly, though how far this is attributable to the inherent qualities of the doctrine and how far to the rationalism of English judges is a matter for debate.

C THE HISTORICAL DEVELOPMENT OF LAW REPORTING

As stated at the beginning of this chapter, the doctrine of binding precedent became a part of English law only when the system of law reporting had become comprehensive. The doctrine of precedent, as such, is of far greater antiquity but it was only in the nineteenth century that precedents became

---

[1] In *Esso Petroleum, Ltd.* v. *Harper's Garage (Stourport), Ltd.*, [1966] 2 Q.B. 514; [1965] 2 All E.R. 933, MOCATTA, J., in the Queen's Bench Division, declined to follow the decision of BUCKLEY, J., (as he then was) in the Chancery Division, in the case of *Petrofina, Ltd.* v. *Martin*, [1965] Ch. 1073; [1965] 2 All E.R. 176. The conflict was finally resolved by the House of Lords on appeal in the former case: [1968] A.C. 269; [1967] 1 All E.R. 699. For other illustrations of clashes between first instance judges see: *Receiver for the Metropolitan Police District* v. *Croydon Corporation*, [1956] 1 W.L.R. 1113; [1956] 2 All E.R. 785; and *Monmouthshire C.C.* v. *Smith*, [1957] 1 All E.R. 78; [1956] 1 W.L.R. 1132; *Wood* v. *Luscombe*, [1966] 1 Q.B. 169; [1964] 3 All E.R. 972 and *Randolph* v. *Tuck*, [1962] 1 Q.B. 175; [1961] 1 All E.R. 814: see p. 473, *post*.

binding rather than merely persuasive. As late as 1762 LORD MANSFIELD, a bitter opponent of mulish adherence to precedent, could state:[1]

"the reason and spirit of cases make law, not the letter of particular precedents".

Nevertheless the growth of a comprehensive system of law reporting brought with it the modern doctrine of binding precedent. If it were possible to mark the turning point, the decision of PARKE, B. in *Mirehouse* v. *Rennell* in 1833[2] would appear to herald the evolution of the modern system.

It is, therefore, instructive to trace the evolution of law reporting and, incidentally, to note the methods of citation and reference.

The history of law reporting can be roughly divided into three periods: first, the period of the Year Books extending approximately from 1272 to 1535; secondly, the period of the private named[3] reporters extending from 1535 to 1865 and, thirdly, the modern semi-official system of reporting which began in 1865.

1　The Year Books

The Year Books are the first available law reports. They were first compiled during the reign of Edward I. Exactly what function they were intended to and did fulfil at that time is uncertain. They were certainly not intended for use by the judges as precedents, and were probably simply notes compiled by students and junior advocates for use, by advocates, as guides to pleading and procedure. While they contain legal argument of counsel and notes of exchanges between bench and bar they are very far from being law reports in the modern sense. Since most litigation in the thirteenth and fourteenth centuries took the form of disputes over title to land it is natural to find that most Year Book cases are land law cases, generally being decisions of the Court of Common Pleas.

Although Year Book reports were in no sense official and were not, apparently, intended for use by the judges, there are indications that they may have been used by some judges as a direct source of precedent. Thus in 1310 STANTON, J. referred to a case decided at least ten years earlier[4] while BEREFORD, C.J. in 1312 cited a decision some twenty-five years old.[5] Even allowing for the longevity of judicial recollection of case law, it seems likely that these judges were basing their knowledge upon some written record of the cases in question. By the fifteenth century there are many examples of Year Book cases in which the judge is reported as having relied upon a number of very old authorities. This is the origin of the doctrine of precedent in English law and there is ample evidence[6] that the judges were conscious that their decisions were being recorded for use as precedents.

With the introduction of printing in the fifteenth century many Year Book

---

[1] *Fisher* v. *Prince* (1762), 3 Burr. 1363. This theme runs through many of LORD MANSFIELD's judgments. See, for example: *Jones* v. *Randall* (1774), Cowp. 37; *R.* v. *Bembridge* (1783), 3 Doug. 327.

[2] (1833), 1 Cl. & F. 527.

[3] Private reports are still published, though not, as formerly, under the name of the individual reporter.

[4] *Kembeare* v. *K.*, Y.B. 4 Ed. 2 (S.S. iv), 153. Note the method of citation by regnal year.

[5] *Anon.*, Y.B. 6 Ed. 2 (S.S. xiii), 43.

[6] For examples see Allen, *Law in the Making* (7th Edn.), pp. 190 *et seq.*

manuscripts were printed in the so-called "Black Letter" editions. The most widely used modern printed editions of the Year Books are the Rolls Series (R.S.) and the Selden Society Series (S.S.). Both were published early in the present century and contain the original text of the Year Book manuscripts, which are in "law French", a peculiar combination of Norman French, English and Latin, together with an English translation. Citation of Year Book cases is usually by reference to one of these two editions.

Abridgements

The excellence of the printed editions of the original Year Books which are available has rather lessened the value of the Abridgements. These are merely collections of Year Book cases according to their subject matter in chronological order compiled by judges and lawyers, generally for their own use. Some of these Abridgements were published and may be compared to modern case books. The best known Abridgements are those of Fitzherbert and Brooke, published in 1516 and 1568 respectively.

2 The private reports

Compilation of the Year Books ceased in about 1535. Almost immediately private sets of reports began to be produced, printed and published under the name of the law reporter. At first the private reports were scarcely fuller than the Year Book reports had been. Very soon, however, many sets of private reports became far more detailed, reproducing much of counsel's argument and virtually the whole of the judgment. The private reporters generally attached themselves to one court, probably the court in which they intended to practise, and took notes of the proceedings. These notes would later be revised and published as reports. The citation of precedents became progressively more common as the private reports became more comprehensive.

The private reporters proliferated in the period 1535 to 1865. The standard of reporting varied greatly. At one end of the scale were the reporters whose reports contain what are still regarded today as classic expositions of the common law. These reporters did not, until the end of the eighteenth century, produce their reports contemporaneously with the decisions they were reporting. Consequently the reporter's invention and personality played no little part in the compilation of the reports. This is particularly true of Coke, possibly the greatest of all law reporters. Coke's Reports (Co. Rep.) are so well known as to be citable merely as "Reports" (Rep.). They contain comprehensive expositions of virtually every aspect of the common law supported by a wealth of authority assiduously gleaned from the Year Books and even the ancient Plea Rolls, which Coke had copied for his own use. Coke's great industry and scholarship have made his Reports and text-books a primary literary source of the common law. Nowadays there is rarely any need to look beyond Coke to trace the origin of any common law rule. His Reports, published between 1600 and 1658, contain many of the great constitutional cases of the seventeenth century, such as *Prohibitions del Roy*,[1] *Proclamations*,[2] and *Magdalen College*.[3]

---

[1] (1607), 12 Rep. 63.
[2] (1610), 12 Rep. 74.
[3] (1615), 11 Rep. 666.

It will be observed that Coke was a judge as well as a law reporter. This is true of many of the great reporters, notably Dyer, who was Chief Justice of the Common Pleas, and Saunders, Chief Justice of the King's Bench. To the great names of Coke, Dyer and Saunders may be added those of Plowden and, later, Burrow. Burrow's Reports are of cases in the Court of King's Bench between 1751 and 1772 and thus include many of Lord Mansfield's famous judgments. They are widely regarded as the first set of law reports produced in the modern pattern. They contain headnotes and the argument of counsel is carefully separated from the judgment. Nevertheless they were not contemporaneous reports. The first reports which attempted to be contemporaneous were the Term Reports which are of cases in the King's Bench in the period 1785–1800.

It must not be thought that every one of the private law reporters was a Plowden or a Coke. At the other end of the scale were reporters such as Barnardiston, Atkyns and Espinasse whose reports became virtually uncitable, so low were they held in judicial esteem.[1] Lord Mansfield, in particular, would not permit certain series of reports to be cited to him, while HOLT, C.J. observed feelingly that "these scambling reports ... will make us appear to posterity for a parcel of blockheads".[2]

Citation of private reports

The private reports are cited by the name of the reporter (usually abbreviated) and a volume and page number. The date of the report is not part of the reference but is usually inserted in ordinary round (not square) brackets. Thus the reference to the case of *Ashford* v. *Thornton* is

(1818), 1 B. & Ald. 405

which indicates that the case is reported in volume 1 of Barnewall and Alderson's Reports at page 405. The reference to *Pillans* v. *Van Mierop*,

(1765), 3 Burr. 1663

indicates that the case can be found in the third volume of Burrow's Reports at page 1663.

In practice most law libraries have the reports of the private reporters in the reprinted edition known as "The English Reports" (E.R. or Eng. Rep.). The English Reports are published in 176 volumes and contain all the available reports of the private reporters. With the English Reports is published a reference chart showing in which volume the reports of any individual reporter are contained.

3 The present system of law reporting

a The Law Reports

In 1865 the system of private reporting gave way to the system which still exists at the present day. A Council was established to publish, as cheaply as possible, reports of decisions of superior courts. The Council was, from its inception, under professional control and contained representatives of the Inns of Court and The Law Society. The Council was incorporated in 1870 as the

---

[1] For an assessment of the relative merits of the private reporters see Allen, *Law in the Making* (7th Edn.), pp. 221 *et seq.*
[2] *Slater* v. *May* (1704), 2 Ld. Raym. 1072.

Incorporated Council of Law Reporting for England and Wales.[1] The reports which the Council produces are described simply as the "Law Reports" and have superseded most of the private series of reports. The Law Reports are not an official publication but, by convention, they are the series of reports to which counsel should refer when citing a case which is reported in the Law Reports.[2] In addition the judges are given the opportunity of revising reports of their own judgments. The reporters for the Law Reports are, of course, barristers and they must be present in court when judgment is delivered. This demonstrates that, even at the present day, a precedent is not citable merely because it is reported but only if it is vouched for by a barrister who was present when judgment was delivered.

b The Weekly Law Reports

Up to and including 1952 the Incorporated Council of Law Reporting published "Weekly Notes" (W.N.). These reports were in the form of a current précis and did not enjoy the authority of the Law Reports. They were, indeed, not strictly citable as reports.[3]

Weekly Notes were replaced in 1953 by the Weekly Law Reports. The Weekly Law Reports include a report of every decision which will ultimately appear in the Law Reports proper. The cases are reported in full, except that legal argument is omitted because of the restriction on space. In addition many cases are published in the Weekly Law Reports which it is not intended to include subsequently in the Law Reports. These cases are published in Volume 1 of the Weekly Law Reports whereas cases which are destined to reach the Law Reports are published in Volumes 2 and 3.

c Citation of the Law Reports and the Weekly Law Reports

The citation of the Law Reports prior to 1891 was somewhat complex. Before 1875 a case was cited by reference to the court in which it was decided and a serial number dating from 1865, prefixed by the letters L.R. The date, not being part of the reference, was inserted in ordinary round brackets. Thus

> *Irving v. Askew* (1870), L.R. 5 Q.B. 208

was reported in the fifth volume of Reports of cases in the Court of Queen's Bench at page 208.

Between 1875 and 1890 citation was by an abbreviation of the appropriate division of the High Court (Ch. D.; Q.B.D.; P.D.; C.P.D.; Ex. D.[4]) or App. Cas. for an appeal case. The date was still not part of the reference and the serial number dated from 1875. The prefix L.R. was dropped. An example of citation during this period is

> *Symons v. Rees* (1876), 1 Ex. D. 416.

---

[1] The Council is a charity; *Incorporated Council of Law Reporting for England and Wales* v. *A.-G.*, [1972] Ch. 73; [1971] Ch. 626; [1971] 3 All E.R. 1029.

[2] An advantage of the Law Reports over other series is that legal argument, as well as the judgments, is published. Where the court has adjourned to take time to consider its decision judgment is said to be "reserved". This fact is indicated in reports by the insertion of the words *curia advisari vult* (*cur. ad. vult* or *c.a.v.*) before the judgment. Reserved judgments are generally accorded greater weight than *ex tempore* judgments.

[3] See *Re Loveridge*, [1902] 2 Ch. 859, at p. 865, *per* BUCKLEY, J.

[4] The last two were abolished in 1880 with the fusion of the Common Pleas Division and the Exchequer Division into the Queen's Bench Division; see p. 59, *ante*.

In 1891 the date was, for the first time, made part of the reference in place of a serial number and the letter D. (for Division) was dropped. The fact that the date is part of the reference is signified by its inclusion in square brackets. There is a separate volume of Reports for each division of the High Court (Q.B.; Ch.; Fam.[1]) and a separate volume for House of Lords and Privy Council cases (A.C.).[2] Court of Appeal decisions are reported in the volume for the division of the High Court from which the appeal came. County court appeals and appeals to the criminal division of the Court of Appeal are usually reported in the volume for the Queen's Bench Division. There is thus nothing in the reference to distinguish a Court of Appeal decision from a decision at first instance. This is the modern method of citation.

In the case of the Weekly Law Reports the year is, as with the Law Reports, part of the reference and appears in square brackets. There is, however, no attempt to classify cases by the court in which they were decided. All cases appear in 1 W.L.R., 2 W.L.R. or 3 W.L.R. irrespective of whether they are House of Lords or first instance decisions.

d Other series of reports

A case which is reported in the Law Reports should be cited by its Law Report reference in preference to any other reference, though only as a matter of practice. Although the Law Reports superseded most of the series of private reports, certain series of private reports are still published. The most highly regarded of these private reports are the All England Law Reports. These are published weekly and their virtue lies principally in the speed with which they follow the decision. In addition many cases are reported in the All England Law Reports which do not find their way into the Law Reports. The All England Law Reports are cited by the year in square brackets followed by the abbreviation All E.R. and a page number. There are usually three volumes of All England Law Reports published each year though, unlike the Weekly Law Reports, there is no significance in the volume number.

The Law Journal Reports (L.J.) and Law Times Reports (L.T.) have been incorporated in the All England Law Reports. The Times Law Reports (T.L.R.) have also ceased to function independently. However, the Criminal Appeal Reports (C.A.R. or Cr. App. Rep.), first published shortly after the creation of the Court of Criminal Appeal, are still produced and report a number of criminal cases not reported elsewhere. Similarly Lloyd's List Law Reports (Lloyd's Rep.) contain a number of commercial cases not reported elsewhere while the Road Traffic Reports (R.T.R.) contain, as the title would suggest, reports of road traffic cases. Periodicals such as the *Solicitors' Journal*, *Justice of the Peace*, *Estate Gazette* and *Current Law* include notes of cases to which

---

[1] When the Family Division was named the Probate, Divorce and Admiralty Division, this volume of Reports was cited by the letter P.

[2] It may be noted that when a case reaches the House of Lords (or Privy Council or divisional court on appeal) the appellant's name is cited first. Thus, for example, the case known in the Court of Appeal as *Lever Brothers, Ltd.* v. *Bell*, [1931] 1 K.B. 557 became *Bell* v. *Lever Brothers, Ltd.*, [1932] A.C. 161 in the House of Lords because the defendant, Bell, was the appellant in the House of Lords. The same method of citation prevails in criminal cases with the additional oddity that the *Director of Public Procecutions* is substituted for *Rex* (or *Regina*), a practice which appears to date from *Director of Public Prosecutions* v. *Beard*, [1920] A.C. 479.

reference may be made in the absence of a full report in a recognised series.[1] Among newspapers only the reports of *The Times* are commonly cited (not to be confused with the Times Law Reports).

The chief criticism which may be advanced of the present system of law reporting in England is its informality. Although there cannot be many cases of importance which escape the elaborate net of the law reporters there are undoubtedly some. The citation of unreported cases in court is still by no means unknown while the citation of cases reported only in series of reports other than the Law Reports is quite common.[2]

A second criticism of the system is the unnecessary duplication of effort. Many cases are reported more or less fully in three or four different series of reports and noted in many periodicals.

On the initiative of the then Lord Chancellor a Committee was set up to report on the state of law reporting. Its report, published in 1940, was somewhat negative in character. It rejected the proposal to grant a monopoly to the Incorporated Council of Law Reporting, being content to state that the Law Reports should be cited in preference to any other series. The Committee also rejected, in the interest of publicity of judicial proceedings, a proposal to grant licences to reporters without which they would be incompetent to report. Most of the positive recommendations in the 1940 Report were contained in the minority report of Professor Goodhart. Professor Goodhart's main suggestion was that each court, through an official shorthand writer and the judge, should produce an authenticated transcript which would be filed with the court records. Copies of these transcripts would be available for sale to law reporters and other interested persons. This would amount to making law reports official. The majority of the Committee rejected Professor Goodhart's proposal as expensive and inconvenient. At the present day the main objection to Professor Goodhart's proposal would be the additional strain it would impose upon an already overworked judiciary. Also there is no reason to suppose that important decisions would not become lost in the archives of the Public Record Office unless there were a comprehensive system of indexing and filing which would be certain to involve great expense in its installation and maintenance.[3]

---

[1] See *Worthy* v. *Lloyd*, [1939] 2 K.B. 612; [1939] 1 All E.R. 474.

[2] For examples see Allen, *Law in the Making* (7th Edn.) pp. 367 *et seq*; see also *Barrington* v. *Lee*, [1971] 3 All E.R. 1231; [1971] 3 W.L.R. 962 from which it appears that the Court of Appeal in *Ryan* v. *Pilkington*, [1959] 1 All E.R. 689; [1959] 1 W.L.R. 403 may have gone wrong because two important unreported authorities were not before the Court. These cases, decided in 1948 and 1958 have since been reported (in [1971] 2 All E.R. 628, 631; [1971] 2 W.L.R. 939, 942).

[3] The modern phenomenon of the computer could, it has been suggested, obviate this difficulty.

CHAPTER 8

Text Books

A text book differs from a statute or a law report in that it is not an original literary source of law. Text books, even if of the highest authority, contain only opinions as to the state of the law. In short they are descriptive rather than creative. Nevertheless it would be unrealistic in any consideration of the literary sources of English law to ignore text books for they are, in some cases, the earliest authority for the existence of a common law rule. The importance of text books as a source of law is, historically, in inverse proportion to the availability of law reports. Thus, in modern times text books are of comparatively little value since direct authority can almost always be found in a law report. Conversely, in the infancy of law reporting when such reports as existed were of a highly personalised nature the text books were, and are, the main source of authority. Indeed the line between a law report and a text book opinion is often a narrow one, particularly in the case of Coke whose *Institutes* (*Inst.*) are cited quite as often as his Reports and are generally accorded equivalent authority.

It will thus be apparent that there are two types of legal text book. The first is the ancient text book which is commonly used as an original source of common law. This type of book is a book of authority. The second type of text book is the modern text book which, however well respected and frequently cited, is not a book of authority. That is to say it is not a source of law and is only of use in that it indicates where a direct source, such as a statute or a law report, may be found. The dividing line between books of authority and modern text books is purely historical and depends, as stated above, on the availability of direct literary sources. Blackstone's *Commentaries on the Laws of England*, published in 1765, is probably the watershed in that, although it is often cited as a book of authority, it was also the forerunner of the modern text book.

A SOME BOOKS OF AUTHORITY

Text books of English law have not become books of authority merely by reason of their antiquity. Of the many works produced as legal text books, only about a dozen are universally accepted by the legal profession and the judiciary alike as books of authority. It is no accident that almost all the authors of these works were judges. The academic lawyer in the modern sense did not appear until Blackstone, in the eighteenth century, and Blackstone himself was also a judge. The following are some of the major text book writers whose works may be said to be sources of English law.

1 Glanvill and Bracton

Glanvill's treatise *De Legibus et Consuetudinibus Angliae* (concerning the laws and customs of England), written in about 1187, is the first major commentary on the common law in existence. Written in Latin, the manuscripts merely indicate that the treatise was written in the time of Glanvill who was Henry II's chief justiciar,[1] so that it is doubtful whether Glanvill was personally responsible for its composition. The subject matter of the treatise principally concerns land law, the basis of the common law. The form of the treatise set the pattern for legal writing for centuries to come in that it approached the common law from the standpoint of procedure, setting out the existing forms of action with a commentary on the scope of each. Glanvill is still cited as a book of authority[2] though not as frequently as the larger and more comprehensive treatise of Bracton.

Bracton's treatise, written in about 1250, was, like Glanvill's treatise, written in Latin and intituled *De Legibus et Consuetudinibus Angliae*. Although uncompleted it is a far more ambitious and comprehensive survey of English law than Glanvill's work. It adopted Glanvill's pattern of a summary of the forms of action glossed with a commentary but went further in that it illustrated the commentaries with case law. The cases in Bracton's treatise are set out very fully, generally including as much detail as the Year Books. In addition the treatise contains a long exposition of English law by way of introduction. Bracton appears to have been thoroughly grounded in Roman law and his treatise draws many Roman law analogies. Virtually all the principles of Roman law which have found their way into English law have done so *via* Bracton.[3] Perhaps the best known case in which Bracton's civilian analogies have been adopted into English law is *Coggs* v. *Bernard*[4] in which HOLT ,C.J. developed the law of bailments in accordance with Roman law concepts gleaned from Bracton. The development of the law of easements also owes much to Bracton's exposition of Roman law.[5] Nevertheless, Bracton is first and foremost a chronicler of the common law and his treatise stands as the major academic work on the common law prior to Coke's *Institutes*.

2 Littleton

After Bracton there is no book of authority until the late fifteenth century when Littleton's treatise *Of Tenures* was published. This important work was the first comprehensive study of English land law which was, at the time, exceedingly complex. The work differs from that of Bracton in that it approaches the

---

[1] The justiciar was the forerunner of the Chancellor.
[2] See, for example: *Ashford* v. *Thornton* (1818), 1 B. & Ald. 405; *Warner* v. *Sampson*, [1959] 1 Q.B. 297; [1959] 1 All E.R. 120.
[3] See p. 52, *ante*.
[4] (1703), 2 Ld. Raym. 909.
[5] *Dalton* v. *Angus* (1881), 6 App. Cas. 740.

subject from the standpoint of substantive law rather than of procedure.   Also it appears that the work was intended for use as a text book and it was, in fact, used for this purpose for centuries after its composition.   Coke's praise of Littleton was fulsome and he described the work as being of absolute perfection, "the ornament of the common law, and the most perfect and absolute work that ever was written in any human science".   Indeed, the first of Coke's *Institutes* is a commentary on Littleton's *Of Tenures*.

The work is also notable as being the first major legal work to be printed, rather than written.

3   Coke

Probably the greatest of text book writers was Coke himself.   This may be added to his other accomplishments as a judge, Parliamentarian and law reporter. Coke's great contribution to academic literature, apart from the Reports which undoubtedly contain much subjective exposition, are his *Institutes of the Laws of England*.   Coke's *Institutes* were composed chiefly towards the end of his life after he had ceased to hold judicial office.   They are so well known as to be citable merely as *Inst.* without reference to the author.

There are four *Institutes*.   The first, published in 1628, is a treatise on Littleton's *Of Tenures* and is commonly cited as *Co. Litt.*   The second, and perhaps least valuable, Institute is a summary of the principal medieval statutes.   The third is concerned with criminal law, defining and describing all the Pleas of the Crown, and the fourth Institute deals with the jurisdiction of the courts.   The reason for the exalted position of the *Institutes* as a direct source of the common law is Coke's acquaintance with the Year Books.   Coke's mastery of the Year Books has probably never been equalled and his recollection in the *Institutes* is so accurate that, even shortly after his death, virtually no one would look beyond Coke as a direct source.   For this reason the Year Books are cited comparatively infrequently while the *Institutes* have been cited to English courts probably more frequently than any other book of authority.

The only weakness in Coke's work is his total devotion to the common law to the exclusion of every other branch of English law.   His total abhorrence of equity and admiralty undoubtedly did much to maintain the separate administration of these branches of the law for so long.

4   Blackstone

After Coke a large number of legal text books were produced.   A few of these, such as the works of Hale, Hawkins and Foster are citable as books of authority particularly in relation to the criminal law.[1]   Due to the poverty of early reports of criminal cases judges, when faced with a question of basic principles of criminal law, usually look no further than the early text books, particularly those of Coke, Hale, Hawkins, Foster and Blackstone.   In the leading case of *Joyce* v. *Director of Public Prosecutions*[2] the House of Lords, in deciding that a foreigner who enjoyed the protection of the Crown could be guilty of treason under the Treason Act 1351, relied almost entirely on Foster's *Crown Cases*,

---

[1] See *Ashford* v. *Thornton* (1818), 1 B. & Ald. 405; *R.* v. *Casement*, [1917] 1 K.B. 98; *Joyce* v. *Director of Public Prosecutions*, [1946] A.C. 347; [1946] 1 All E.R. 186.
[2] [1946] A.C. 347; [1946] 1 All E.R. 186.

Hale's *Pleas of the Crown*, Hawkins' *Pleas of the Crown*, East's *Pleas of the Crown* and Coke's *Institutes*. More recently, in defining the common law offence of affray in the House of Lords, LORD GARDINER, L.C. referred (*inter alia*) to Fitzherbert, Coke, Hale, Hawkins and Blackstone.[1]

Blackstone's *Commentaries on the Laws of England*, published in 1765, is probably the last book of authority to be written. It differs from works such as those of Hale and Hawkins in that it covers a far wider field. The four books comprising the *Commentaries* deal with constitutional law, family law, the law of real and personal property, succession, contract and tort, criminal law and civil and criminal procedure. It is, however, in the fields of tort and criminal law that Blackstone's authority is greatest. The authority of the *Commentaries* is rather less weighty than the authority of the earlier works cited in this section. There are two reasons for this. First, the scope of the work is so wide that it cannot do more than state principles where works of narrower range can probe detail. Secondly, the *Commentaries* are later in point of time than Coke, Hale, Foster and the others so that in the event of an inconsistency between them the earlier work is almost bound to prevail. This is well illustrated by the recent case of *Button v. Director of Public Prosecutions*[2] in which a statement in Blackstone[3] to the effect that a common law affray could take place only in a public place was rejected by the House of Lords as inconsistent with earlier statements in the works of Hale and Hawkins.

B MODERN TEXT BOOKS

The growth of law reporting after Blackstone's era and the fact that the basic principles of the common law were well established and chronicled by that time have made it unnecessary to look at any more recent text book as a direct source of a common law rule. Nineteenth-century works such as Stephen's *Commentaries on the Laws of England* are sometimes consulted but only as guides, not as sources. They are not books of authority. There are, in addition, many standard text books widely used by the legal profession, and even by judges, which are of the highest persuasive authority. Virtually every branch of the law has its standard work and the judge will think twice before gainsaying a statement of law appearing in such a work. Nevertheless judges never lose sight of the fact that these works are not books of authority and, in the event of a statement in a standard text book being inconsistent with a principle contained in a precedent or a statute, the latter will always prevail. For example, in the recent case of *Watson v. Thomas S. Whitney & Co., Ltd.*[4] the Court of Appeal, in deciding that an appeal from the registrar of the (now defunct) Liverpool Court of Passage lay to the Court of Appeal, declined to adopt clear statements in Halsbury's *Laws of England* and the *Annual Practice 1966*, p. 1752, to the effect that the appeal lay to the divisional court of the Queen's Bench Division. Similarly, in *Button v. Director of Public Prosecutions*[5] the House of Lords drew attention to errors in Archbold's *Pleading, Evidence & Practice in Criminal Cases* and Russell

---

[1] *Button v. Director of Public Prosecutions*, [1966] A.C. 591; [1965] 3 All E.R. 587.
[2] *Supra.*
[3] 4 Comm. 145.
[4] [1966] 1 All E.R. 122; [1966] 1 W.L.R. 57.
[5] *Supra.*

on *Crimes and Misdemeanours*, both standard works on the criminal law. In *Shenton* v. *Tyler*[1] the then Master of the Rolls, in considering the scope of marital privilege, referred to some dozen text books on evidence, including those of Best, Cockle, Phipson and Stephen, before deciding that all were wrong.

The above, however, are exceptional occurrences. On the whole the persuasive authority of a standard text book is of considerable weight. There have been several cases in which a court has been willing to accept almost *verbatim* the view of a distinguished academician upon the law. Thus the description of easements contained in Cheshire's *Modern Real Property* was adopted by the Court of Appeal in *Re Ellenborough Park*,[2] while the House of Lords in *Attorney-General* v. *De Keyser's Royal Hotel, Ltd.*[3] expressly accepted Dicey's definition of the royal prerogative. To go one step further, counsel for the respondents in *Rookes* v. *Barnard*[4] postulated the rather startling proposition that the tort of intimidation had been created by Sir John Salmond in his leading work on the law of torts.

There was formerly a rule of practice that a text book could not be cited in court during the lifetime of its author. The rule, which appears to have rested on no very logical foundation, has now been discounted and several text book writers, and even the authors of articles in legal periodicals, have had the satisfaction of seeing their opinions judicially endorsed during their own lifetimes.[5]

---

[1] [1939] Ch. 620; [1939] 1 All E.R. 827.
[2] [1956] Ch. 131; [1955] 3 All E.R. 667.
[3] [1920] A.C. 508.
[4] [1964] A.C. 1129; [1964] 1 All E.R. 367.
[5] See, for example, *Performing Right Society, Ltd.* v. *Mitchell and Booker (Palais de Dance), Ltd.*, [1924] 1 K.B. 762; *Read* v. *J. Lyons & Co., Ltd.*, [1945] K.B. 216; [1945] 1 All E.R. 106 (affirmed [1947] A.C. 156; [1946] 2 All E.R. 471).

PART III

The Administration of Justice

SUMMARY

CHAPTER 9

The Royal Prerogative

Historically the Sovereign is the fountain of justice in England. For this reason the administration of justice is, strictly speaking, a prerogative of the Crown. This prerogative has, however, been substantially whittled away. Thus it was decided by COKE, C.J. in the case of *Prohibitions del Roy*,[1] that the King (James I) could not, in his own person, judge any case. The general immunity from civil proceedings which the Crown enjoyed at common law has been drastically curtailed by the Crown Proceedings Act 1947, although the personal immunity which the Sovereign enjoys from both civil and criminal proceedings remains. It is customarily accepted that the Crown no longer has a general power to create new courts by prerogative although it can, apparently, create courts to administer only the common law. This was established by the Privy Council in *Re Lord Bishop of Natal*.[2] Nevertheless this power is worthless since any court so created would be powerless to apply any rules of law other than common law rules and would, presumably, have difficulty in obtaining Parliamentary authority for the finance required to maintain such a court.[3]

Most of the remaining vestiges of prerogative control over the administration of justice are now found in formality rather than in substance. The superior courts are termed the "Queen's Courts" and the judges of those courts styled "Her Majesty's Judges". All proceedings, whether civil or criminal, are pursued in the name of the Queen. Writs in civil actions are issued in the name of the Queen and all criminal proceedings are conducted on behalf of the Crown, usually in the Queen's name. These so-called prerogatives are, however, illusory. Judges are appointed "on the advice of" the Lord Chancellor or, in some cases, the Prime Minister. There is no power in the Crown to intervene in civil proceedings and criminal proceedings may usually be commenced by any private individual. The substantial remnants of the royal prerogative over the administration of justice are few. Among them may be included the

---

[1] (1607), 12 Co. Rep. 63.
[2] (1865), 3 Moo. P.C. N.S. 115.
[3] The creation of the Criminal Injuries Compensation Board is, however, a recent example of a tribunal created by prerogative act; see p. 186, *post*.

power of the Attorney-General to stop a prosecution on indictment by entering a *nolle prosequi*, the power to pardon a convicted person and the prerogative of mercy under which the Crown may, through the Home Secretary, suspend, commute or remit any sentence.

Thus the administration of justice has gradually become a function which is independent of the Crown although the bodies which in practice administer the English judicial system derive their jurisdiction directly or indirectly from the Crown. The two chief organs of the administration of justice are Parliament and the courts. The general legislative power of Parliament is described elsewhere in this book.[1] Consequently the remainder of this section is concerned with examining the constitution and jurisdiction of the courts of law, and the roles and positions of the individuals who administer justice in the courts; the judges, juries and the legal profession. Finally there is a description of the legal aid scheme which is an increasingly important factor in the contemporary administration of justice.

---

[1] See p. 93, *ante*.

CHAPTER 10

The Courts

A INTRODUCTION

All English courts derive their jurisdiction directly or indirectly from the Crown, the jurisdiction of judges being, in theory, an extension of the royal prerogative. There are, within the English legal system, a large number of courts of varying degrees of standing and jurisdiction. There are various ways of classifying courts. The two fundamental divisions of English courts are; (1) courts of record and courts not of record; and (2) superior and inferior courts. Before explaining further the significance of this classification it may be noted that there are other classifications, though these are not of universal application. Thus it is possible to classify courts according to their functions. The obvious classification in this respect would be into courts of civil and courts of criminal jurisdiction. This classification is not, however, a valid one since, although certain courts do exercise a purely civil or criminal jurisdiction, most English courts hear both civil and criminal cases. Thus the House of Lords, Court of Appeal, High Court, Crown Court and magistrates' courts exercise jurisdiction in both civil and criminal matters. A second classification would be into courts of original and courts of appellate jurisdiction. Nor is this division of general application. Although certain courts, such as the Court of Appeal and the House of Lords, exercise a purely appellate jurisdiction, while other courts, such as magistrates' courts, have no appellate jurisdiction, many courts, notably the High Court and the Crown Court, exercise both original and appellate jurisdiction.

1 Superior and inferior courts

A traditional classification of English courts is their division into superior and inferior courts. The nature of superior courts is that their jurisdiction is limited neither by the value of the subject matter of an action nor geographically. The jurisdiction of inferior courts is limited both geographically and according to the value of the subject matter of the dispute. The superior courts are the House of Lords, Court of Appeal, High Court, Crown Court, Judicial Committee of the Privy Council, Restrictive Practices Court and the National Industrial Relations Court. One of the distinctive features of inferior courts is that they are amenable to the supervisory jurisdiction of the High Court exercised by prerogative order,[1] though this applies also to the Crown Court in the exercise of its appellate jurisdiction even though the Crown Court is, as stated above, a superior court.[2] The most important of the inferior courts are county courts and magistrates' courts although all courts not listed above as superior are inferior courts.

2   Courts of record

An ancient division of courts is into courts of record and courts which are not courts of record. The basic historical distinction depended upon whether or not the court in question maintained a record of its proceedings. The records of courts of record are preserved in the Public Record Office. Courts of record may be inferior or superior. The essential characteristic of a court of record is no longer that it maintains a record; it is that it has power to punish for contempt. Consequently any court which has jurisdiction to punish contempt is a court of record. The jurisdiction of inferior courts of record, such as the county courts, to punish contempt is generally limited to contempt committed in the face of the court whereas superior courts of record have far wider powers to commit for contempt. Conduct which would amount to contempt if committed before a court of record but which is committed before a court which is not a court of record, a magistrates' court for example, may be punished by the High Court as a contempt.[3]

Before considering individually the constitution and jurisdiction of English courts attention may be drawn to the general principle that courts should sit in public. Ever since the abolition of the Court of Star Chamber English judges have rebelled against the notion of private sittings of courts. In the famous words of LORD HEWART, C.J. in *R. v. Sussex Justices, Ex parte McCarthy*:[4]

> "A long line of cases shows that it is not merely of some importance but is of fundamental importance that justice should not only be done, but should manifestly and undoubtedly be seen to be done."

This is not to say that English courts never sit in private. There are several situations in which courts are justified in sitting *in camera*. These are, principally, in wardship proceedings, proceedings involving a secret process, cases involving evidence of sexual capacity in suits for nullity of marriage, proceedings relating to declarations of legitimacy, certain proceedings for financial relief in matrimonial causes, juvenile court proceedings,[5] proceedings under the Official Secrets Act[6] and other proceedings where the presence of the public would make the administration of justice impracticable.[7] In addition where an appeal

---

[1] See p. 164, *post*.
[2] See p. 165, *post*.
[3] *R. v. Davies*, [1906] 1 K.B. 32; see p. 196, *post*.
[4] [1924] 1 K.B. 256, at p. 259; see also *Scott v. Scott*, [1913] A.C. 417.
[5] Though *bona fide* representatives of the press may not be excluded: Children and Young Persons Act 1933, s. 37.
[6] Official Secrets Act 1920, s. 8.
[7] The National Industrial Relations Court may sit in private in certain cases; Industrial Relations Act 1971, Sch. 3, part II, para. 20; Industrial Court Rules 1971, r. 66.

or an application for leave to appeal is brought against the decision of a court which had power to sit in private, the appellate court has similar power.[1]

In exercising its discretion whether to conduct proceedings *in camera*, the court must take into account the effect of publicity on the parties, particularly in relation to their health and occupations and on third parties who, for example, might be distressed by the disclosure of family secrets and weigh against that the value of publicity in eliciting further evidence and the traditional rule of public policy that justice should be administered publicly.[2] Where the public is wrongly excluded from proceedings, those proceedings may be set aside.[3]

It is now necessary to consider the constitution and jurisdiction of English courts.

B THE HOUSE OF LORDS

1 Constitution and procedure

Parliament is the oldest court of the common law although it is not usual nowadays to refer to it as a court. Nevertheless reference is still made to the High Court of Parliament as a judicial body. Leaving aside the jurisdiction of each House to regulate its own procedure, the judicial function of Parliament is now exercised by the House of Lords.

In theory, though not in fact, an appeal to the House of Lords is an appeal to the whole House, not merely to those members who are in fact sitting to hear the appeal. Until the nineteenth century this was literally true in that any member of the House could and did vote in judicial sessions. Not unnaturally decisions of the House of Lords at that time enjoyed no very great authority, particularly since those peers who were lawyers and took the most prominent part in the exercise of the House's jurisdiction were by no means the senior and most respected judges of their day, a remark which also applies to certain Lord Chancellors of the nineteenth century. As a matter of practice puisne judges were frequently invited to advise their Lordships on the law. Indeed this is still possible though it does not appear to have been done since 1898.[4] However it was not until the Appellate Jurisdiction Act 1876 provided for the creation of salaried life peers to hear appeals that the convention against lay peers participating in judicial sittings of the House was firmly established.[5]

This Act provided that at the hearing of an appeal there should be present at least three of the following—the Lord Chancellor, the Lords of Appeal in Ordinary ("law lords") and such peers who hold or have held "high judicial office" as defined in the Act. In practice most appeals are heard solely by the Lords of Appeal in Ordinary. These are the senior members of the judiciary and are generally appointed from the ranks of the Court of Appeal, though exceptionally a first instance judge may be elevated directly to the "chill and

---

[1] Domestic and Appellate Proceedings (Restriction of Publicity) Act 1968, s. 1.
[2] *Barritt* v. *A.-G.*, [1971] 3 All E.R. 1183; [1971] 1 W.L.R. 1713.
[3] *McPherson* v. *McPherson*, [1936] A.C. 177.
[4] *Allen* v. *Flood*, [1898] A.C. 1.
[5] An earlier attempt to create life peers by prerogative had been rejected by the House— *Wensleydale Peerage Case* (1856), 5 H.L.Cas. 958.

distant heights". They must either have held high judicial office for two years or be practising barristers of not less than fifteen years' standing.[1] They have the same rights as other peers but in practice they sit on the cross benches and take no part in political sittings of the House unless the matter concerns the administration of justice. By custom, one or two of the law lords are Scots and the Scottish members generally sit when the House is hearing appeals from the Court of Session, which is the Scottish equivalent of the Court of Appeal. The number of law lords, originally fixed at two, is now not less than seven nor more than eleven.[2]

Argument in appeals no longer takes place, as it used to do, in the chamber of the House. The appeal is argued in one of the committee rooms, their lordships sitting unrobed. The opinions of their lordships are not usually read in the chamber[3] although they retire to the chamber to state whether they would allow or dismiss the appeal. These opinions are not strictly "judgments" but speeches in support of the members' votes on the motion made by the Lord Chancellor or senior Lord. Where the House is equally divided the appeal is dismissed. Equal division does not in practice occur because an uneven number of members invariably sits. Nevertheless the situation has arisen on a few occasions and arose recently in the case of *Kennedy* v. *Spratt*.[4] In that case the appeal would have been dismissed by a majority of three to two but for the fact that one of the majority, LORD UPJOHN, died between the hearing of the appeal and the delivery of judgment having, however, recorded his opinion before his death. In the result, the votes being equal, the appeal was dismissed in any event.[5] The House of Lords has no power to pass judgment. It may only remit the case to the trial judge with its recommendations which must then be translated by the judge into a judgment.

2   Jurisdiction

a   Original jurisdiction

The House of Lords has very little original jurisdiction. The right of a peer to be "tried by his peers", which was thought to have been created by Magna Carta, was finally abolished by the Criminal Justice Act 1948 and now all persons, whether peer or commoner, are subject to the ordinary jurisdiction of the English criminal courts.

Impeachment is a procedure whereby persons may be prosecuted by the House of Commons before the House of Lords. It has always been confined to the prosecution of political offenders. Although impeachment has not been abolished it is in practice obsolete and the jurisdiction has not been exercised

---

[1] Appellate Jurisdiction Act 1876, s. 6.
[2] Appellate Jurisdiction Act 1947; Administration of Justice Act 1968, s. 1 (1) (*a*); this number may be increased by Order in Council (*ibid.*, s. 1 (2)).
[3] See *Practice Direction*, [1963] 1 W.L.R. 1382.
[4] [1971] 1 All E.R. 805; [1971] 2 W.L.R. 667.
[5] See *Kennedy* v. *Spratt* (*Background Note*), [1972] A.C. 99. Had LORD UPJOHN's written opinion indicated that he was in favour of allowing the appeal an anomalous situation would have arisen whereby his death would, in effect, have deprived the appellant of success. In such an event the members of the House would surely have changed their votes so that the appeal would be allowed or, possibly, taken no vote and had the appeal reheard by a differently constituted committee.

since the impeachments of Warren Hastings and Viscount Melville in 1795 and 1805 respectively.

The Committee of Privileges, which is by convention composed of lawyers in the House, makes recommendations to the whole House arising out of the Committee trying, at the instance of the Sovereign, a disputed claim to a peerage.

Finally both the House of Lords and the House of Commons have jurisdiction over breaches of privilege, which include contempt of the House in question and wrongs committed within the precincts of each House. Either House may imprison the offender who has no right of appeal and may not move for habeas corpus.

b Appellate jurisdiction

The jurisdiction of the House of Lords is almost entirely appellate.

In civil cases it hears appeals from the Court of Appeal but only with leave of either the Court of Appeal or the Appeals Committee of the House itself.[1] The ground of appeal does not have to be a point of law as it does in criminal cases but most cases which reach the House of Lords do in fact involve a point of law of public importance. The Administration of Justice Act 1969 introduced a "leap-frog" procedure whereby there can be an appeal direct from the trial court to the House of Lords without the need for a prior appeal to the Court of Appeal. Such an appeal lies subject to two conditions; first the trial judge must grant a certificate,[2] which he may do only if all parties consent and the case involves a point of law of general public importance which either relates wholly or mainly to the construction of an enactment or is one in respect of which the judge was bound by a previous decision of the Court of Appeal or House of Lords; secondly the House of Lords must grant leave.[3]

The appeal to the House of Lords in criminal cases is of modern origin. Although a writ of error was available before this century, there was no general right of appeal until the Criminal Appeal Act 1907, which provided for an appeal from the Court of Criminal Appeal[4] established by that Act. The right of appeal from the divisional court of the Queen's Bench Division was created by the Administration of Justice Act 1960 and the conditions for appealing to the House of Lords in a criminal matter are now contained in that Act. These conditions are discussed fully in Part V of this book.[5]

Appeal lies, subject to similar conditions, from the Court of Criminal Appeal in Northern Ireland and from the Courts-Martial Appeal Court.

C THE COURT OF APPEAL

The Supreme Court of Judicature was the product of the complete reorganisa-

---

1 Administration of Justice (Appeals) Act 1934. The House also hears appeals from the equivalent civil courts of Scotland and Northern Ireland.

2 Act of 1969, s. 12 (1); there is no appeal against the grant or refusal of a certificate (s. 12 (5)).

3 *Ibid.*, s. 13. The grant of leave precludes appeal to the Court of Appeal. The "leap-frog" procedure was adopted in *Ealing London Borough* v. *Race Relations Board*, [1972] 1 All E.R. 105; [1972] 2 W.L.R. 71; see p. 112, *ante*.

4 The jurisdiction of this Court was transferred to the criminal division of the Court of Appeal by the Criminal Appeal Act 1966.

5 See pp. 430, 444, *post*.

tion of the English superior courts effected by the Supreme Court of Judicature Acts 1873–1875. These Acts are now consolidated in the Supreme Court of Judicature (Consolidation) Act 1925, generally referred to as the Judicature Act 1925. The Acts created the Supreme Court of Judicature to which was transferred the original and appellate jurisdiction of the existing superior courts of first instance and appeal.[1] The Supreme Court now consists of the Court of Appeal, the High Court and the Crown Court. The appellate jurisdiction of the superior courts of law and equity was transferred to the Court of Appeal, while the original jurisdiction was, broadly speaking, transferred to the High Court, the Crown Court having been added by the Courts Act 1971.[2]

1 Constitution

The Court of Appeal is composed of the Lord Chancellor, the Lord Chief Justice, the Master of the Rolls, the President of the Family Division of the High Court, former Lord Chancellors, the Lords of Appeal in Ordinary (all the above being *ex officio* judges) and the Lords Justices of Appeal. In practice, of the *ex officio* judges only the Master of the Rolls (in civil cases) and the Lord Chief Justice (in criminal cases) sit in the court. The Master of the Rolls was a first instance judge in the Court of Chancery, and, indeed, in the Chancery Division of the High Court until 1881. In modern times some of the greatest lawyers of their day have held the office of Master of the Rolls. The Lords Justices of Appeal are appointed by Her Majesty by letters patent. They must have been judges of the High Court or barristers of at least fifteen years' standing.[3] There must be not less than eight nor more than fourteen Lords Justices.[4]

In addition to the regular judges of the court the Lord Chancellor may require a judge of the High Court to augment the court from time to time. This power exists under section 7 of the Judicature Act 1925. The Criminal Appeal Act 1966 supplements this provision by providing that the Lord Chief Justice may, after consultation with the Master of the Rolls, at any time request the attendance of any judge of the High Court to sit at sittings of the criminal division of the Court of Appeal.[5] While it is fairly rare for High Court judges to be required to sit in the civil division under section 7 of the 1925 Act, the criminal division more often than not contains a Queen's Bench Division judge. Indeed, though this is not set out in the Criminal Appeal Act 1966, the first court of the criminal division usually consists of the Lord Chief Justice, a Lord Justice of Appeal and one puisne judge while a second court comprises one Lord Justice of Appeal and two puisnes.

By section 2 (1) of the Criminal Appeal Act 1966 any number of courts of either division of the Court of Appeal may sit at the same time. Appeals against final orders and judgments to either division of the Court of Appeal

---

[1] See p. 58, *ante*.   [2] See p. 165, *post*.

[3] Judicature Act 1925, s. 9.

[4] Administration of Justice (Judges and Pensions) Act 1960, ss. 1, 6 and Sch. 2; Administration of Justice Act 1968, s. 1 (1) (*b*) (i); this number may be increased by Order in Council (*ibid.*, s. 1 (2)) and was so increased (from thirteen to fourteen) in 1970.

[5] Section 1 (3), as amended by Courts Act 1971, s. 56; Sch. 8.

must be heard by not less than three judges.[1] However, interlocutory appeals may be heard by two judges and, in the criminal division, a single judge (who may be a judge of the High Court) has certain jurisdiction under the Criminal Appeal Act 1968, s. 31, notably to hear applications for leave to appeal. Occasionally a "full court" of five or more members is convened to hear appeals involving novel or difficult points of law in both the civil and criminal divisions, although such a court has no wider powers than the normal court.

2 Jurisdiction

Since October 1, 1966, the date upon which the Criminal Appeal Act 1966 came into operation, the Court of Appeal has consisted of a civil and a criminal division.

a Civil division

The civil division exercises the jurisdiction exercisable by the Court of Appeal immediately before the passing of the 1966 Act.[2] This is set out more fully in Chapter 23 of this book.[3] It is sufficient to note at this stage that the civil division has no criminal jurisdiction and hardly any original jurisdiction. Its jurisdiction is entirely civil and almost entirely appellate. It hears appeals from the High Court, county courts, the Restrictive Practices Court, the National Industrial Relations Court and various tribunals, notably the Lands Tribunal. Appeal is by way of rehearing, except in the case of certain appeals from tribunals where it is by case stated.[4]

b Criminal division

The criminal division of the Court of Appeal is the successor of the Court of Criminal Appeal, the jurisdiction of the latter being transferred to the former by section 1 (1) of the Criminal Appeal Act 1966.

The Court of Criminal Appeal emerged as a result of the deficient system of criminal appeals which existed prior to 1907. The court was created by the Criminal Appeal Act 1907 and superseded the Court for Crown Cases Reserved and the right of appeal by writ of error to the Queen's Bench Division.

The jurisdiction of the criminal division is set out fully in Part V of this book.[5] Briefly, it hears appeals by persons convicted[6] on indictment or coroner's inquisition at the Crown Court. It also hears appeals against sentence from this court. In addition the Home Secretary may refer a case to the division, under section 17 of the Criminal Appeal Act 1968, for assistance on any point or for determination as an appeal. The criminal division of the Court of Appeal has no civil jurisdiction and no original jurisdiction, its jurisdiction being solely

---

[1] Judicature Act 1925, s. 68 (1); Criminal Appeal Act 1966, s. 2 (2). In the criminal division the number of judges must be uneven save that the criminal division may consist of two judges, but not for the purpose of determining an appeal or an application for leave to appeal to the House of Lords or of refusing an application for leave to appeal to the Court of Appeal other than an application which has been refused by a single judge under s. 31 of the Criminal Appeal Act 1968: Administration of Justice Act 1970, s. 9.

[2] Criminal Appeal Act 1966, s. 1 (2) (a).

[3] See p. 333, post.

[4] Rules of the Supreme Court (Revision) 1965, O. 61.

[5] See p. 421, post.

[6] See Chapter 26, post.

appellate. It may be noted that the prosecution has no right of appeal to the criminal division, even though the prosecution has the same right to appeal from the division to the House of Lords as has the defendant.

D THE HIGH COURT OF JUSTICE

The High Court was established by the Judicature Acts and to it was transferred the jurisdiction of the three superior common law courts of first instance, the Court of Chancery, the Courts of Admiralty, Probate, Divorce and Matrimonial Causes and other superior courts of civil and criminal jurisdiction (except the Chancery Courts of the Counties Palatine of Lancaster and Durham[1]). Prior to 1971 the High Court sat in the Royal Courts of Justice in the Strand, London, though High Court judges constituted a court of the High Court for all purposes when they tried cases on assize. Nevertheless their jurisdiction on assize derived not from their office but from the Commissions under which they sat. The Courts Act 1971, s. 1 abolished all courts of assize but s. 2 provides that sittings of the High Court may be conducted at any place in England or Wales; the centres at which sittings of the High Court are, in fact, held are determined in accordance with directions of the Lord Chancellor. The jurisdiction of the High Court is both civil and criminal and both original and appellate. It has virtually unlimited jurisdiction in civil actions, though this is not generally an exclusive jurisdiction and where the action concerns a small sum it is usually brought in the county courts.

The High Court, when created, consisted of five divisions, but these were reduced in 1880 to the three which now exist (save that the Probate, Divorce and Admiralty Division has been re-named the Family Division[2]). Although all three divisions have equal competence each division, in fact, exercises a separate jurisdiction. This is not dictated by convenience but by the Rules of the Supreme Court which govern procedure and practice throughout the Supreme Court (except in the Crown Court where there are separate rules, the Crown Court Rules).[3] These Rules specify the manner in which an action or matter may be commenced and prosecuted in the High Court. Consequently certain types of action are confined to a particular division. Thus matrimonial causes in the High Court may only be heard in the Family Division and not in either of the two other divisions. In certain cases the jurisdiction of the divisions

---

[1] These courts, which were superior courts, continued to exercise a Chancery jurisdiction equivalent to that of the High Court in the County Palatine of Lancaster and the County Borough of Teesside until their abolition by the Courts Act 1971, s. 41 which merged them with the High Court.

[2] Administration of Justice Act 1970, s. 1. The same section also effected redistribution of business between the divisions as a consequence of the main purpose of the change which was to create a division which deals solely with family and domestic matters. Thus the Admiralty jurisdiction of the High Court was assigned to the Queen's Bench Division to be exercised by the new "Admiralty Court" created by s. 2 of the Act, while contentious probate business was assigned to the Chancery Division, thereby eradicating the unsatisfactory duality of jurisdiction which had hitherto existed, whereby disputes concerning the validity of wills were heard in the Probate, Divorce and Admiralty Division, while questions of the construction of wills were determined in the Chancery Division.

[3] See p. 170, *post*; though the inherent jurisdiction of the High Court is exercisable by a judge of any Division; see *Re L*, [1968] P. 119; [1968] 1 All E.R. 20; p. 59, *ante*.

overlap and it is possible to start certain proceedings in one or other of them. For example, two recent cases concerning similar conditions in similar contracts were tried within a short space of time. The first[1] was tried in the Chancery Division, the second[2] in the Queen's Bench Division. It is important to bear in mind that the divisions of the High Court are not different courts, so that the jurisdiction of any one High Court judge is exercisable by any other other High Court judge, irrespective of the division to which he is assigned.[3] Nevertheless, as a matter of practice, the effect of statutes and rules of procedure is usually to confer upon each division jurisdiction which is independent of that exercised by the other two divisions.

As the volume of litigation has increased so has the number of High Court judges. The maximum number is now seventy-five and this number may be increased by Order in Council.[4] High Court judges, sometimes styled "puisne" judges, must be barristers of not less than ten years' standing. In practice High Court judges are appointed from the ranks of Queen's Counsel and it seems likely that they will in future be appointed also from the ranks of Circuit judges. High Court judges are appointed to a particular division by the Lord Chancellor, depending usually on the practice which the appointee had at the bar prior to appointment. This is particularly true of the Chancery Division where the very specialised nature of the cases heard requires that new judges be appointed from the Chancery Bar, whose members are usually to be found in chambers in Lincoln's Inn. Appointments are made by the Crown on the advice of the Lord Chancellor.[5]

a   Chancery Division

The Chancery Division consists of the Lord Chancellor, who, although nominal head of the Division, never sits at first instance, a Vice-Chancellor and at least four other puisne judges.[6] Before 1972, sittings of the Chancery Division were held only in the Royal Courts of Justice and Chancery judges did not go on assize (though a concurrent Chancery jurisdiction was exercised by the now defunct Chancery Courts of the Counties Palatine of Lancaster and Durham). Although the Courts Act 1971 authorises sittings of the High Court to be held at any place in England and Wales, in practice it is likely that most Chancery business will continue to be taken in London, members of the Chancery bench and bar not being noticeably peripatetic. However by a recent *Practice Direction*[7] the Vice-Chancellor of the County Palatine of Lancaster (who is now a Circuit judge[8]) sits as a judge of the High Court[9] at Liverpool, Manchester and Preston

---

[1] *Petrofina (Great Britain), Ltd.* v. *Martin*, [1965] Ch. 1073; [1965] 2 All E.R. 176.
[2] *Esso Petroleum Co., Ltd.* v. *Harpers Garage (Stourport), Ltd.*, [1966] 2 Q.B. 514; [1965] 2 All E.R. 933.
[3] See *Re Hastings (No. 3)*, [1959] Ch. 368; [1959] 1 All E.R. 698; *Re Kray*, [1965] Ch. 736; [1965] 1 All E.R. 710; *Re L*, [1968] P. 144; [1968] 1 All E.R. 20.
[4] Under the Administration of Justice Act 1968, s. 1 (2); the number was so increased from 70 to 75 in 1970.
[5] For details of the position of Her Majesty's judges, see p. 191, *post*.
[6] There are at present nine.
[7] Reported at [1972] 1 All E.R. 103; [1972] 1 W.L.R. 1.
[8] By virtue of Courts Act 1971, s. 16; Sch. 2.
[9] Pursuant to the request of the Lord Chancellor made under s. 23 of the Courts Act 1971, under which section Circuit judges or Recorders may sit as judges of the High Court.

and, time permitting, at Leeds and Newcastle-upon-Tyne for the hearing of proceedings assigned to the Chancery Division.

Original jurisdiction—Section 34 of the Judicature Act 1873[1] assigned to the Chancery Division jurisdiction over matters which were heard in the Court of Chancery prior to the abolition of that court in 1875. The most important of these matters are the administration of estates, the execution of trusts, the redemption and foreclosure of mortgages, the rectification and cancellation of deeds, specific performance of contracts for the sale or lease of interests in land, partnership actions. This jurisdiction has been augmented by statutes and rules of procedure. Thus the Chancery Division, in addition to the matters set out above, exercises jurisdiction over the winding-up of companies, bankruptcy, revenue matters, town and country planning, adoption and landlord and tenant disputes. In addition judges of the Division when sitting as the Court of Protection[2] hear applications under the Mental Health Act 1959 concerning the management of the property and affairs of mental patients. In addition contentious probate business has recently been transferred to the Division by the Administration of Justice Act 1970.

Probate jurisdiction and procedure—Probate procedure differs according to whether the deceased died testate, i.e. leaving a valid will, or intestate, i.e. leaving no will or leaving a will which is invalid, generally through failure to comply with the due formalities which are principally contained in the Wills Act 1837.

If a person dies testate his will should appoint one or more executors. These executors must first apply to the Principal Registry of the Family Division or to a District Probate Registry for a grant of probate. This application must be accompanied by the will itself, the executors' affidavit of undertaking to administer the estate, an affidavit of all the deceased's property for estate duty purposes and various other documents. In the overwhelming majority of cases no-one will dispute the validity of the will and the grant of probate will be made as a formality. However any person who disputes the validity of a will in respect of which a grant is sought may enter a *caveat* at the Registry in question. In that event the proceedings become contentious and there will have to be a trial as to the validity of the will. This trial may take place in the county court for the district where the testator resided before his death if the net value of the estate is less than £1,000.[3] In practice this is rare and the trial will almost always be in the Chancery Division.[4]

If a person dies intestate a person will have to apply to be appointed an administrator of the estate. There will then be a grant of letters of administration rather than a grant of probate. The effect is similar in that it vests the deceased's property in the administrators who must then distribute it in accordance with the intestacy provisions.

Appellate jurisdiction—Although the jurisdiction of the Chancery Division is predominately original, there is some appellate jurisdiction. A single judge of the

---

[1] Now s. 56 of the Judicature Act 1925.

[2] See p. 184, *post.* The wardship jurisdiction of the Chancery Division was assigned to the Family Division by the Administration of Justice Act 1970, s. 1; Sch. 1.

[3] County Courts Act 1959, s. 62.

[4] The procedure is governed by R.S.C. O.76; a probate action must be commenced by writ (O.75, r. 2).

Division has jurisdiction by statute to hear certain appeals, for example income tax appeals from the Commissioners of Inland Revenue under section 64 of the Income Tax Act 1952. A divisional court of the Chancery Division, comprising at least two judges of the Division, has a limited jurisdiction, notably the hearing of appeals from county courts in bankruptcy matters.

b Queen's Bench Division

The jurisdiction of the Queen's Bench Division is wider in scope than that of the other two divisions of the High Court. It is both civil and criminal and both original and appellate. In addition it exercises the supervisory jurisdiction formerly exercised by the Court of King's Bench. The jurisdiction of the Division is equivalent to the jurisdiction exercised by the three superior common law courts of first instance prior to 1875, as altered by subsequent statutes and rules. Procedure in this division is dealt with at length in Part IV of this book.

Original civil jurisdiction—By far the most important aspect of the business of the Division is its first instance jurisdiction over civil matters, principally actions in contract and tort. Jurisdiction over commercial matters is exercised in the Commercial Court, which is one of the lists in the Division, maintained in London, Liverpool and Manchester.[1] Admiralty jurisdiction, assigned to the Division by the Administration of Justice Act, is exercised by the "Admiralty Court", the judges of which are those judges nominated to be Admiralty Judges by the Lord Chancellor.[2] Admiralty business includes actions to enforce a claim for damage, loss of life or personal injury arising out of a collision between ships, claims to the possession or ownership of ships, claims for loss of or damage to goods carried in a ship, towage claims and other specified proceedings.[3] When trying admiralty actions the judge often sits with lay assessors.

Appellate civil jurisdiction—The appellate jurisdiction of the Queen's Bench Division in civil matters is fairly minor. Appeal lies from an interlocutory order of a Queen's Bench Division master to a judge in chambers[4] and a single judge also has jurisdiction to hear certain appeals from tribunals, for example from the Pensions Appeal Tribunal.[5] A divisional court of the Queen's Bench Division consisting of two or more judges of the Division has a limited civil jurisdiction in hearing appeals by way of case stated from magistrates' courts, other than matrimonial proceedings, and the Crown Court, from the Solicitors Disciplinary Committee and in certain other cases.

Criminal and supervisory jurisdiction—The criminal jurisdiction of the High Court is exercised exclusively by the Queen's Bench Division.

This is entirely appellate[6] and exercised by the divisional court consisting of at least two but usually three judges of the Division. The Lord Chief Justice

---

1 For details of procedure in the Commercial Court see p. 288, *post*.
2 Administration of Justice Act 1970, s. 2. Procedure in the Admiralty Court is governed by R.S.C., O. 75; see p. 289, *post*.
3 Administration of Justice Act 1956, s. 1.
4 See p. 335, *post*.
5 Pensions Appeal Tribunals Act 1943; Tribunals and Inquiries Act 1971, s. 13.
6 Prior to 1972 the Division exercised a limited original criminal jurisdiction in the form of a trial "at bar", a procedure adopted in the notorious case of *R. v. Casement*, [1917] 1 K.B. 98; the jurisdiction was, however, virtually obsolete and was abolished by the Courts Act 1971, s. 6 of which provides that all proceedings on indictment must be brought before the Crown Court.

often sits and the hearing will then take place in his own court in the Royal Courts of Justice. The jurisdiction is exercised over appeals by way of "case stated"[1] from magistrates' courts and the Crown Court (in the exercise of that court's appellate jurisdiction).

The supervisory jurisdiction of the Division is also exercised by the divisional court. This includes jurisdiction to issue the prerogative writ of habeas corpus and to make orders of mandamus, prohibition and certiorari by which inferior courts and tribunals are compelled to exercise their powers properly and restrained from exceeding their jurisdiction. Thus a magistrates' court which refuses to "state a case" for the consideration of the divisional court of the Queen's Bench Division in a case where it ought to do so may be compelled by order of mandamus so to do. Similarly if there has not been a proper trial it may be restrained by prohibition from imposing any sentence on the accused. Finally, if a magistrates' court exceeds its jurisdiction or conducts a case improperly or if one of the bench has some interest in the proceedings the proceedings may be removed by order of certiorari to the High Court for consideration.

Disputed Parliamentary elections are determined by an election court which consists of two judges of the Queen's Bench Division.[2]

It should be noted finally that the "first-tier" jurisdiction of the Crown Court is exercised principally by the judges of the Queen's Bench Division.[3] Judges of the Queen's Bench Division on average spend approximately half their time in the Royal Courts of Justice and half "on circuit".

c   Family Division

This Division (formerly named the Probate, Divorce and Admiralty Division[4]) consists of the President and not less than three puisne judges.[5] The jurisdiction of the Division is set out in the first Schedule to the Administration of Justice Act 1970 and is both original and appellate.

The original jurisdiction comprises all defended matrimonial causes, proceedings for a decree of presumption of death and dissolution of marriage, proceedings for a declaration as to legitimacy, the validity of a marriage or matrimonial status, wardship, adoption, guardianship of minors and proceedings under section 17 of the Married Women's Property Act 1882 (determination of title to property in dispute between spouses) and section 1 of the Matrimonial Homes Act 1967 (means whereby a spouse can continue in occupation of, or obtain entry to, a dwelling-house which is, or has been the matrimonial home). The general effect of these provisions is that the Division has exclusive jurisdiction over matrimonial disputes and children. Prior to the 1970 Act the Chancery Division dealt with wardship and embarrassing conflicts sometimes arose between the Divisions involving issues such as whether the Divorce

---

[1] For details of the procedure see p. 441, *post*.
[2] Representation of the People Act 1949, ss. 107 *et seq.*
[3] See p. 170, *post*.
[4] The Division was re-named by the Administration of Justice Act 1970, s. 1. The late Sir Alan Herbert described the jurisdiction as "wills, wives and wrecks"; of these, "wills" have gone to the Chancery Division and "wrecks" (other than the wrecks of marriages) to the Queen's Bench Division (*supra*).
[5] There are at present sixteen.

judge in, say, custody proceedings could disregard the order of a Chancery judge made in wardship proceedings.[1]

The appellate business of the Division comprises principally appeals from magistrates' courts and county courts under the Guardianship of Minors Act 1971 from magistrates' courts under the Adoption Act 1958, and the Matrimonial Proceedings (Magistrates' Courts) Act 1960 and from magistrates' courts and the Crown Court in affiliation proceedings.

E THE CROWN COURT

1 Creation of the Crown Court

The Crown Court was created by the Courts Act 1971. In order to appreciate the jurisdiction of this court and its place in the hierarchy, it is necessary to examine briefly the system of courts that the Crown Court replaced.

Prior to the 1st January 1972, the date upon which the Courts Act came into operation, trials on indictment took place either at quarter sessions or at assizes.[2] The essential characteristics of both quarter sessions and assizes was that their jurisdiction was local. This meant not only that the courts (as a rule) tried only offences committed within the locality of their jurisdiction but also that the administration of the courts was organised on a local basis, so that the methods of administration and organisation varied from area to area.

The most serious offences were tried at assizes before a court presided over by a judge sitting, not by virtue of his normal judicial office, but under Royal commissions of *oyer and terminer* and *gaol delivery*; the persons named in the commissions usually included at least two High Court judges, almost invariably judges of the Queen's Bench Division, who would sit at the assize town for the duration of the assize. The jurisdiction of assizes was equivalent to that of the High Court since a commissioner when engaged in the exercise of his jurisdiction constituted a court of the High Court of Justice.[3]

All save the most serious offences tried on indictment were tried at quarter sessions of which there were almost 150 separate courts. Quarter sessions were of two kinds—county quarter sessions and borough quarter sessions. These courts, which as their name would indicate were held at least four times a year, were composed, in the case of county quarter sessions, by the justices of the peace of the county, almost invariably presided over by a legally qualified chairman, and in the case of borough quarter sessions, by a Recorder who sat alone and was a practising barrister of at least five years' standing. The jurisdiction of quarter sessions was both civil and criminal and original and appellate. The criminal jurisdiction comprised the trial of all indictable offences, save those which had, by statute, to be tried at assizes, jurisdiction to sentence persons

---

[1] This occurred, for example, in *Hall* v. *Hall*, [1963] P. 378; [1963] 2 All E.R. 140.

[2] Although trial "at bar" in the High Court was still, theoretically, possible; see p. 163 (*n*), *ante*.

[3] Judicature Act 1925, s. 70 (4). In addition to the High Court judges, county court judges and Queen's Counsel were often included in the commissions; furthermore the Master of the Rolls, Lords Justices of Appeal and former Lords Justices and High Court judges might be included in the commissions but in practice were not (*ibid.*, s. 70 (3)). The Commissioners of Assize also tried civil cases as a court of the High Court; in this respect the *status quo* is maintained by section 2 of the Courts Act which enables sittings of the High Court to be held at any place in England or Wales.

committed for sentence following summary conviction and the hearing of appeals from the decisions of magistrates' courts. The whole of this jurisdiction has been transferred to the Crown Court together with the civil jurisdiction of quarter sessions which comprised principally matters concerned with various forms of licensing.[1]

Before leaving the pre-1972 system, mention must also be made of the Central Criminal Court and of the Crown Courts of Liverpool and Manchester. The Central Criminal Court, established by the Central Criminal Court Act 1834 and popularly known as the "Old Bailey" after the name of the street in London in which the court is situated, was the assize court exercising criminal jurisdiction in the Greater London area. The court was a court of the High Court and its jurisdiction extended over indictable offences committed in Greater London or on the high seas; the judges of the court sat under the commissions of *oyer and terminer* and *gaol delivery* and consisted of the Lord Chancellor, the Lord Mayor of the City of London, the Lord Chief Justice and the judges of the Queen's Bench Division, the Aldermen of the City of London, the Recorder and the Common Serjeant and a number of additional judges who had to be judges of at least ten years' standing; of these only the Queen's Bench Division judges, the Recorder, the Common Serjeant and the additional judges sat in practice.

The Criminal Justice Administration Act 1956 established, as something of an experimental innovation, Crown Courts in Liverpool and Manchester presided over by the Recorders of Liverpool and Manchester who were the full time judges of the courts. The jurisdiction of these courts was solely criminal but was both original and appellate since the courts exercised the criminal jurisdiction of both assizes and quarter sessions within the area of their respective jurisdictions. These courts, which were abolished by the Courts Act 1971, must not be confused with the present Crown Court. Apart from the difference in the judiciary of the courts, the jurisdiction of the Crown Courts of Liverpool and Manchester was, as in the case of all courts of quarter session and assize, local.

Of the system of courts described above one commentator has observed:[2]

"Not only have the courts been tied to geographical areas but their judges have been tied to them. This is true both of courts of quarter sessions in boroughs and counties and also of courts of assize where the judges of the High Court have been obliged to follow rigid itineraries which, since the beginning of the last century, have borne little relation to the volume of business to be dealt with or the populations which the assize towns were intended to serve. When populations are small, business is light and travelling slow, such a system has its obvious advantages and represents perhaps no more than a marginal waste of resources which is more than adequately offset by the benefit of having justice readily available on a local basis. The urbanisation of England from the late eighteenenth century, together with the vast increase in population and the introduction of a rapid and efficient system of transport, have rendered a rigid system of locally organised justice no longer adequate to absorb the consequent increases in the volume of work."

---

[1] Although certain administrative functions have been transferred to local authorities (Courts Act 1971, ss. 53, 56; Sch. 8).

[2] M. D. Huebner, *An Outline of the New System*, 121 New Law Journal, p. 1136.

In the result a Royal Commission was established under the chairmanship of Lord Beeching and the so-called Beeching Report[1] that followed contained recommendations which formed the basis for the system introduced by the Courts Act 1971.

The Courts Act 1971 abolished all courts of assize and quarter sessions and established in their place a single court to be known as the Crown Court, which court is expressly made part of the Supreme Court of Judicature and a superior court of record.[2] The Act further abolished the Crown Courts of Liverpool and Manchester and the Central Criminal Court, though the latter has been retained in name since it is expressly provided that when the Crown Court sits in London it shall be known as the Central Criminal Court.[3]

As already indicated the essential feature of the Crown Court is that its jurisdiction is in no sense local. Section 4 (4) of the 1971 Act provides that:

"(*a*) any Crown Court business may be conducted at any place in England or Wales,

(*b*) sittings of the Crown Court at any place may be continuous or intermittent or occasional,

(*c*) judges may sit simultaneously to take any number of different cases in the same or in different places, and all or any of them may adjourn cases from place to place at any time."

Thus it is important to remember that there are not various Crown Courts throughout the country, in the way that there were various quarter sessions; there is one Crown Court, sittings of which may be held anywhere at any time as indicated above.

2 Constitution

The judges of the Crown Court are all the judges of the High Court, the Circuit judges and Recorders; judges of the Court sit alone as a rule, though there is provision for justices of the peace to sit, but only with one of the judges of the

---

[1] *Report of the Royal Commission on Assizes and Quarter Sessions:* Cmnd. 4153 of 1969.

[2] This, however, appears to be little more than a matter of terminology since, in the exercise of its appellate jurisdiction, the Crown Court (as were Quarter Sessions) is amenable to the supervisory jurisdiction of the High Court as if it were an inferior court (Courts Act 1971, s. 10 (5); see p. 153, *ante*). In addition s. 57 of the 1971 Act, the interpretation section, provides that except where the context otherwise requires a reference in the 1971 Act, or in any other Act, to a judge of the Supreme Court shall not include a reference to a judge of the Crown Court.

[3] Section 4 (7); the Lord Mayor of the City and any Alderman of the City are entitled to sit as judges of the Central Criminal Court with any High Court judge, Circuit judge or Recorder. The reasons behind the preservation of this obsolete tradition are not clear. There used to be a rule to the effect that an Alderman of the City had to be present in the court; although this rule has disappeared, the central seat in the No. 1 court at the Old Bailey is still traditionally left vacant for the Lord Mayor. As a further concession to the City of London the 1971 Act provides that the holders of the offices of Recorder of London and Common Serjeant, although Circuit judges *ex officio*, continue to be appointed and remunerated in accordance with the provisions of the City of London (Courts) Act 1964 rather than in accordance with the provisions of the 1971 Act, which govern the appointment and remuneration of all other Circuit judges (s. 16; Sch. 2); finally judges sitting in the Central Criminal Court continue to be addressed as "my Lord" as opposed to "your Honour", which is the appropriate form of address for Circuit judges.

Court.[1]   This is in contrast to the former county quarter sessions which were composed entirely of justices of the peace, albeit almost always sitting with a legally qualified chairman.   In addition to the regular judges of the Court any judge of the Court of Appeal may, on the request of the Lord Chancellor, sit and act as a judge and when so sitting and acting is regarded as a judge of the High Court.[2]   There is also provision for the temporary appointment of deputy High Court and Circuit judges.[3]

There are thus basically three tiers of judiciary.   At the highest level are the High Court judges who, it is anticipated, will invariably be judges of the Queen's Bench Division and will try principally those cases formerly heard at assizes.[4]

Below the High Court judges are the Circuit judges.   The office of Circuit judge is a new one created by the 1971 Act.   Circuit judges are appointed by Her Majesty on the recommendation of the Lord Chancellor and must have been barristers of at least ten years' standing or have held the office of Recorder for at least five years.[5]   In addition, before recommending any person for appointment the Lord Chancellor must take steps to satisfy himself that the proposed appointee's health is satisfactory.[6]   Circuit judges retire at the age of 72 though the Lord Chancellor may authorise continuance in office from time to time up to the age of 75.   The Lord Chancellor may remove a Circuit judge from office on the ground of incapacity or misbehaviour.

Whereas Circuit judges are full time appointments, Recorders are part time judges of the Crown Court.   They are appointed by Her Majesty on the recommendation of the Lord Chancellor and must be barristers or solicitors of at least ten years' standing.[7]   Recorders must be under the age of 72 and, like Circuit judges, are removable by the Lord Chancellor on the ground of incapacity or misbehaviour.   Unlike Circuit judges, however, Recorders are appointed on a temporary basis and their appointment specifies the term for which they are appointed and the frequency and duration of the occasions during that term on which they will be required to be available to undertake the duties of Recorder; failure to comply with the requirements specified in the terms of appointment is a ground for removal from office.[7]

Finally there are the provisions for justices of the peace to sit in the Court. Their attendance is mandatory on the hearing by the Crown Court of any appeal or of proceedings on committal to the Court for sentence, on the hearing of which proceedings the judge of the Court sits with not less than two nor more than four justices of the peace.[8]   In addition any jurisdiction or power of

---

[1] Courts Act 1971, ss. 4 (1) (c), 5.   A further unimportant exception to the rule that the judges of the Court sit alone is the right of the Lord Mayor and Aldermen of the City of London to sit in the Central Criminal Court (*supra*).

[2] *Ibid.*, s. 4 (3).

[3] *Ibid.*, s. 24.

[4] As to the distribution of business, see p. 169 *post*.

[5] *Ibid.*, s. 16.   Since solicitors are eligible for appointment as Recorders (and indeed several solicitors have already been appointed as Recorders), it follows that the office of Circuit judge is open to members of that branch of the profession.

[6] *Ibid.*, s. 16 (4); this presumably means that proposed appointees will be required to submit to medical examination.

[7] *Ibid.*, s. 21.

[8] *Ibid.*, s. 5 (1), although under s. 5 (5) the Lord Chancellor may give directions dispensing with the requirements for justices to sit in such cases.   In addition no objection can subsequently be taken to a decision on the ground that the court was not properly constituted

the Court may be exercised by a regular judge of the Court sitting with not more than four justices.[1] Where justices sit the decision of the Court is by majority and if the members of the Court are equally divided the regular judge has a second and casting vote.[2] As a final illustration of the departure from the principle of localised jurisdiction, section 5 (9) of the 1971 Act provides that a justice of the peace shall not be disqualified from acting as a judge of the Crown Court for the reason that the proceedings are not at a place within the area for which he was appointed as a justice, or because the proceedings are not related to that area in any way.

It will be noted that the judges of the Crown Court are not, as it were, full time criminal judges (as were the Recorders of the former Crown Courts of Liverpool and Manchester). The High Court judges sit, of course, in civil cases in the High Court; the Circuit judges, as well as exercising the very limited civil jurisdiction which the Crown Court inherited from Quarter Sessions, discharge the functions of county court judges;[3] Recorders sit almost exclusively to try criminal cases though, as well as having the civil jurisdiction of the Crown Court, there is provision for Recorders to sit as county court judges.

The immediate effect of the Courts Act was a large number of new judicial appointments, which is thought to have placed some strain on the resources of the bar. In fact the majority of Circuit judges were simply translated from judicial offices held before the Courts Act came into force. Thus, on the 1st January 1972, the date upon which most of the provisions of the Courts Act came into force, the Vice-Chancellor of the County Palatine of Lancaster, the Recorder of London, the Common Serjeant, the Official Referees of the Supreme Court,[4] the Recorders of Liverpool and Manchester, the additional judges of the Central Criminal Court, the assistant judge of the Mayor's and City of London Court,[5] all county court judges and all whole-time chairmen and deputy chairmen of courts of quarter sessions for Greater London, Cheshire, Durham, Kent and Lancashire automatically became Circuit judges.[6]

3 Jurisdiction and procedure

The Crown Court has exclusive jurisdiction over all trials on indictment for offences wherever committed, including proceedings on indictment for offences

---

as required by section 5 unless objection was taken at the time; this nullifies the effect of *R. v. Inner London Quarter Sessions, Ex parte D'Souza*, [1970] 1 All E.R. 481; [1970] 1 W.L.R. 376.

[1] Courts Act 1971, s. 5 (3).
[2] *Ibid.*, s. 5 (8).
[3] *Ibid.*, s. 20; see p. 177, *post*.
[4] The office of Official Referee was abolished by section 25 of the Act, but the functions conferred on official referees by statute are discharged by such of the Circuit judges as the Lord Chancellor may from time to time determine, these functions being described as "official referees' business" (s. 25 (2), (3); see p. 288 (*n*), *post*).
[5] This court was abolished by section 42 of the Act, though the name survives, rather in the same way as the Central Criminal Court, since the county court for the City of London is known as the Mayor's and City of London Court and the Circuit judge assigned to that district under section 20 of the Act is known as the judge of the Mayor's and City of London Court.
[6] Courts Act 1971, s. 16; Sch. 2.

within the jurisdiction of the Admiralty in England.[1] In addition all jurisdiction formerly exercised by any court of quarter sessions is vested in the Crown Court.[2] This, as indicated above, includes the hearing of appeals by persons convicted summarily in magistrates' courts,[3] the sentencing of persons committed for sentence following summary conviction[4] and a limited civil jurisdiction, principally concerned with licensing appeals.

Procedure in the Court is governed by Crown Court rules[5] and follows closely procedure in quarter sessions prior to 1972. Details of criminal procedure are to be found in Part V of this work.

The Lord Chief Justice has power under section 4 (5) of the 1971 Act, with the concurrence of the Lord Chancellor, to give directions relating to the distribution of Crown Court business and, on 14th October 1971, LORD WIDGERY, C.J. gave such directions.[6] The directions classify offences, for the purposes of distribution, into four classes,[7] the first of which, being the most serious, are to be tried by a High Court judge. Class 2 offences are to be tried by a High Court judge unless a particular case is released by or on the authority of a presiding judge, that is to say, a High Court judge assigned to have special responsibility for a particular circuit. All other indictable offences form Class 3 and may be listed for trial by a High Court judge, Circuit judge or Recorder, while offences which may, in appropriate circumstances, be tried either on indictment or summarily constitute Class 4 and may be tried by a High Court judge, Circuit judge or Recorder but will normally be listed for trial by a Circuit judge or Recorder.[8]

F   NATIONAL INDUSTRIAL RELATIONS COURT

1   Constitution   NO LONGER EXISTS

This court,[9] established by section 99 of the Industrial Relations Act 1971, consists of such number of judges as may be nominated from time to time by the

---

[1] Courts Act 1971, s. 6.

[2] *Ibid.*, s. 8; Sch. 1; this is subject to the provisions of Sch. 8, Part I which transferred certain administrative functions of quarter sessions to local authorities.

[3] See p. 439, *post*.

[4] See p. 357, *post*.

[5] Section 15 of the 1971 Act confers power to make Crown Court rules upon a Crown Court rule committee consisting of the Lord Chancellor together with any four or more of the following persons, namely the Lord Chief Justice, two other judges of the Supreme Court, two Circuit judges, the registrar of criminal appeals, a justice of the peace, two practising barristers and two practising solicitors. The first set of rules is the Crown Court Rules 1971 (S.I. No. 1292).

[6] Reported in *Practice Note*, [1971] 3 All E.R. 829; *Sub. nom. Practice Direction*, [1971] 1 W.L.R. 1535.

[7] For further details of the classification of offences and the distribution of business, see p. 386, *post*.

[8] As to when Class 4 offences will be tried by a High Court judge, see p. 387, *post*.

[9] The new National Industrial Relations Court is often referred to as the Industrial Court. It should not be confused with the Industrial Court, established under the Industrial Courts Act 1919. The latter has been re-named the Industrial Arbitration Board (Industrial Relations Act 1971, s. 124). This Board has jurisdiction both under the 1919 Act and under the 1971 Act to consider industrial disputes referred to it. Nor should the National Industrial Relations Court be confused with the Industrial Tribunals; see p. 185, *post* as to the jurisdiction of the latter.

Lord Chancellor from the judges of the High Court and the Court of Appeal, one of whom is appointed President,[1] at least one nominated judge of the Court of Session and such other members as may be appointed from time to time by Her Majesty.[2] The characteristic of the court's constitution is that, although the President is a lawyer, the court will consist of laymen with specialised knowledge of industrial relations. The members of the court may resign by notice in writing and may be removed by the Lord Chancellor and the Secretary of State on the ground of incapacity or misbehaviour.[3] The court, which is a superior court of record, has a central office in London and may sit at any time and in any place in Great Britain in any number of divisions concurrently. It is duly constituted when sitting with a judge and not less than two nor more than four other members (or a judge and one other member by consent of the parties).[4]

The express purpose of the Industrial Relations Act 1971 is the promotion of good industrial relations in accordance with the following general principles, that is to say—

"(*a*) the principle of collective bargaining freely conducted on behalf of workers and employers and with due regard to the general interests of the community;

(*b*) the principle of developing and maintaining orderly procedures in industry for the peaceful and expeditious settlement of disputes by negotiation, conciliation or arbitration, with due regard to the general interests of the community;

(*c*) the principle of free association of workers in independent trade unions, and of employers in employers' associations, so organised as to be representative, responsible and effective bodies for regulating relations between employers and workers; and

(*d*) the principle of freedom and security for workers, protected by adequate safeguards against unfair industrial practices, whether on the part of employers or others."[5]

By section 1 (2) of the Act the National Industrial Relations Court is expressly required to regard the above as guiding principles.

2 Jurisdiction

The jurisdiction of the court is expressly limited to that which is conferred upon it by the 1971 Act[6] and encompasses numerous matters arising out of industrial disputes between employers, employees, trade unions and employers' associations. These include applications by workers refused employment by reason of a pre-entry "closed shop",[7] applications to approve certain closed shop agreements,[8] applications for reference to the Commission on Industrial

---

[1] The first President of the court is Sir JOHN DONALDSON.
[2] Industrial Relations Act 1971, s. 99 (2).
[3] *Ibid.*, Sch. 3, Part II, paras. 3–6.
[4] *Ibid.*, Sch. 3, Part II, paras. 13–17.
[5] *Ibid.*, s. 1 (1).
[6] *Ibid.*, s. 136.
[7] *Ibid.*, s. 7.
[8] *Ibid.*, s. 17; Sch. 1.

Relations of questions relating to the recognition of "sole bargaining agents" or the withdrawal of such recognition,[1] applications by the Chief Registrar of Trade Unions and Employers' Association, or his appointed assistant, to cancel the registration of an organisation as a trade union or an employers' association[2] and applications by the Secretary of State for an order discontinuing or deferring industrial action or for an order requiring a ballot to be taken relating to industrial action such as a strike.[3] In addition the court hears complaints of the various unfair industrial practices specified in the Act, on the hearing of which complaints the court may make an order determining the rights of the complainant and respondent, an award of compensation to be paid by the respondent to the complainant or an order directing the respondent to refrain from taking or continuing to take certain action.[4] The Act lays down principles upon which compensation awarded under the Act is to be assessed; the basic principle is that—

> "the amount of compensation shall ... be such amount as the Court ... considers just and equitable in all the circumstances, having regard to the loss sustained by the aggrieved party in consequence of the matters to which the complaint relates, in so far as that loss was attributable to action taken by or on behalf of the party in default."[5]

Finally, the National Industrial Relations Court has an appellate jurisdiction, set out in sections 114 and 115 of the Act, to hear appeals on specified questions of law from Industrial Tribunals, notably under the Contracts of Employment Act 1963, the Redundancy Payments Act 1965 and the Industrial Relations Act itself, and from certain decisions of the registrar under the 1971 Act.

3　Procedure

The hallmarks of procedure in the National Industrial Relations Court are speed, informality and simplicity, as the President declared at the opening of the court. The Lord Chancellor has power to make rules[6] with respect to the conduct of proceedings but, subject to these rules, the court has power to regulate its own procedure and the Act expressly provides that[7]—

> "in exercising that power the Industrial Court shall seek to avoid formality in its proceedings so far as it appears to the Court to be appropriate to do so; and [subject to exceptions principally concerned with appeals to the court] the Industrial Court shall not be bound by any enactment or rule of law relating to the evidence which is admissible in proceedings in other courts."

---

[1] Industrial Relations Act 1971, ss. 45, 51.
[2] *Ibid.*, ss. 76, 77.
[3] *Ibid.*, ss. 138–142.
[4] *Ibid.*, s. 101.
[5] Section 116. These principles, it will be observed, differ considerably from the normal principles upon which damages are awarded at common law, where the plaintiff is entitled *as of right* to be compensated for all loss suffered as a result of the wrongful conduct of the defendant. In addition ss. 117 and 118 prescribe statutory maxima of compensation; under s. 117 the maximum liability of a trade union is governed by the size of its membership and is £1 for every member with a maximum liability of £100,000.
[6] The first rules are the Industrial Court Rules 1971 (S.I. 1971 No. 1777).
[7] Sch. 3, part II, para. 18 (5).

All that is required to initiate proceedings is completion of a simple form setting out the names and addresses of the applicant and other parties, the nature of the assistance required and a brief statement of the facts. At the opening of the court the President stated that any attempt to turn these forms into complex legal documents would be resisted. Nevertheless any person appearing before the court may be represented by counsel or by a solicitor or, indeed, may appear in person or be represented by a representative of a trade union or employers' association or by any other person whom he desires to represent him.[1]

The procedure at hearings is designed to combine informality with order. The judges of the court are called "Sir", there is no traditional courtroom, no-one appears robed, there is no bench or witness box, parties and their advisers sit at tables and may address the court seated. The informality is doubtless an innovation to be welcomed, though whether abandonment of the rules of evidence is likely to be a profitable exercise remains open to doubt. A further departure from normal court practice is that no party is to be ordered to pay costs unless, in the opinion of the court, the proceedings were unnecessary, improper or vexatious or there has been unreasonable delay or other unreasonable conduct in bringing or conducting the proceedings.[2]

The court has all the powers of the High Court in relation to compelling the attendance and examination of witnesses, the production and inspection of documents, the enforcement of its orders and all other matters incidental to its jurisdiction under the Act, save that no person can be punished for contempt except by, or with the consent of, a judge who is a member of the court.[3]

Appeals.—Any decision of the National Industrial Relations Court on a question of fact is final (except in the case of committal for contempt) but appeal on a point of law lies to the Court of Appeal.[4] The absence of an appeal on a question of fact appears to be a dangerous precedent, bearing in mind that the court, being a superior court of record, is not subject to the supervisory jurisdiction of the High Court.[5]

G MAGISTRATES' COURTS

1 Constitution

A magistrates' court is defined by the Magistrates' Courts Act 1952, section 124, as any justice or justices of the peace acting under any enactment or by virtue of his or their commission or under common law. Consequently magistrates' courts are composed of justices of the peace.[6] A magistrates' court must be composed of at least two and not more than seven justices of the peace in order to try an information summarily, hear a complaint or conduct an examination into the means of a person whom it is proposed to commit to prison for non-payment of a fine. However an exception is provided by the presence of a

---

[1] Sch. 3, part II, para. 21.
[2] Sch. 3, part II, para. 24.
[3] Sch. 3, part II, para. 27.
[4] Sch. 3, part II, para. 29.
[5] See p. 153, *ante.*
[6] See pp. 10-11, *ante.*

stipendiary magistrate who has all the powers of two lay justices.[1] A single lay justice has a limited jurisdiction and cannot order a person to pay more than one pound or impose imprisonment for more than fourteen days.[2] It should be noted that a single justice may discharge the function of conducting a preliminary investigation.[3]

The jurisdiction of magistrates' courts is local. Every county and many boroughs have a separate commission of the peace. Most counties are further divided into petty sessional divisions and the jurisdiction of the justices is generally confined to matters arising in or near these divisions.

2 Jurisdiction

It is common to suppose that the jurisdiction of the magistrates' courts is entirely criminal. This is very far from being true since magistrates have a wide and varied civil jurisdiction. The feature of both the civil and the criminal matters within the jurisdiction of the magistrates' courts is that they are matters of minor importance compared with the civil matters heard in the High Court and the county courts and the criminal cases tried at the Crown Court. The compensating advantage of summary procedure is its cheapness and speed.

Before examining more closely the civil and criminal jurisdiction of justices it should be remembered that sitting as magistrates' courts is not the only function of justices of the peace. They also sit in the Crown Court.[4] Furthermore such important functions as the conduct of preliminary investigations, the issue of summonses and warrants and the grant of bail are exercised by justices though not sitting as magistrates' "courts". It has only recently been confirmed that licensing sessions are "courts".[5]

a Criminal jurisdiction

The criminal jurisdiction of the magistrates' courts exists principally over summary offences. Such offences are offences triable without a jury and are all statutory offences since all summary jurisdiction derives from statute. These offences are of a minor character since the maximum penalty which can be imposed in respect of a summary offence is usually six months imprisonment and a fine of £400. In practice most summary offenders are convicted of motoring offences under the Road Traffic Acts and Regulations made under those Acts. Indeed so numerous are the number of convictions for minor offences such as speeding and unauthorised parking that a new procedure was introduced by the Magistrates' Courts Act 1957 enabling persons to plead guilty to minor summary offences by post.[6] There are now more than one million persons a year found guilty of summary offences in England and Wales.

In addition to their jurisdiction over summary offences magistrates' courts also have jurisdiction to try certain indictable offences, although if the accused is seventeen or over he cannot be deprived of his right to a jury without his consent. Although these offences are not numerous, in practice only a very

---

[1] Magistrates' Courts Act 1952, s. 121 (1) (b), (c).
[2] *Ibid.*, s. 98 (5).
[3] See p. 380, *post.*
[4] See p. 167, *ante.*
[5] *Jeffrey* v. *Evans*, [1964] 1 All E.R. 536; [1964] 1 W.L.R. 505.
[6] For details of the procedure see p. 436, *post.*

small proportion of indictable offences are actually tried on indictment. The remainder are either tried summarily in the magistrates' courts or in juvenile courts if the offender is under seventeen.

The third class of offences triable by magistrates are the so-called "hybrid" offences which are triable either summarily or on indictment. There is a special procedure for determining the method of trial of these offences.[1]

See P. 366

Juvenile courts

These courts are magistrates' courts which exercise jurisdiction over offences committed by, and other matters concerning, children and young persons. The aim of the procedure in these courts is to disassociate the juvenile offenders from the criminal atmosphere and environment of the ordinary magistrates' courts, and to avoid undue publicity. Thus a juvenile court must not sit in a room in which sittings of another court are held if a sitting of that other court has been or will be held there within an hour. Proceedings are not open to the public and the only persons admitted to the court are the court officers, the parties to the case and their representatives, witnesses, bona fide members of the press and other persons authorised by the court to be present. In addition, to protect the juvenile, the press must not publish or broadcast the identity of any person under seventeen unless the court or the Home Secretary so orders.

A juvenile court consists of justices drawn from a special panel, the chairman of which sits permanently though the other members change by rotation. There must be three lay justices to form a juvenile court of whom one at least must be a woman.[2]

A completely new procedure for the treatment of children and young persons was laid down by the Children and Young Persons Act 1969. At the time of writing, certain fundamental parts of that Act are not yet in operation, in particular sections 4 and 5 which impose an absolute prohibition on charging a child with any offence except homicide and impose severe restrictions on the prosecution of young persons. The basic concept of the Act is to replace criminal proceedings, in respect of children and young persons, with "care proceedings" under section 1 of the Act.[3] Under that section any local authority, constable or authorised person who reasonably believes that there are grounds for an order may bring the child or young person in question before a juvenile court where, if one or more of the qualifying conditions is present, the court may make such an order, which may be an order requiring his parent or guardian to enter into a recognisance to take proper care of him and exercise proper control over him, a supervision order (an order placing him under the supervision of a local authority designated by a probation officer), a care order (an order committing him to the care of a local authority), a hospital order or a guardianship order. One of the qualifying conditions for the making of one of the above orders is that the child or young person is guilty of an offence, excluding homicide. Thus the child or young person may be found guilty of an offence without a trial, as such, but that finding is in no sense a conviction and he is dealt with not as a criminal but as any other child

---

[1] See p. 366, *post.*

[2] *Re J.S. (an infant)*, [1959] 3 All E.R. 856; [1959] 1 W.L.R. 1218.

[3] Part V of this work deals with criminal procedure as it is at the time of writing rather than as it will be when the whole of the 1969 Act is fully operational.

or young person in need of help. Nevertheless the court is not to find the "offence condition" satisfied unless it would have found him guilty of that offence in ordinary criminal proceedings, so that the ordinary onus of proof applies; furthermore if the "offence condition" is satisfied, the court has power to make orders for compensation (even if it makes no order under section 1) up to a maximum of £100 which the court may, in the case of a young person, and must (subject to exceptions) in the case of a child, order to be paid by the parent or guardian.[1] The power to order detention of children and young persons is limited to special circumstances where it is necessary for the protection of the public and detention will normally be in a "community home". Borstal training will, when section 7 (1) of the Act is implemented, not be permissible in the case of young persons, the lower age limit being raised from 15 to 17 by that section.

b Civil jurisdiction

This aspect of the magistrates' courts' jurisdiction is very varied. It extends over the recovery of certain civil debts such as income tax, national insurance contributions, electricity, gas and water charges, rates, the grant, revocation and renewal of licences, adoption orders, affiliation proceedings and domestic proceedings. This latter category is probably the most important aspect of the magistrates' civil jurisdiction; it is exercised principally under the Matrimonial Proceedings (Magistrates' Courts) Act 1960. Under that Act either spouse may apply to the magistrates' court for the petty sessions area in which either of them ordinarily resides for a matrimonial order. There are some nine grounds for complaint including desertion, persistent cruelty to the complainant or to an infant child of the family, adultery and wilful neglect to maintain.[2] Although the Divorce Reform Act 1969 substituted "irretrievable breakdown" as the only ground for divorce, thus departing from the former concept of the "matrimonial offence", the old principle of relief on the ground of a matrimonial offence still obtains in magistrates' courts. Thus, for example, adultery on the part of a wife is still an absolute bar to her obtaining an order for maintenance for herself in magistrates' courts though it plays but a small part nowadays in the assessment of maintenance for a wife in the divorce county courts and the Family Division of the High Court. A matrimonial order may contain various provisions,[3] the most important of which being that the complainant be no longer bound to cohabit with the defendant (non-cohabitation clause), that the defendant pay a reasonable weekly sum to the complainant, and that either or both spouses make weekly payments for the maintenance of any child of the family. The court also has power to make orders relating to the custody of any child of the family under sixteen and may, in particular, commit the child to the care of a local authority.

Appeals relating to matrimonial orders lie to a divisional court of the Family Division. Further appeal lies to the Court of Appeal and then to the House of Lords, in each case with leave.

---

[1] Children and Young Persons Act 1969, s. 3.
[2] Matrimonial Proceedings (Magistrates' Courts) Act 1960, s. 1.
[3] *Ibid.*, s. 2.

H COUNTY COURTS

The county courts are courts of exclusively civil jurisdiction dealing, in the main, with minor civil claims such as small debts. They were established by the County Courts Act 1846 to meet the need for a system of courts to deal with small claims. There are two important limitations to the extent of the county courts' jurisdiction. First, the jurisdiction is entirely statutory so that if, in any matter, statute provides no jurisdiction then none exists. Nevertheless statutes which are likely to affect a large section of the community frequently confer jurisdiction on the county courts. Modern examples are to be found in the Hire-Purchase Act 1965 and the Rent Act 1968. The general common law and equity jurisdiction of the county courts is contained in the County Courts Act 1959 (as amended) and is principally limited by the value of the plaintiff's claim. The Administration of Justice Act 1969 raised the upper limit of the jurisdiction of the county courts to £750 in most actions.[1]

The second limitation on the jurisdiction of the courts is geographical. The jurisdiction of county courts is local in nature so that there must be some connecting factor between the action and the county court district in which it is tried. There are about four hundred county court districts in England and Wales grouped into circuits, each of which has at least one Circuit judge assigned to it. The administrative business of the court is supervised by the county court registrar who is a solicitor of at least seven years' standing and frequently holds the post of district registrar of the High Court. The registrar has a limited jurisdiction to try cases in which cases appeal lies to the judge. Apart from this, county courts have no appellate jurisdiction. Appeal lies from a county court to the Court of Appeal, subject to certain conditions, except in bankruptcy matters where appeal lies to a divisional court of the Chancery Division.

Details of jurisdiction and procedure in the county courts are contained in Part IV of this book.[2]

I CORONERS' COURTS

1 The office of coroner

This ancient office dates from the twelfth century when it principally concerned the custody of the King's revenue, particularly that revenue accruing from fines and forfeiture. In addition the coroner from time to time exercised the jurisdiction of the sheriff and enquired into such matters as deodands, treasure trove and unexplained deaths. Some of these functions, together with the administrative functions once exercised by coroners, have been removed.

The modern coroner's appointment and jurisdiction are governed by statute.[3] He must be a barrister, solicitor or registered medical practitioner of not less than five years' standing. Coroners are appointed, for historical reasons, by county councils in counties and by borough councils in certain boroughs. They are removable by the Lord Chancellor for misbehaviour.

---

[1] In equity proceedings the figure is £5,000; these figures may be increased by Order in Council (Administration of Justice Act 1969, s. 10).
[2] See p. 312, *post.*
[3] Coroners Acts 1887–1954.

2 Jurisdiction

Although the coroner has jurisdiction over such matters as treasure trove and, in London, enquiring into the outbreak of fires, his jurisdiction is principally concerned with inquests into the death of persons dying within his district where there is reasonable cause for suspecting that the person has died a violent or unnatural death, or a sudden death the cause of which is unknown, or has died in prison.

To hold an inquest the coroner may, and in some cases must summon a jury of between seven and eleven members. Witnesses attend and give evidence and the coroner may compel the attendance of a witness and fine a witness for failing to attend in answer to a summons. The procedure is entirely inquisitorial in that, although interested persons may be represented and may ask questions of the witnesses, it is the coroner who conducts the proceedings and there are no speeches made to the jury. The jury return their verdict which need not be unanimous provided there are not more than two dissentients. This verdict is recorded in a document termed an "inquisition". If there is a verdict of murder, manslaughter or infanticide by a named person, the coroner has power to commit that person for trial in the same way as examining justices. In such a case the inquest is rather like a preliminary investigation and the inquisition takes the place of an indictment at the subsequent trial.[1] However, where criminal proceedings are pending in respect of the death the inquest is adjourned pending their determination. There is no appeal from a coroner's inquisition although it may be quashed by an order of certiorari by the High Court.

Proceedings before a coroner's court are absolutely privileged.[2]

J JUDICIAL COMMITTEE OF THE PRIVY COUNCIL

1 Constitution

Prior to the Judicial Committee Act 1833 the jurisdiction of the Privy Council was exercised principally by laymen. This Act, as amended by the Judicial Committee Act 1844, the Appellate Jurisdiction Acts 1876–1947 and other Acts, created the Judicial Committee composed of the Lord President of the Council, the Lord Chancellor, ex-Lord Presidents, the Lords of Appeal in Ordinary and those members of the Privy Council who hold or have held high judicial office within the meaning of the Appellate Jurisdiction Acts 1876 and 1887. Membership has also been extended from time to time by Order in Council to persons who have held high judicial office in Commonwealth countries. In practice the Lord Chancellor and the Lords of Appeal in Ordinary are the members of the Committee who usually sit, with the result that decisions of the Privy Council enjoy great authority although they are not strictly binding on English courts.[3]

The hearing of appeals takes place at the bar of the Privy Council before not less than three and usually five members of the Committee. The members of the Committee sit unrobed and procedure is similar to procedure in the House of Lords.

---

[1] See p. 380, *post.*

[2] *McCarey* v. *Associated Newspapers, Ltd.,* [1964] 2 All E.R. 335; [1964] 1 W. L. R. 855.

[3] See p. 127, *ante.*

2 Jurisdiction

Although all English courts derive their jurisdiction directly or indirectly from the Sovereign, the Judicial Committee of the Privy Council is slightly different in that its jurisdiction is that of the Sovereign in Council. Consequently the Privy Council does not pass judgment. It merely tenders advice to the Sovereign in person. This is by convention followed and implemented by an Order in Council. For this reason only one opinion is usually read and dissents were until recently not recorded.[1] However it is now provided by Order in Council that dissenting opinions may be delivered in open court.[2]

The main aspects of the jurisdiction of the Privy Council are as follows.

a Appeals from courts outside the United Kingdom

Since the Sovereign is the fountain of justice for all her Dominions the Privy Council has jurisdiction to hear appeals from the Isle of Man, the Channel Islands, British Colonies and Protectorates and from the highest courts of independent Commonwealth countries. However, since the Statute of Westminster 1931 Commonwealth legislatures have been competent to pass legislation excluding appeal to the Privy Council and several have done so. Thus the Privy Council held in 1947 that Canada could validly enact that the decision of its own Supreme Court be final and exclusive in civil and criminal matters.[3]

b Admiralty jurisdiction

Prior to 1875 appeal lay from the High Court of Admiralty to the Privy Council. When the Judicature Acts assigned jurisdiction to hear appeals from the Probate, Divorce and Admiralty Division of the High Court to the newly formed Court of Appeal the jurisdiction of the Privy Council was limited to appeals from that Division when sitting as a "prize court". The jurisdiction of the High Court to sit as a prize court is now exercised, in common with all Admiralty jurisdiction, by the Admiralty Court of the Queen's Bench Division.[4] A prize court is a court convened to determine issues concerning the ownership of ships and cargo and the validity of their capture by enemy warships.

c Appeals from ecclesiastical courts

Since the jurisdiction of the ecclesiastical courts was drastically curtailed in 1857[5] their jurisdiction has been confined to matters affecting members of the clergy and church buildings. The highest ecclesiastical courts are the Canterbury Court of Arches and the Chancery Court of York. Appeal from these courts lies to the Privy Council.[6] Although archbishops and bishops are not members of the Privy Council, whenever the Council is hearing an ecclesiastical appeal summonses are sent to one archbishop or the Bishop of London and four other bishops to sit as assessors, i.e. in an advisory capacity.

---

[1] Cf., Judgment in the criminal division of the Court of Appeal where only one judgment is delivered as a rule but for different reasons.

[2] Judicial Committee (Dissenting Opinions) Order in Council 1966.

[3] *A.-G. for Ontario* v. *A.-G. for Canada*, [1947] A.C. 127; [1947] 1 All E.R. 137.

[4] Administration of Justice Act 1970, s. 2; see p. 163, *ante*.

[5] Court of Probate Act 1857; Matrimonial Causes Act 1857; see p. 58, *ante*.

[6] Ecclesiastical Jurisdiction Measure 1963, s. 8.

d   Appeals from medical tribunals

The Privy Council hears appeals by persons who have had their names erased from the medical register by the disciplinary committee of the General Medical Council under the Medical Act 1956.[1]

e   Special references

Apart from its appellate jurisdiction outlined above, the Privy Council is sometimes required to advise on matters of law at the instance of the Sovereign.[2] In the exercise of this jurisdiction the Judicial Committee has advised on such diverse matters as the powers of colonial judges,[3] legislation in Jersey[4] and the eligibility of a person to sit and vote in the House of Commons.[5]

K   COURTS OF PARTICULAR JURISDICTION

Prior to 1972 there were courts of local jurisdiction which constituted exceptions to the normal hierarchy of courts in that their constitution and jurisdiction were controlled locally.   However all such courts which actively exercised jurisdiction were abolished by the Courts Act 1971.   Certain courts are outside the ordinary hierarchy because their jurisdiction is concerned with matters wholly outside the scope of the ordinary civil and criminal law.   Some of these courts, such as courts-martial, derive their jurisdiction from statute while others, notably the ecclesiastical courts, are autonomous although, of course, they are recognised by the Crown.   The jurisdiction of these specialist courts is usually applicable only to certain members of society who have impliedly agreed to submit to their jurisdiction, though in some instances it extends to all members of the community.

1   Courts-martial

Courts-martial exercise jurisdiction over members of the armed forces.   Their constitution, jurisdiction and procedure are governed by various statutes, principally the Army and Air Force Acts 1955 and the Naval Discipline Act 1957.

Air Force and military courts-martial are similar in constitution and procedure.[6]   The accused may be arrested for any offence against military law by a superior officer.   In many instances his offence will only be a "summary" offence against Queen's Regulations in which case he will be tried by superior officers.   In other cases the accused has a choice as to whether to be tried summarily or at a court-martial.[7]   Serious offences are always tried at courts-martial, except that murder, manslaughter, treason and rape committed within the United Kingdom cannot be tried at courts-martial but must be tried in the

---

[1] Similar powers exist under the Dentists Act 1957 and the Opticians Act 1958.
[2] Judicial Committee Act 1833, s. 4.
[3] *Re Wills* (1840), 3 Moo. P.C.C. 216.
[4] *Re Jersey States* (1853), 9 Moo. P.C.C. 185.
[5] *Re Macmanaway,* [1951] A.C. 161.
[6] Naval courts-martial differ slightly in their composition, although their jurisdiction and procedure are similar.
[7] Cf. procedure in criminal courts where the accused is charged with a "hybrid" offence; see p. 366, *post.*

ordinary criminal courts. In all other cases the jurisdiction of civilian and military courts is concurrent. However a person who has already been convicted or acquitted by a civilian court cannot be subsequently tried at a military or Air Force court-martial, and *vice-versa.*[1]

The trial of an offence at a court-martial is in many ways similar to a trial in the ordinary criminal courts. It is preceded by an inquiry which is similar to a preliminary investigation. The accused is sent for trial on a charge sheet which may be compared with an indictment. The trial will be before at least three (or five in the case of a general court-martial) officers who are assisted by a judge advocate from the Judge Advocate General's department[2] who is a lawyer and advises on the law. Proceedings are in open court and both counsel and solicitors have a right of audience. The prosecution case is conducted by an Army or Air Force officer either personally or through a civilian counsel. The order of proceedings and rules of evidence applicable are similar to those applicable in other criminal proceedings. The accused may appear in person or be represented by counsel, solicitor or a defending officer. There is no jury and at the conclusion of the evidence the judge advocate sums up and advises on the law, leaving the members of the court to arrive at their decision which is by majority, except that the court must be unanimous where sentence of death is to be imposed.[3] An acquittal is final whereas a finding of guilt is subject to confirmation by a superior officer. Prior to confirming the finding of guilt the confirming authority may remit the finding to the court for reconsideration and may refuse to confirm the decision if it could not be supported by the evidence, was wrong in law or there was a miscarriage of justice.

The necessity for confirmation of a finding of guilt affords a safeguard to the accused against injustice. A further safeguard is provided by the power of the High Court to prevent excesses or abuses of jurisdiction by means of the prerogative orders of prohibition and certiorari and by habeas corpus.[4]

Although courts-martial cannot generally exercise jurisdiction over civilians this can be done where Her Majesty's forces are in armed occupation of hostile territory. In these circumstances a state of martial law may be declared by Her Majesty's commanders. A state of martial law may also be declared in time of insurrection although it is doubtful whether such a declaration would be valid within the United Kingdom.

Courts-Martial Appeal Court. Until 1951 there was no appeal from conviction by a court-martial, the only remedy being a petition to the reviewing authority or, where an excess of jurisdiction was alleged, an application for prohibition, certiorari or habeas corpus.

The Courts-Martial (Appeals) Act 1951[5] created the Courts-Martial Appeal Court which is now composed of the *ex-officio* and ordinary members of the Court of Appeal, judges of the Queen's Bench Division nominated by the Lord Chief Justice, certain Scottish and Irish judges and other persons of legal

---

[1] Armed Forces Act 1966, s. 25.

[2] The corresponding department in naval courts-martial is the Judge Advocate of the Fleet's department. The Judge Advocate General and the Judge Advocate of the Fleet are appointed by the Queen on the advice of the Lord Chancellor.

[3] Army Act 1955, s. 96.

[4] R. v. *Governor of Wormwood Scrubs Prison, ex parte Boydell,* [1948] 2 K.B. 193; [1948] 1 All E.R. 438.

[5] Now the Courts-Martial (Appeals) Act 1968.

experience appointed by the Lord Chancellor. In practice the composition of the court resembles closely that of the criminal division of the Court of Appeal.[1] As in the latter court, there must be at least three judges. Only one judgment is delivered and procedure is similar to that in the criminal division of the Court of Appeal. The grounds of appeal to the Courts-Martial Appeal Court and the powers of that court on determining appeals are substantially similar to those of the Court of Appeal except that there is no right of appeal against sentence.

Appeal lies from the Courts-Martial Appeal Court to the House of Lords at the instance of the prosecutor or the defence subject to the conditions under which an appeal lies from the criminal division of the Court of Appeal to the House of Lords.[2]

2   Ecclesiastical courts

These courts have a history which is as old as the common law itself. Although they have been subject to control by the Sovereign since the reign of Henry VIII and although their jurisdiction over laymen has by stages been abolished there remains a hierarchy of courts within the Church of England. In addition the National Assembly of the Church of England has statutory power[3] to pass Measures concerning any matter affecting the Church of England and even concerning Acts of Parliament. These measures have statutory force upon receiving the Royal Assent. The most significant recent measure has been the Ecclesiastical Jurisdiction Measure 1963 which altered the hierarchy of ecclesiastical courts and abolished a large number of obsolete courts and their jurisdiction.

The ecclesiastical judicial system may now be summarised as follows. In each diocese there is a consistory court the judge of which is a chancellor appointed by the bishop. He must be at least 30 years old and either be a barrister of seven years' standing or have held high judicial office. The consistory courts' jurisdiction is principally concerned with investigating allegations of conduct unbecoming a clerk in Holy Orders and persistent neglect of duty. Appeal lies from the consistory courts to the Arches Court of Canterbury, presided over by the Dean of the Arches, or the Chancery Court of York, presided over by the Auditor, both officers being barristers of ten years' standing or persons who have held high judicial office. Appeal from these two courts lies to the Privy Council.[4]

Jurisdiction equivalent to that of the consistory courts is exercised over bishops and archbishops by Commissions of Convocation. Jurisdiction over all members of the clergy in matters involving "doctrine, ritual or ceremonial" is exercised by the Court of Ecclesiastical Causes Reserved composed of five judges appointed by Her Majesty including two persons who have held high judicial office and three diocesan bishops. Finally petition lies from both the Commissions of Convocation and the Court of Ecclesiastical Causes Reserved to a Commission of Review composed of three Lords of Appeal in Ordinary and two Lords Spiritual.

---

[1] See p. 158, *ante*.
[2] See p. 430, *post*; Courts-Martial (Appeals) Act 1968, s. 39.
[3] Under the Church of England Assembly (Powers) Act 1919.
[4] See p. 179, *ante*.

The penalties which ecclesiastical courts may impose range from rebuke to deprivation of Orders and disqualification from subsequent preferment. In addition such deprivation and disqualification are automatic where a priest or deacon is sentenced to imprisonment, has an affiliation order made against him, has a decree of divorce or judicial separation pronounced against him on the ground of adultery, desertion, cruelty, rape, sodomy or bestiality, is found to have committed adultery in matrimonial proceedings or has had a magistrates' court order made against him in similar circumstances.[1]

Excesses of jurisdiction by the ecclesiastical courts may be controlled by the High Court by means of the prerogative orders of mandamus and prohibition. Certiorari does not, however, lie since these courts exercise and administer a different system of law.

3 Naval courts

A naval court may be summoned by an officer in command of one of Her Majesty's ships on any foreign station on a complaint to him by any member of the crew which appears to require immediate investigation, or where any British ship is wrecked, abandoned or lost in the area, or where the interests of the owner of any British ship or its cargo so require.[2] Such a court, consisting of naval officers, must investigate the matter judicially and may impose imprisonment or fine or forfeiture of wages, suspend or cancel officers' certificates, send an offender home for trial and order a ship to undergo a survey for unseaworthiness. Appeal lies from its decision to the divisional court of the Queen's Bench Division and thence, with leave, to the Court of Appeal.

4 Court of Chivalry

The jurisdiction of an English court can only be removed by statute. Nevertheless the jurisdiction of most local courts and feudal courts has fallen into obsolescence. However a recent sitting was held of the Court of Chivalry, an ancient feudal court, to decide the entitlement of a theatre to display the coat of arms of the City of Manchester.[3] Prior to this case the court had not been convened since 1737. The court determines disputes over the right to use armorial bearings and ensigns. It is presided over by the Earl Marshal, although he appointed the Lord Chief Justice to sit as his deputy in the recent case in question. The court appears to have no power to enforce its decisions.[4]

5 Restrictive Practices Court

This court of record was created by the Restrictive Trade Practices Act 1956. The function of the court is to consider agreements which restrict prices or the conditions of supply of goods. Cases are referred to the court by the Registrar of Restrictive Trading Agreements or by parties to such an agreement who have been ordered to furnish particulars to the court. The scope of the court's business was temporarily increased by the Resale Prices Act 1964 which restricted minimum resale price maintenance. Any supplier or trade association

---

[1] Ecclesiastical Jurisdiction Measure 1963, s. 55.
[2] Merchant Shipping Act 1894, s. 480.
[3] *Manchester Corporation* v. *Manchester Palace of Varieties, Ltd.*, [1955] P. 133; [1955] 1 All E.R. 387.
[4] *Ibid.*

was able to apply to the Restrictive Practices Court for exemption for a class of goods on the grounds that this would be in the public interest.[1]

The court consists of three judges of the High Court appointed by the Lord Chancellor, a judge of the Court of Session of Scotland, a judge of the Supreme Court of Northern Ireland and not more than ten lay members appointed by the Queen on the recommendation of the Lord Chancellor. The court is duly constituted with a presiding judge and two lay members. Appeal lies from the court on a question of law to the Court of Appeal, the Court of Session or the Court of Appeal of Northern Ireland, as the case may be.

6   Court of Protection

At common law the Sovereign has always assumed care and custody of persons of unsound mind and their property. As keeper of the Queen's conscience the Lord Chancellor was detailed to exercise this authority. At the present day the Lord Chancellor and the judges of the Chancery Division administer the property of persons of unsound mind within the meaning of the Mental Health Act 1959. When exercising this function the Chancery judge sits as the Court of Protection, the constitution and jurisdiction of which is now governed by the 1959 Act.[2]

The jurisdiction of the Court of Protection should not be confused with the jurisdiction of courts under various statutes to make orders for admission of persons to approved hospitals[3] nor with the general statutory powers of justices of the peace to make reception orders in the case of persons of unsound mind wandering at large.[4]

L   TRIBUNALS AND INQUIRIES

1   Nature of tribunals and inquiries

a   Statutory Tribunals

The second characteristic of Dicey's Rule of Law is that all categories of people are subject to the control of the courts. There are some who regard the modern concept of administrative justice as a denial of this principle. Nonetheless administrative justice is an increasingly important aspect of the English legal system. Because of the comparative speed, cheapness and informality of tribunals as compared with the ordinary courts Parliament has during the last hundred or so years tended more and more to confer jurisdiction upon bodies which are outside the normal hierarchy of the courts. These tribunals exercise differing functions which may be administrative or judicial. They differ from ordinary courts of law in several respects but particularly in their composition. The members of the tribunals are often lawyers and sometimes even judges but equally frequently they are laymen with specialised knowledge of the sphere of activity with which the tribunal is dealing but with little or no knowledge of the law.

---

[1] Resale Prices Act 1964, s. 5. All applications have now been determined.
[2] Though the power is exercisable in the High Court if the sum involved is a small one: Re K., [1969] 2 Ch. 1; [1969] 1 All E.R. 194.
[3] E.g., Mental Health Act 1959, s. 60.
[4] Magistrates' Courts Act 1952, s. 30.

In recent years the control exercised by outside forces, notably the ordinary courts, over administrative tribunals has increased. A committee was set up in 1955 under the chairmanship of Sir Oliver Franks to consider administrative tribunals and inquiries. The committee reported in 1957[1] and its recommendations were substantially implemented by the Tribunals and Inquiries Act 1958 (now the Tribunals and Inquiries Act 1971). The 1971 Act provides that in the case of certain specified tribunals the chairman is to be selected from a panel appointed by the Lord Chancellor.[2] In addition there is a Council on Tribunals consisting of not more than fifteen nor less than ten members appointed by the Lord Chancellor and the Secretary of State.[3] The members are disqualified from membership of the House of Commons. The Council keeps under review the working of tribunals and reports on them from time to time. The tribunals subject to the scrutiny of the Council on Tribunals are listed in the First Schedule to the Act and include Agricultural Land Tribunals, the Lands Tribunal, Mental Health Review Tribunals, National Insurance Tribunals, Rent Tribunals and the General and Special Commissioners of Income Tax. In this way the Lord Chancellor is able to exercise direct extrajudicial control over some of the more important tribunals.

b Domestic tribunals

There are a number of private or professional associations which have set up their own tribunals for resolving disputes between their own members or exercising control or discipline over them. The jurisdiction of these tribunals is based primarily on contract in that, by becoming a member of the association or professional body, a person contracts to accept the jurisdiction of the governing tribunal. Nevertheless in many cases these tribunals exist on a statutory basis with a right of appeal to the courts. Examples of domestic tribunals constituted under statute are the Solicitors' Disciplinary Committee, set up under the Solicitors' Act 1957,[4] and the Disciplinary Committee of the General Medical Council, set up under the Medical Act 1956. Where the tribunal is not constituted under a statute then there is no appeal to the ordinary courts. However, the High Court exercises a supervisory jurisdiction over tribunals, even where their jurisdiction is not based on statute and will intervene to prevent an abuse of natural justice.[5]

c Industrial Tribunals

These tribunals were first established under section 12 of the Industrial Training Act 1964 with a very limited jurisdiction under that Act. Since that date, however, the jurisdiction of the tribunals has been greatly enlarged by statutes, notably the Contracts of Employment Act 1963, the Redundancy Payments Act 1965 and the Docks and Harbours Act 1966. The jurisdiction of these

---

[1] Cmnd. 218.
[2] Tribunals and Inquiries Act 1971, s. 7.
[3] *Ibid.*, s. 2 (1); the Parliamentary Commissioner for Administration is also a member of the Council (s. 2 (3)).
[4] See p. 205, *post.*
[5] *Lee* v. *Showmen's Guild of Great Britain*, [1952] 2 Q.B. 329; [1952] 1 All E.R. 1175; *Byrne* v. *Kinematograph Renters Society, Ltd.*, [1958] 2 All E.R. 579; [1958] 1 W.L.R. 762; *Nagle* v. *Feilden*, [1966] 2 Q. B. 633; [1966] 1 All E.R. 689.

tribunals has recently been widened still further by the Industrial Relations Act 1971. Thus, for example, the industrial tribunals have jurisdiction under section 106 of that Act to hear complaints of various forms of unfair industrial practice on the part of employers, on the hearing of which the tribunal may make an order determining the rights of the complainant and of the employer and may award compensation to be paid by the employer to the complainant.[1] There is, further, power under section 113 to confer jurisdiction on industrial tribunals to hear actions for damages for breach of any contract of employment (other than for damages in respect of death or personal injury) though the power has not yet been exercised.

Appeal from industrial tribunals lies on questions of law to the National Industrial Relations Court in proceedings under the Contracts of Employment Act 1963, the Redundancy Payments Act 1965, the Equal Pay Act 1970 and the Industrial Relations Act 1971. In other proceedings appeal lies to a divisional court of the Queen's Bench Division.

d   Tribunals of Inquiry

When a matter of urgent public importance arises Parliament may resolve to set up a tribunal to inquire into it. The tribunal is then set up by Her Majesty or a Secretary of State and upon the tribunal may be conferred many of the procedural powers of the High Court, such as summoning witnesses, compelling the production of documents and taking evidence on oath. If a witness refuses to answer a question put to him he may be reported to the High Court and punished for contempt of court.[2] A tribunal of inquiry must generally sit in public unless the public interest requires otherwise. The tribunal has discretion whether or not to allow representation by counsel or solicitor before it.

e   Local statutory inquiries

There are a number of statutes which confer jurisdiction upon Ministers to hold local inquiries. In practice these inquiries are conducted by local inspectors but ultimately it is the Minister who assumes responsibility in Parliament. Inquiries of this nature often arise when objections are lodged against orders submitted by a local or public authority to a Minister for confirmation, or, sometimes, submitted by the Minister himself but subject to confirmation. The usual circumstance is the making of an order for the compulsory acquisition of land,[3] or planning schemes affecting land development.[4]

Procedure at these inquiries is governed by the statute under which they are held and often there is no right of appeal. Nevertheless the rules of natural justice must be observed and, since the Tribunals and Inquiries Act 1958, the Minister has been required to give reasons for his decision on request unless national security justifies not giving a reason.

f   Criminal Injuries Compensation Board

Tribunals are sometimes established for the purpose of determining individuals' rights to compensation from public funds. The right to compensation arises

---

[1] See also Industrial Relations Act 1971, ss. 107–11.
[2] Tribunals of Inquiry (Evidence) Act 1921, s. 1; A.-G. v. Clough, [1963] 1 Q.B. 773; [1963] 1 All E.R. 420; A.-G. v. Mulholland, [1963] 2 Q.B. 477; [1963] 1 All E.R. 767.
[3] Acquisition of Land (Authorisation Procedure) Act 1946.
[4] Town and Country Planning Act 1962.

where a person has suffered loss or damage, often by reason of an act of the legislature or the executive; compulsory acquisition of land is an obvious example.

A recent and most important addition to compensation tribunals is the Criminal Injuries Compensation Board. The scheme was established as an experimental measure in 1964 and provides *ex gratia* compensation to victims of crimes of violence (or if the victim dies, his dependants). Compensation is assessed on the same basis as common law damages (where the application is by a dependant the principles of the Fatal Accidents Acts 1846–1959 apply) and takes the form of a lump sum payment. Although there is no right to compensation claims are determined by the Board consisting of a chairman and eight qualified members.

An interesting feature of the Board is the method of its creation. Whereas tribunals are usually established by statute, the Board was set up by prerogative act. The Government set out in a White Paper[1] the draft scheme, it was debated in both Houses of Parliament and, in an amended form, was announced by both Houses on June 24, 1964.[2]

The scheme is financed by a grant-in-aid, approved annually by the Appropriation Act. Despite being a non-statutory tribunal the Board, since its jurisdiction is of a public rather than a domestic nature, is subject to the prerogative order of *certiorari*.[3]

2 Control by the courts of administrative tribunals and inquiries

It is well recognised that administrative justice is a dangerous institution unless it is subject to effective safeguards and control. The Donoughmore Committee on Ministers' Powers, a predecessor of the Franks Committee, in its report in 1932 recommended four types of safeguard: first, that the supervisory jurisdiction of the High Court over tribunals be maintained in respect of excesses of jurisdiction; secondly, that the tribunals be compelled by the High Court to observe natural justice; thirdly, that reports of statutory inquiries be published; and finally, that there should be an appeal to the High Court on a question of law. The third of these safeguards is not judicial and was, in fact, implemented by the Tribunals and Inquiries Act 1958, section 12. The same Act introduced the additional safeguard of control by the Council on Tribunals. The first, second and last of the four safeguards specified by the Donoughmore Committee depend upon control by the courts through the exercise of supervisory and appellate jurisdiction.

a Supervisory control

The supervisory jurisdiction of the High Court, exercised in practice by the Queen's Bench Division, is a common law jurisdiction and does not depend upon statute. Any provision in an Act passed before August, 1958 which

---

[1] Cmnd. 2323 of 1964.

[2] Further amendments to the scheme were announced by the Home Secretary on August 3, 1965 and May 21, 1969.

[3] *R. v. Criminal Injuries Compensation Board, ex parte Lain,* [1967] 2 Q.B. 864; [1967] 2 All E.R. 770.

excludes any of the powers of the High Court does not have effect so as to prevent the High Court from making orders of mandamus or certiorari.[1]

In R. v. Electricity Commissioners, Ex parte London Electricity Joint Committee Co. (1920) Ltd.[2] ATKIN, L.J. (as he then was) laid down four requirements as conditions precedent to the exercise of the supervisory jurisdiction of the High Court. This jurisdiction is exercised over bodies which (1) have legal authority, (2) have power to determine questions affecting the rights of subjects, (3) have a duty to act judicially, and (4) act in excess of their legal authority.

There are two ways in which the High Court may purport to exercise its supervisory control over tribunals. The usual method is by the issue of prerogative orders; however these orders lie only against tribunals which are statutory, or at least of a public character[3] and do not extend to tribunals exercising a purely voluntary jurisdiction. A person aggrieved by the decision of a voluntary tribunal may, however, invoke the High Court's supervisory jurisdiction by bringing an action against the officers of the tribunal, claiming an injunction or a declaration as to his rights.[4]

Whichever procedure is adopted the court will interfere to prevent the tribunal exceeding its jurisdiction or acting contrary to natural justice. The rules of natural justice are not clearly defined and indeed may vary according to the nature of the tribunal[5] but they generally include the right of each party to state his case, the prohibition on a person being a judge in his own cause and the right of parties to be informed of the reasons for the decision.

In recent years the High Court has shown an increased willingness to intervene in the affairs of trade and professional bodies which have the power to deprive individuals of their livelihood.[6]

b Appeals from tribunals

An application for a prerogative order is not an appeal. There is no common law right of appeal from a tribunal so that an appeal only lies where statute so provides. The Tribunals and Inquiries Act 1971, section 13, provides for any party to appeal or to require the tribunal to state a case on a point of law from certain administrative tribunals to the High Court. These appeals are heard by the divisional court of the Queen's Bench Division. Other statutes provide rights of appeal to various branches of the Supreme Court and, in the case of doctors, dentists and opticians, to the Judicial Committee of the Privy Council.[7]

---

1 Tribunals and Inquiries Act 1971, s. 14.
2 [1924] 1 K.B. 171.
3 R. v. Criminal Injuries Compensation Board, ex parte Lain, [1967] 2 Q.B. 864; [1967] 2 All E.R. 770.
4 Under R.S.C. (Revision) 1965, O. 15, r. 16; see p. 266, post.
5 Thus even the rule audi alteram partem does not always apply; R. v. Senate of University of London, ex parte Roffey, [1969] 2 All E.R. 964. Observance of the law of evidence is not a rule of natural justice; T. A. Miller, Ltd. v. Minister of Housing and Local Government, [1968] 2 All E.R. 633; [1968] 1 W.L.R. 992, nor is the right to legal representation before a domestic tribunal; Enderby Town Football Club, Ltd. v. Football Association, Ltd., [1971] Ch. 591; [1971] 1 All E.R. 215; Pett v. Greyhound Racing Association, Ltd. (No. 2), [1970] 1 Q.B. 46; [1969] 2 All E.R. 221.
6 Bonsor v. Musicians' Union, [1956] A.C. 104; [1955] 3 All E.R. 518; Byrne v. Kinematograph Renters Society, Ltd., [1958] 2 All E.R. 579; [1958] 1 W.L.R. 762. Nagle v. Feilden, [1966] 2 Q.B. 633; [1966] 1 All E.R. 689.
7 See p. 179, ante.

M ARBITRATION

1 Provisions for reference to arbitration

As an alternative to proceedings in the ordinary courts, parties, particularly in the sphere of commerce, often prefer to refer their disputes to arbitration. The jurisdiction of arbitrators usually arises out of contract, though there are numerous statutory provisions which provide for the reference of disputes to arbitration.

An agreement to refer disputes to arbitration is a contract and, as such, is subject to the ordinary law of contract. Any provision purporting to oust the jurisdiction of the courts is void, as being contrary to public policy, though there is no objection to a clause which makes reference to arbitration a condition precedent to a right of action. The effect of such a clause, known as a *Scott v. Avery*[1] clause, is that if a party does institute proceedings without referring the dispute to arbitration the clause may be pleaded as a defence in those proceedings and the other party may, after entering appearance but before taking any other step in the proceedings, apply to the court for an order staying the proceedings.[2] The order is discretionary but, in the absence of some good reason, the court will stay the proceedings.

2 Procedure

Procedure on arbitrations is governed (except, in relation to statutory references, where the statute in question otherwise provides) by the Arbitration Act 1950. The issues arising must (in the absence of contrary agreement) be decided according to the ordinary rules of English law and the normal judicial procedure will apply, including the rules of evidence (though these are often dispensed with by agreement). The arbitrator has implied power to examine witnesses, order the discovery and inspection of documents, pleadings, interrogatories and the like.

3 Appointment and powers of arbitrators and umpires

In the absence of specific provision reference to arbitration connotes reference to a single arbitrator.[3] Where specific provision is made for the appointment of two arbitrators there is an implied term that, immediately after they are appointed, they shall appoint an umpire who, if the arbitrators cannot agree, may enter on the reference in their stead.[4] Under section 10 of the Act the High Court has various powers to appoint arbitrators and umpires in default of appointment by the parties. The High Court also has power to revoke the authority of an arbitrator or umpire on the ground of delay, bias or improper conduct[5] and has inherent jurisdiction to stay arbitration proceedings by injunction.

An arbitrator or umpire may, and must if so directed by the High Court or the agreement so provides, state in the form of a special case for the opinion of the High Court (1) any question of law arising in the course of the reference; (2) any award.[6]

---

[1] (1856), 5 H.L. Cas. 811.
[2] Arbitration Act 1950, s. 4 (1).
[3] *Ibid.*, s. 6.
[4] *Ibid.*, s. 8.
[5] *Ibid.*, s. 23.
[6] *Ibid.*, s. 21.

This power cannot be restricted by the terms of the agreement[1] and if the arbitrator or umpire wrongly refuses to state a case the High Court may compel him so to do.

The decision of the arbitrator is in the form of an "award", dealing with all the issues on which reference was made. The award may contain provision for the payment of money, costs or an order of specific performance (except of a contract relating to land).[2] As between the parties the award gives rise to an estoppel *in personam*[3] in relation to the issues decided, thus extinguishing any cause of action in relation thereto.

4 Intervention by the court

An arbitration award may, with leave of the High Court, be enforced in the same way as a judgment or order of that court and, where leave is granted, judgment may be entered in the terms of the award. In addition action may be brought on the award as a contractual debt.

The court's powers over arbitration proceedings are strictly limited. There is no right of appeal to the courts (other than the procedure by special case, referred to above). However if the award (which usually sets out findings of law) is erroneous on its face, the High Court has power to set aside the award or remit the case for reconsideration;[4] similar powers exist where the award is uncertain or ambiguous, where the arbitrator has been guilty of misconduct or when fresh evidence becomes available. However, a mere wrong decision of a point of law is not a ground for upsetting an award.

The parties may nominate any person they wish to act as arbitrator. Members of the bar are not infrequently appointed. In addition, by section 4 of the Administration of Justice Act 1970 a judge of the Commercial Court may, if in all the circumstances he thinks fit, accept appointment as sole arbitrator or as umpire where the dispute appears to him to be of a commercial character and provided the Lord Chief Justice has informed him that, having regard to the state of business in the High Court, he can be made availalble to do so.

---

[1] *Czarnikow v. Roth, Schmidt & Co.*, [1922] 2 K.B. 478.
[2] Arbitration Act 1950, s. 15.
[3] See p. 472, *post*.
[4] Arbitration Act 1950, s. 23.

CHAPTER 11

The Judiciary

A APPOINTMENT AND CONDITIONS OF TENURE OF OFFICE

The Lord Chancellor, the Lord Chief Justice, the Master of the Rolls, the President of the Family Division of the High Court, the Lords of Appeal in Ordinary and the Lords Justices of Appeal are appointed by the Queen on the advice of the Prime Minister. Of these only the Lord Chancellor's appointment is made on a political basis. The puisne judges of the High Court, Circuit judges and Recorders are appointed by the Queen on the advice of the Lord Chancellor. Justices of the peace are appointed by the Lord Chancellor directly.

Until Stuart times judges held office only during the King's pleasure and could be, and were, removed at the will of the King. Their position was altered in consequence of the Revolution settlement by the Act of Settlement 1700 which provided that:

> "Judges' commissions be made *quamdiu se bene gesserint*, and their salaries ascertained and established, but upon the address of both Houses of Parliament it may be lawful to remove them."

Thus, as long as they conducted themselves properly (*quamdiu se bene gesserint*) judges of the superior courts[1] could be removed only on an address by both Houses of Parliament. Presumably a judge who was guilty of serious neglect or misconduct could be removed by the Crown without the need for an address by Parliament.[2] This prohibition still applies to judges of the Supreme Court of Judicature, except, however, for Circuit judges and Recorders who are removable by the Lord Chancellor on the ground of incapacity or misbehaviour or, in the case of a Recorder, failing to comply with the conditions of his appointment.[3]

---

[1] Except the Lord Chancellor who, because he is a Minister of the Crown, holds office at the Queen's pleasure: Judicature Act 1925, s. 12.

[2] See *Earl of Shrewsbury's Case* (1611), 9 Co. Rep. 42a, at P. 50. No English judge has been removed under the Act of Settlement procedure, though an Irish judge was so removed in 1830.

[3] Courts Act 1971, ss. 17 (4), 21 (6); see p. 168, *ante*.

Judges of the Supreme Court (excluding Circuit judges and Recorders) and Lords of Appeal in Ordinary must, unless appointed before 1959, retire at the age of 75.[1] Their salaries are fixed by statute and charged on the Consolidated Fund.

Justices of the peace may be removed from the Commission by the Lord Chancellor without showing cause. Several justices have been so removed, generally for refusing to administer a law with which they were not in sympathy. Although there is no retiring age for justices of the peace they are put on the supplemental list at the age of 75,[2] which is *de facto* retirement in that they cease to be entitled to exercise judicial functions. Justices may be put on the supplemental list before they have reached this age, either at their own request or on the ground of "age or infirmity or other like cause".[3]

A peculiar feature of the English system of judicial appointments has been its almost Salic preference for males over females. This tradition was only recently broken when, in 1965, Mrs. Justice Lane, having already been the first female county court judge, was accorded the distinction of being the first woman to be made a judge of a superior court in England, being appointed a puisne judge of the Probate, Divorce and Admiralty Division.

B   CONSTITUTIONAL POSITION

Much has been written on the question of whether judges are "servants" of the Crown. The better view seems to be that they are servants for they are appointed and, in certain circumstances, removable by the Queen and are paid out of the Consolidated Fund, although they cannot be controlled in the exercise of their office by the Queen or her Ministers. Generally the question of whether judges are properly describable as servants is unimportant though the question did arise in an acute form in 1931 when the National Economy Act of that year conferred power upon the Commissioners of Inland Revenue to reduce the remuneration of "persons in His Majesty's Service". The Commissioners purported to reduce judicial salaries. The validity of this measure, though strenuously disputed, was not decided since the Inland Revenue soon abolished these reductions under pressure of public opinion.

Whether judges are or are not Crown servants there is no doubt that the judicial function is not under the control of the legislature or the Executive. Judicial independence is a fundamental of English constitutional law. An offshoot of this principle of judicial independence is the doctrine of judicial immunity. The degree of this immunity varies with the status of the judge. No action lies against a judge of a superior court in respect of anything he does or says in the exercise of his judicial office even if he is malicious or acts in bad faith.[4] It is uncertain whether this immunity is lost if the judge of a superior court exceeds his jurisdiction.[5] Judges of inferior courts enjoy immunity only when

---

[1] Judicial Pensions Act 1959. Circuit judges retire at the age of 72 (though the Lord Chancellor may authorise continuance in office until 75); Courts Act 1971, s. 17 (1), (2).
[2] In most cases this will be done at the age of 70: Justices of the Peace Act 1968, s. 2.
[3] Justices of the Peace Act 1949.
[4] *Anderson* v. *Gorrie*, [1895] 1 Q.B. 668.
[5] *Hamond* v. *Howell* (1677), 2 Mod. 218. The acts of a superior court are presumed to be within its jurisdiction: *Peacock* v. *Bell* (1677), 1 Saund. 73.

acting within their jurisdiction. A judge of an inferior court who exceeds his jurisdiction has no immunity from civil proceedings, and the burden is on the judge to show that he acted within his jurisdiction.[1] The immunity of magistrates is narrower and is governed by the Justices Protection Act 1848. The effect of this Act is that magistrates may be sued in respect of any act done in excess of their jurisdiction and, also, in respect of any act done within their jurisdiction maliciously and without reasonable cause.

The immunity which attaches to judicial proceedings is not personal to the judge. Thus no civil action lies in respect of words spoken in the course of proceedings by parties,[2] witnesses,[3] advocates[4] or in respect of the verdict of a jury.[5] Fair and accurate contemporaneous newspaper and broadcast reports of judicial proceedings in the United Kingdom are also absolutely privileged in the law of defamation.[6]

C THE JUDICIAL FUNCTION

Most of the work of the judges is judicial in the sense that they have to adjudicate upon disputes. In the exercise of this function judges must apply the existing rules of law to the case in hand. They cannot, in strict theory at least, create rules of law. The term "judge-made law" has traditionally been used in a perjorative sense. There are two aspects of this function—the interpretation of statutes and the application of the doctrine of precedent. It is the duty of judges to ascertain the intention of the legislature, if the rule of law in question is statutory, or to apply the existing law where the rule of law in question is a rule of common law or equity. The traditional view is that judges are not competent to interpret a statute other than in accordance with the literal meaning of the words used, or to alter any existing rule of common law or equity. Nevertheless there is no doubt that, in practice, only the most traditional of judges always adhere to this rule.[7] Indeed the rule cannot be applied in interpreting an Act of Parliament which makes no provision for the case in question or in deciding a case of "first impression", i.e., a case for which there is no precedent. In such a case the judge must create new law. This traditional view of the judicial function is, it must be said, changing. As LORD SIMON frankly stated in the recent case of *Jones* v. *Secretary of State for Social Services*:[8]

> "In this country it was long considered that judges were not makers of law but merely its discoverers and expounders. The theory was that every case was governed by a relevant rule of law, existing somewhere and discoverable somehow, provided sufficient learning and intellectual rigour were brought to bear. But once such a rule had been discovered, frequently the pretence was tacitly dropped that the rule

---

[1] *Houlden* v. *Smith* (1850), 14 Q.B. 841; *Peacock* v. *Bell* (*supra*).
[2] *Astley* v. *Younge* (1759), 2 Burr. 807.
[3] *Hargreaves* v. *Bretherton*, [1959] 1 Q.B. 45; [1958] 3 All E.R. 122.
[4] *Munster* v. *Lamb* (1883), 11 Q.B.D. 588.
[5] *Bushell's Case* (1670), Vaugh. 135.
[6] Defamation Act 1952, s. 8.
[7] For a detailed discussion of the judicial approach to statutory interpretation and to the doctrine of judicial precedent, see pp. 102, 122 *et seq.*, *ante*.
[8] [1972] 1 All E.R. 145, at p. 198; [1972] 2 W.L.R. 210, at p. 271; see p. 129, *ante*.

was pre-existing; for example, cases like *Shelley's Case*,[1] *Merryweather* v. *Nixan*[2] or *Priestley* v. *Fowler*[3] were (rightly) regarded as new departures in the law. Nevertheless the theory, however unreal, had its value—in limiting the sphere of law making by the judiciary (inevitably at some disadvantage in assessing the potential repercussions of any decision, and increasingly so in a complex modern industrial society), and thus also in emphasising that central feature of our constitution, the sovereignty of Parliament. But the true, even if limited, nature of judicial lawmaking has been more widely acknowledged of recent years."

There are other circumstances in which the judicial function goes far beyond the strict application of existing legal rules. Thus, in many cases, a judge has a discretion. This discretion is usually fettered by precedent and is always subject to principles of natural justice but it is, nonetheless, a discretion. There is no good reason why a judge should not evolve a new rule of equity at the present day. Indeed DENNING, J. (as he then was) virtually did this in *Central London Property Trust, Ltd.* v. *High Trees House, Ltd.*[4] However the existing framework of the law of property makes it very difficult for a new equitable right to be recognised.[5]

In addition to the power to apply, and to a lesser extent create, rules of law, judges exercise certain administrative functions. This is particularly true of justices of the peace who exercise many functions which are not properly termed judicial, such as licensing and the issue of summonses and warrants. Judges of the Chancery Division sitting as a Court of Protection supervise the affairs and administer the property of persons of unsound mind. The Lord Chancellor and all High Court judges are "visitors" of the Inns of Court and, as such, hear appeals from orders of the Inns of Court and the Senate of the Inns of Court.[6] In addition much litigation in the courts is non-contentious and concerns such matters as the administration of trusts, the winding-up of companies, adoption and legitimacy. Finally the Judicature Acts[7] confer power upon a Rule Committee consisting of the Lord Chancellor, the Lord Chief Justice, the Master of the Rolls, four judges, two barristers and two solicitors to make Rules of Court to govern practice and procedure in the Supreme Court while the Courts Act 1971[8] confers similar power upon the Crown Court Rule Committee created by that Act to make "Crown Court Rules" prescribing the procedure and practice to be followed in the Crown Court.

D CONTEMPT OF COURT

1 General nature of contempt

Her Majesty's judges control the due administration of justice and have an inherent jurisdiction to punish conduct which is calculated to prejudice or interfere with the process of the law. Such conduct is termed a contempt of court.

---

[1] (1581), Moore K.B. 136.
[2] (1799), 8 Term Rep. 186.
[3] (1837), 3 M. & W. 1.
[4] [1947] K.B. 130; [1956] 1 All E.R. 256n.
[5] *National Provincial Bank, Ltd.* v. *Ainsworth,* [1965] A. C. 1175; [1965] 2 All E.R. 472.
[6] See p. 216, *post.*
[7] Judicature Act 1925, s. 99.
[8] S. 14.

Contempt may be of a criminal nature or of a procedural nature, the latter being generally termed civil contempt.

Criminal contempt is a common law misdemeanour punishable by fine and imprisonment. It consists of conduct, in or out of court, which amounts to a contemptuous interference with the administration of justice. Perhaps the best known perpetrator of a criminal contempt was the prisoner who, at the Salisbury summer assizes, 1631, before Chief Justice RICHARDSON:

> "Ject un Brickbat a le dit Justice que narrowly mist, & pur ceo immediately fuit Indictment drawn per Noy envers le prisoner, & son dexter manus ampute & fix al Gibbet sur que mesme immediatement hange in presence de Court."

There are many more subtle forms of criminal contempt such as: interfering with jurors or witnesses, the publication of matter during a pending case which is calculated to prejudice a fair trial,[1] failure of a witness to attend court in pursuance of a subpoena, witness order or witness summons,[2] removal of a ward of court from the jurisdiction, publication of the identity of a child in juvenile court proceedings without the express consent of the court and scandalous abuse of a judge with reference to his office. Innocence and mistake are not defences to a charge of contempt at common law. However, section 11 of the Administration of Justice Act 1960 provides that a person shall not be guilty of contempt of court on the ground that (1) he has published matter calculated to prejudice the course of justice in proceedings pending or imminent at the time of publication, if at the time he did not know and had no reason to suspect that proceedings were pending or imminent; or (2) he has distributed a publication containing such matter if at that time he did not know and had no reason to suspect that it contained such matter.

Whereas criminal contempt consists of a positive act of interference with the administration of justice, civil (or procedural) contempt is generally committed by inaction. It is a failure to comply with an order of the court or an undertaking given to the court. Examples of civil contempt are: failure of a solicitor to comply with an undertaking,[3] failure to swear an account, refusal to comply with an order for discovery of documents or to answer interrogatories[4] and failure to comply with an injunction. Similarly mere failure to pay a judgment debt is not contempt, although wilful refusal to do so is.[5]

2 Jurisdiction to punish contempt

Civil contempt was formerly punishable by writ of attachment but the Rules of the Supreme Court (Revision) 1965 abolished attachment so that civil

---

[1] E.g., *R.* v. *Bolam, Ex parte Haigh* (1949), 93 Sol.Jo. 220 in which the editor of the *Daily Mirror* was gaoled for three months and the proprietors fined £10,000 for comments made pending a murder trial. On the other hand, criticism of the decision of a court does not amount to contempt, even if it contains error, provided that it was made in good faith and is reasonable. Thus in *R.* v. *Metropolitan Police Commissioner, Ex parte Blackburn* (*No.* 2), [1968] 2 Q.B. 150; [1968] 2 All E.R. 319 a description of a Court of Appeal decision (by none other than the present Lord Chancellor, before his appointment) as "a strange example of the blindness which sometimes descends on the best of judges" was held not to amount to contempt.

[2] Criminal Procedure (Attendance of Witnesses) Act 1965; see p. 380, *post*.

[3] *Re Kirby*, [1901] 1 Ch. 467.

[4] See pp. 277, 283, *post*.

[5] Debtors Act 1869, as amended by Administration of Justice Act 1970, s. 11.

contempt is now punishable by committal in the same way as criminal contempt.

The jurisdiction to punish for contempt, whether committed in or out of court, is inherent in superior courts of record. Such courts may commit for contempt and also punish contempt committed in the face of the court by immediate fine and imprisonment.

Inferior courts of record have more limited powers. They have no jurisdiction at common law to punish contempt summarily unless committed in the face of the court.[1]

Justices in magistrates' courts do not constitute a court of record and therefore have no jurisdiction to punish for contempt. However, the Queen's Bench Division, as the successor of the Court of King's Bench, protects inferior courts against contempt by punishing contempts committed in inferior courts.[2]

Until 1960 there was no appeal against punishment for criminal contempt. The law was altered by the Administration of Justice Act 1960, section 13, which provides that the defendant shall have a right of appeal from any order or decision of a court or tribunal in the exercise of jurisdiction to punish for contempt, including criminal contempt. Appeal lies to the Court of Appeal, divisional court or House of Lords as the case may be.

It should be noted, in conclusion, that punishment for contempt of court is by no means the only legal sanction for abuse of legal process. Many forms of conduct which appear to have the characteristics of criminal contempt are not punishable as contempts because they are separate criminal offences. Where they cause damage to another person they may also be torts, although contempt of court is not in itself tortious. Thus a person who intimidates a witness commits a contempt of court but may not be sued by that witness in tort.[3]

---

[1] See: County Courts Act 1959, ss. 30, 127, 157 (county courts); Army Act 1955, s. 101 (courts-martial).

[2] *R. v. Davies*, [1906] 1 K.B. 32; *R. v. Daily Herald, Ex Parte Bishop of Norwich*, [1932] 2 K.B. 402. The High Court also has statutory power under the Parliamentary Commissioner Act 1967 to deal with a person whom the Commissioner certifies as having been guilty of conduct in the nature of contempt in relation to an investigation held by the Commissioner under the Act.

[3] *Chapman* v. *Honig*, [1963] 2 Q.B. 502; [1963] 2 All E.R. 513.

CHAPTER 12

Juries

A HISTORICAL GROWTH OF THE JURY SYSTEM

There is ample evidence that a jury system existed in England prior to the Norman Conquest. However, although the jury system was not the creation of the common law, it was certainly one of the cornerstones of common law procedure both in civil and criminal trials.

In criminal cases there were, until 1948, two juries. The first of these was the grand jury. The grand jury was not principally a trial jury in the modern sense. It originated in the jury of presentment of the hundred and its function was to present persons for trial before the royal judges at assizes or the justices in quarter sessions.[1] This function was later assumed by justices of the peace in the form of the modern system of preliminary investigation. For this reason the grand jury (of 24 members) ceased to be functional and its duties had been reduced virtually to formality long before its abolition. It was virtually abolished by the Administration of Justice (Miscellaneous Provisions) Act 1933, save for a few purposes, and entirely abolished by the Criminal Justice Act 1948.

The second jury in criminal cases was the petty jury (of 12 members). This was the equivalent of the modern trial jury. The trial of criminals by jury evolved in the thirteenth century to replace trial by ordeal, which the Church condemned in 1215.[2] Originally the grand jury of presentment also exercised the function of the trial jury but by the middle of the fourteenth century the petty jury had become distinct from its predecessor. The petty jury was originally summoned for its local knowledge and the members were really witnesses rather than judges of fact. Their function changed gradually as the practice grew of examining independent witnesses and by the fifteenth century the trial jury had assumed its modern function as judges of fact. Nevertheless not until *Bushell's Case* in 1670[3] was it established that jurors could not be punished for returning a verdict contrary to the evidence or the direction of the trial judge.

In civil cases there was only ever one type of jury—the trial jury of 12

---

[1] See p. 14, *ante.*
[2] See p. 15, *ante.*
[3] Vaugh. 135.

members, which had its origins in the Assize of Clarendon 1166.[1]   By 1304 it was the rule of the common law courts that all trespass actions had to be tried with a jury.   The result was that, with the decline of the real actions and the personal actions of debt and detinue,[2] virtually all actions in the common law courts came to be tried with a jury and this was the position until 1854 when the steady decline of the jury in civil cases began.   The function of civil juries was, originally, that of witnesses but, as with criminal juries, a similar transition from witnesses to judges of fact took place.

B   THE JURY SYSTEM AT THE PRESENT DAY

Before the present century the jury system was widely pronounced to be one of the chief safeguards of the individual against the abuse of prerogative and judicial power.   The vast majority of cases, both civil and criminal, were tried by a jury and this right was thought to be essential and inviolable.   Blackstone, writing of the jury in criminal cases, saw the jury as a barrier between the liberties of the people and the prerogative of the Crown.[3]   LORD CAMDEN, reflecting the mood of the age, observed:

> "Trial by jury is indeed the foundation of our free constitution; take that away, and the whole fabric will soon moulder into dust."[4]

By the middle of the nineteenth century this concept of the sanctity of jury trial was disappearing.   Consequently the jury began to decline as a factor in the administration of justice in both civil and criminal cases.   The principal reasons for this decline were the eclipse of the royal prerogative in the administration of justice, the rapid growth in the volume of litigation in civil cases, the even more rapid growth of summary jurisdiction in criminal cases and a general appreciation that juries were both unpredictable and fallible.

1   Criminal cases

In criminal cases the loss of faith in the jury system has been far less marked than in civil cases.   The situation is still that a person aged seventeen or over[5] who has a common law right to jury trial cannot be deprived of that right without his consent.   Since all common law offences were triable by jury an accused person still has a right to claim trial by jury for any common law offence.   He can, however, often elect to be tried summarily and, in fact, only a very small proportion of indictable offences are actually tried by a jury.   In addition the number of trials of indictable offences is minimal compared with the number of trials for summary offences.   Modern legislation, especially that concerned with road traffic, has created a vast number of summary offences.   Almost all of these are tried summarily although the accused generally has a right to claim jury trial if liable to a punishment in excess of three months' imprisonment.[6]

---

[1] See p. 27, *ante.*
[2] See p. 20, *ante.*
[3] 3 Comm. 379.
[4] See Jackson, *The Machinery of Justice in England* (5th Edn.), pp. 302 *et seq.*
[5] There are special provisions for children and young persons: see p. 175, *ante.*
[6] Magistrates' Courts Act 1952, s. 25: see p. 362, *post.*

2 Civil actions

It is in civil actions that the decline of the jury has been most marked. Until 1854 most civil actions in the common law courts had to be tried before a jury. The Common Law Procedure Act 1854 provided for trial by a judge alone but only with the consent of both parties. This trend was continued by the Judicature Acts and by 1933 only about one half of civil actions in the Queen's Bench Division were tried with a jury. The Administration of Justice (Miscellaneous Provisions) Act 1933 was a landmark in the decline of the civil jury. By section 6 of that Act the right to claim a jury in a civil action was limited to cases of libel, slander, malicious prosecution, false imprisonment, seduction or breach of promise of marriage on the application of either party or on the application of a party against whom fraud is alleged.[1] Even in these cases a jury may be refused if the court considers that the trial will involve a prolonged examination of documents or accounts or a scientific or local investigation. In all other cases the grant of a jury is at the discretion of the court. It was widely thought that this discretion was absolute or "completely untrammelled".[2] However in the leading case of *Ward* v. *James*[3] the full Court of Appeal established that this was not so and that the discretion had, in the same way as any other discretion, to be exercised judicially. Furthermore, the Court of Appeal stated that in actions for damages for personal injuries trial should be by a judge alone in the absence of special circumstances, such as a substantial dispute on the facts. The basic reason for this opposition to jury trial in personal injury cases is the unpredictability of jury awards of damages. Juries, no doubt swayed by the knowledge that the substantive defendant in a "running-down" case is almost always an insurance company[4] with apparently bottomless resources, have sometimes made disproportionate awards to successful plaintiffs in this type of action. It was following two awards of £50,000 to victims in personal actions in 1963[5] that the courts became acutely aware of the unsuitability of juries in this type of case. Since some 40 *per cent* of actions in the Queen's Bench Division are actions for damages for personal injuries, *Ward* v. *James* is a further landmark in the decline of the civil jury. Immediately before this decision approximately 2 *per cent* of trials in the Queen's Bench Division took place before a jury. The figure is now likely to be less than 1 *per cent*.

Consequently, in little more than a century, jury trial in civil cases has virtually been superseded by trial by a judge alone. Outside the Queen's Bench Division of the High Court juries are hardly ever encountered in civil actions. The Chancery Amendment Act 1858 provided power to summon a jury in the Court of Chancery. This power was transferred to the Chancery Division by the Judicature Acts but has been totally ignored. There may be a jury in defended divorce petitions and contentious probate proceedings

---

[1] Of these, actions for seduction and breach of promise of marriage have been abolished by the Law Reform (Miscellaneous Provisions) Act 1970.

[2] *Hope* v. *Great Western Rail. Co.*, [1937] 2 K.B. 130; [1937] 1 All E.R. 625, *per* LORD WRIGHT, M.R.

[3] [1966] 1 Q.B. 273; [1965] 1 All E.R. 563.

[4] Although the court should not be informed that the defendant in a personal injuries action is insured.

[5] *Warren* v. *King*, [1963] 3 All E.R. 521; [1964] 1 W.L.R. 1; *Morey* v. *Woodfield*, (*No. 2*), [1964] 1 Q.B. 1; [1963] 3 All E.R. 584.

though there seldom is in either type of case. A jury of eight may be summoned in the county court in the same circumstances as in the Queen's Bench Division but this is extremely unusual mainly because of the disproportionately high costs which it would entail. Juries may also be summoned in many of the courts of local jurisdiction. Finally coroners must, in certain cases,[1] summon a jury of between seven and eleven persons.

Majority verdicts were permitted in criminal cases by the Criminal Justice Act 1967.[2] In civil cases majority verdicts (save by consent of the parties) were not receivable until the Courts Act 1971, s. 39 in effect extended the Criminal Justice Act provisions to civil cases.

C CRITICISMS OF THE JURY SYSTEM

There are several criticisms which are commonly levelled at the present-day jury system, many of which have no doubt been instrumental in its current decline. The most frequent criticism concerns the composition of juries. Jurors must be between the ages of twenty-one and sixty. They must satisfy a property qualification.[3] They must not have been sentenced to imprisonment for five years or more nor, during the preceding ten years, to imprisonment for three months or more.[4] Persons who are either exempt or may claim exemption include judges, justices of the peace, solicitors, barristers, peers, members of Parliament, medical practitioners, ministers of religion, members of the armed forces or sheriff's, police or prison officers.[5] The result is that the jury is, in the words of an eminent authority "predominantly male, middle-aged, middle-minded and middle-class".[6] This results in certain common prejudices which are alleged to exist in juries. The tendency to high awards of damages to victims of motor accidents has already been noted. There is also alleged to be a bias against newspapers in libel actions and against the police in malicious prosecution and false imprisonment suits. On the other hand juries are commonly supposed to sympathise with the motorist in criminal prosecutions under the Road Traffic Acts. Other commonly encountered criticisms of juries are their susceptibility to rhetoric and their lack of experience in weighing evidence. Nor is the system popular with most jurors themselves. The compulsory element of jury service is undoubtedly unpopular with many

---

[1] See Coroners (Amendment) Act 1926, s. 13.

[2] Section 13; see p. 413, *post* as to the procedure.

[3] The Criminal Justice Bill currently before Parliament is likely, when implemented, to abolish the property qualification (presently contained in the Juries Act 1825, as amended) and to raise the maximum age to 65. It is uncertain whether the minimum age will be reduced from 21 to 18.

[4] Criminal Justice Act 1967, s. 14. The verdict of a jury is not void only because a juror was disqualified from jury service (Criminal Justice Act 1967, s. 15) and no verdict can be challenged on the ground that a juror was not included in the relevant list of jurors or was misnamed or misdescribed or (unless objection was taken at the time) that the provisions of the Courts Act 1971 as to the impanelling or selection of jurors has not been complied with (Courts Act 1971, s. 40).

[5] Juries Act 1870, s. 9; Criminal Justice Act 1967, s. 16.

[6] Devlin, *Trial By Jury*, p. 20.

because of the loss of time and money it may involve, although jurors are paid travelling and subsistence allowances and compensation for loss of earnings.[1]

Nevertheless, despite these criticisms, the jury remains a fundamental of the English legal system. LORD DENNING, M.R. in *Ward* v. *James* explained the place of the modern jury as follows:[2]

> "Let it not be supposed that this court is in any way opposed to trial by jury. It has been the bulwark of our liberties too long for any of us to seek to alter it. Whenever a man is on trial for serious crime, or when in a civil case a man's honour or integrity is at stake, or when one or other party must be deliberately lying, then trial by jury has no equal."

---

[1] See Courts Act 1971, Part V. "Special juries" whose members were paid and specially qualified were finally abolished by the Courts Act 1971, s. 40 (1).
[2] [1966] 1 Q. B. 273, at p. 295; [1965] 1 All E.R. 563, at p. 571.

CHAPTER 13

The Legal Profession

A THE DIVISION OF THE LEGAL PROFESSION

A distinctive feature of the English legal system is the division of the legal profession into two separate branches—solicitors and barristers. This precise division is unknown outside Britain and the Commonwealth. Elsewhere all practitioners are described as "lawyers", a word which has no particular application in England. The division of the legal profession dates back to about 1340, the time at which professional advocacy evolved. The advocates with audience in the common law courts were the serjeants[1] and barristers while the preparatory stages of an action were carried through by officers of the court in question known as attorneys. There thus developed two classes of legal practitioner; serjeants and barristers on the one hand and attorneys who were, as solicitors still are, officers of the court. Solicitors, as distinct from attorneys, first appeared in the fifteenth century and practised in the Court of Chancery. They were, at first, inferior to attorneys and could not bind their clients as attorneys could. By the eighteenth century the offices of attorney and solicitor were frequently held by the same person and the distinction between them was finally abolished by the Judicature Act 1873.

The separation of barristers and solicitors was preserved by the Inns of Court. Barristers had to be members of one of the Inns of Court and these Inns, after the sixteenth century, refused to admit attorneys or solicitors to membership. As a result the latter banded together and by 1739 had formed their own professional organisation in London. This was styled "The Society of Gentlemen Practisers in the Courts of Law and Equity" and was the forerunner of The Law Society.

Thus the separation of the legal profession has an historical foundation as has the nature of the respective functions which barristers and solicitors perform. Barristers are still primarily advocates, although many barristers in fact spend most of their time engaged in "paper-work" such as the drafting of pleadings,

---

[1] Serjeants (*servientes regis ad legem*) were the senior advocates and had exclusive audience in the Court of Common Pleas. The rank of serjeant was abolished by the Judicature Act 1873.

divorce petitions, complex settlements and opinions on specialised matters such as taxation and company law. Solicitors deal with the preparatory stages of litigation such as the preparation of evidence, interviewing witnesses, issuing writs and, usually, conducting interlocutory proceedings. Solicitors have a limited right of audience in open court, which is confined to county courts, magistrates' courts, certain proceedings in the Crown Court,[1] the National Industrial Relations Court, certain tribunals and to bankruptcy matters in the High Court.[2] In addition solicitors deal with a large number of non-litigious matters such as the drafting of wills, the supervision of trusts and settlements the administration of estates and, above all, conveyancing.

There are other important distinctions between the two branches of the profession. Solicitors may enter into partnership; barristers may not. Solicitors, since they stand in a contractual relationship to their clients, may sue for their fees; barristers, whose fees are regarded as honorary rather than contractual payments, may not. For the same reason solicitors may be liable to their clients for professional negligence; barristers are historically immune from such liability. Barristers appear in court (other than magistrates' courts) in wig and gown; solicitors appear in gown in certain courts, notably the county court, but are never bewigged. Solicitors are instructed by their clients directly; barristers may be instructed only by a solicitor and not by a lay client direct.[3]

B SOLICITORS

1 The Law Society

The controlling body in the case of solicitors is The Law Society, constituted under a Royal Charter of 1845 as amended by supplemental charters,[4] and being given the name "The Law Society" by the Supplemental Charter of 1903. Membership of the Society is voluntary although there is power under the Solicitors Act 1957, section 75, to provide for the introduction of compulsory membership.[5] The Society is governed by a Council of 65 members, elected annually, of whom 30 practice in London and 35 in the provinces.

The objects of the Society remain, as defined in the Charter of 1845, as "promoting professional improvement and facilitating the acquisition of legal knowledge". Notwithstanding its voluntary composition The Law Society has statutory powers in respect of all solicitors and in certain matters affecting the public generally. These powers derive mainly from the Solicitors Act 1957, a consolidating statute.

---

[1] See *Practice Direction (Crown Court: Right of Audience)*, [1972] 1 All E.R. 608; [1972] 1 W.L.R. 307.

[2] In *Rondel* v. *Worsley*, [1967] 1 Q.B. 443; [1966] 3 All E.R. 657 (affirmed [1969] 1 A.C. 191; [1967] 3 All E.R. 993) a written brief composed by the plaintiff's solicitor was read to the Court of Appeal since the plaintiff was not represented by counsel. DANCKWERTS and SALMON, L.JJ., deprecated this occurrence and expressed a hope that it would not be permitted to be repeated.

[3] This is a custom rather than a rule of law but is, nevertheless, strictly observed. It is a custom of fairly recent origin for, until the eighteenth century, it was customary for counsel to be instructed directly by lay clients.

[4] In 1872, 1903, 1909 and 1954.

[5] In fact over 85 *per cent* of a total of more than 20,000 solicitors holding practising certificates are members of the Society.

By section 3 of the 1957 Act the Society may, with the concurrence of the Lord Chancellor, the Lord Chief Justice and the Master of the Rolls, make regulations (at present the Students Regulations 1962, as amended) governing service under articles, legal education and examinations. A person wishing to enter into articles must satisfy the Society as to his character, fitness and suitability[1] and no person may be admitted as a solicitor until he has obtained a certificate that the Society is satisfied as to his satisfactory completion of articles, legal education and examinations and also as to his moral fitness to be an officer of the Supreme Court. The Society maintains the Roll of Solicitors and, in order to practise as a solicitor, a person must have his name on the Roll and hold a current practising certificate.

Section 29 of the 1957 Act[2] requires the Council of The Law Society to make rules governing the handling by solicitors of clients' and certain trust moneys and the right to interest thereon. Section 30[3] requires the Council to make rules governing the annual submission by solicitors of an accountant's report. Section 28 empowers the Council to make rules regulating professional practice, conduct and discipline.

As well as exercising these powers and duties The Law Society also looks after the welfare of solicitors generally and attempts to maintain good relations with other bodies and with the public. To this end the Council examines the activities of unqualified persons doing the work of solicitors and, in appropriate cases, institutes proceedings. It also organises refresher lectures on changes in the law, annual study courses, study groups and pamphlets on certain matters of general importance to solicitors, such as new legislation.

The only matters concerning solicitors which are not within the province of The Law Society are scales of remuneration, which are fixed by statute, and disciplinary proceedings, which are dealt with by the Disciplinary Committee, an independent statutory body.

In addition to its control over its own members and other solicitors the Society in at least two spheres protects the interests of the public generally. First it administers the Legal Aid and Advice Scheme and secondly it maintains a Compensation Fund[4] out of which it may make a hardship grant to any person who suffers hardship through the failure of a solicitor to account for money due in connection with his practice as a solicitor or with any trust of which he is a trustee. The result is that members of the public are indemnified against loss which might be suffered as a result of any solicitor's default in the handling of their moneys. The Law Society is subrogated to the rights and remedies of the person to whom the grant was made to the extent of the grant.

2 Liabilities of a solicitor

a Liability to disciplinary proceedings

Solicitors are, of course, subject to the general criminal law. However, conduct

---

[1] For this purpose there is an interviewing panel nominated by the Society.

[2] As amended by s. 8 of the Solicitors Act 1965. The present rules are the Solicitors' Accounts Rules, 1945–1959, the Solicitors' Trust Accounts Rules 1945, and the Solicitors' Accounts (Deposit Interest) Rules 1965.

[3] As amended by s. 9 of the Solicitors Act 1965.

[4] Solicitors Act 1957, s. 32 and Sched. II as amended by Solicitors Act 1965, ss. 15, 16. The fund is made up of special annual contributions payable by solicitors on application for practising certificates.

on the part of a solicitor which falls short of a criminal offence may still result
in sanctions. These are usually enforced by the Disciplinary Committee although, since solicitors are officers of the Supreme Court, the High Court and
Court of Appeal have inherent jurisdiction to strike the name of a solicitor from
the roll or suspend him for misconduct.[1] In addition to this inherent jurisdiction the High Court has a limited statutory jurisdiction in disciplinary matters.
The High Court must strike off the Roll the name of a solicitor who wilfully
and knowingly assists an unqualified person to practise or act as a solicitor;[2] it
must strike off the Roll or suspend from practice a person who, without the
written permission of The Law Society, knowingly employs a person who has
been struck off the Roll involuntarily or suspended from practice.[3] However
the Disciplinary Committee has, in all these cases, corresponding jurisdiction
and, since it also has a wider jurisdiction than the High Court, proceedings are
generally instituted before the Disciplinary Committee.

The Disciplinary Committee is constituted by the Master of the Rolls from
up to 12 past or present members of the Council of The Law Society.[4] It is,
nonetheless, independent of The Law Society. The Committee is a judicial
tribunal and proceedings before it are absolutely privileged for the purposes of
the law of defamation.[5] It may sit in two or more divisions, the quorum being
three, receive evidence on oath and compel the attendance of witnesses by
subpoena. It may also, with the concurrence of the Master of the Rolls, make
rules regulating its own procedure.

Its jurisdiction is threefold. First, it hears applications by a solicitor to have
his own name removed from the Roll, generally in order that he may qualify
for call to the Bar. Secondly, it hears hostile applications by another party
against a solicitor based either upon common law disciplinary offences of professional misconduct or upon specific offences under the 1957 Act, such as
failure to comply with the Solicitors' Accounts Rules or the Solicitors' Trust
Accounts' Rules[6] or making a false statement in a declaration for obtaining a
practising certificate.[7]

Finally, the Committee hears applications by The Law Society under section
38 of the 1957 Act[8] to restrain the employment by solicitors, without the written
permission of The Law Society, of clerks who have been convicted of criminal
offences of dishonesty rendering their employment in a solicitor's practice
undesirable or have been parties to disciplinary offences by solicitors.

The major part of the Committee's business is concerned with the second type
of matter—hostile applications against solicitors in respect of professional misconduct or offences under the Solicitors Act 1957. In dealing with these applications the Committee may make such order as it thinks fit. In particular it
may strike the solicitor's name off the Roll, suspend him from practice, order
him to pay a penalty not exceeding £750, to be forfeit to Her Majesty, and

---

[1] This jurisdiction is preserved by the Solicitors Act 1957, s. 50 (2).
[2] Solicitors Act 1957, s. 34 (1).
[3] *Ibid.*, s. 36 (1).
[4] *Ibid.*, s. 46 as amended by the Solicitors (Amendment) Act 1959.
[5] *Addis* v. *Crocker*, [1961] 1 Q.B. 11; [1960] 2 All E.R. 629.
[6] Solicitors Act 1957, s. 29 (3).
[7] *Ibid.*, s. 9 (3).
[8] As amended by Solicitors Act 1965, s. 18.

order him to pay a reasonable contribution towards the costs of the proceedings.[1] In two cases the punishment imposable by the Committee is mandatory. It must strike off the Roll a solicitor who has committed an offence under s. 34 of the 1957 Act (assisting an unqualified person to practise) and it must either strike off or suspend from practice a solicitor who has committed an offence under s. 36 (employment of a person involuntarily disqualified from practice).

Any party may appeal from the decision of the Disciplinary Committee to a divisional court of the Queen's Bench Division[2] and thence, with leave of either that court or the Court of Appeal, to the Court of Appeal.[3] However no appeal lies against the dismissal of a complaint against a solicitor since this would amount to an appeal against acquittal which English law does not allow.[4] Where the application is to restrain the employment of a clerk under s. 38, appeal lies only at the instance of the clerk and the decision of the High Court is final.

b   Liability as an officer of the court

As stated above, the Supreme Court has both an inherent and a limited statutory jurisdiction over solicitors since they are officers of the Supreme Court. This jurisdiction is merged in the wider jurisdiction of the Disciplinary Committee. In addition to this jurisdiction, the sanction for which is striking off the Roll, the High Court has further powers to impose liability upon solicitors as court officers. Thus solicitors may be, and sometimes are, ordered to pay personally costs thrown away by their neglect or improperly incurred. These costs may be made payable either to the solicitor's own client or to a third party. This provision is both punitive and compensatory so that a solicitor may be ordered to pay costs even where the defaulting party is his partner or a clerk.[5] Examples of the type of default which may render a solicitor personally liable for costs are: failing to warn the court that an action has been settled or postponed, entering into a champertous agreement, acting for both sides in an action and instituting proceedings without his client's authority.

A solicitor may also be liable, as an officer of the court, for loss occasioned by his negligence or breach of duty.[6] This liability may be summarily enforced by any party who has suffered loss. This may be compared with the general civil liability of a solicitor to his client, discussed below, which is enforceable by civil proceedings.

A further way in which a solicitor may incur liability as an officer of the court is by giving an undertaking to the court or in his capacity as a solicitor. The court often makes an order, or refrains from making an order, on the faith of a personal undertaking by a solicitor appearing; for example, an undertaking to stamp a document or an unconditional undertaking not to issue execution if payment of a judgment debt is expedited. The court will enforce a solicitor's undertaking summarily, not as a contractual obligation but in order to secure the proper conduct of its officers. An undertaking to pay money is an obliga-

---

[1] Solicitors Act 1957, s. 47 (2) as amended by the Solicitors Act 1965, s. 27, Sched. 2.
[2] *Ibid.*, s. 48.
[3] Judicature Act 1925, s. 27 (1), s. 31 (1) (*f*).
[4] Subject to exceptions; see Chapters 26, 28, *post*.
[5] *Myers* v. *Elman*, [1940] A.C. 282; [1939] 4 All E.R. 484.
[6] *Marsh* v. *Joseph*, [1897] 1 Ch. 213.

tion *sui generis* enforceable summarily by the court and is neither a contractual obligation nor a judgment debt.[1]

Finally a solicitor is liable to be committed for contempt of court. A solicitor's liability for contempt of court is basically no different from the liability of laymen. Nevertheless solicitors, because of their close association with the court, may be guilty of contempt in a wider variety of ways. Furthermore there are various statutes and rules which impose special liability to committal upon a solicitor, for example for neglecting to inform his client of a judgment against the latter or for defaulting in an order to pay costs personally for misconduct.[2] Failure to comply with an undertaking is a contempt of court as well as rendering the solicitor liable to perform his undertaking.

c Civil liability

The solicitor, by his position, may render himself liable to civil proceedings either at the suit of his client or of some third party, in a variety of ways. The duty which the solicitor owes to his own client is an incident of the solicitor-client relationship and is dealt with in the following section.

There are, in addition, several ways in which a solicitor may incur civil liability to persons other than his own client. In contract the solicitor's liability to third parties is governed usually by the ordinary law of agency. Thus if the solicitor contracts on behalf of an undisclosed client, the other party may elect to sue either the solicitor or the client.[3] If the solicitor acts without authority on behalf of a client he may, in accordance with general principles, be sued for breach of warranty of authority.[4] An exception to the general law of agency is that the solicitor is personally responsible for certain items of expenditure even though incurred as agent for his client, such as jury fees and the costs of a shorthand writer. A solicitor's liability in tort is governed by the general law of torts. Thus, for example, a solicitor who fraudulently induces a third party to buy an estate with a defective title commits the tort of deceit. The position of solicitors in the tort of negligence is uncertain. The question is whether the liability for negligent advice introduced by the House of Lords in *Hedley Byrne & Co., Ltd.* v. *Heller and Partners, Ltd.*[5] extends to solicitors. It has been held, at first instance, that there is no liability in negligence where the plaintiff is the client of the defendant solicitor[6] but it is, as yet, undecided whether there may be liability in tort in respect of negligent advice where there is no contractual relationship between the solicitor and the plaintiff. On principle there seems to be no good reason why such liability should not exist.[7]

---

[1] *Re Hudson*, [1966] Ch. 209; [1966] 1 All E.R. 110. However the obligation will only be enforced summarily in clear cases; in cases where there is a triable issue the plaintiff must bring an action in the normal way: *Silver and Drake* v. *Baines*, [1971] 1 Q.B. 396; [1971] 1 All E.R. 473.
[2] Debtors Act 1869, s. 4 (4).
[3] *Foster* v. *Cranfield* (1911), 46 L.Jo. 314.
[4] *Yonge* v. *Toynbee*, [1910] 1 K.B. 215.
[5] [1964] A.C. 465; [1963] 2 All E.R. 575.
[6] *Clark* v. *Kirby-Smith*, [1964] Ch. 506; [1964] 2 All E.R. 835.
[7] See *The Law Society's Gazette* (1965), 688, at p. 692 where Sir Thomas Lund, C.B.E., the then Secretary-General of The Law Society, suggested that such liability would exist.

3   Incidents of the solicitor–client relationship

a   *Solicitor's duty of care to his client*

A solicitor's authority derives from the retainer given to him by his client. The effect of this retainer is to create a contractual relationship between the solicitor and the client. In most respects this relationship is, therefore, subject to the ordinary law of contract and in particular to that part of contract law concerning agency since the relationship created is, for purposes within the scope of the retainer, a principal and agent relationship. Consequently the solicitor has a right to be indemnified by his client for acts done within the scope of his authority.

If the solicitor is negligent the client may have an action against him for damages. Indeed, as one writer has observed:[1]

> "The pursuit of actions for negligence, once rare occurrences, has now become the pastime of the disgruntled client whose affairs have gone wrong whether through ill luck, his own fault or otherwise, and no professional man or indeed technician is safe from them."

The action lies, however, in contract not in tort.[2] In *Rondel* v. *Worsley*[3] the majority opinion of the House of Lords was that a solicitor should not be liable for negligence in carrying out work in litigation which would have been carried out by counsel, had counsel been engaged in the case.

b   *Fiduciary obligations*

The solicitor–client relationship is regarded in equity as a fiduciary one. Several consequences flow from this. In general the solicitor must act in good faith in all dealings with his client. This involves making a full and honest disclosure of facts within the solicitor's knowledge in any financial transaction with his client. This principle derives from the equitable doctrine of fraud and has differing consequences which depend upon the nature of the transaction.

The principle is at its strongest in the case of gifts to the solicitor by his client. There is a presumption of undue influence in the case of such a gift, the effect of which is to make the gift voidable at the instance of the client. The solicitor can retain the gift only by showing that it was made after the fiduciary relationship had ceased, or that it was ratified by the client after the relationship had ceased or that the client had independent legal advice.[4]

This presumption of undue influence, which applies to gifts *inter vivos*, does not apply to gifts by will although any person may allege and prove actual undue influence by the solicitor. Nevertheless, where a solicitor prepares a will under which he receives a large benefit the court requires affirmative proof that the testator knew and fully approved of the contents of the will.[5] Where a client intends to give a large benefit to a solicitor in his will the latter should insist on the will being prepared by another solicitor.

---

[1] *Cordery on Solicitors* (6th Edn.), p. 148.
[2] *Groom* v. *Crocker*, [1939] 1 K.B. 194; [1938] 2 All E.R. 394; *Clark* v. *Kirby-Smith*, [1964] Ch. 506; [1964] 2 All E.R. 835.
[3] [1969] 1 A.C. 191; [1967] 3 All E.R. 993.
[4] *Gibson* v. *Jeyes* (1801), 6 Ves. 266; *Lancashire Loans, Ltd.* v. *Black*, [1934] 1 K.B. 380.
[5] *Wintle* v. *Nye*, [1959] 1 All E.R. 552; [1959] 1 W.L.R. 284.

A purchase by a solicitor from his client, or a sale to his client, is not necessarily bad but the solicitor must show that the bargain is as good as the client
could have obtained with due diligence elsewhere in order to rebut the presumption of undue influence. This means that the price must be fair and that the
solicitor must make a full disclosure. In practice the solicitor should see that
the client has independent advice. Similar conditions apply to loans between
solicitor and client.[1]

c   Obligations to preserve confidence

One particular aspect of the fiduciary relationship between solicitor and client
is the confidential nature of communications between them. This gives rise
to two types of privilege; privilege in the tort of defamation and privilege
from disclosure in evidence.

For the purposes of the law of defamation professional communications between solicitor and client are undoubtedly privileged though it is not finally
decided whether this privilege is absolute or only qualified, i.e., rebuttable by
proof of malice. The Court of Appeal in *More* v. *Weaver*[2] held the privilege
to be absolute, but the House of Lords in *Minter* v. *Priest*[3] expressly left the point
open and the better view probably is that the privilege is only qualified.[4] In
this event it is rebuttable by malice but the malice of a client is not attributable
to his solicitor.[5]

The second category of privilege is privilege from disclosure in evidence of
communications, oral or written, which are made between the client and his
solicitor in a professional capacity. This privilege is for the protection of the
client rather than the solicitor and exists so that the client may make the fullest
disclosure to his solicitor. The client (but not the solicitor) may waive the
privilege and, in addition, it is lost if the communication is made in furtherance
of a criminal purpose, for example criminal conspiracy or an unlawful threat by
the client to his solicitor. The privilege does not extend to collateral matters not
disclosed confidentially such as the client's name and address. However where
the privilege does exist it does not end with the termination of any proceedings
to which it relates, nor with the termination of the retainer, nor with the death
of the client.[6]

With these privileges, which exist for the better operation of the solicitor and
client relationship, may be compared the wider privilege which attaches to all
statements made in the course of judicial proceedings, such as statements made
by a solicitor or witness to the court. This privilege exists for the better operation of the judicial system and its effect is to confer absolute immunity from
proceedings in defamation and other torts.[7] It does not, however, create evi-

---

[1] See, generally, *Cordery on Solicitors* (6th Edn.), pp. 122–143; cf. *Spector* v. *Ageda*, [1971]
3 All E.R. 417; [1971] 3 W.L.R. 498.
[2] [1928] 2 K.B. 520.
[3] [1930] A.C. 558.
[4] But see observations of DEVLIN, L.J., (as he then was) in *Lincoln* v. *Daniels*, [1962] 1 Q.B.
237, at p. 260; [1961] 3 All E.R. 740 at p. 751.
[5] *Egger* v. *Viscount Chelmsford*, [1965] 1 Q.B. 248; [1964] 3 All E.R. 406.
[6] *Bullivant* v. *A.-G. for Victoria*, [1901] A.C. 196.
[7] *Lincoln* v. *Daniels*, [1962] 1 Q.B. 237; [1961] 3 All E.R. 740; *Marrinan* v. *Vibart*, [1963]
1 Q.B. 528; [1962] 3 All E.R. 380; *Roy* v. *Prior*, [1971] A.C. 470; [1969] 3 All E.R. 1153.

dential privilege, except in relation to those proceedings to which the statement relates.

So stringent is the solicitor's professional duty to maintain his client's confidences that he should not disclose a communication by his client to the effect that the latter has committed a criminal offence. His duty to his client in such a case overrides his public duty and he would not be guilty of any criminal offence by reason of his non-disclosure.[1]

4 Remuneration

Solicitors are entitled to remuneration for their services. However the way in which this remuneration is assessed and recovered is not primarily governed by the ordinary law of contract even though the right to remuneration arises out of a contractual relationship. It is governed by various statutes and rules, passed generally for the benefit of clients, and is subject to the supervision of the courts. Even where solicitor and client make an agreement as to costs, the court may still examine its reasonableness.

The way in which a solicitor's remuneration is assessed depends upon whether the business done on behalf of the client is contentious or non-contentious. "Contentious business" is defined by the Act[2] as:

> "Business done, whether as solicitor or advocate, in or for the purpose of proceedings begun before a court or before an arbitrator appointed under the Arbitration Act 1950, not being business which falls within the definition of non-contentious or common form probate business contained in subsection (1) of section one hundred and seventy-five of the Supreme Court of Judicature (Consolidation) Act 1925;"

The test is thus whether or not proceedings are begun. If they are, all business relating to these proceedings is contentious. If proceedings are not begun, as for example where a dispute is settled before a writ is issued, the proceedings are treated as non-contentious. Non-contentious business is any business which is not contentious within the above statutory definition and comprises a very wide range of matters including conveyancing, drafting wills and settlements, advice and many other matters. The basic difference between contentious and non-contentious business in relation to the assessment of remuneration is that in the former the amount is usually fixed by the court by taxation while in the latter it is not, being generally subject to a statutory scale.

a Assessment of remuneration in contentious business

The Solicitors Act 1957, section 59 expressly authorises a solicitor to enter into a written agreement with his client regulating remuneration in contentious business.[3] In the absence of such an agreement the solicitor may submit either a bill containing detailed items or one charging a gross sum.[4]

---

[1] *Sykes* v. *Director of Public Prosecutions*, [1962] A.C. 528, at p. 564; [1961] 3 All E.R. 533, at p. 564, *per* LORD DENNING. However the duty yields to a contrary statutory provision; thus a solicitor's duty to produce his books of account to The Law Society for inspection overrides his contractual duty not to disclose his client's affairs; *Parry-Jones* v. *Law Society*, [1968] Ch. 195; [1968] 1 All E.R. 177.
[2] Solicitors Act 1957, s. 86 (1).
[3] See p. 212, *post.*
[4] Section 64.

The client has a right to have this bill taxed, in which case the appropriate basis of taxation is (unless the bill is to be paid out of the Legal Aid Fund) the "solicitor and own client" basis.[1] On this basis:

> "All costs shall be allowed except in so far as they are of an unreasonable amount or have been unreasonably incurred".[2]

All costs incurred with the express or implied approval of the client are conclusively presumed to have been reasonably incurred and, where the amount has been so approved, are presumed to have been reasonable in amount.[3] However the solicitor must expressly inform his client of any costs which are of an unusual nature and might not be allowed on a "party and party" taxation; otherwise such costs are deemed to be unreasonably incurred.[4] Many items of costs are charged on a fixed scale[5] while in respect of other items a maximum and a minimum charge are prescribed by scale.[6] Nevertheless items may be allowed on a solicitor and own client taxation which do not appear in the scale and even where a maximum amount is prescribed in the scale the taxing master may, in his discretion, allow an amount higher than that prescribed by the scale.[7]

An exception to the above basis of taxation applies where the client is legally aided. In such a case in the High Court the solicitor receives from the Legal Aid Fund only his disbursements and 90 *per cent* of his costs taxed on a "common fund" basis. On this basis, which is less liberal than the "solicitor and own client" basis of taxation, there is allowed "a reasonable amount in respect of all costs reasonably incurred".[8]

b Assessment of remuneration in non-contentious business

Whereas remuneration in contentious business is usually fixed by the court, remuneration in non-contentious business is controlled differently. For this purpose non-contentious business is divisible broadly into conveyancing (comprising completed sales, purchases, mortgages, leases and agreements for leases of land) and other non-contentious business.[9]

Conveyancing charges are fixed by scale under Schedule I of the Solicitors' Remuneration Orders 1883 to 1959.[10] This scale is calculated according to a percentage of the monetary consideration involved, such as the purchase price of land or the premium for a lease. Schedule I only applies to completed conveyancing transactions. Thus it is not appropriate where the transaction is left incomplete or where the work involved is the negotiation of sales, purchases or leases. The scale fee prescribed by Schedule I does not include such items as stamps, counsel's fees, search fees, registration fees, costs of extracts from any

---

[1] See p. 302, *post.*
[2] R.S.C. (Revision) 1965, O. 62, r. 29 (1).
[3] O. 62, r. 29 (2).
[4] O. 62, r. 29 (3).
[5] O. 62, Appendix 3.
[6] O. 62, Appendix 2.
[7] O. 62, r. 32 (2).
[8] O. 62, r. 28 (4).
[9] There is a third class of special business, where charges are regulated by statutes or rules, preserved by s. 74 of the 1957 Act.
[10] These Orders are passed by a committee under powers conferred by the Solicitors Act 1957, s. 56.

register or similar disbursements though it does include law stationers' charges and allowances for the time of the solicitor and his clerks. A separate scale of charges is fixed for conveyancing transactions involving registered land,[1] the amounts being rather lower than in the case of unregistered land. A solicitor may, whether dealing with registered or unregistered land, elect by writing under his hand to charge Schedule II remuneration provided he does so before undertaking any business in connection with the transaction in question.

Schedule II governs other non-contentious business. The basis of remuneration under this Schedule is a lump sum which is fair and reasonable having regard to all the circumstances of the case and in particular to:

(1)   the complexity of the matter or the difficulty or novelty of the questions raised;

(2)   the skill, labour, specialised knowledge and responsibility involved on the part of the solicitor;

(3)   the number and importance of the documents prepared or perused, without regard to length;

(4)   the place where and the circumstances in which the business or any part thereof is transacted;

(5)   the time expended by the solicitor;

(6)   where money or property is involved, its amount or value; and

(7)   the importance of the matter to the client.

The client has no right to have a lump sum bill under Schedule II itemised. He has, nevertheless, two safeguards against an excessive charge. First, he has a right to have the bill taxed and secondly, without prejudice to this right, he has a right, at any time before the bill is taxed or paid, to require the solicitor to obtain a certificate from The Law Society that the sum charged is fair and reasonable, or, if it is not, what is a fair and reasonable sum. It is for the solicitor to show that the charge is fair and reasonable. Furthermore, the solicitor can bring no proceedings on a lump sum bill until he has drawn his client's attention to the latter's rights which are set out above. If the taxing master allows less than one half the amount charged on a Schedule II bill he must bring the facts of the case to the attention of The Law Society.

c   Special agreements as to remuneration

Solicitor and client may, in both contentious and non-contentious business, agree the amount of the solicitor's remuneration. Such agreements are, however, not freely enforceable in the same way as commercial contracts since their enforceability is regulated by statute.

In contentious business the client may enforce an agreement against the solicitor irrespective of whether it is written or oral. The solicitor can only enforce such an agreement if it is in writing[2] or if it is generally favourable to the client.[3] There is no prescribed form for the agreement and it may be contained

---

[1] Solicitors' Remuneration (Registered Land) Orders 1925 to 1959.

[2] Solicitors Act 1957, s. 59.

[3] This was the position at common law and since s. 59 does not state that the agreement "shall be in writing", as does s. 57 (3) (which governs agreements in non-contentious business), there seems to be no reason why the solicitor's common law right to enforce an oral agreement should be affected: see *Electrical Trades Union* v. *Tarlo*, [1964] Ch. 720; [1964] 2 All E.R. 1.

in letters passing between solicitor and client provided that the terms of the agreement can be ascertained with certainty. However there are certain other restrictions attaching to such an agreement. Any provision exempting the solicitor from liability for negligence or any other responsibility is void.[1] The agreement itself is void if it is champertous or amounts to maintenance of civil proceedings.[2] The agreement cannot prejudice the rights of third parties although it may indirectly benefit them since the client cannot recover more costs from a third party than he has agreed to pay his solicitor.[3]

A provision relating to remuneration in contentious business cannot be enforced by action,[4] even though the agreement as a whole can be so enforced. It may, however, be enforced summarily by the High Court or a county court on application.[5] The court may, if it considers the agreement unfair or unreasonable, declare it void and order the costs covered thereby to be taxed as if the agreement had never been made.[6]

An agreement for remuneration in non-contentious business must be in writing whether the solicitor or the client is seeking to enforce it.[7] It must also be signed by the party to be bound or his agent, a provision which is not mandatory, though desirable, in the case of agreements relating to contentious business. Such an agreement is subject to the ordinary law of contract and may be sued on in the ordinary way. Nevertheless the court has an inherent jurisdiction to order taxation in order to determine whether the sum agreed is fair and reasonable, and may cancel the agreement or reduce the amount payable if the taxing officer certifies that it is unfair or unreasonable.[8]

d Recovery of costs

By section 68 of the Solicitors Act 1957 no action shall be brought to recover any costs due to a solicitor until one month after delivery of a bill signed by the solicitor, or by a partner in the firm if the costs are due to a firm, or accompanied by a letter so signed and referring to the bill.

Within one month of the delivery of a bill the client has a right to have it taxed and no action may be commenced on the bill until the taxation is completed.[9] After one month has elapsed the court may, upon such terms as it thinks fit, order taxation on the application of solicitor or client and may stay proceedings on the bill, or order that no action shall be taken, until taxation is completed.[10] However, except in special circumstances, the client will not

---

[1] Solicitors Act 1957, s. 60 (4).
[2] This rule presumably survives the abolition of champerty as both a crime and a tort by the Criminal Law Act 1967, ss. 13, 14. A solicitor is, however, justified in acting for an impoverished client on terms that he shall receive no costs or reduced costs unless the action succeeds.
[3] Solicitors Act 1957, s. 60 (2).
[4] *Ibid.*, s. 61 (1).
[5] The appropriate court is the one in which the business to which the agreement relates was done if this is the High Court or a county court, or, if not, the High Court in respect of agreements to pay more than £50 or the county court for sums of less than £50 (1957 Act, s. 61 (7)). Application to the High Court is usually by originating summons; application to a county court is by originating application.
[6] Solicitors Act 1957, s. 61 (2) (5).
[7] *Ibid.*, s. 57.
[8] Proviso to s. 57 (4).
[9] *Ibid.*, s. 69 (1).
[10] *Ibid.*, s. 69 (2).

obtain an order for taxation more than twelve months after the delivery of the bill or after payment, and in no event will he obtain an order more than twelve months after payment. Unless the client does not appear on the solicitor's application to have the bill taxed or the order for taxation otherwise provides the costs of the taxation depend upon its outcome. If one-sixth (or in some cases one-fifth) of the amount of the bill is taxed off the solicitor pays the costs; otherwise the client pays the costs.[1]

Subject to the above restrictions the solicitor may proceed to recover his costs as a contractual debt. He may do so by action or by proving in the client's bankruptcy or in the liquidation of a client company. As an alternative to action the solicitor may exercise his common law lien.[2] He has a general lien over all of the client's personal property in the solicitor's possession except his will. This entitles the solicitor to retain the property until payment of the full amount due. In addition the solicitor has a particular lien over property, other than real property[3], recovered or preserved or the proceeds of any judgment obtained in an action, for his costs in relation to that action.

5 Offences by unqualified persons

An "unqualified person" means, in the Solicitors Act 1957, a person who is not qualified under section 1 of that Act. No person shall be qualified to act as a solicitor unless:

(a) he has been admitted as a solicitor; and
(b) his name is for the time being on the Roll; and
(c) he has in force a practising certificate.

Thus a solicitor who has been disqualified or does not have a current practising certificate is in no better position than any layman.[4]

It is an offence for an unqualified person to act as a solicitor or as such to take a step in any court proceeding. This is a misdemeanour and a contempt of the court in which the action or matter is proceeding. In addition it renders the offender liable to a penalty of £50 for each offence, enforceable by action in the High Court or a county court by The Law Society.[5]

It is also an offence for an individual or a body corporate[6] to pretend to be a solicitor. This is punishable, in the case of an individual, by a penalty not exceeding £50 on summary conviction,[7] or, in the case of a body corporate, £100.[6]

Any unqualified person, not being a barrister, notary public or public officer acting in the course of his duty, who prepares for reward any instrument relating to real or personal estate is liable to a fine not exceeding £50 on summary

---

[1] Solicitors Act 1957, s. 69 (5).
[2] See, generally, *Cordery on Solicitors* (6th Edn.), pp. 416–453.
[3] But see s. 72 of the Solicitors Act 1957 which enables the Court to make a charging order in favour of the solicitor over any property including real property.
[4] He is still, however, a solicitor within the meaning of the Solicitors' (Disciplinary Proceedings) Rules 1957: *Re A Solicitor* (1963), 107 Sol. Jo. 216.
[5] Solicitors Act 1957, s. 18.
[6] *Ibid.*, s. 22 reversing the effect of *The Law Society* v. *United Service Bureau, Ltd.*, [1934] 1 K.B. 343.
[7] *Ibid.*, s. 19; see *Carter* v. *Butcher*, [1966] 1 Q.B. 526; [1965] 1 All E.R. 994

conviction. There are savings for wills, agreements under hand only, powers of attorney and simple stock transfers.[1]

None of the above provisions affect the right of any person to act for himself in any matter, contentious or non-contentious. Thus a litigant may appear in person without the need for representation by solicitor or counsel. However there are exceptional cases in which the litigant cannot appear in person. Thus in the High Court neither a corporate body nor the next friend or guardian *ad litem* of a person under disability (infant or patient) may appear in person. A solicitor must be retained.[2]

C BARRISTERS

1 General organisation of the Bar

a The Inns of Court

Persons may only practise as counsel in England if they have been "called to the Bar" of one of the four Inns of Court, Lincoln's Inn, the Inner Temple, the Middle Temple and Gray's Inn. These Inns are as old as professional advocacy itself in England and appear to have originated as living quarters for those legal practitioners who were not serjeants.[3] The Inns' jurisdiction is in no way statutory. It is derived from the judges (and thus indirectly from the Crown) and is subject to control by the judges.[4] One member of the Court of Appeal has explained the Inns' functions as follows:[5]

> "I would regard the Inns of Court in their disciplinary power in relation to the practising member of the Bar as equivalently established over the centuries by its practice and acceptance as if the power had been derived from statute and as unassailable. If the Inns of Court had not controlled the professional conduct of the Bar the judges themselves would have had to do so. The judges themselves, deriving their authority from the Crown, were minded in the distant past to delegate, and the undisputed view in Lord Mansfield's time was that the judges had delegated their disciplinary power over the Bar to the Inns of Court."

In the Inns of Court there are three classes of members; benchers, who are the governors of the Inn, barristers, who are called by the benchers, and students who are admitted to membership by the benchers. The benchers of an Inn, who are judges or senior members of the Bar, have absolute control over the admission of students and the call of barristers. There is an appeal from their decisions to the Lord Chancellor and the judges of the High Court sitting as "visitors", a domestic tribunal. They cannot, however, be sued in respect of any act done in their official capacity nor can they be compelled by mandamus to

---

[1] Act of 1957, s. 20. No offence is committed if the unqualified person proves that the instrument was not prepared in expectation of any fee or reward. He need not, however, have a legal right to remuneration. It is sufficient that he has an expectation of gain: *Pacey* v. *Atkinson*, [1950] 1 K.B. 539; [1950] 1 All E.R. 320.

[2] R.S.C. (Revision) 1965, O. 5, r. 6.

[3] Serjeants had their own Inns ("Serjeants' Inns"). There were also several Chancery Inns (e.g. New Inn, Clifford's Inn). All these have ceased to exist.

[4] *R.* v. *Gray's Inn* (1780), 1 Doug. K.B. 353, *per* LORD MANSFIELD.

[5] SELLERS, L.J. in *Lincoln* v. *Daniels*, [1963] 1 Q.B. 237, at p. 250; [1961] 3 All E.R. 740, at p. 745; cf. *Re S. (a barrister)*, [1970] 1 Q.B. 160; [1969] 1 All E.R. 949.

admit a person as a student or call a student to the Bar.[1]   The principal conditions which a student must satisfy before applying for call to the Bar are payment of the requisite fees, passing the Bar Final Examination and keeping eight terms.[2]   No person under the age of 21 can be called to the Bar.   Before a barrister can practise he must serve a pupillage under a senior member of the Bar (not a Queen's Counsel) for not less than twelve months.

b   The Senate of the Inns of Court

In 1966 the four Inns, by a resolution passed by each Inn (and confirmed by a resolution of the judges of the High Court) established a new joint body known as the Senate of the Inns of Court.   The Senate consists of thirty-seven members, comprising the Attorney-General, the Chairman of the Bar Council, six representatives appointed by the Benchers of each Inn and six appointed by the Bar Council.   The Senate has authority, within limits, to make decisions on behalf of the whole Bar.   Its functions include the regulation of the admission of students and of call to the Bar, legal education and the exercise of certain disciplinary power over members of the Bar.   The Inns of Court are bound by decisions of the Senate, which also acts in an advisory capacity to the Inns.   The Senate also controls the policy of the Council of Legal Education, though the functions of the Bar Council remain independent.   The Senate, through a special disciplinary committee composed entirely of practising barristers, hears and determines disciplinary charges against barristers, though the penalty to be imposed upon a barrister found guilty of professional misconduct is still imposed upon him by his own Inn, which therefore acts simply as a "rubber stamp" for the decisions of the Senate.

In a recent case[3] a barrister, who had been disbarred by his Inn following a hearing before the disciplinary committee of the senate, appealed to five judges of the Queen's Bench Division sitting as visitors to the Inn;   his contention was that the benchers of the Inn, having derived their disciplinary powers by delegation from the judges could not, because of the principle *delegatus non potest delegare*, delegate those powers to the Senate.   The visitors rejected this contention on the ground that the judges had a duty to determine who should have right of audience in the courts and that, although they had for three centuries acquiesced in that duty being performed by the benchers, they had never divested themselves of the duty.   Consequently the transfer of jurisdiction to the Senate was not a delegation but simply a change in the manner in which the judges chose to discharge their primary duty.

> "The judges remain under the same duty unimpaired;   the machinery by which they exercise their judicial duty has been changed."[4]

---

[1] *R. v. Lincoln's Inn Benchers* (1825), 4 B. & C. 855.

[2] The latter obligation is not imposed upon solicitors wishing to become barristers. There are four dining terms a year in the Inns of Court: Michaelmas, Hilary, Easter and Trinity.   A term is kept by dining in Hall on a number of occasions (usually three) during the term.

[3] *Re S. (a barrister)*, [1970] 1 Q.B. 160; [1969] 1 All E.R. 949.

[4] [1970] 1 Q.B., at p. 175; [1969] 1 All E.R. at p. 959, *per* PAULL, J.   In the instant case the visitors allowed the appeal in respect of 2 out of 6 charges and substituted for the order of disbarment an order of suspension for 12 months.

c   The General Council of the Bar

The Bar Council, like the Inns of Court, has no statutory foundation. However its jurisdiction does not derive from the judges but from the consent of the Bar. In addition it is not a judicial body and has no disciplinary powers, although it does investigate complaints about the conduct of barristers.[1]   It is of far more recent creation than the Inns, being created by consent of the whole Bar in 1894. The Council is supported by financial assistance from the four Inns of Court and by contributions from individual barristers.   Its function is principally administrative and may be compared to the function which The Law Society exercises in respect of solicitors.   It deals with such matters as remuneration, professional etiquette and the general organisation of the circuit system.

2   Rights and duties of barristers

The barrister's function is primarily advocacy although he deals also with such matters as drafting conveyances, pleadings and other legal documents and advising on the law.   He has a right of audience in virtually all judicial proceedings and in the House of Lords, the Judicial Committee of the Privy Council, the Court of Appeal and the High Court of Justice this right is exclusive, except in interlocutory proceedings and bankruptcy proceedings where solicitors have a concurrent right.   This exclusive right of audience does not usually prejudice the right of a litigant to appear in person.   However, in certain exceptional cases counsel must be retained.   In criminal proceedings in the Crown Court, prosecutions must be conducted by barristers and prosecutors cannot appear in person.   All petitions of appeal to the House of Lords from the Court of Appeal must be signed by two counsel.

Barristers have, in most cases, exclusive eligibility by statute for judicial offices and the offices of Lord Chancellor, Attorney-General and Solicitor-General are always filled by barristers.

In addition to these rights and privileges barristers have various duties both to the court and to their clients.   Their duties to the court are all based on professional etiquette.   Barristers are not, in the way that solicitors are, officers of the court so that they are not strictly subject to control by the courts.   It is doubtful whether the courts would exercise jurisdiction to suspend a barrister from practising, since this power is left by the judges to the Inns of Court. Nevertheless a barrister may clearly be fined or imprisoned for contempt of court to the same extent as a solicitor or, indeed, any other person.   Counsel cannot, in general, be heard in court unless they are "robed", a term which includes the wearing of wig, gown and bands.   A barrister may, however, appear unrobed in magistrates' courts and also when appearing as litigant in person.[2]   Although counsel are not officers of the court they are officers of justice.   This is particularly true in criminal proceedings so that prosecuting counsel's function is to assist the court, not to press for a conviction.   Even in civil cases barristers are under a duty to draw to the attention of the court authorities which do not support their client's case.   Furthermore, counsel must not mislead the court by actively concealing facts[3] from the court which

---

[1] See *Lincoln* v. *Daniels*, [1962] 1 Q.B. 237; [1961] 3 All E.R. 740.
[2] *Practice Note*, [1961] 1 All E.R. 319.
[3] *Meek* v. *Fleming*, [1961] 2 Q.B. 366, [1961] 3 All E.R. 148.

are material to the case, nor must he set up any affirmative case or defence inconsistent with any admission or confession made to him by his client, nor should he take a point of law which he knows to be bad.

3   Relationship between counsel and client

The relationship between a barrister and his client is *sui generis*. It is not a contractual relationship. The payment which a barrister receives by way of a brief fee is not a contractual payment but an *honorarium*. The result is that a barrister cannot sue for his fees.[1] Nor can he sue upon a promise to pay fees, nor prove for fees in bankruptcy. Fees due to counsel which have been paid to a firm of solicitors but have not been paid over to counsel cannot be attached or garnished.[2] Counsel's fees are, however, chargeable to income tax and are allowable as costs on taxation.

The principal safeguard that counsel has in connection with his fee is that he may refuse to accept a brief if the fee is not paid when the brief is delivered. However, as a matter of etiquette, the Council of The Law Society has stated that solicitors are personally liable to see that counsel's fees are paid whether or not the solicitor has been put in funds by the client. If the solicitor has been paid counsel's fee by the client, it is professional misconduct on the part of the solicitor not to pay it over and the matter may be referred to the Disciplinary Committee.[3] In exceptional cases The Law Society may authorise payment of counsel's fees out of the Compensation Fund.[4] Also, as a matter of etiquette, counsel's "right" to his fees derives from delivery of the brief not from his retainer. Thus a brief must not be marked after the termination of the proceedings to which it relates, with certain exceptions, notably in legal aid cases.

The corollary of barristers' inability to sue for their fees is their immunity from being sued in contract for professional negligence. Historically barristers have always been immune from actions in negligence because such actions could only be based on contract and were thus not possible against a barrister, with whom the client could not enter into a contractual relationship. There is a long line of authorities going back to the Year Books for the reign of Henry VI which support this immunity.[5] However, when all these old cases were decided there was no thought of the existence of the modern action for negligence in respect of professional advice. Following statements of the House of Lords in *Hedley Byrne & Co., Ltd.* v. *Heller and Partners, Ltd.*[6] that a person giving professional advice may owe a duty of care in negligence:

> "Many at the Bar have been watching carefully for signs of the cold wind of change blowing across the Strand into the Temple; some are said to have protected

---

[1] *Wells* v. *Wells*, [1914] P. 157.
[2] *Re Le Brasseur and Oakley*, [1896] 2 Ch. 487. See *Rondel* v. *Worsley*, [1969] 1 A.C. 191; [1967] 3 All E.R. 993, in which the position of a barrister is examined and the authorities reviewed.
[3] Annual Statement of the Bar Council 1930, p. 10.
[4] Annual Statement of the Bar Council 1954, p. 26.
[5] The leading case is *Swinfen* v. *Lord Chelmsford* (1860), 5 H. & N. 890. The authorities are reviewed in *Rondel* v. *Worsley*, [1969] 1 A.C. 191; [1967] 3 All E.R. 993.
[6] [1964] A.C. 465; [1963] 2 All E.R. 575.

themselves with the comforting embraces of Lloyd's and others who provide like services."[1]

However, in the recent case of *Rondel* v. *Worsley*[2] the House of Lords, faced with this very question whether a barrister might now be held liable in negligence, decided not and dismissed the plaintiff's appeal from an order that his statement of claim be struck out as disclosing no cause of action. LORD DENNING, M.R., in the Court of Appeal, reviewed the authorities at length before distinguishing *Hedley Byrne & Co., Ltd.* v. *Heller and Partners, Ltd.*[3] The Master of the Rolls conceded that, since *Hedley Byrne*, a barrister's immunity could not be justified on the ground of his inability to sue for his fees. Consequently LORD DENNING based counsel's immunity upon various grounds of public policy and upon long usage from which the public interest did not require a departure. The grounds of public policy to which LORD DENNING adverted may be summarised as follows:[4]

(1) *Independence*—"that he may do his duty fearlessly and independently as he ought and to prevent him being harassed by vexatious actions."
"If a barrister is to be able to do his duty fearlessly and independently he must not be subject to the threat of an action for negligence."
(2) *Professional obligation to act*—"A barrister cannot pick or choose his clients. He is bound to accept a brief for any man who comes before the Courts. No matter how great a rascal the man may be. No matter how given to complaining. No matter how underserving or unpopular his cause. The barrister must defend him to the end;"
(3) *Duty to the court*—"He has a duty to the court which is paramount. It is a mistake to suppose that he is the mouthpiece of his client to say what he wants: or his tool to do what he directs. He is none of these things. He owes allegiance to a higher cause. It is the cause of truth and justice. . . . He must disregard the most specific instructions of his client, if they conflict with his duty to the court;"
(4) *Protraction of litigation*—"If a barrister could be sued for negligence, it would mean a retrial of the original case. . . . If this action were to be permitted, it would open the door to every disgruntled client. . . . If this action is to go for trial, it will lead to dozens of like cases."

Although the appellant's claim was "clearly as devoid of merit as it was of any prospect of success"[5] the House of Lords gave leave to appeal in view of the importance of the question of law involved. In the event the House of Lords affirmed the decision of the Court of Appeal. While their lordships differed slightly as to the emphasis to be placed upon individual heads of public policy they concurred, in the result, in each of the above four heads adverted to by LORD DENNING in the Court of Appeal.

The House of Lords also considered, as the Court of Appeal had done, the question of whether barristers' immunity extended to work done in chambers in advising, settling documents and other matters which might never come before a court. Although the majority view of the Court of Appeal had been that the immunity did so extend the House of Lords, with the exception of

---

[1] LAWTON, J. (as he then was) at first instance in *Rondel* v. *Worsley*, [1967] 1 Q.B. 443, at p. 455; [1966] 1 All E.R. 467, at p. 470.
[2] [1969] 1 A.C. 191; [1967] 3 All E.R. 993.
[3] [1964] A.C. 465; [1963] 2 All E.R. 575.
[4] [1967] 1 Q.B., at pp. 501–504; [1966] 3 All E.R., at pp. 665–666.
[5] [1967] 1 Q.B., at 516; [1966] 3 All E.R., at p. 674, *per* SALMON, L.J. (as he then was); [1969] 1 A.C., at p. 226; [1967] 3 All E.R., at p. 998, *per* LORD REID.

LORD PEARCE who favoured the wider immunity, expressed the opinion that, while the immunity from action extended to pleadings and other work done while litigation was pending, it did not extend to advisory work or work done on documents outside the context of litigation. These opinions are, of course, no more than *obiter dicta* so that the question awaits authoritative determination.

Other incidents of the barrister's relationship with his client which may be noted briefly are the former's obligation to preserve the latter's confidences and counsel's authority to conduct proceedings on behalf of the client. The scope of this authority is determinable in accordance with ordinary principles of the law of agency and includes the authority to compromise proceedings on behalf of the client and the authority to make admissions on the latter's behalf in civil proceedings, though not to plead guilty in a criminal prosecution.

4 Professional etiquette

The duties of solicitors towards their clients is governed both by statute and by their code of professional etiquette. In the case of barristers the obligations are governed solely by the dictates of professional etiquette.[1] The rules of etiquette may change from time to time and may be altered by the Bar Council on behalf of the whole Bar, by the Inns of Court on behalf of their members or by the Senate of the Inns of Court. In no case are the rules enforceable in any way other than by complaint to the Bar Council or the individual barrister's Inn followed by disciplinary proceedings before the Senate of the Inns of Court which may result in the barrister being disbarred or suspended from practising.

Etiquette at the Bar is a complex study[2] but certain important rules of etiquette should be carefully noted. Perhaps the most important rule of etiquette is that, subject to a few exceptional cases, counsel may accept instructions only from a solicitor and not from a client direct.[3] This rule applies to all civil contentious business and to all criminal business with the unimportant exception of a "dock brief."[4] Touting for business among solicitors and advertisement[5] are clearly contrary to etiquette. So too is any form of partnership or profit sharing. Counsel should not normally interview witnesses before or during a trial, nor should he consult with a client except in the presence of the solicitor. A Queen's Counsel must appear with a junior, may not have pupils and may not do drafting work or give written opinions on evidence.

---

[1] *Re Harrison*, [1908] 1 Ch. 282.
[2] For details see Boulton, *Conduct and Etiquette at the Bar*.
[3] *Doe d. Bennett* v. *Hale* (1850), 15 Q.B. 171.
[4] The prisoner, on a trial on indictment, may instruct from the dock any barrister who is robed and sitting in court for the sum of £2·25. The dock brief is virtually obsolete by reason of the extension of legal aid in criminal proceedings. It may be noted that the litigation in *Rondel* v. *Worsley* (*supra*) arose out of a dock brief, the plaintiff having been refused a legal aid certificate.
[5] Though it is not improper for a Queen's Counsel (Q.C.) to describe himself by this title.

D LAW OFFICERS

1 Attorney-General and Solicitor-General

The "Law Officers", legal advisers to the Crown, are the Attorney-General and the Solicitor-General. The Attorney-General is the head of the English Bar, though neither he nor the Solicitor-General may engage in private practice while they hold office. They are assisted by Junior Counsel to the Treasury who, holding no political office, are practising barristers.

Apart from his political duties, which include advising Government Departments and answering questions in the House of Commons, the Attorney-General represents the Crown in certain civil proceedings and, as a matter of practice, in trials for treason and other important offences with a political or constitutional element. In addition he exercises the prerogative power of staying prosecutions on indictment by the entry of a *nolle prosequi* and, by statute, leave of the Attorney-General is required for the commencement of certain criminal proceedings. Mention may also be made of "relator" proceedings in which the Attorney-General appears on behalf of a section of the public, for example to restrain a public nuisance.

The Solicitor-General's position is basically that of the Attorney-General's deputy and he may exercise any power vested by statute in the Attorney-General (unless the statute in question otherwise provides) if the office of Attorney-General is vacant, the Attorney-General is unable to act through illness or the Attorney-General authorises the Solicitor-General to act.[1]

2 Director of Public Prosecutions

The term "Law Officers" does not strictly include the Director of Public Prosecutions but mention may be made at this stage of this official who is a barrister or solicitor appointed by the Home Secretary but working under the supervision of the Attorney-General. Although most prosecutions in England are instituted by private persons (usually police officers) the Director of Public Prosecutions must under some statutes prosecute[2] and does in practice investigate and prosecute crimes of great gravity or complexity, notably murder and crimes of interference with the judicial process, such as perjury. Finally certain statutes prescribe the consent of the Director of Public Prosecutions as a condition precedent to the institution of criminal proceedings.[3]

---

[1] Law Officers Act 1944, s. 1.
[2] E.g. for election offences under the Representation of the People Act 1949.
[3] E.g. Sexual Offences Act 1967, s. 8. If consent is not first obtained the subsequent trial is a nullity: *R. v. Angel*, [1968] 2 All E.R. 607 n.; [1968] 1 W.L.R. 669.

CHAPTER 14

Legal Aid and Advice

A GENERAL ADMINISTRATION OF THE LEGAL AID SCHEME

Prior to 1949 there were various provisions to enable persons to sue or be sued *in forma pauperis* and to prosecute and defend both civil and criminal proceedings with the financial assistance of various societies and authorities. These provisions have now been almost totally replaced by statute. The statutes which govern the grant of legal aid in all civil matters and, to a lesser extent, in criminal matters are the Legal Aid and Advice Act 1949, the Legal Aid Act 1960 and the Legal Aid Act 1964 together with numerous regulations passed under these Acts. The Legal Aid Acts create a national scheme for providing legal aid and advice to persons within the means limits, the expense being met out of a public fund known as the Legal Aid Fund financed by the State.[1] The annual cost to the public of the legal aid scheme is currently slightly over £13 million, much of which is accounted for by the costs of matrimonial proceedings, most of which are undefended petitions for divorce. It is this factor which was the principal argument for removing undefended divorce petitions from the High Court to the county court where the costs of proceedings are somewhat lower.[2]

The general administration of Part I of the 1949 Act, which concerns legal aid in civil litigation, legal aid in matters not involving litigation and legal advice, is in the hands of The Law Society which acts in consultation with the Bar Council and under the general guidance of the Lord Chancellor.[3] For the purposes of the scheme England and Wales is divided into twelve areas each with an Area Committee consisting of practising solicitors and barristers, subordinate to which are a number of Local Committees comprising solicitors and barristers. The principal function of the Local Committees is to consider applications for legal aid certificates in courts of first instance and, where appropriate, to issue certificates. Other responsibilities are in the hands of the Area Committees themselves and include the supervision of the remuneration of barristers

---

[1] In criminal proceedings (save in the Queen's Bench Divisional Court) the costs are paid out of local authority funds: Criminal Justice Act 1967, s. 81 (1).
[2] This change was effected by the Matrimonial Causes Act 1967.
[3] Legal Aid and Advice Act 1949, s. 8 (9).

and solicitors acting in the Scheme and the preparation and maintenance of separate panels of solicitors and barristers who are willing to act for persons who are given legal aid and of solicitors willing to give legal advice. Area Committees also deal with complaints against solicitors and barristers on these panels which may result in their names being removed.[1] Finally, Area Committees assess costs in certain cases in which taxation by the court is not required.

The means of an applicant for legal aid are determined by the Supplementary Benefits Commission.[2]

B LEGAL ADVICE

Legal advice is provided only by solicitors, not by barristers. There are two Schemes for legal advice; the Voluntary Legal Advice Scheme made by the Council of The Law Society and the Statutory Scheme under section 7 of the Act.[3]

The Voluntary Scheme does not depend upon the applicant's means. Any person may apply to a solicitor on the panel for advice. The solicitor may decline to give advice without giving any reason. Otherwise he must give advice for not more than 30 minutes for a fee of not more than £2 to be paid by the applicant. The advice is oral but the solicitor may, if he thinks fit, give a written note confirming the advice. If the matter cannot be disposed of in 30 minutes the solicitor should give an approximate estimate of the cost of any further advice which may be necessary.

A person may apply for advice under the Statutory Scheme only if he can satisfy certain conditions specified in the Legal Advice Regulations 1959, as amended. The applicant must be over the age of 16 and must either have an interest in the question on which advice is sought whether directly, indirectly or in a representative, fiduciary or official capacity, or represent a person so interested who cannot appear in person. In addition the applicant must satisfy the solicitor that he cannot afford to obtain advice in the ordinary way, that his capital does not exceed £125,[4] and that his disposable income in the seven days up to and including the date of his application does not exceed £9·50 (unless he is in receipt of a supplementary benefit[5]).

If the solicitor is satisfied as to the above conditions the applicant may obtain oral advice on questions of English law, including assistance in preparing an

---

[1] In criminal proceedings any practising barrister or solicitor may be assigned to act for a legally assisted person unless excluded, by order of a tribunal established by the Lord Chancellor, as being unfit to act by reason of professional misconduct: Criminal Justice Act 1967, s. 82 (1).

[2] Established by the Ministry of Social Security Act 1966 to exercise certain of the functions formerly exercised by the National Assistance Board which was abolished by the same Act.

[3] References in this chapter to "the Act" are to the Legal Aid and Advice Act 1949, unless a contrary intention appears. The Legal Advice and Assistance Bill currently before Parliament makes extensive changes in the schemes set out hereafter.

[4] In assessing this figure the value of the applicant's dwelling house, furniture and effects, articles of personal clothing and the tools and implements of his trade are excluded: Legal Advice Regulations 1959, reg. 3 (3).

[5] Either a "supplementary pension", if he has attained pensionable age, or a "supplementary allowance", if he has not: Ministry of Social Security Act 1966, s. 4.

application for legal aid,[1] for not more than 1 hour and 30 minutes, unless the Area Committee specifies a longer period. The solicitor must exercise the same degree of care and skill in giving advice as he would normally[2] and must preserve the applicant's confidence except that he must complete and forward to the Area Committee the appropriate form provided by The Law Society and must give to the Area Committee any additional information that it may require.

In return for this advice the applicant pays to the solicitor the decimal equivalent of half a crown unless he or his spouse is receiving supplementary benefit. The solicitor must keep this sum on account of sums due to him from the Fund, which are £2 for every half hour spent (with a maximum of £2 if the time spent is 40 minutes or less) to a maximum of £6, unless the Area Committee has authorised advice for more than 1 hour and 30 minutes.

C LEGAL AID IN CLAIMS NOT INVOLVING LITIGATION

Section 5 of the Act provides for legal aid in taking steps to assert or dispute a claim, where the question of litigation has not yet arisen, but if it did arise, the proceedings would be such that legal aid could be granted in connection therewith. A certificate under this section is termed a "claim certificate" and is often a preliminary to the grant of a full legal aid certificate under section 1 of the Act. Where it is anticipated that litigation may follow, it is useful to apply for a claim certificate for two reasons. First, the claim certificate may authorise obtaining counsel's opinion as to whether or not to institute or defend proceedings, an opinion which the Area Committee is often willing to accept in deciding whether to grant a certificate for those proceedings. Secondly, if proceedings are taken, the claim certificate may be amended by the Area Committee to extend it to such proceedings.[3]

The application is to the Local Committee, with no appeal from a refusal to issue a certificate. The applicant must satisfy the Committee that he has reasonable grounds for taking steps to assert or dispute the claim and that he is within the financial limits. In the case of an application for a claim certificate the applicant's disposable capital must not exceed £125 and he must either be in receipt of supplementary benefit at the date of the application or have a disposable income not exceeding £325.[4] These amounts are assessed by the secretary of the Local Committee. Where the applicant's disposable income exceeds £303 he is required to pay a contribution[5] to the Fund of not more than one-third of the amount by which his disposable income exceeds £300; for example, if his disposable income is £324 his maximum contribution is £8. A contribution may be made payable forthwith, within a reasonable time or by instalments.

A claim certificate will entitle the assisted person to the aid of a solicitor. It

---

[1] Legal Aid and Advice Act 1949, s. 7 (2).
[2] *Kitchen* v. *Royal Air Force Association*, [1958] 2 All E.R. 241; [1958] 1 W.L.R. 563.
[3] Legal Aid (General) Regulations 1971, reg. 9.
[4] *Ibid.*, reg. 5 (4) and Sch. 2.
[5] *Ibid.*, reg. 6 (6).

cannot extend to counsel,[1] though it may authorise the solicitor to obtain counsel's opinion upon which a "proceedings" (section 1) certificate may be made conditional. A claim certificate authorises expenditure of a sum not exceeding a specified amount.[2] It does not authorise the taking of any step towards the issue or defence of proceedings.

A solicitor acting under a claim certificate must apply to the Area Committee for remuneration which is assessed by the Committee on the basis of disbursements and a fair remuneration for the work properly done.

D LEGAL AID IN CIVIL PROCEEDINGS

1 Courts and proceedings in which legal aid is authorised by the Act

Legal aid is now available in connection with proceedings (unless specifically excepted) in the House of Lords, the Supreme Court of Judicature, any county court and the Lands Tribunal. It is also available in certain proceedings in magistrates' courts, namely proceedings under the Affiliation Proceedings Act 1957, the Matrimonial Proceedings (Magistrates' Courts) Act 1960, the Guardianship of Minors Act 1971, the Small Tenements Recovery Act 1838 and in certain proceedings under the Children and Young Persons Acts 1933, 1963 and 1969 and the Education Act 1944.

Legal Aid is not available in proceedings before judicial and administrative tribunals (except the Lands Tribunal), which many consider a notable omission in view of the increasing volume of business dealt with therein.

There are, however, excepted proceedings in respect of which Aid is not, at present, authorised under the Act. Of these the more important are proceedings wholly or partly in respect of defamation.[3]

2 Conditions under which aid may be granted

Any person, not being a body corporate or an unincorporated body,[4] may apply for legal aid irrespective of nationality or residence. He must, however, be within the prescribed financial limits, this being the first condition precedent to the grant of legal aid. His "disposable income"[5] must not exceed £950 a year and, if required, the applicant must show that his "disposable capital" does not exceed £500 or, if it does, that he could not afford to proceed without legal aid.[6] Disposable income and disposable capital are assessed by the Supplementary Benefits Commission in accordance with the Legal Aid (Assessment of Resources) Regulations 1960 as amended. These Regulations are complex. It

---

[1] Legal Aid and Advice Act 1949, s. 5 (2).

[2] Legal Aid (General) Regulations 1971, reg. 6 (4).

[3] Though the making of a counterclaim in respect of defamation in proceedings in which legal aid is available does not prevent the grant of legal aid to a defendant to the counterclaim: Legal Aid (Extension of Proceedings) Regulations 1969.

[4] Legal Aid and Advice Act 1949, s. 17 (1).

[5] Legal Aid and Advice Act 1949, ss. 2, 4 and sch. 2, as amended by the Legal Aid Act 1960, s. 1 (1); Legal Aid (Assessment of Resources) Regulations 1960 as amended. The figure was raised from £700 to £950 by the Legal Aid (Financial Contributions) Regulations 1970.

[6] Legal Aid and Advice Act 1949, s. 2.

is sufficient to say that disposable income is far less than gross income.   Generous allowances are made for tax, National Insurance contributions, dependants and other outgoings, so that a disposable income of £950 may represent, in extreme cases, a gross income of £2,500 or more.

The second condition precedent to a grant of legal aid is that the applicant must show that he has reasonable grounds for taking, defending or being a party to the proceedings.[1]   In particular a certificate will not be granted in respect of proceedings at first instance where it appears to the Local Committee that the proceedings are too trivial or simple to warrant the assistance of a solicitor.

If a certificate is granted it may be marked with a contribution payable by the assisted litigant.   The maximum contribution in proceedings is all the assisted person's disposable capital above £125 and one-third of the amount by which his disposable income exceeds £300 a year.[2]

3   Application for a certificate under section 1

In the case of proceedings in an appellate court the application is to one of the Area Committees.   Application is also to an Area Committee to amend an existing claim certificate to extend it to proceedings.   In all other cases application is to a Local Committee, with an appeal from refusal to grant a certificate to the appropriate Area Committee, except in the case of summary proceedings, where there is no appeal. If the application is approved the appropriate Committee will draw to the applicant's attention his potential liability for contribution and the costs of an opponent and the conditions upon which a certificate will be issued to him.   He then has 28 days in which to accept these conditions.   If he does he must choose a solicitor from the panel and inform the Committee of his choice.   He may also choose any counsel from the panel if this is authorised by the certificate.

4   The effects on the proceedings of a party being aided

a   Relationship between the assisted litigant and his solicitor and counsel

The professional relationship of solicitor and client is not prejudiced by the fact of the client being in receipt of legal aid.   The solicitor's general duties are still owed to the client and he has authority to act for the client, unless the act performed is not within the scope of the certificate.   The solicitor must preserve his client's confidences though he is in some cases obliged to furnish information to the Area Committee which would normally be privileged.

The chief effect of legal aid on the solicitor–client relationship is upon costs. The solicitor has no right to any costs from the client and he must not charge or take any sum in respect of costs.   It follows that any item of costs incurred by a solicitor which is not allowed by the Area Committee or by the court on taxation is irrecoverable so that a disbursement of this nature will have to be met by the solicitor personally.   In certain cases costs are assessed by the Area

---

[1] Legal Aid and Advice Act 1949, s. 1 (6).
[2] *Ibid.*, s. 3 (1) as amended by the Legal Aid Act 1960, s. 1 (2).   The figure was raised from £250 to £300 by the Legal Aid (Financial Contributions) Regulations 1970.

Committee.[1]   Otherwise in High Court proceedings the court must order the assisted person's costs to be taxed pursuant to the third schedule of the 1949 Act. These costs are taxed on a "common fund" basis.[2]   After taxation the solicitor may recover from the Fund the full amount allowed on taxation for disbursements and 90 *per cent*[3] of the amount allowed in respect of profit costs.   Counsel receives 90 *per cent*[3] of the fee allowed on taxation (his brief is not marked with a fee before the proceedings as it must be in other cases).

b   Assisted litigant's liability for costs

An assisted person has, as stated above, no liability for costs towards his own solicitor and counsel.   His primary liability to the Legal Aid Fund is limited to the amount of his contribution.   However, if he loses his action he may be ordered to pay the costs of the other side.   This does not mean that he must pay the full taxed costs of his opponent.   His liabilities are limited to such amount (if any) which is a reasonable one for him to pay, having regard to the means of all the parties and their conduct in connection with the dispute.[4] In determining this amount, the assisted person's dwellinghouse, household furniture and tools and implements of his trade are not to be taken into account.[5]   In addition the order may direct payment by instalments or may suspend payment *sine die*. The order may, however, be varied within six years if circumstances change.

An assisted person cannot be required by the court to pay the costs of an unsuccessful interlocutory application forthwith.   Also, an assisted person is not usually ordered to give security for costs although such an order can be, and has been, made.[6]

If the assisted litigant is awarded costs, these are payable by his opponent in the ordinary way.   These costs are paid directly into the Legal Aid Fund.   If the sums paid out by the Fund to the assisted person's solicitor and counsel exceed the amount paid in, comprising the assisted person's contribution and costs recovered from the other side, the Fund has a first charge for the balance on any property recovered or preserved in the proceedings, with certain exemptions, notably maintenance in matrimonial proceedings.[7]   Thus if an assisted person is successful the public will not generally be the loser, which is the reason for the public cost of the Legal Aid Scheme being relatively so low.

---

[1] (a) In the case of summary proceedings in accordance with rules contained in the schedule to the Legal Aid (General) Regulations 1971; (b) in other cases where the retainer of the assisted person's solicitor or counsel is ended before proceedings are actually begun; and (c) in certain exceptional cases specified in the Legal Aid (Assessment of Resources) Regulations 1960, reg. 19.

[2] Legal Aid and Advice Act 1949, sch. 3, para. 4 (1).   See Rules of the Supreme Court (Revision) 1965, O. 62, r. 28 (4); p. 302, *post*.

[3] The full amount is recoverable in respect of proceedings in county courts.

[4] Legal Aid and Advice Act 1949, s. 2 (2) (*e*).   See *Peeling* v. *Guidice* (1963), 186 Estates Gazette, 133.

[5] *Ibid.*, s. 2 (4).   On the other hand the court, in considering what is a reasonable amount for the assisted litigant to pay, may take into account the fact that he has been awarded damages: *Nolan* v. *C. and C. Marshall, Ltd.*, [1954] 2 Q.B. 42; [1954] 1 All E.R. 328.

[6] *Wyld* v. *Silver (No. 2)*, [1962] 2 All E.R. 809; [1962] 1 W.L.R. 863.

[7] Legal Aid and Advice Act 1949, s. 3 (4).

c Unassisted person's rights to costs

It follows from the preceding paragraph that the unassisted litigant appearing
against an assisted litigant is at a substantial disadvantage in the matter of costs.
If he loses he pays full costs; if he wins he recovers only limited costs, unlikely
to amount to more than about £100. It was to remedy this serious abuse that
the Legal Aid Act 1964 was passed. This Act was at first interpreted and applied
by the courts in a very restrictive manner,[1] so much so that over the period of
three years after the passing of the Act, Parliament provided no less than
£120,000 for the purposes of the Act, of which only £1,155 was used. However, in *Hanning* v. *Maitland (No. 2)*[2] the Court of Appeal laid down broader
principles for the application of the Act, stating that if the legally aided party
lost the action it was usually just and equitable that the unassisted party should
recover his costs from public funds, unless, for example, he has done something
to bring the action on himself or has been guilty of misconduct.

The 1964 Act, by section 1 provides that an unassisted party appearing against
an assisted party may be awarded the whole or any part of his costs out of the
Legal Aid Fund, provided that the proceedings are finally decided in favour of
the unassisted party, that those proceedings were instituted by the assisted party
in the court of first instance and provided "the court is satisfied that the unassisted party will suffer. severe financial hardship unless the order is made".[3]
"Severe financial hardship" is not, however, strictly interpreted so that in
Hanning v. *Maitland (No. 2)*, LORD DENNING, M.R. stated that the condition
should not be construed as to exclude people of modest income or modest
capital who would find it hard to bear their own costs. Furthermore no order
is to be made unless an order in favour of the unassisted party would be made
apart from this Act; thus, in divorce suits (to which legal aid so often relates)
a wife is not usually ordered to pay her husband's costs unless she has sufficient
separate estate. If an assisted wife would not be required to pay her unassisted
husband's costs apart from the 1964 Act, the latter has no recourse to the Fund.[4]

Where both parties are legally aided the court may make such order as to
costs as the circumstances warrant.

Apart from the above provisions, which affect costs, proceedings are not
generally affected by one or more of the parties being legally aided. Indeed
proceedings may be lengthened since litigants are naturally not anxious to
compromise proceedings which they are fighting at the public expense. This
is one of the principal criticisms of the scheme to which may be added the
fact that legal aid is not available before most tribunals and the inequitable
position of the unassisted litigant, despite the 1964 Act.

---

[1] See *Nowotnik* v. *Nowotnik*, [1967] P. 83; [1965] 3 All E.R. 167; *Re Spurling's Will Trusts*,
[1966] 1 All E.R. 745; [1966] 1 W.L.R. 920; *Re Sl. (infants)*, [1967] 3 All E.R. 538;
[1967] 1 W.L.R. 1379.

[2] [1970] 1 Q.B. 580; [1970] 1 All E.R. 812.

[3] The need to show "severe financial hardship" exists only in relation to proceedings at first
instance (s. 1 (3)) and not to proceedings on appeal where the applicant need only show
that it is "just and equitable" that an order be made (s. 1 (2)): *Parker (infants)* v. *Thompson*
[1966] 3 All E.R. 766; [1967] 1 W.L.R. 28; *Gallie* v. *Lee (No. 2)*, [1971] A.C. 1039;
[1971] 1 All E.R. 243 (in which case a Building Society was awarded its costs out of the
Legal Aid Fund).

[4] Legal Aid Act 1964, s. 1 (4); *Nowotnik* v. *Nowotnik (supra)*; *Povey* v. *Povey*, [1972]
Fam. 40; [1970] 3 All E.R. 612.

E LEGAL AID IN CRIMINAL PROCEEDINGS

Criminal proceedings (save those in the Queen's Bench Divisional Court) are outside the scope of the above Scheme. Legal aid in criminal proceedings is now governed by Part IV of the Criminal Justice Act 1967 as amended.

There are two basic differences between legal aid in criminal proceedings and legal aid in civil proceedings. The first is that, due to the importance of expedition in criminal proceedings, there is not time for the elaborate formalities relating to applications for certificates to Committees and assessment of resources which take place in civil cases. The result is that application is usually to the court of trial and any assessment of resources or contribution by the accused may take place after an order has been made. However a court, before it makes a legal aid order, must require the applicant to furnish a written statement of means and, if it appears from this statement that he will be required to make a contribution and has the means to make an immediate payment, may refuse an order unless the applicant first makes a payment on account.[1]

The second essential difference between civil and criminal legal aid is that, while in civil proceedings there is a wide discretion in the matter of granting certificates, legal aid must be granted where it is desirable in the interests of justice,[2] and an accused will rarely be refused legal aid, on grounds other than financial ones, where he is charged with a serious crime, even if he intends to plead guilty.[3] Moreover on committal for trial on a charge of murder or on the prosecution appealing, or applying for leave to appeal, from the criminal division of the Court of Appeal or the Courts-Martial Appeal Court to the House of Lords, the court must make a legal aid order.[2]

The House of Lords does not grant legal aid although aid may be granted by the court below in respect of an appeal to the House. Where the appeal is from or the proceedings are before a divisional court of the Queen's Bench Division application is, anomalously, to the appropriate Area Committee of The Law Society since these are treated as civil proceedings for the purpose of legal aid.

In relation to all other criminal proceedings the power to grant legal aid is now contained in section 73 of the Criminal Justice Act 1967.[4]

In magistrates' courts the court before which the accused appears may make the order.

Where a person appears before the Crown Court, whether for trial or sentence, a legal aid order may be made either by the court by which or by the court to which he is committed. Similarly on appeal from a magistrates' court to the Crown Court either of these courts may make an order.

In relation to appeals to the criminal division of the Court of Appeal, that

---

[1] Criminal Justice Act 1967, s. 75 (3), (4).
[2] *Ibid.*, s. 75 (1).
[3] See *R. v. Howes*, [1964] 2 Q.B. 459; [1964] 2 All E.R. 172.
[4] The Children and Young Persons Act 1969, s. 33 and Sch. 1 extend s. 73 to certain proceedings under the 1969 Act which are not, strictly, criminal proceedings, namely "care proceedings" brought under section 1 of the Act (see p. 175, *ante*), proceedings under sections 15 and 21 of the Act (variation and discharge of supervision and care orders) and under section 31 (removal to borstal institutions of persons committed to the care of local authorities).

court may grant legal aid for the purposes of the appeal and any proceedings preliminary or incidental thereto.

As a rule legal aid consists of representation by a solicitor and counsel and includes advice on the preparation of the accused's case. However in magistrates' courts legal aid does not extend to representation by counsel except in the case of an unusually grave or difficult indictable offence,[1] while in certain cases there is power to order legal aid to consist of representation by counsel only.[2]

An assisted person may, after the disposal of his case, be ordered by the court to pay such contribution as appears reasonable, having regard to his commitments and resources.[3] A contribution may be ordered to be paid by instalments. If the assisted person fails to pay any contribution, or any instalment thereof, this may be recovered in a magistrates' court as a civil debt or enforced as a judgment debt in the High Court or a county court.[4]

---

[1] Criminal Justice Act 1967, s. 74 (2).

[2] Ibid., s. 74 (3), (4).

[3] Ibid., s. 76.   For this purpose the court may require the Supplementary Benefits Commission to enquire into the assisted person's means (s. 77).   Where the assisted person is under the age of 16, the order for payment of contributions may be made against anyone who is an "appropriate contributor" in relation to the assisted person (Children and Young Persons Act 1969, s. 33 (1); Sch. 1), which expression includes the assisted person's father, any person who has been adjudged to be his putative father or his mother.

[4] Ibid., s. 79 (3), (4), (6).

PART IV

Civil Procedure

SUMMARY

The jurisdiction of the various English courts has been considered. The chapters in this section deal with civil proceedings in the Queen's Bench Division of the High Court, county court proceedings and appeals in civil cases. Procedure in the Chancery Division is basically similar to procedure in the Queen's Bench Division though there are, of course, certain differences due to the specialised nature of many Chancery matters. Procedure in the Family Division, to which brief reference has been made in Chapter 10, differs substantially from Queen's Bench Division procedure and will not be considered further in this work.

CHAPTER 15

Preliminary Considerations in an Action in the Queen's Bench Division

A RULES OF THE SUPREME COURT

Procedure in the Queen's Bench Division is governed by the Rules of the Supreme Court. These Rules are delegated legislation, being made by a Rule Committee under powers conferred by the Judicature Acts.[1]

The Rules were recently revised; the current Rules[2] are the Rules of the Supreme Court (Revision) 1965. The Rules themselves together with guides to their interpretation are to be found in the current edition of the Supreme Court Practice (the "White Book"). It must be stressed that the Rules are purely procedural and cannot affect substantive rules of law. In the words of a Master of the Rolls:

> ". . . The relation of the rules of practice to the work of justice is intended to to be that of handmaiden rather than mistress . . ."[3]

Thus the Court of Appeal has in two recent cases declared certain of the Rules to be *ultra vires*, as being substantive rather than procedural.[4]

---

[1] At present, Judicature Act 1925, s. 99.
[2] The Rules of the Supreme Court have their source in the Common Law Procedure Acts 1852 and 1854 and the Court of Chancery Procedure Act 1852 (15 & 16 Vict., c. 86). These were substantially reproduced in a Schedule to the Judicature Acts 1873–1875 and later embodied in the Rules of the Supreme Court 1883, a statutory instrument drawn up by the Rule Committee.
[3] Sir RICHARD HENN-COLLINS M.R. in *Re Coles and Ravenshear*, [1907] 1 K.B. 1, at p. 4.
[4] *Re Grosvenor Hotel, London (No. 2)*, [1965] Ch. 1233; [1964] 3 All E.R. 354; *Ward* v. *James*, [1966] 1 Q.B. 273; [1965] 1 All E.R. 563; the Rules in question have since been amended.

B DISCOVERY, INSPECTION AND RELATED PROCEDURES BEFORE COMMENCEMENT OF PROCEEDINGS

Questions concerning discovery and inspection of documents and the inspection, preservation and the like of property are dealt with during the course of proceedings, usually after the close of pleadings, and these matters are dealt with below in that context.[1] However recent statutory provisions enable parties to obtain orders of this type prior to the commencement of proceedings. There are two distinct procedures.

1 Discovery and inspection of documents

By section 31 of the Administration of Justice Act 1970 a person who appears to the High Court to be likely to be a party to subsequent proceedings in that court in which a claim in respect of personal injuries to a person or in respect of a person's death is likely to be made, may apply to the court[2] whereupon a party who appears to be likely to be a party to the proceedings and to be likely to have or have had in his possession, custody or power any relevant documents may be ordered to disclose whether those documents are in his custody, possession and power and, if so, to produce them to the applicant, save that if they would be privileged from production he may claim privilege from production in the normal way.[3]

It will be noted that the above procedure is limited to personal injuries litigation. It may be utilised, for example, by a plaintiff to enable him to see his employer's accident reports or documents relating to the maintenance of a vehicle or machine which has proved defective. The object of this provision is to enable personal injuries litigation to be conducted openly and with a view to early settlement if possible.

2 Inspection etc. of property

Section 21 of the Administration of Justice Act 1969 empowers the High Court, in such circumstances as may be specified in rules of court, to make an order providing for the inspection, photographing, preservation, custody or detention of property (including land or chattels) which appears to the court to be property which may become the subject-matter of subsequent proceedings in the court or as to which any question may arise in such proceedings, or for the taking of samples of any such property and the carrying out of any experiment on or with any such property.

Although the section is not confined to personal injuries actions the only rule

---

[1] See pp. 275 *et seq.*, *post.*

[2] The application is by originating summons supported by an affidavit which must (*a*) state the grounds upon which it is alleged that the applicant and the person against whom the order is sought are likely to be parties to subsequent proceedings of the type specified in section 31; and (*b*) specify or describe the documents concerned and showing, if practicable by reference to a draft pleading, their relevance.

The summons and copy affidavit are served on the other party and require him to make an affidavit stating whether any documents specified or described are or have been in his custody, possession or power and, if not then in his custody, possession or power, what has become of them; O. 24, r. 7A (1), (3)–(5).

[3] O. 24, r. 7A (6); see p. 277, *post.*

so far made under the section[1] is limited to such actions and the objects of the section, as thus far implemented, are clearly similar to the objects of section 31 of the 1970 Act. Unlike that section, however, section 21 of the 1969 Act is not limited to prospective parties.

C ALTERNATIVE METHODS OF COMMENCING A CIVIL ACTION

An action in the Queen's Bench Division[2] is in most cases commenced by writ of summons, generally referred to as a writ. However there is an alternative method of proceeding—by originating summons.[3] The latter method is appropriate where the parties' dispute is such that it can be peremptorily determined. As the name indicates it is a summons which actually originates the action as opposed to the issue of an ordinary summons which is an interlocutory step in an action commenced by writ. The method which the plaintiff chooses is not in all cases optional. Thus the following proceedings in the Queen's Bench Division must be begun by writ:

(1) in which a claim is made by the plaintiff for any relief or remedy for any tort, other than trespass to land;

(2) in which a claim made by the plaintiff is based on an allegation of fraud;

(3) in which a claim is made by the plaintiff for damages for breach of duty where the damages claimed consist of or include damages in respect of the death of any person or in respect of personal injuries to any person or in respect of damage to any property;[4]

One type of action must be commenced by originating summons; where any Act requires an application to be made to the High Court other than an application in pending proceedings and no other method is prescribed.[5] A common example is an application, made before commencing an action, under the Limitation Act 1963.[6] All other proceedings may be commenced by writ or

---

[1] O. 29, r. 7A. The application is by originating summons and the procedure is similar to that under O. 24, r. 7A (*supra*).

[2] By R.S.C., O. 1, r. 4A (*a*) "any reference to proceedings in the Queen's Bench Division shall be construed as including a reference to proceedings in the Commercial Court but not to proceedings in the Admiralty Court." The Admiralty Court is part of the Queen's Bench Division (Administration of Justice Act 1970, s. 2) but procedure differs in many respects from procedure in the remainder of the Division and a code of procedure is prescribed by Order 75; see p. 289, *post*.

[3] The extension of originating summons procedure in the Queen's Bench Division was an important innovation of the 1962 Rules. Prior to 1964 originating summonses were far more common in the Chancery Division and, in the Queen's Bench Division, were confined mainly to applications under s. 17 of the Married Women's Property Act 1882 (which are now assigned to the Family Division).

[4] O. 5, r. 2.

[5] O. 5, r. 3.

[6] This Act, as amended by the Law Reform (Miscellaneous Provisions) Act 1971, enables the plaintiff to defeat the defence of limitation, which would normally arise three years after the accrual of his cause of action, in actions for damages for death or personal injury. Under the Act, if the plaintiff can prove that material facts relating to his cause of action were or included facts of a decisive character which were outside his knowledge during the relevant period and that he has issued proceedings within three years of such knowledge (or of death where the action is in respect of the death of the injured person) he may defeat the defence which the defendant would otherwise have under the Limitation

originating summons but the following proceedings are appropriate to be commenced by originating summons:

(1)   in which the sole or principal question at issue is, or is likely to be, one of the construction of an Act, or of any instrument made under an Act, or of any deed, will, contract or other document, or some other question of law, or

(2)   in which there is unlikely to be any substantial dispute of fact.[1]

Since these actions are not concerned with disputes as to fact it would be pedantic for the parties to have to exchange pleadings.   The originating summons procedure is not, therefore, appropriate where there is a significant dispute upon the facts.   Nor is it appropriate where the plaintiff intends to apply for summary judgment under Order 14, since this important Order applies only to actions commenced by writ.   The tort of trespass to land is excepted from those proceedings which must be begun by writ because this action frequently involves a dispute as to title which can be resolved by reference to a single deed or contract—the very type of case with which originating summons procedure is appropriate to deal.

The following chapters are almost exclusively concerned with the course of an action commenced by writ.   However in a later chapter we shall return to consider the procedure applicable to an action begun by originating summons.

Having considered which is the appropriate method of proceeding the plaintiff must, before issuing his writ, consider two further preliminary matters. First he must ensure that his cause of action has accrued since, in order to succeed in his action, the plaintiff must prove a cause of action which was complete at the date of the issue of the writ.   So, for example, an action for the recovery of a debt would be bound to fail if the debt had not fallen due before the issue of the writ even though, when the action came to trial, the debt was clearly overdue.   It is axiomatic that English courts will not adjudicate upon hypothetical, as opposed to actual, disputes.[2]

The second matter which he must consider concerns the proper parties to the action.

Act 1939, s. 2 (1) (as amended).   The plaintiff does not have to issue a summons before commencing his action;   he can simply ask for "leave" to rely on the conditions of the 1963 Act at the trial if the defence of limitation is pleaded.   However, with a view to ascertaining his position, he may apply *ex parte* on affidavit for "leave" to rely upon the Act, in which case he must apply by originating summons, procedure being governed by R.S.C., O. 110.   The procedure is widely used in practice though it is difficult to see why, since even if leave is granted it is still open for the defendant to plead the defence of limitation, in which event the trial court must independently consider whether the plaintiff is within the provisions of the 1963 Act, so that having obtained "leave" before the action commenced will be of no avail to him.

[1]   O. 5, r. 4.

[2]   *Re Barnato*, [1949] Ch. 258;   cf. *Ealing London Borough Council* v. *Race Relations Board*, [1972] 1 All E.R. 105;   [1972] 2 W.L.R. 71 and authorities referred to therein.   The power of the High Court to make a declaratory judgment or order (O. 15, r. 16;   see p. 266, *post*) can be exercised in relation to future rights but is only so exercised in exceptional cases, for example where future rights affect the present situation.   A declaration which relates to a purely hypothetical issue or which would serve no useful purpose will not be made;   cf. *Mellstrom* v. *Garner*, [1970] 2 All E.R. 9;   [1970] 1 W.L.R. 603.   If a writ is issued prematurely the defect is incurable by amendment since amendment dates back to the issue of the writ (*Eshelby* v. *Federated European Bank*, [1932] 1 K.B. 254);   the plaintiff's only course is to apply to discontinue the action (see p. 251, *post*).

D PARTIES

1 Joinder of parties

The names of all intended parties must appear at the head of the writ. There may be any number of plaintiffs or defendants, or both, to the action. At common law the effect of misjoinder or non-joinder of proper parties was to defeat the plaintiff's claim but nowadays "no cause or matter shall be defeated by reason of the misjoinder or nonjoinder of any party".[1] However the plaintiff must still weigh carefully his choice of parties. On the one hand he may fail to join a party from whom he is entitled to relief in which case his whole action may fail. Alternatively he may add parties whose presence is unnecessary in which event he will usually have to pay the costs occasioned by his error.

Subject to the court's power to order separate trials or add or strike out parties,[2] two or more persons may be joined as plaintiffs or defendants in the following circumstances:

(1) where (*a*) if separate actions were brought by or against each of them, as the case may be, some common question of law or fact would arise in all the actions; and

(*b*) all rights to relief claimed in the action (whether they are joint, several or alternative) are in respect or arise out of the same transaction or series of transactions; and

(2) in any other case with leave of the court.[3]

The plaintiff should join all potential defendants whether relief is alleged to exist against them jointly, severally or in the alternative, for even in the latter circumstance the plaintiff, although he obviously must fail against one or more defendant, may not suffer by it. The reason is that if the court is satisfied that it was a proper course for the plaintiff to join the defendants, it may order the costs of the successful defendant to be added to the costs payable by the unsuccessful defendant,[4] Thus if a plaintiff is injured in a "running down" case he should join the drivers of all the vehicles (unless the liability of one driver, to the exclusion of the others, is *prima facie* obvious, in which event a wise course is to sue only one driver and then to join, by amendment, such other persons as the defendant "blames" in his defence); where he seeks an injunction to abate a nuisance he should join both the landlord and the tenant of the premises from which the alleged nuisance comes; where he is uncertain whether a woman has contracted with him as agent of her husband or as a principal he should join both the husband and wife.[5]

In addition, under O. 15, r. 6 (2), at any stage of the proceedings the court may, of its own motion or on application (*a*) strike out any party who is not a necessary or proper party; or (*b*) add as a party any person whose presence is

---

[1] O. 15, r. 6 (1)
[2] O. 15, rr. 5 (1), 6 (2).
[3] O. 15, r. 4.
[4] See p. 299, *post.*
[5] *Morel Brothers* v. *Earl of Westmorland*, [1904] A.C. 11; unless, of course, prior correspondence or negotiation has disclosed that there is no issue on the point.

necessary to ensure that all matters in dispute may be effectively and completely determined or any person between whom and any party there may exist a question or issue connected with the action which in the opinion of the court it would be just and convenient to determine.[1] Thus in *Gurtner* v. *Circuit*[2] the Motor Insurers Bureau was added as a defendant to an action for damages by a pedestrian against a motor cyclist, on the basis that, since neither the original defendant nor his insurers could be traced, the Bureau might, by reason of its agreement with the Minister of Transport to satisfy all unpaid damages awarded against an uninsured motorist, have to pay any damages awarded. This gave the Bureau a legal and pecuniary interest in the proceedings sufficient to justify its joinder, notwithstanding that the plaintiff had no cause of action against the Bureau.

As in all branches of the law there are special rules which apply only to certain classes of person, usually by reason of a status. The prospective plaintiff must in particular determine whether a prospective defendant is the subject of any of these special rules.

2 Special parties

a The Crown[3]

Until 1948, as an offshoot of the principle of sovereign immunity, the Crown could not be made a party to an action in the courts, the only redress being against Crown servants in their personal capacity. However, by the Crown Proceedings Act 1947 the Crown may now be sued in contract or tort with minor exceptions. The immunity now extends only to the reigning monarch, although there is still a rule of statutory interpretation that the Crown is not bound by a statute unless expressly named in it. An action is commenced by or against the Crown through its appropriate government department as named in a list issued by the Treasury and service is on the solicitor for that department. If there is no appropriate department proceedings are carried on in the name of the Attorney-General. Although the Crown now has few relics of substantive immunity it enjoys certain procedural advantages; for example that judgment in default of appearance or defence cannot be entered against the Crown without leave, that judgment under Order 14 cannot be entered against the Crown and that the Crown is not liable to have any judgment enforced against it.

Heads of foreign sovereign states and their envoys enjoy an immunity from process in the English courts. The scope of this immunity is a matter of constitutional law and will not be discussed further.[4]

---

[1] The latter part of (*b*) was added by R.S.C. (Amendment No. 4) 1971 and appears to negative the decision of the House of Lords in *Re Vandervell's Trusts*, [1971] A.C. 912; [1970] 3 All E.R. 16).

[2] [1968] 2 Q.B. 587; [1968] 1 All E.R. 328.

[3] The special rules of procedure applicable in proceedings to which the Crown is a party are contained in O. 77.

[4] But see, for example, such cases as *Mighell* v. *Sultan of Johore*, [1894] 1 Q.B. 149; *Duff Development Co., Ltd.* v. *Kelantan (Government)*, [1924] A.C. 797; *Mellenger* v. *New Brunswick Development Corporation*, [1971] 2 All E.R. 593; [1971] 1 W.L.R. 604.

b Incorporated associations

An association may be incorporated either by Royal charter or under a statute, usually one of the Companies Acts. In either case the creation is a legal *persona* with an existence, for the purposes of the law, completely independent of its members.[1] It is this factor which distinguishes a corporation or company from an unincorporated association, which is merely a group of individuals referred to by a collective name. An incorporated association may enter into contracts and may commit torts and even crimes. As a legal personality it may sue and be sued in its corporate title or registered name. However, since it has no physical existence, it can only appear through a solicitor.[2] Service on a company is effected by delivering or posting the document to be served to the company's registered office.[3] In one respect a plaintiff company is at a disadvantage; if it has insufficient assets it may be required to give security for costs.[4]

c Unincorporated associations

An association which is not incorporated, under Royal charter or statute, has no legal existence independent of the members of the association. There are for procedural purposes three classes of unincorporated association; partnerships, registered associations and unregistered associations.

Partnerships—Partners may sue and be sued in the firm name.[5] However if suing in the firm name they must on request disclose the name and address of every member of the firm.[6] If they are sued in the firm name, the partners must enter an appearance in their own names individually although proceedings continue in the name of the firm. Any person who denies that he is or was a partner when the cause of action arose should enter an appearance under protest.[7] A judgment against a partnership may be executed against partnership property or against any partner who has entered an appearance.[8]

Registered associations—Certain associations are by statute registrable. This does not affect the position of the members but it does enable the association to appear in its registered name. The most common examples of such associations are Trade Unions[9] and Friendly Societies.[10]

Other unincorporated associations—Where an association is unregistered and not a partnership it cannot appear in its group name, since that name is no more than a convenient label for the members collectively.[11] Frequently the proper parties to the action will be members of the association in their private

---

[1] *Salomon* v. *Salomon & Co., Ltd.*, [1897] A.C. 22.

[2] So that the litigant's right to appear in person (O. 5, r. 6) does not extend to corporations or companies.

[3] Companies Act 1948, s. 437 (1). Service on the company solicitor is also usual. Corporations are served by serving the appropriate officer, e.g. mayor, town clerk (O. 65, r. 3.)

[4] Companies Act 1948, s. 447.

[5] O. 81, r. 1.

[6] O. 81, r. 2.

[7] O. 81, r. 4; see p. 248, *post.*

[8] O. 81, r. 5; such a judgment may also be executed against the private property of any other partner, but only with leave.

[9] Industrial Relations Act 1971 (repealing and replacing earlier legislation).

[10] Friendly Societies Acts 1896–1971.

[11] But see *London Association for Protection of Trade* v. *Greenlands, Ltd.*, [1916] 2 A.C. 16, where the rules of procedure appear to have been flouted.

capacity. Where, however, the right or liability is common to all the members it is inconvenient, although possible, to join them all as parties. The appropriate procedure is a "representative action".

In a representative action, where numerous persons have the same interest in any proceedings, whether as plaintiffs or defendants, one or more persons may be authorised to appear on behalf of all persons so interested.[1] However a representative action is only appropriate where all the persons to be represented have a common grievance and will all benefit from the relief claimed if plaintiffs,[2] or are jointly liable if defendants.[3] Thus where the liability of defendants is several, for example in conspiracy[4] or defamation,[3] they cannot be represented and must be sued in their own names. Nevertheless an action for negligence has been allowed to proceed against representatives of the members of a club on the ground that they were joint occupiers of the club premises.[5] A judgment against representative defendants is binding on them all. However it can be executed against the actual parties but not against the persons represented without out leave. An order for costs cannot be made against a person represented. The writ must define clearly the parties and the names of persons represented. Thus an order to represent "all the persons who were members of the City Livery Club on June 29, 1949" was made in one case, being a sufficient identification of the persons represented as defendants.[5]

It is important to distinguish a representative action from a "test case". The latter is popular terminology for an action the function of which is to determine the legal position of numerous individuals who are not parties to the action; for example an action based on the interpretation of a Finance Act upon which depend the tax obligations of a large section of the populace. The expression "test case" has, however, no legal meaning and only the parties to a test case are bound by the judgment. However, rights are determined conclusively through the operation of the doctrine of precedent.

d   Persons under disability: infants and patients

A married woman has, since 1935, ceased to be a person under a disability[6] and that phrase now applies only to infants and patients. An infant is a person under the age of 18.[7] A patient is a person who, by reason of mental disorder within the meaning of the Mental Health Act 1959, is incapable of managing and administering his property and affairs.[8] Infants and patients cannot appear personally.

They sue by their "next friend".[9] In the case of an infant this is usually

---

[1] O. 15, r. 12.
[2] *Smith* v. *Cardiff Corporation*, [1954] 1 Q.B. 210; [1953] 2 All E.R. 1373; distinguished in *John* v. *Rees*, [1970] Ch. 345; [1969] 2 All E.R. 274.
[3] *Mercantile Marine Service Association* v. *Toms*, [1916] 2 K.B. 243.
[4] *Hardie and Lane, Ltd.* v. *Chiltern*, [1928] 1 K.B. 663.
[5] *Campbell* v. *Thompson*, [1953] 1 Q.B. 445; [1953] 1 All E.R. 831.
[6] Law Reform (Married Women and Tortfeasors) Act 1935, s. 1; and see Law Reform (Husband and Wife) Act 1962.
[7] Family Law Reform Act 1969, s. 1 (1); the terms "infant" and "minor" are synonymous (*ibid.*, s. 1 (2)).
[8] This definition of a "patient" in O. 80, r. 1 is narrower than the definition in s. 147 (1) of the Mental Health Act 1959, i.e. a person suffering or appearing to be suffering from mental disorder.
[9] O. 80, r. 2 (1).

the father or person *in loco parentis*; in the case of a patient, his receiver. In any case where there is no person competent or willing to appear as next friend, the Official Solicitor will do so. The next friend is not a party to the action (though he may, of course, be a co-plaintiff in his own right). Nevertheless his name must appear on the writ, *viz.* "AB an infant, by CD of (address) his next friend", and he is personally liable for costs with a right of indemnity from the infant or patient for costs properly incurred. Since he is not a party he cannot counterclaim in his personal capacity; nor can he be required to give security for costs.[1] The next friend cannot act in person and so must be represented by a solicitor[2] who must file two documents: (1) the next friend's written consent to act, and (2) a certificate that the next friend has no interest in the proceedings adverse to that of the infant or patient.[3]

They defend by a "guardian *ad litem*" who will be the same person as the next friend would have been, or the Official Solicitor. The solicitor must file the same two documents as above. However the guardian *ad litem* is not personally liable for costs except where he has been guilty of gross misconduct, and in this respect his position differs from that of the next friend.

It is also important to note the following procedural points.

(1) Judgment in default of appearance cannot be entered against an infant or patient. The proper course is to apply to the court to appoint a guardian *ad litem*.[4]

(2) No settlement of an action on behalf of an infant or patient is valid unless approved by the court.[5]

(3) Any money recovered by or on behalf of an infant or patient must be dealt with in accordance with the court's direction.[6]

(4) Allegations in a statement of claim or counterclaim are not deemed to be admitted by an infant or patient by reason only of his failure to traverse them.[7]

e Estates of deceased persons

Prior to 1971, if at the commencement of proceedings a person named as a party was dead the action by or against that person was a nullity and could not be cured by amendment to substitute executors as parties.[8] The action had to be brought by or against the executors or administrators. However the

---

[1] Since he is not a "nominal plaintiff" within O. 23, r. 1 (1) (*b*); *Fellows* v. *Barrett* (1836), 1 Keen 119. Nor can he give a receipt for money recovered in settlement of an action, *Leather* v. *Kirby*, [1965] 3 All E.R. 927n.; [1965] 1 W.L.R. 1489.

[2] O. 80, r. 2 (3).

[3] O. 80, r. 3.

[4] O. 80, r. 6.

[5] O. 80, rr. 10, 11. If a settlement or compromise is reached before a writ is issued, the court's approval to it can now be sought by originating summons to which no appearance need be entered (O. 80, r. 11). If a settlement is reached after proceedings have begun, the application for the approval of the court is by ordinary summons, or to the trial judge if the settlement is reached during the trial. It seems arguable that O. 80, r. 10 is *ultra vires* in that, insofar as it purports to declare certain contracts void, it is more than a rule of procedure.

[6] O. 80, r. 12. In *Leather* v. *Kirby*, [1965] 3 All E. R. 927n.; [1965] 1 W.L.R. 1489, the House of Lords stated that the money should usually be paid into court or, in the case of a patient, to the Court of Protection.

[7] O. 80, r. 8; see O. 18, r. 13 (1); also p. 267, *post*.

[8] *Dawson (Bradford), Ltd.* v. *Dove*, [1971] 1 Q.B. 330; [1971] 1 All E.R. 554.

Proceedings Against Estates Act 1970[1] and Order 15, rule 6A enable an action to be brought against the estate of a deceased person even though no grant of probate or administration has been made; the defendant should be named in the proceedings "the personal representatives of A.B. deceased." The plaintiff must then, during the period of validity for service of the writ or originating summons, apply to the court for an order appointing a person to represent the deceased's estate or, if a grant of probate or administration has been made since the commencement of proceedings, an order that the personal representative be made a party.[2] Before making such order the court may require notice to be given to any insurer of the deceased who has an interest in the proceedings as well as to any other person having an interest in the estate.

---

[1] The Act, which implemented recommendations of the Law Commission (Cmnd. 4010 of 1969), together with the new O. 15, r. 6A, came into operation on January 1st 1971. Notwithstanding the new Act and Rule, proceedings commenced in the name of a dead man as plaintiff are still a nullity.

[2] O. 15, r. 6A (4). Where no grant of probate or administration has been made any judgment or order binds the estate as if a personal representative of the deceased had been a party to the proceedings (O. 15, r. 6A (7)).

CHAPTER 16

Commencing an Action by Writ

A THE WRIT AND ITS CONTENTS

A writ is a royal command to the defendant to enter an appearance in an action instituted by the plaintiff. The writ must state the names of all the intended parties to the action, whether plaintiffs or defendants, the persons on whose behalf they are appearing, if they are appearing in a representative capacity, and the division of the High Court in which the plaintiff is suing. In addition the writ must bear certain indorsements. These are of two kinds; indorsements of the plaintiff's claims and formal indorsements.

1 Indorsements of claim

The writ must be indorsed either:

(1) with a statement of claim.[1] In this event, the statement of claim on the writ will be the statement of claim in the action and the plaintiff may not serve another, except by way of amendment. The advantage is a saving of time for the plaintiff may proceed to apply for summary judgment under Order 14 as soon as the defendant has entered an appearance. Also where the plaintiff's claim is for an injunction or a declaration, he cannot obtain judgment in default until he has served a statement of claim; or

(2) with a concise statement of the nature of the claim made or the relief or remedy required in the action.[2] In this case the plaintiff will have to serve his statement of claim, setting out his claim in detail, at the same time as service of the writ, or subsequently. However he must still indorse his writ with particulars which are sufficient to enable the defendant to identify the cause of action against him.[3] Thus "the plaintiff claims damages for breach of contract",

---

[1] This is usually termed a "special indorsement", though this expression does not appear in the current Rules. The plaintiff may in one action claim relief against the same defendant in respect of more than one cause of action.
[2] Usually described as a "general indorsement".
[3] Although failure so to do does not render the writ a nullity. The defect may be cured by amendment, by service of a statement of claim, or even by the defendant's delay in applying to have the writ set aside; *Pontin* v. *Wood*, [1962] 1 Q.B. 594; [1962] 1 All E.R. 294.

or "the plaintiff claims damages for slander" are insufficient. The plaintiff must identify the contract which he alleges has been broken, or the publication which he alleges to defame him. In addition; in actions for libel the actual publication complained of must be identified;[1] in actions by moneylenders for the return of money lent, the writ must be indorsed with a statement that the plaintiff at the time of the loan was a licensed moneylender;[2] where the claim is for possession of land the writ must be indorsed with a statement showing whether the claim relates to a dwelling house and, if it does, whether the rateable value exceeds, in Greater London, £400 or £200 elsewhere; where the action is brought to enforce a right to recover possession of goods the writ must be indorsed with a statement showing the value of the goods.[4]

2 Formal indorsements

a "Fourteen-day" costs

Where the plaintiff's claim is for a debt or liquidated demand *only*, the writ must be indorsed with a claim for fixed costs, the amount being determined by the amount of the claim, and a statement that further proceedings will be stayed if, within the time limited for appearing, the defendant pays the amount claimed and costs. This indorsement is only made where the claim is for a debt or liquidated demand, i.e. a specific sum of money either ascertained or readily ascertainable by arithmetic. Thus such a claim cannot be made where the action is founded on tort since damages in tort are always unliquidated.

b Solicitor and address

The writ must be indorsed with the plaintiff's address within the jurisdiction and his solicitor's name and address if the plaintiff has a solicitor.[6] The latter is essential if the plaintiff is a body corporate, an infant or patient or a person who has no address within the jurisdiction, since these plaintiffs, contrary to the general rule, cannot appear in person.

c District registry actions

Where the writ is issued out of a district registry and the cause of action arose wholly or in part in the district of that registry, the writ may be indorsed with

---

The court has power to amend a defective indorsement even after expiry of the current period of limitation, at least where the defendant has had sufficient knowledge of the true nature of the claim; *Sterman* v. *E. W. & W. J. Moore*, [1970] 1 Q.B. 596; [1970] 1 All E.R. 581.

[1] O. 82, r. 2.
[2] O. 83, r. 2.
[3] O. 6, r. 2 (1) (c). This amendment, together with corresponding amendments to O. 13, r. 4 and O. 19, r. 5, was made (by R.S.C. (Amendment No. 3) 1966) following the Court of Appeal decision in *Peachey Property Corporation., Ltd.* v. *Robinson*, [1967] 2 Q.B. 543; [1966] 2 All E.R. 981. Where the premises are within the Rent Act 1968 the landlord ought to issue his proceedings in a county court since, in the High Court, he can no longer sign judgment in default of appearance or defence without leave and, furthermore, cannot recover any costs.
[4] O. 6, r. 2 (1) (d).
[5] O. 6, r. 2 (1) (b). Where the claim is for less than £100, no claim for costs should be indorsed since no costs are recoverable (unless the action is one which could not be brought in a county court or is brought by the Crown); County Courts Act 1959, s. 47, as amended (see p. 330, *post*). The scale of fixed costs is set out in Order 62B.
[6] O. 6, r. 5.

a statement to that effect.[1] The effect is that the defendant must in these circumstances enter an appearance in the district registry.

Where a writ does not bear the proper formal indorsements it will not be issued until the defects have been corrected. Where, however, an indorsement of claim lacks particularity the writ will be issued and will be valid. The defect must then be cured by amendment unless the defendant acquiesces in the fault.

B ISSUE AND SERVICE OF THE WRIT

1 Issue

The writ must be issued using the prescribed form, but that form is not a writ until it has been issued. To issue his writ the plaintiff takes or sends two copies of his form to the Central Office or a district registry where one copy is stamped with the court fee (usually £10)[2] and filed, and the other is sealed and returned to the plaintiff. The action has now been commenced for the purpose of any statute of limitation. Leave is not generally required to issue a writ but to this rule there are five exceptions of which the two more important are: (1) where the defendant is outside the jurisdiction[3] (England and Wales); and (2) where the plaintiff has been declared a vexatious litigant.[4]

2 Service

Once issued the writ is valid for twelve months beginning with the date of issue.[5] However it may on application be renewed for periods of up to twelve months if the court is satisfied that it has not been possible to serve it during that period. Such an application is made *ex parte* (without giving notice to the other party) on affidavit. An extension will only be granted in exceptional circumstances, generally where the defendant is untraceable; it is not an exceptional circumstance that the plaintiff failed to serve the writ through accident, mistake or a delay in obtaining a legal aid certificate.[6] While in force the writ may be served at any time of the day or night including Sunday.[7] The following are permitted methods of service.

---

[1] O. 6, r. 4. There are in most large towns district registries which may be regarded as branch offices of the Central Office of the Supreme Court. The district registrar exercises in his registry the same powers as the masters exercise in the Central Office (O. 32, r. 23). However, whereas a master must be a barrister of ten years' standing, a district registrar must be a solicitor of seven years' standing.

[2] Where the claim is only for a liquidated sum not exceeding £750, the sum is £6.

[3] O. 6, r. 7 (1); see p. 247, *post*.

[4] Judicature Act 1925, s. 51. The other three cases in which leave is required are under the Mental Health Act 1959, s. 141 (2), under the Leasehold Property (Repairs) Act 1938, s. 1, and under the Crown Proceedings Act 1947, s. 9 (3).

[5] O. 6, r. 8 (1). Thus a writ issued on the 10th September 1965 can validly be served on the 9th September 1966 but not on the following day; see *Trow* v. *Ind Coope* (*West Midlands*) *Ltd.*, [1967] 2 Q.B. 899; [1967] 2 All E.R. 900.

[6] *Baker* v. *Bowkett's Cakes, Ltd.*, [1966] 2 All E.R. 290; [1966] 1 W.L.R. 861; *Stevens* v. *Services Window and General Cleaning Co., Ltd.*, [1967] 1 Q.B. 359; [1967] 1 All E.R. 984.

[7] The Sunday Observance Act 1677 having been repealed by the Statute Law (Repeals) Act 1969.

a   Personal service

This is the usual method of service. It involves the plaintiff or his agent tendering the defendant a copy of the writ and allowing him to see the original on request.[1]

b   Service on the defendant's solicitor

This is an alternative to personal service. The defendant's solicitor must indorse on the writ a statement that he accepts service on behalf of the defendant.[2]

c   Unconditional appearance

Where the defendant enters an unconditional appearance to the writ he submits to the jurisdiction of the court and is deemed to have been served with the writ on the day that he entered an appearance.[3] This renders actual service unnecessary.

d   Substituted service

Where the plaintiff is unable to effect service as above, he may apply *ex parte* on affidavit to a master for an order for substituted service.[4] The master, if he makes such an order, will specify the form which substituted service must take, for example, service by registered or recorded delivery post to the defendant's last known address, service on the defendant's solicitor or agent or service by advertisement in the press.[5]

e   Service in pursuance of contract

The parties may by contract agree upon a method of service, in which case service in accordance with this method is sufficient.[6]

f   Actions for the recovery of land

Where no person appears to be in possession of land, the plaintiff in an action for the recovery of that land may, with leave, serve the writ by affixing it to some conspicuous part of the land, such as the door. In summary proceedings for possession of land commenced by originating summons the summons may be served by leaving a copy at the premises and where the occupants are not identified, by affixing a copy of the summons to the main door or other conspicuous part of the premises.[7]

---

[1] O. 65, r. 2. If the person served will not accept the copy, it is sufficient to tell him of its contents and leave it as nearly as possible in his possession.

[2] O. 10, r. 1 (2).

[3] O. 10, r. 1 (3); see *The Gniezno*, [1968], P. 418; [1967] 2 All E.R. 738.

[4] O. 65, r. 4. An action in the Queen's Bench Division is assigned to one of the masters when the first summons in the action is issued. Masters have, with a few exceptions (set out in O. 32, r. 11), all the powers of a judge in chambers in relation to interlocutory matters. In addition masters have jurisdiction to try cases, with the consent of the parties, to assess damages and to make final orders in interpleader and garnishee disputes.

[5] *Porter* v. *Freudenberg*, [1915] 1 K.B. 857. Where the defendant is insured against his potential liability, service may be ordered on his insurers: *Gurtner* v. *Circuit*, [1968] 2 Q.B. 587; [1968] 1 All E.R. 328.

[6] O. 10, r. 3; see *British Controlled Oilfields, Ltd.* v. *Stagg* (1921), 127 L.T. 209.

[7] O. 113, r. 4.

There is only one case in which leave is needed to serve, as well as to issue, a writ. That is where it is proposed to serve it outside the jurisdiction. Leave is also needed to issue the writ in such a case and one application both to issue and serve is usually made. The jurisdiction of the English courts comprises England, Wales, Berwick-on-Tweed and such part of the sea as the Crown may from time to time claim as territorial waters.[1] Leave in any case is discretionary but can only be given in those cases specified in Order 11, rr. 1 and 2. This important Order lists some twelve cases in which leave may be granted, for example; where the subject matter of the action is land situate within the jurisdiction, where the defendant is domiciled or ordinarily resident within the jurisdiction, where the action is founded on a tort committed within the jurisdiction or concerns a contract made or broken within the jurisdiction. Since the grant of leave is discretionary, leave may be refused if the court considers that another forum could more properly and conveniently try the case. This particularly applies where it is proposed to serve the writ in Scotland or Northern Ireland.[2] Unless service is to be effected in Scotland, Northern Ireland, the Isle of Man or the Channel Islands, notice of the writ is served and not the writ itself.[3] The effect is similar in that the plaintiff may obtain judgment in default of appearance following service of notice of the writ.

If the defendant is in Scotland, Ireland, the Isle of Man, the Channel Islands or the Commonwealth the writ or notice of the writ may be served in accordance with the English methods of service. Elsewhere it must be served through the British consul, or the foreign government (where it is willing), or the foreign judicial authority in any country with which there is a Civil Procedure Convention.[4]

Where personal service or substituted service is effected the person who serves the writ must within 3 days after service complete an indorsement on the writ, setting out the time, place and method of service. If this is not done the plaintiff will not be allowed to enter judgment in default of appearance or defence.[5]

C APPEARANCE

1 Method of entering appearance

The defendant must enter an appearance within 14 days of service (including the day of service) to avoid being in default.[6] This is done by delivering or posting[7] to the Central Office or a district registry a memorandum of appearance in duplicate. This is not a defence but a formal document the sole function of

---

[1] *R. v. Kent Justices, Ex parte Lye,* [1967] 2 Q.B. 153; [1967] 1 All E.R. 560.

[2] Leave cannot be granted under O. 11, r. 1 (1) (*f*) (contract (*inter alia*) made within the jurisdiction) if the defendant is domiciled or ordinarily resident in Scotland, nor under O. 11, r. 1 (1) (*g*) (breach within the jurisdiction) if the defendant is domiciled or ordinarily resident in Scotland or Northern Ireland.

[3] O. 11, r. 3.

[4] O. 11, rr. 5, 6.

[5] O. 10, r. 1 (4).

[6] Where service is out of the jurisdiction extra time is allowed.

[7] The use of registered or recorded delivery post is not required. Ordinary pre-paid post is sufficient but it must be remembered that an appearance is entered when the documents actually arrive at the court office, not when they are posted.

which is to get an appearance on record. The memorandum is filed; the duplicate sealed. The memorandum contains the defendant's address for service, which will be his solicitor's address if he has one, and must be signed by the defendant or his solicitor. Where the defendant enters an appearance by delivery the sealed copy of the memorandum is handed back to him and he must, on the same day, send it to the plaintiff. The court does this where the appearance is entered by post.

2 Place for entering appearance[1]

(1) Where the writ was issued out of the Central Office appearance must in all cases be entered in the Central Office.

(2) Where the writ was issued out of a district registry and is indorsed with a statement that the cause of action arose wholly or in part in the district or the defendant resides or carries on business in the district, appearance must be entered in that district registry.

(3) In any other case the defendant may enter an appearance either in the Central Office or in the district registry out of which the writ was issued.

3 Conditional appearance[2]

Any defendant who enters an appearance is deemed to submit to the jurisdiction of the court. Thus if he wishes to contest either the jurisdiction of the English courts to try the case or the validity of the writ or its service, he should enter a conditional appearance, alternatively called an appearance under protest. The effect of this is to get an appearance on record without submitting to the jurisdiction of the court or waiving any irregularity. The defendant must then within 14 days apply by summons to have the writ or an order for service set aside. The master may on this application try the issue of jurisdiction as a preliminary point. If the defendant does not so apply his appearance becomes unconditional and he is deemed to have submitted to the jurisdiction (unless he is a foreign sovereign, who may refuse to submit to the jurisdiction at any stage of the proceedings). An appearance may be withdrawn with leave of the court but where a defendant, acting on competent legal advice and not by mistake, enters an appearance (thereby submitting to the jurisdiction) he will not be permitted to withdraw it.[3]

4 Judgment in default of appearance

If any defendant fails to enter an appearance within the time limited the plaintiff is entitled to enter judgment in default of appearance. He must either file an affidavit of service setting out the date, place and method of service and a statement that the indorsement of service was completed within 3 days, or produce the writ indorsed with a statement by the defendant's solicitor that he accepts service on the defendant's behalf. In some cases leave must also be obtained: examples are cases where the defendant is the Crown or the plaintiff a licensed moneylender (including actions arising out of agreements within the Hire-Purchase Act 1965), or where the action is an action in tort between

---

[1] O. 12, r. 2.
[2] O. 12, r. 7.
[3] *Somportex* v. *Philadelphia Chewing Gum Corporation.*, [1968] 3 All E.R. 26.

spouses. In addition judgment in default cannot be entered against an infant or patient.

Where there are several defendants, some of whom do not appear, the plaintiff may enter judgment against those who do not appear without prejudice to his right to proceed against the others, if their liability is joint or several. However, where the liability of defendants is alternative, a judgment against one, albeit a default judgment, is a bar to a claim against any other.[1]

The type of default judgment which the plaintiff obtains depends upon the indorsements on the writ.

(1) Where the writ was indorsed with a claim for a debt or liquidated demand or for the recovery of land the plaintiff is entitled to *final* judgment in default for the amount claimed or the recovery of land and costs on a fixed scale.[2] Thus a final judgment is final both as to liability and as to *quantum*.

(2) Where the writ was indorsed with a claim for unliquidated damages or for the return of specific goods the plaintiff is entitled to *interlocutory* judgment in default.[3] This is final as to liability but leaves the amount of damages and costs to be assessed. Notice of the assessment, which will take place before a master or referee, is served upon the defendant who may attend the hearing and give evidence affecting the amount of liability, although he can no longer dispute his liability.

(3) Where the writ was indorsed with any other claim, for example for an injunction, a declaration, a decree of specific performance, an account or the appointment of a receiver, the plaintiff cannot obtain judgment in default of appearance. He must first serve a statement of claim, unless this was indorsed on the writ, and the action proceeds as if an appearance had been entered. Then if the defendant does not serve a defence within the time limited, the plaintiff may apply for judgment in default of defence, for such relief as he appears entitled to on his statement of claim.[4]

5 Setting aside a default judgment[5]

If the default judgment was irregularly or fraudulently obtained or is for an amount larger than is due the defendant has a right to have it set aside. In any other case, he may apply to have it set aside but he will have to show why he has failed to enter an appearance, and also that he has a triable defence, which he will normally have to disclose by affidavit. In addition a third party who is affected by the judgment may apply to have it set aside even though not a party to the action. Thus an insurance company may apply to have a judgment against the insured set aside;[6] so also may a person in possession of land which the plaintiff has recovered by default.

Where a judgment regularly obtained is set aside it will usually be on condition that the defendant pay the extra costs incurred.

---

[1] *Morel Brothers* v. *Earl of Westmorland*, [1903] 1 K.B. 64, (affirmed [1904] A.C. 11).

[2] O. 13, rr. 1, 4. Leave is required where the action is for possession of premises to which the Rent Act 1968 applies: R.S.C. (Amendment No. 3) 1966, r. 3.

[3] O. 13, rr. 2, 3.

[4] O. 19, r. 7 (1). The application may be by motion, but is usually by summons unless an injunction is sought (which is generally outside the master's jurisdiction: O. 32, r. 11).

[5] O. 13, r. 9.

[6] *Windsor* v. *Chalcraft*, [1939] 1 K.B. 279; [1938] 2 All E.R. 751.

CHAPTER 17

Proceedings After Appearance

After the defendant has entered an appearance, the action will normally proceed to the stage where the parties disclose their respective cases by the exchange of pleadings; however there are several courses which the action may take before that stage is reached and the procedure applicable to each of these must be considered. The principal possibilities are as follows.

A The proceedings may be stayed, discontinued or dismissed for want of prosecution.

B The proceedings may be settled.

C There may be an application for summary judgment under Order 14.

D There may be a summons for an account to be taken under Order 43, rule 1.

E The defendant may make a payment into court.

F There may be an application for a trial without pleadings under Order 18, rule 21.

G There may be an application for interim relief.

Each of these courses merits individual consideration.

A STAY, DISCONTINUANCE AND DISMISSAL

1. Stay

The Rules in addition to certain Acts of Parliament[1] contain various specific provisions empowering or requiring the court to stay proceedings, generally until a party complies with an order. In addition it appears from a recent decision of the Court of Appeal that there is inherent jurisdiction to order a stay

---

[1] For example, the Law Reform (Husband and Wife) Act 1962, s. 1 (2) enables actions in tort to be stayed if the court considers that no substantial benefit would accrue to either party from the continuation of the proceedings or that the dispute could more conveniently be disposed of under s. 17 of the Married Women's Property Act 1882. In addition, under s. 131 of the Industrial Relations Act 1971 a court before which proceedings in tort are brought may stay the proceedings where proceedings under the Act have already been brought before the Industrial Court or an Industrial Tribunal or the act complained of is one in respect of which (being an unfair practice or a breach of duty imposed by or under the Act) proceedings under the Act could be brought before the Industrial Court or an Industrial Tribunal.

whenever it is just and reasonable to do so, even though no party has failed to comply with any specific obligation. The case in question is *Edmeades* v. *Thames Board Mills, Ltd.*[1] The plaintiff, in an action for damages for personal injuries, refused to submit to a medical examination by the defendant's doctor for the purpose of enabling the defendant to check on the injuries which the plaintiff claimed to have sustained. The Court of Appeal ordered a stay of the action until the plaintiff submitted to such examination. The decision is a remarkable one, since there is no power in any court to order a person to submit to medical examination.[2] It is odd that a person should be denied the use of the legal process to enforce his rights simply because he refuses to do that which he is in no way obliged to do[3].

2. Discontinuance

The parties and their solicitors will, at every stage of the proceedings, be attempting to resolve their dispute without the expense of a trial. In fact very few actions come to trial. If the plaintiff is satisfied that his cause of action was misconceived or has ceased to exist he may at any time consent to judgment being entered against him with costs. The result will be to determine finally the issues he has raised on his writ and pleadings. However the plaintiff is better advised simply to discontinue his action since this course will not prevent him from suing again at a more convenient time. If he acts before a defence is served or within 14 days of service of a defence, the plaintiff may without leave serve a written notice on the defendant to the effect that he is discontinuing the whole or any part of his action.[4] He may serve a notice of discontinuance at a later stage of the action but only with leave (unless the defendant agrees in writing), and a condition of the grant of leave may be that the plaintiff shall take no further proceeding in the matter. Alternatively leave may be refused and judgment entered for the defendant. If a defendant has served a defence, he may withdraw it in whole or in part by giving written notice to the plaintiff.[5] The plaintiff may then enter judgment in default of defence. If a subsequent action is brought in respect of a cause of action previously discontinued, the master may order the proceedings to be stayed until the costs of the discontinued action have been paid.[6]

3 Dismissal for want of prosecution

If the time limits prescribed by the Rules were strictly observed most actions would be disposed of in a matter of months. In practice the time limits are,

---

[1] [1969] 2 Q.B. 67; [1969] 2 All E.R. 127.

[2] Although the creation of such a power has been recommended: *Report of the Committee on Personal Injuries Litigation* (Cmnd. 3691 of 1968), para. 312.

[3] This view was apparently shared by LAWSON, J. who in holding in *Baugh* v. *Delta Water Fittings, Ltd.*, [1971] 3 All E.R. 258; [1971] 1 W.L.R. 1295 that there was no power to require a widow to submit to medical examination by staying the action if she refused, (at any rate in the absence of any reason for supposing that her medical condition was out of the ordinary), expressed the opinion that *Edmeades* was wrongly decided, an opinion which soon brought a sharp rebuke by the Court of Appeal in *Lane* v. *Willis*, [1972] 1 All E.R. 430; [1972] 1 W.L.R. 326, in which case *Edmeades* was approved.

[4] O. 21, r. 2 (1).

[5] O. 21, r. 2 (2) (a).

[6] O. 21, r. 5.

for one reason or another, not observed and even the simplest actions often take an unconscionable time to come to trial. The blame for delay must, as a rule, rest with the plaintiff and the ultimate sanction is that the action may be dismissed for want of prosecution. A dismissal, not being an adjudication on the merits, does not estop the plaintiff from issuing a fresh writ founded on the same cause of action.[1] However in most cases the cause of action will by then have become statute-barred and the plaintiff's only remedy will be to sue his solicitor for professional negligence.[2]

There have, recently, been numerous reported cases on this topic, starting with *Allen v. Sir Alfred McAlpine & Sons, Ltd.*[2] in which the Court of Appeal set out the principles on which the court would approach applications to dismiss. These are: (1) that the delay must be inordinate, (2) that it must be inexcusable, and (3) that the defendant must have been prejudiced by the delay. In considering whether delay has been inordinate, the whole history of the action is considered including delay prior to the issue of the writ and delay for which the defendant has been responsible. An inordinate delay will be inexcusable unless the plaintiff has some excuse for it. Even if the delay is inordinate and inexcusable the action may not be struck out if the defendant has not been prejudiced, for example where liability is admitted.[3] Nevertheless actions may be, and have been, struck out even where liability has been admitted by the defendant (thus providing an unexpected windfall for the defendant or, more often, his insurers). Thus in the recent case of *Paxton* v. *Allsopp*[4] an action for damages for personal injuries arising out of a car accident was struck out even though liability had been admitted and, indeed, an offer of £2,050 had been made by the defendant's solicitors and rejected some years earlier. The reason for striking out was that, not only was the delay inordinate and inexcusable, but the defendant was prejudiced in that oral examination of the medical witnesses would be impossible after such a length of time. The case was, it should be pointed out, an extreme one since the application to strike out was made more than 13 years after the accident.

Without prejudice to the above, O. 3, r. 6 provides that where a year or more has elapsed since the last proceeding in an action, the party who desires to proceed must give to every other party not less than one month's notice of intention to proceed (whereupon the other party may, of course, apply to have the action dismissed for want of prosecution).

B   SETTLEMENT

The parties (or their insurance companies) are likely to be in constant communication to effect a settlement of the action. This they may do with complete candour since letters which pass between them are privileged from

---

[1] *Pople* v. *Evans*, [1969] 2 Ch. 255; [1968] 2 All E.R. 743.
[2] *Allen* v. *Sir Alfred McAlpine & Sons, Ltd.*, [1968] 2 Q.B. 299; [1968] 1 All E.R. 543. If a new writ would not be statute-barred there is, of course, little point in dismissing the action for want of prosecution (see *Instrumatic, Ltd.* v. *Supabrase, Ltd.*, [1969] 2 All E.R. 131, [1969] 1 W.L.R. 519) since this will simply cause added costs.
[3] *Marlton (an infant)* v. *Lee-Leviten*, [1968] 2 All E.R. 874; [1968] 1 W.L.R. 1214.
[4] [1971] 3 All E.R. 370; [1971] 1 W.L.R. 1310; see also *Gloria* v. *Sokoloff*, [1969] 1 All E.R. 204.

production and any offer or admission of liability made therein is said to be made "without prejudice".[1] The nature of a settlement is that it is a contract whereby the parties abandon their previous rights and obligations in return for the creation of new rights and obligations. Since the new obligations are contractual, they must, in accordance with general principles, either be under seal or made for consideration. These releases are termed, therefore, a "release under seal" and a "release by way of accord and satisfaction"; the latter is more common and has been defined as:[2]

> "The purchase of a release from an obligation, whether arising under contract or tort, by means of any valuable consideration, not being the actual performance of the obligation itself. The accord is the agreement by which the obligation is discharged. The satisfaction is the consideration which makes the agreement operative."

The parties may effect a settlement without the consent of the court by giving notice of withdrawal before trial. Where an order of the court is required, which will usually be the case when the action is settled during the trial, the required terms will be drawn up and indorsed on counsels' briefs, or, more usually, the parties will submit to judgment on agreed terms. The settlement of any action on behalf of an infant or patient must be approved by the court.[3]

C SUMMARY JUDGMENT UNDER ORDER 14

This procedure was introduced by the Judicature Acts 1873–1875, and involves the only order which is universally recognised by number. It will be appreciated that the defendant's purpose in entering an appearance to a writ is frequently to gain time. Order 14 procedure enables the plaintiff to bring the matter to an early determination where the defendant has no triable defence to liability.[4]

The rule applies to every action in the Queen's Bench Division (or Chancery Division) begun by writ other than one which includes:

(*a*) a claim by the plaintiff for libel, slander, malicious prosecution, or false imprisonment; or,

(*b*) a claim by the plaintiff based on an allegation of fraud.[5]

Provided the defendant has entered an appearance and the plaintiff has served a statement of claim, the plaintiff may issue the appropriate summons. To do so he or a person duly authorised by him must first swear an affidavit setting out his cause of action, the amount claimed, if liquidated, and his belief that there is no defence to his claim except as to the amount of damages. The plaintiff should not swear to this lightly, for if he issues an Order 14 summons

---

[1] See p. 536 *post*.

[2] *British Russian Gazette, Ltd.* v. *Associated Newspapers, Ltd.*, [1933] 2 K.B. 616, at pp. 643–644.

[3] O. 80, rr. 11, 12.

[4] O. 86 provides a procedure, similar to O. 14, in actions commenced by writ in the Chancery Division for specific performance or rescission of agreements relating to land or for the forfeiture or return of any deposit made under such an agreement.

[5] O. 14, r. 1 (2). "Fraud" appears to be confined to common law deceit: *Barclays Bank, Ltd.* v. *Cole*, [1967] 2 Q.B. 738; [1966] 3 All E.R. 948.

where the case is not a proper one, or where he must have known that the defendant had a triable defence, the master may order him forthwith to pay the whole costs of the application.[1]

The plaintiff, having filed his affidavit, then takes out a summons which must be served on the defendant, together with a copy of his affidavit, not less than 10 clear days before the return day (i.e. the day appointed for the hearing of the summons).[2] The defendant, if he contests the summons, must attend on the return day and show that he has a triable defence. This is usually done by an affidavit, but it can be done "otherwise",[3] for example by oral testimony.

At the hearing of the summons the master[4] may make the following orders.

(1) He may give judgment for the plaintiff, final or interlocutory. This must unless the defendant satisfies the court "that there is an issue or question in dispute which ought to be tried or that there ought for some other reason to be a trial."[5] If he has any defence on a question of law or fact then he must be given leave to defend the action, even if the master strongly doubts that the defence will succeed.

(2) He may give the defendant unconditional leave to defend the action. In this case the action will proceed to trial in the usual way.

(3) He may give the defendant conditional leave to defend. This may be done where the master is almost, but not quite, sure that there is no triable defence.[6] The effect is that the defendant may present his defence provided he makes a payment into court of the whole or part of the sum claimed. The defendant may appeal to a judge in chambers against any condition imposed.

(4) He may give judgment for the plaintiff as to part and to the defendant leave to defend as to part of the claim.

(5) He may give judgment for the plaintiff with a stay of execution pending the trial of a counterclaim.

(6) If the application was not made in good faith or the case was not within the order, a libel action for example, the master may order the plaintiff to pay

---

[1] O. 14, r. 7 (1); except where the plaintiff is an assisted person. See the remarks of LORD GODDARD, C.J. in *M. Pocock* v. *A.D.A.C., Ltd.*, [1952] 1 T.L.R. 29 *(infra).*

[2] O. 14, r. 2. As to the meaning of "clear days" in the Rules, see O. 3, r. 2 (4).

[3] O. 14, r. 4 (1). The defendant must show that he has a triable defence, although he need not set out every element of that defence. A general denial of liability is not sufficient. There is no express requirement for the defendant to serve his affidavit on the plaintiff. However the summons contains a notice requiring the defendant to send a copy of his affidavit to the plaintiff to reach him not less than three days before the return day (so that the plaintiff may swear an affidavit in answer if he wishes). If the defendant sends his affidavit late or not at all, thereby necessitating an adjournment of the summons, he will usually have to pay the costs thrown away in any event; see *Practice Direction (Order 14: Return Date)*, [1970] 1 All E.R. 343; [1970] 1 W.L.R. 258.

[4] The summons is almost always returnable before a master. However if an injunction is sought (which a master has no power to grant) the summons should be made returnable before a judge; *Shell-Mex and B.P. Ltd.* v. *Manchester Garages, Ltd.*, [1971] 1 All E.R. 841; [1971] 1 W.L.R. 612.

[5] O. 14, r. 3 (1); the latter part of this sub-rule is wide enough to enable leave to defend to be given where, even though the defendant cannot point to a specific defence, it is just that the plaintiff be put to strict proof of his case: *Miles* v. *Bull*, [1969] 1 Q.B. 258; [1968] 3 All E.R. 632.

[6] *Fieldrank, Ltd.* v. *E. Stein*, [1961] 3 All E.R. 681 n.; [1961] 1 W.L.R. 1287.

the costs of the application forthwith.[1] This is an extreme sanction which will rarely be invoked although LORD GODDARD, C.J. has suggested otherwise:[2]

> "I wish it to be known as a practice rule that the proper course for a Master to take, if he considers that in a summons under O.14 it is clear that the plaintiff knew that there was an arguable defence to the claim, is to dismiss the summons with costs. Masters should use their powers under O.14 much more freely."

(7) He may transfer the action to a county court if he gives leave to defend a claim in contract or tort of not more than £750, or more by written agreement of the parties.[3]

(8) If the master gives leave to defend or orders a stay of execution pending the trial of a counterclaim, he must give all directions as to the further conduct of the action as if the summons were a summons for directions; in particular he may, with the consent of all parties, order the action to be tried by himself or another master.[4]

A defendant may apply for summary judgment on a counterclaim, provided it is not a claim which is outside the scope of the Order.[5] In addition any judgment under Order 14 may be set aside by the court on such terms as it thinks just. This rather likens a judgment under Order 14 to a judgment in default of appearance.[6]

D ACCOUNT SUMMONS

The plaintiff may indorse his writ with a claim for an account to be taken. This procedure dates back to the early days of the common law where it was available to the feudal lord against his bailiff or steward. It was extended in equity to any principal and agent relationship, such as landlord and rent-collector.[7] It is appropriate where the defendant is an accounting party, that is to say a person who has received money on the plaintiff's behalf. The plaintiff is not in possession of sufficient details to frame an action for a debt. His remedy is to ask the court to compel his agent to account for monies received and to pay them to the plaintiff.

To do so he may, at any time after the time limited for entering an appearance to the writ (whether or not appearance has been entered), take out a summons. The application is usually supported by an affidavit setting out the grounds on which the plaintiff relies. Unless the defendant can show that there is some preliminary issue to be tried or that he has already accounted, the master will order an account to be taken and the amount found due to be paid to the plaintiff within a specified time. The plaintiff's rights thus become crystallised into a judgment debt in the normal way. Simple accounts may be taken by a

---

[1] O. 14, r. 7 (1).
[2] *M. Pocock* v. *A.D.A.C., Ltd.*, [1952] 1 T.L.R. 29, at p. 34.
[3] O. 14, r. 4 (3); County Courts Act, 1959, ss. 42, 45, 67 as amended.
[4] O. 14, r. 6.
[5] O. 14, r. 5.
[6] O. 14, r. 11. This rule was introduced in 1964 to nullify *Spira* v. *Spira*, [1939] 3 All E.R. 924.
[7] See *London, Chatham and Dover Rail. Co.* v. *South Eastern Rail. Co.*, [1892] 1 Ch. 120.

master in the Queen's Bench Division, but the proceedings are usually transferred to the Chancery Division or to a Circuit judge nominated by the Lord Chancellor to take "official referees business."[1]

E PAYMENT INTO COURT

1 Method of payment

In any action for debt or damages the defendant may, at any time after entering an appearance, pay money into court in satisfaction of any or all of the plaintiff's claims.[2] To do so he deposits his payment at the Bank of England, Law Courts Branch, and serves a written notice to this effect on the plaintiff and on every co-defendant.[3] Where the plaintiff has included in his writ two or more claims the defendant may either; (1) make a separate payment in respect of each, or (2) make one payment in respect of any or all of those claims.[4] The latter course is usually disadvantageous to the plaintiff, since he must either continue with all of his claims or accept the payment and abandon them all. Accordingly where the payment in of a lump sum in respect of several causes of action embarrasses the plaintiff, he may apply to the court by summons for an order that the defendant apportion his payment in respect of the several causes of action.[5] However, the defendant will not be required to sever his payment in unless the causes of action are substantially different, i.e. where a jury might be directed to make separate awards of damages. Where the causes of action are technically different but substantially the same, for example several meanings of the same words in a defamation action, the defendant, if he makes one payment in respect of them all, will not be required to sever it.[6]

Where the defendant has a counterclaim for damages he may expressly take this into account when paying money into court;[7] thus if he values the plaintiff's claim at £1,000 and his counterclaim at £200, he will pay into court £800. It will be appreciated that where he values his counterclaim in excess of the plaintiff's claim, he should not take it into account when paying in since, as we shall see, the effect of the plaintiff accepting the payment will be that the defendant cannot proceed with his counterclaim.

2 Effects of a payment into court

The plaintiff must, within 3 days of receiving the defendant's notice of payment in, acknowledge receipt. He may then within 14 days, or later with leave,

---

[1] Courts Act 1971, s. 25; this section effectively abolished the office of official referee.

[2] O. 22, r. 1 (1). This may be done after the trial of an action has begun.

[3] Money standing in court carries no interest unless the court orders it to be placed in a deposit or short-term investment account. Consequently, if the sum is of any size, the defendant should apply to a master for the money to be transferred to the Short-Term Investment Account established under section 6 (1) of the Administration of Justice Act 1965; for the procedure applicable, see *Practice Direction (Short-Term Investment Account)*, [1970] 1 All E.R. 1107; [1970] 1 W.L.R. 602.

[4] O. 22, r. 1 (4). Until 1965 this was not possible in defamation actions.

[5] O. 22, r. 1 (5). This order cannot be made in relation to money paid into court after the trial or hearing of the action has begun (O. 22, r. 3 (3)).

[6] *Pedley* v. *Cambridge Newspapers, Ltd.*, [1964] 2 All E.R. 794; [1964] 1 W.L.R. 988; decided under O. 82, r. 4, before that rule was amended; see fn. 4, *supra*.

[7] O. 22, r. 2.

take the money out of court in respect of any cause of action for which a payment in was made.[1] If the defendant made a general payment in the plaintiff must take "all or nothing". The effect is that all the causes of action in respect of which the plaintiff accepted a payment in are stayed, as is any counterclaim which the defendant took into account under O. 22, r. 2. The plaintiff may then:

(1) tax and sign judgment for his costs to the date of payment in (but only if his whole claim is satisfied);[2] and

(2) in actions for defamation, apply to a judge in chambers by summons for leave to make in open court a statement in terms approved by the judge.[3] This is so that he may vindicate his reputation publicly.

Alternatively the plaintiff may leave the money in court and continue with his action. In this event the court must not be told of the existence of a payment into court until all questions of liability and damages have been determined.[4] This is especially so in jury actions, notably defamation, for if the jury knew of a substantial payment into court they would obviously be likely to look upon it as an admission of liability by the defendant, rather than a genuine attempt to effect a settlement. To this rule there are two exceptions—the defences of tender before action and apology under section 2 of the Libel Act 1843. In both these cases payment into court is an element in a defence and will therefore appear on the pleadings and be disclosed to the court.

As long as the plaintiff recovers more than the amount paid in the payment in will have been of no avail to the defendant. However, if he recovers less or no more than the amount paid in then, although costs are discretionary, the plaintiff will usually have to pay the whole costs of the action in respect of which payment was made, from the date of payment in.[5] The modern tendency of the courts is to look at the action as a whole and not as several causes of action tried together. Thus if the plaintiff does not recover in the aggregate more than the total payment in by the defendant he may have to pay the costs of the whole action from the date of payment in.[6] To put it simply, the plaintiff is gambling to "beat the payment in".[7]

---

[1] O. 22, r. 3. He requires, under O. 22, r. 4, an order of the court in some cases; *viz.* (a) where the payment is made by some, but not all, defendants sued jointly or in the alternative by him, (b) where the payment in was made as part of a plea of tender before action, (c) in actions by an infant or patient (O. 80, r. 12), (d) in actions both under the Fatal Accidents Acts and the Law Reform (Miscellaneous Provisions) Act 1934, or under the Fatal Accidents Acts alone where more than one person is entitled to the money. Where the payment in was made or increased after the trial has begun the plaintiff may accept the money within two days of receiving notice but before the judge begins to deliver judgment or sum up to the jury.

[2] O. 62, r. 10 (2).

[3] O. 82, r. 5 (1).

[4] O. 22, r. 7; *Monk* v. *Redwing Aircraft Co.*, [1942] 1 K.B. 182; [1942] 1 All E.R. 133; *Millensted* v. *Grosvenor House (Park Lane), Ltd.*, [1937] 1 K.B. 717; [1937] 1 All E.R. 736.

[5] O. 62, r. 5. *Findlay* v. *Railway Executive*, [1950] 2 All E.R. 969.

[6] *Hultquist* v. *Universal Pattern and Precision Engineering Co., Ltd.*, [1960] 2 Q.B. 467; [1960] 2 All E.R. 266.

[7] LORD DENNING, M.R. in *Mason* v. *Mason*, [1965] 3 All E.R. 492; [1966] 1 W.L.R. 757 pointed out the desirability of a new rule which would have the effect of concealing the existence and amount of a payment in from the Court of Appeal which may be, at

Since a claim for interest on a debt or damages is not in itself a cause of action, no payment into court can or should be made in respect of interest. By the same token if the plaintiff recovers less by way of damages than the sum in court, but a greater total sum by reason of interest, he has not "beaten the payment in" and will be liable for costs after the date of payment in the normal way.[1] However, if the plaintiff accepts a payment into court he is not entitled to any interest and indeed the court has no power to award interest since there is no "judgment".[2] This may put the plaintiff (and his advisers) in an invidious position in a case in which, possibly because of the delay in coming to trial, there is a large amount of potential interest accrued and a sum in court which might exceed the damages awardable but not the interest.[3]

Where a defendant claims an indemnity or contribution from a third party or tortfeasor liable in respect of the same damage, that third party or tortfeasor cannot make a payment into court. He can, however, obtain a similar advantage by making a written offer to the defendant to pay a specified contribution to any debt or damages recovered against the defendant. If the defendant refuses this offer it may be drawn to the attention of the trial judge, who may take it into account when making an order as to costs, as if the offer were a payment into court.[4]

Finally it should be noted that the plaintiff may make a payment into court in respect of a counterclaim against him.[5]

F   TRIAL WITHOUT PLEADINGS

This procedure enables either the plaintiff or the defendant to obtain a trial without pleadings or without further pleadings as the case may be. The application may be made in any action commenced by writ other than one which includes:

(a)   a claim by the plaintiff for libel, slander, malicious prosecution or false imprisonment; or

(b)   a claim by the plaintiff based on an allegation of fraud,

provided that any defendant has entered an appearance.[6] The object of this procedure is to enable the parties to determine their dispute without the delay and expense of pleadings or other interlocutory applications. However it is

---

present, embarrassed by its knowledge of a payment in. As yet, no such rule has been introduced; cf. *Thornton* v. *Swan Hunter (Shipbuilders), Ltd.*, [1971] 3 All E.R. 1248; [1971] 1 W.L.R. 1759.

[1] See, generally, *Jefford* v. *Gee*, [1970] 2 Q.B. 130; [1970] 1 All E.R. 1202.

[2] *Jefford* v. *Gee (supra)*; *Waite* v. *Redpath Dorman Long, Ltd.*, [1971] 1 Q.B. 294; [1971] 1 All E.R. 513.

[3] Thus if the plaintiff assessed the value of the claim at £9,000 and there was £9,500 in court he would, presumably, feel compelled to accept the payment in. However if the potential accrued interest was £3,000 the plaintiff would forfeit this by accepting the payment in. On the other hand failure to take the money out of court would (assuming his assessment to be correct) render him liable to a possibly heavy bill of costs to deduct from his extra £3,000. Some amendment to the rule would appear desirable.

[4] O. 16, r. 10; O. 62, r. 5; *Bragg* v. *Crosville Motor Services, Ltd.*, [1959] 1 All E.R. 613; [1959] 1 W.L.R. 324.

[5] O. 22, r. 6.

[6] O. 18, r. 21.

only appropriate where there is no substantial dispute as to fact, as, for example, where the action turns on the construction of a document. In this respect, and also in the conduct of the proceedings, the procedure is very similar to originating summons procedure, except that it applies to a wider range of proceedings in the Queen's Bench Division, such as a negligence action where the sole issue is the assessment of damages. Since there are no pleadings the parties must agree on a statement of the issues in dispute. This may be done by letter.[1] In a commercial case application for a trial without pleadings is frequently made in conjunction with an application for transfer to the Commercial Court.[2]

If the master makes an order for a trial without pleadings he must, and if he dismisses the application he may, give directions as to the further conduct of the action as if the summons were a summons for directions.

G INTERIM RELIEF

1 Interlocutory injunction

The power of the High Court to grant injunctions is, of course, inherited from equity. In addition to the court's inherent power to grant an injunction by way of final remedy, section 45 of the Judicature Act 1925[3] empowers the court to grant an injunction by an interlocutory order "in all cases in which it appears to the court to be just or convenient so to do."

The power is thus defined very widely and, in practice, an injunction will usually be granted where the plaintiff satisfies the court that there is a serious question to be tried and that he is probably entitled to relief, or where the plaintiff can show a *prima facie* case and the defendant is threatening an act which will cause the plaintiff irreparable damage.[4] In such cases the court will maintain the *status quo* pending the trial. The court takes into account the "balance of convenience" between the plaintiff and the defendant as well as the extent to which the plaintiff can be adequately compensated by damages.[5]

A master having no power to grant injunctions, application must be made to a judge. In cases of extreme urgency application can be made *ex parte* on affidavit, in which event an injunction will be granted for a very short period until an application by summons or motion can be brought before the court. Otherwise application is by summons to a judge in chambers in the Queen's Bench Division or by motion in open court in the Chancery Division.[6]

As an alternative to injunction the court will usually accept an undertaking from the defendant (which has precisely the same effect). In addition, as a condition of being granted an interlocutory injunction the plaintiff is always

---

[1] *Hill* v. *Scott*, [1895] 2 Q.B. 371.
[2] See p. 288, *post*.
[3] Replacing Judicature Act 1873, s. 25 (8).
[4] However an injunction, final or interlocutory, will only be granted to protect a legal right, so that even if the defendant threatens an irreparable injury to the plaintiff, an injunction will not be granted if the defendant will not thereby infringe a right protected by law; *Ballard* v. *Tomlinson* (1884), 26 Ch. D. 194.
[5] *Donmar Productions, Ltd.* v. *Bart*, [1967] 2 All E.R. 338n; [1967] 1 W.L.R. 740; cf. *Hampstead and Surburban Properties, Ltd.* v. *Diomedous*, [1969] 1 Ch. 248; [1968] 3 All E.R. 545.
[6] O. 29, r. 1.

required to give his undertaking as to damages, that is an undertaking to indemnify the defendant in respect of any damages which the latter sustains by reason of the injunction. For this reason it is generally improvident for a plaintiff to apply for an interlocutory injunction unless he has a strong case in circumstances in which the injunction will cause the defendant heavy expense, for example by delaying building works.

2 Interim payment of damages

One long-standing criticism of civil procedure in the English courts was that wholly innocent parties, such as injured passengers in road accidents, had to wait for long periods for their damages while disputes between other parties, such as the car drivers (in fact, their insurers) were being resolved. The Report of the Committee on Personal Injuries Litigation[1] recommended that in such litigation, courts should have power to make interim payments and effect was given to this recommendation by section 20 of the Administration of Justice Act 1969 which authorised rules of court to enable the court:

> "in such circumstances as may be specified in the rules, to make an order requiring a party to the proceedings to make an interim payment of such amount as may be specified in the order, either by payment into court or (if the order so provides) by paying it to another party to the proceedings".

The power has been exercised[2] in relation to "actions for personal injuries", a term which comprises actions in which there is a claim for damages in respect of death or personal injuries. The application for an interim payment may be made at any time after expiry of the time limited for appearance and is by summons supported by an affidavit which must verify the special damages, if any, claimed by the plaintiff to the date of the application and must exhibit the hospital and medical reports, if any, relied upon by the plaintiff. In addition the affidavit must state "the grounds on which the application is made."[3] Herein lies the restriction on interim payments for by O. 29, r. 12 an interim payment is only to be made in three circumstances:

(*a*)   where the defendant has admitted liability;
(*b*)   where the plaintiff has obtained judgment against the respondent to the application for damages to be assessed;   or
(*c*)   where if the action proceeded to trial the plaintiff would succeed on the question of liability without any substantial reduction for contributory negligence. Thus the power to order a payment on account of damages is limited to the clearest cases.[4]

The fact of the interim payment being made must not be pleaded nor disclosed to the court at the trial until all questions of liability and damages have

---

[1] Cmnd. 3691 of 1968.
[2] By R.S.C. (Amendment No. 2) 1970, creating a code which is contained in the revised O. 29, rr. 9–17.
[3] O. 29, r. 11 (1).
[4] It is further limited in that no order can be made unless the defendant is insured against his liability, a public authority or a person whose means and resources are such as to enable him to make the interim payment; O. 29, r. 12 (2).

been decided.[1]   On giving final judgment the court may make an order so as to adjust the position between the parties in relation to sums already paid by way of interim payment; such an adjustment may involve repayment by the plaintiff or compensating payments between two or more defendants.[2]

---

[1] O. 29, r. 14; cf. the rules relating to payments into court, p. 256, *ante*.
[2] O. 29, r. 16.

CHAPTER 18

Pleadings

A THE NATURE AND FUNCTION OF PLEADINGS

If the action has not been brought to an end in one of the ways referred to in the preceding Chapter the parties must proceed to the exchange of pleadings. Before embarking upon consideration of this important topic it is important to bear in mind the distinction between modern pleadings and the pleadings which formed the basis of the common law writ system at common law. Pleadings at common law had to state a conclusion of law in one of the prescribed forms. Pleadings in Chancery went to the other extreme and simply set out *en masse* all the relevant facts leaving the judge to decide where equity lay. The modern system of pleading strikes a happy balance between the common law and Chancery systems. The modern system has its origins in the Common Law Procedure Acts 1852 and 1854 and the first set of Rules of the Supreme Court in 1875.[1]

Pleadings are written statements served by each party on his opponent, containing the allegations of fact on which the party pleading relies. They serve various purposes. Principally they enable each party to determine exactly which facts are alleged against him. This may save a party from preparing evidence to meet allegations which are not being made against him. Also it enables parties to establish their "common ground", that is to say facts on which they are in agreement, thus saving the expense of proving these matters at the trial.

Secondly, the action is decided upon the pleadings. Thus the parties and their successors may, by reference to the pleadings, determine in the future exactly what the case decided, so that they may not have to, and indeed may not be allowed to, fight the same issues again. Similarly reference to the pleadings in an action may disclose the *ratio decidendi* of the case for the purpose of the doctrine of precedent, since any fact not pleaded will not usually be regarded as a fact upon which a judgment is based.

The classic definition of what pleadings must contain is now to be found in O. 18, r. 7 (1):

---

[1] See pp. 56–61, *ante.*

"..., every pleading must contain, and contain only, a statement in a summary form of the material facts on which the party pleading relies for his claim or defence, as the case may be, but not the evidence by which those facts are to be proved, and the statement must be as brief as the nature of the case admits ..."

Thus pleadings must contain facts not law.[1] However, this only means that conclusions of law (such as the existence of a duty of care in negligence) need not be pleaded, not that a point of law cannot be raised on the pleadings.[2] Only material facts should be pleaded. Thus immaterial facts, such as character or motive, must not be pleaded since they form no part of a cause of action or defence.[3] Evidence should not be pleaded. However, the line between facts and evidence is by no means clearly defined. It is suggested that evidence be confined to its narrow meaning, viz. the means of proof.[4] By way of exception to the rule that evidence need not be pleaded, Order 18, rule 7A provides that a party intending to adduce evidence of another party's conviction, pursuant to Section 11 of the Civil Evidence Act 1968[5] must include in his pleading a statement of his intention with particulars of the conviction and the date thereof, the court which made the conviction and the issue in the proceedings to which the conviction is relevant. If the person convicted intends to deny the conviction, allege that it was erroneous or deny its relevance he must make the denial or allegation in his pleading.

Finally, pleadings must contain all the material facts. The reason is that at the trial a party will be confined to his pleadings and will not be allowed to raise any matter not pleaded since this would take his opponent by surprise—the very contingency which pleadings are designed to avoid. Thus where, in an action based on negligence, the plaintiffs relied in their pleaded case upon vicarious liability, they were not allowed in the House of Lords to allege that the defendants were negligent personally, since this was an allegation which they had not pleaded.[6] On the other hand a variation from the pleaded case, as opposed to a complete departure, is permissible; thus where, in one case, the plaintiff in his statement of claim alleged that a large stone had struck him on the head, he was not prevented from showing at the trial that his injuries had in fact been caused by several stones.[7]

Without prejudice to the generality of the above principles the Rules prescribe certain criteria as to the contents of pleadings generally. The most important of these are as follows.

(1) Every pleading must contain the necessary particulars of any claim, defence or other matter pleaded, including particulars of any misrepresentation,

---

[1] *North Western Salt Co., Ltd.* v. *Electrolytic Alkali Co., Ltd.,* [1914] A.C. 461; *Gautret* v. *Egerton* (1867), L.R. 2 C.P. 371.

[2] O. 18, r. 11.

[3] *Rassam* v. *Budge,* [1893] 1 Q.B. 571; *Plato Films, Ltd.* v. *Speidel,* [1961] A.C. 1090; [1961] 1 All E.R. 876; but see *Goody* v. *Odhams Press,* [1967] 1 Q.B. 333; [1966] 3 All E.R. 369.

[4] *Davy* v. *Garrett* (1878), 7 Ch.D. 473; *North Western Salt Co., Ltd.* v. *Electrolytic Alkali Co., Ltd.,* [1914] A.C. 461; see p. 447, *post.*

[5] As to the admissibility and effect of such evidence, see p. 465, *post.* The rule also applies to findings of adultery and paternity as evidence in civil proceedings under section 12 of the Civil Evidence Act 1968.

[6] *Esso Petroleum Co., Ltd.* v. *Southport Corporation,* [1956] A.C. 218; [1955] 3 All E.R. 864.

[7] *McCarron* v. *Cementation Co., Ltd.* (1964), *The Times,* October 26th; see also *Waghorn* v. *George Wimpey & Co., Ltd.,* [1970] 1 All E.R. 474; [1969] 1 W.L.R. 1764. A "change of case" may be made by amendment; see p. 272, *post.*

fraud, breach of trust, wilful default or undue influence on which the party pleading relies.[1]

(2) A party must give particulars of any alleged condition of mind of any person other than knowledge (for example, fraudulent intention or malice).[2]

(3) A party must in any pleading *subsequent* to a statement of claim plead any matter, for example any relevant statute of limitation, fraud or any fact showing illegality which he alleges makes any claim or defence of the other party not maintainable or which if not specifically pleaded might take the other party by surprise or which raises issues of fact not arising out of the preceding pleading.[3]

Thus, for example, if in a "running down" action the defendant driver's case is that his vehicle had a latent mechanical defect which caused it to go out of control, he cannot simply deny negligence in his defence and then raise the specific suggestion of latent defect at the trial since this would take the other party by surprise. He must plead the defence of latent mechanical defect specifically so that the plaintiff can inspect the vehicle, or have it inspected by his own expert, and join the manufacturer or the person who last repaired or serviced the vehicle as a second defendant.

It will be observed that the above rules are of two kinds: (3) relates to matters which must be pleaded, whereas (1) and (2) relate to particulars which must be given of matters which are pleaded.

B THE EXCHANGE OF PLEADINGS

1 Statement of claim[4]

The plaintiff may have indorsed his writ with a statement of claim. This is a pleading and the plaintiff may not serve another statement of claim except by way of amendment. If the writ was only generally indorsed the plaintiff may serve his statement of claim at any time before the defendant enters an appearance or within 14 days thereof. If he does not the defendant may (although he is not obliged so to do) apply to have the action dismissed for want of prosecution.

The statement of claim is a statement of all the facts which are alleged to constitute the plaintiff's cause of action, and a statement of the relief or remedy required. Thus if the action is for breach of contract, the statement of claim must set out the date, time and place at which the contract was made, the parties to the contract, the term alleged to have been broken and details of the breach. It is bad pleading to allege a breach of contract without alleging the existence of a contract, since that may be just what the defendant wishes to deny. Similarly in a tort action the plaintiff must allege all the elements of the tort in question,

---

[1] O. 18, r. 12 (1) (*a*).

[2] O. 18, r. 12 (1) (*b*); *Fowler* v. *Lanning*, [1959] 1 Q.B. 426; [1959] 1 All E.R. 290. "Condition of mind" includes the condition of mind of the party pleading, if he relies upon it: *Feeney* v. *Rix*, [1969] Ch. 693; [1968] 3 All E.R. 22. Although the rule excludes "knowledge" it is necessary to give particulars of the facts alleged to give rise to knowledge; O. 18, r. 12 (4).

[3] O. 18, r. 8 (1).

[4] Before 1875 this was called a "declaration"; the modern defence was called a "plea" and the reply, a "replication".

although he need not name the tort. Otherwise, his statement of claim discloses no cause of action. Thus a statement of claim that alleged, "laconically", that at a stated time and place "the defendant shot the plaintiff" was held to disclose no cause of action, since it did not allege a mental element which is an element in the tort of trespass to the person.[1] The one limitation on the contents of the statement of claim is that it must contain only allegations in respect of causes of action mentioned in the indorsement on the writ or arising from facts mentioned on the writ.[2]

In addition to the general criteria for the contents of pleadings, referred to above, there are certain other matters which the plaintiff must have in mind when preparing the statement of claim. The more important of these are as follows.

(1)   In libel and slander the plaintiff must give particulars of facts to support any sense of the words other than their ordinary meaning (innuendo).[3]

(2)   In actions under the Fatal Accidents Acts 1846–1959, the plaintiff must serve:

"a full particular of the person or persons for whom and on whose behalf such action shall be brought, and of the nature of the claim in respect of which damages shall be sought to be recovered".[4]

(3)   The plaintiff should set out in his statement of claim all reliefs and remedies to which he claims to be entitled, though he need not specifically claim either costs or interest.[5] The reliefs and remedies which the plaintiff may claim merit some attention.

a   Damages

For procedural purposes there are only two kinds of damages—general and special.

General damages—These are such damages as the law will presume to have resulted from the defendant's act. These damages (which include damages for pain, suffering, loss of amenities and inconvenience) need not be specifically pleaded and the plaintiff cannot as a rule be required to give particulars of them. However, where a plaintiff has suffered damage of an unusual character he must in his pleadings warn the defendant of the fact that damages will be claimed in respect of such damage, thus showing the defendant the case he has to meet and assisting him in computing a payment into court.[6] Once again the general rule is that the plaintiff must not take the defendant by surprise. So, for example, future loss of earnings in a personal injuries action are general damages; nevertheless a plaintiff who alleges a continuing or future loss of earnings must make this clear. It appears that a claim for exemplary damages need not be expressly

---

[1] *Fowler v. Lanning*, [1959] 1 Q.B. 426; [1959] 1 All E.R. 290.

[2] O. 18, r. 15 (2). The rule is, however, of no great practical importance since the plaintiff can raise a new cause of action by amending the writ; see *Brickfield Properties, Ltd. v. Newton*, [1971] 3 All E.R. 328; [1971] 1 W.L.R. 862.

[3] O. 82, r. 3; *Grubb v. Bristol United Press*, [1963] 1 Q.B. 309; [1962] 2 All E.R. 380; *Lewis v. Daily Telegraph, Ltd.*, [1964] A.C. 234; [1963] 2 All E.R. 151. The precise words of the publications relied upon should be set out *verbatim*; *Collins v. Jones*, [1955] 1 Q.B. 564; [1955] 2 All E.R. 145.

[4] Fatal Accidents Act 1846, s. 4.

[5] O. 18, r. 15 (1).

[6] *Perestrello e Companhia Limitada v. United Paint Co., Ltd.*, [1969] 3 All E.R. 479; [1969] 1 W.L.R. 570. This requirement cuts across the traditional distinction between general and special damages.

pleaded.[1] General damages are claimed generally by the words "and the plaintiff claims damages".

Special damages—These are such damages as the law will not presume in the plaintiff's favour, such as loss of earnings, loss of business profits, and medical expenses. These damages must be specifically pleaded and proved at the trial. Where special damage is an element in the plaintiff's cause of action, he must plead it or his statement of claim will disclose no cause of action. It is important to note that any special damage not pleaded cannot be recovered at the trial, unless leave to amend is given.

b Other relief

There are various other forms of relief available. Of these an order for the possession of land or delivery of a chattel, being common law remedies, are available as of right, whereas the equitable remedies of injunction, specific performance, rectification and rescission are discretionary. Where an order, such as an injunction, is sought it is usual to plead the precise terms of the order sought.

c Declaration

Where the plaintiff claims no relief, legal or equitable, but seeks an adjudication upon his rights he may simply claim a declaration. The power of the High Court to make declarations of right or title is an inherent one deriving from the practice of the Court of Chancery; it is now codified in O. 15, r. 16 and provides a useful means whereby a party may ascertain his legal position before embarking upon a course of action. However, it is axiomatic that the courts will not adjudicate upon hypothetical questions so that no declaration will be granted where the defendant has neither committed nor threatened any wrongful act.[2] The procedure of applying for a declaration is particularly appropriate where a party seeks the court's decision as to status; thus declarations are frequently sought and made on such issues as whether a person is legitimate or whether a foreign divorce decree has effectively dissolved an English marriage.

2 Defence

The defendant must serve a defence on the plaintiff within 14 days of the expiration of the time limited for appearance or of receiving the statement of claim, whichever is the later.[3] If he does not, the plaintiff may enter judgment, final or interlocutory, in default of defence. The procedure is similar to judgment in default of appearance and the same limitations apply. This time limit may, as may all time limits under the Rules, be extended by agreement or by order of the master. Before drafting his defence, there are preliminary matters which the defendant must consider. For example, the statement of claim served on him may disclose no cause of action, or may introduce a new cause of action not indorsed on the writ. In such a case the defendant may apply by summons to a master to strike out the statement of claim.[4] A less radical

---

[1] *Cassell & Co., Ltd.* v. *Broome,* [1972] 1 All E.R. 801; [1972] 2 W.L.R. 645.

[2] *Ealing London Borough* v. *Race Relations Board,* [1971] 1 Q.B. 309; [1971] 1 All E.R. 424; *Mellstrom* v. *Garner,* [1970] 2 All E.R. 9; [1970] 1 W.L.R. 603.

[3] The effect of this is that where the statement of claim is indorsed on the writ, the defendant has 28 days in which to serve a defence.

[4] O. 18, r. 19. This is a most important rule. It enables the court to stay or dismiss an action, or strike out any pleading "on the ground that—(a) it discloses no reasonable cause

course is to apply for particulars.[1] There may be a third party from whom the defendant has a right to relief in respect of the subject matter of the action, the other driver in a running-down action for example. In this case the defendant should institute third party proceedings to join that party to the action.[2] Alternatively the defendant may have found himself in the midst of a dispute in which he has no interest; for example a garage owner may be in possession of a car which is claimed by a hire purchase finance company and by the hirer or an estate agent in possession of a deposit when a sale of property has fallen through. In such a case he should interplead.[3] However if the defendant wishes to serve a defence to the statement of claim, he may frame it in the following ways.

a Defence generally

The defendant must deal individually with each allegation in the statement of claim. A general denial of liability is insufficient and will result in the defendant having to give lengthy particulars, incurring extra costs. In respect of each allegation in the statement of claim the defendant may:

  (i) Admit; or,
  (ii) Traverse; and/or,
  (iii) Confess and avoid; and/or,
  (iv) Object in point of law.

Admissions—An admission on the pleadings may be express or implied. An admission is implied from a failure to traverse, since the Rules expressly provide that every allegation of fact in a statement of claim or counterclaim that is not traversed is deemed to be admitted, except against an infant or patient, and excepting also allegations as to damages.[4] Admission should not be regarded as a sign of weakness on the part of the defendant. Indeed there is no point in denying facts which your opponent can easily prove against you, or which are purely formal.

Thus, if the defendant's case is that his conduct does not amount to a breach of contract, there is no point in denying the existence of the contract. Similarly, in an action for malicious prosecution, where the dispute is invariably as to whether the defendant was malicious and whether he had a reasonable and probable cause for instigating a prosecution, it is pedantic to deny that there was a prosecution which terminated in favour of the plaintiff, since this can easily be proved. Indeed, a party who denies facts that he should properly admit may be penalised in the matter of costs.[5]

---

of action or defence, as the case may be; or (b) it is scandalous, frivolous or vexatious; or (c) it may prejudice, embarrass or delay the fair trial of the action; or (d) it is otherwise an abuse of the process of the court". Apart from this rule the court has an inherent jurisdiction under which it can deal with any case within this rule. This wide power is only exercised in the clearest cases; cf. *Hubbuck & Sons* v. *Wilkinson,* [1899] 1 Q.B. 86; *Remmington* v. *Scoles,* [1897] 2 Ch. 1; *Drummond-Jackson* v. *British Medical Association,* [1970] 1 All E.R. 1094; [1970] 1 W.L.R. 688.
[1] See p. 273, *post.*
[2] See p. 279, *post.*
[3] See p. 280, *post.*
[4] O. 18, r. 13 (1), (4); O. 80, r. 8.
[5] O. 62, r. 3 (5).

Traverses—A traverse is simply a denial. It is unnecessary to traverse allegations of law. On the other hand it is essential that the defendant traverse positively and unambiguously every allegation of fact in the statement of claim that he disputes.[1] A paragraph in the statement of claim may contain two allegations of fact; for example "the plaintiff paid the defendant £5,000." This incorporates two allegations; first, that the plaintiff paid the defendant a sum of money; secondly, that the sum was £5,000. Accordingly a traverse that "the plaintiff did not pay the defendant £5,000" is insufficient if the defendant contends that the plaintiff paid him nothing at all. A proper traverse would be; "the plaintiff did not pay the defendant £5,000 *or any other sum*".

Pleas in confession and avoidance—This form of defence involves admitting the literal truth of an allegation (confession), but at the same time setting up other facts which alter or nullify its effect (avoidance). Thus where the statement of claim alleges the existence of a contract, the defendant may wish to allege that that contract has been discharged or frustrated or that he has been released, or that the action is statute-barred. All these pleas are pleas in avoidance. Similarly, the defendant may be prepared to admit a battery on the plaintiff, but may allege that it was performed in self defence or under a right conferred by law. It is perhaps unfortunate that the Rules allow a party to plead inconsistent defences. Thus the defendant may both traverse and confess and avoid the same facts. For example, he may deny that he struck the plaintiff at all and yet plead that he did so in self-defence.

Objections in point of law—As a rule no party is obliged to take a point of law in his pleadings. Thus even where the statement of claim contains an apparent defect in law or discloses no cause of action, the defendant may elect to remain silent until the trial.[2] Indeed there are occasions where it is politic to do so, since by that time it may be too late for the plaintiff to set his pleadings in order by amendment. However, where the point of law could effectively dispose of the whole question, the Rules provide the means for the defendant to raise this point at an early stage in the proceedings, thus forestalling a trial. The defendant may apply by summons to have the point set down for trial as a preliminary point.[3] In an extreme case the defendant may apply to have the plaintiff's statement of claim struck out on the ground that it is frivolous, vexatious or discloses no cause of action or is otherwise an abuse of the process of the court; for example an action for a gaming debt framed as an application for an account. This provision, due to its stringent nature, is rarely used. The court also has an inherent jurisdiction, which is in no way impaired by the Rules,[4] to stay any proceedings which constitute an abuse of its process.

---

[1] The defendant need not and should not traverse allegations which the plaintiff has not pleaded; although a general traverse is insufficient, it is common form for the defence to conclude with a general traverse in addition to the specific traverses, *viz.* "save as hereinbefore specifically admitted, the defendant denies each and every allegation contained in the statement of claim as though the same were herein set out and traversed *seriatim*". See *Warner* v. *Sampson*, [1959] 1 Q.B. 297; [1959] 1 All E.R. 120.

[2] *MacDougall* v. *Knight* (1890), 25 Q.B.D. 1; *Independent Automatic Sales, Ltd.* v. *Knowles and Foster*, [1962] 3 All E.R. 27; [1962] 1 W.L.R. 974.

[3] O. 33, rr. 2, 4; In addition statutory defences must be specifically pleaded; for example, the Limitation Acts and the Statute of Frauds.

[4] O. 18, r. 19; see fn. 4, p. 266, *ante*.

b Special defences: set-off and counterclaim

In addition to pleading to the statement of claim in any or all of the above ways, in certain cases the defendant may raise a defence which is peculiar to one type of action. Thus the defences of fair comment, justification and offer of amends are peculiar to actions for defamation. These defences must always be specifically pleaded. In particular, the defences of tender before action[1] and apology under the Libel Acts 1843–45[2] are interesting from a procedural standpoint in that both require payment into court as an element in the defence. The payment in differs from a payment under the Rules of the Supreme Court, O. 22 in that the latter can only affect costs[3] while the former is an element in a defence to liability.

At this stage it is appropriate to consider the defence of set-off and, more important still, counterclaim.

Set-off[4]—A defence may contain a set-off which may be pleaded to the whole or to any part of the plaintiff's claim. Thus it may be pleaded in conjunction with a plea of tender before action, whereby the defendant has tendered a sum less than the sum claimed by the plaintiff because he pleads a set-off in respect of the balance.

The common law courts prior to 1875 recognised the set-off although it was limited in its scope to cases where both the plaintiff's claim and the amount to be set off were liquidated. The defence was also recognised in equity, where its scope was, however, greater and extended to unliquidated claims. With the fusion of the administration of law and equity in 1875 the equitable set-off became available throughout the Supreme Court. This is still the case, as evidenced by the wide phrasing of the present Order 18, r. 17:

> "Where a claim by a defendant to a sum of money (whether of an ascertained amount or not) is relied on as a defence to the whole or part of a claim made by the plaintiff, it may be included in the defence and set-off against the plaintiff's claim, whether or not it is also added as a counterclaim."

It must be noted, however, that both the claim and the set-off must be monetary. Thus if the plaintiff seeks an injunction or a declaration of title, for example, there can be no set-off to these claims. There are other limitations to pleading a set-off; *viz.*

(1) Both claim and set-off must exist between the same parties in the same capacity. Thus, if the plaintiff sues as trustee or executor of an estate, the defendant cannot set-off a debt owed to him by the plaintiff in the latter's personal capacity.[5]

(2) If the set-off overtops the plaintiff's claim the defendant cannot recover

---

[1] O. 18, r. 16. This old common law defence can only be pleaded to an action for a debt or liquidated demand; it is that the defendent tendered the whole sum due before issue of the writ.

[2] This defence, which is obsolete, is available to a newspaper or other periodical which publishes a libel without actual malice or gross negligence. The defence is never used because it cannot be pleaded in conjunction with any other defence and, in any event, the defence of unintentional defamation under the Defamation Act 1952, s. 4 is more favourable to the defendant.

[3] See p. 256, *ante*.

[4] O. 18, r. 17.

[5] *Rees* v. *Watts* (1855), 11 Exch. 410; *Phillips* v. *Howell*, [1901] 2 Ch. 773.

the excess except by way of counterclaim. Since a set-off is only a defence, it can only operate to extinguish or reduce *pro tanto* the plaintiff's claim.[1]

(3) If the original claim is settled or discontinued the set-off is *ipso facto* terminated, since it depends for its existence on the original claim.

(4) The amount to be set-off must have been due when the writ was issued.[2]

Counterclaim[3]—A counterclaim is not a defence but, since it is pleaded at this stage, it is conveniently considered here. A counterclaim is a cross action and may best be regarded as the defendant's statement of claim. Thus the subject matter of a counterclaim can be anything which could be the subject matter of an action commenced by writ. It need not relate to the plaintiff's claim, nor indeed need it claim the same remedy as that sought by the plaintiff.[4] If the claim and counterclaim are of a totally different nature and cannot conveniently be tried together, the court may order the counterclaim to be tried separately, or even transferred to a county court. The counterclaim must exist against the plaintiff but not necessarily in the capacity in which he sues (provided that he is a party to the action and not, for example, an infant's next friend). Thus if the plaintiff sues as trustee or executor, the defendant may counterclaim either against the plaintiff personally or against the estate that the plaintiff is representing.[5] In addition the defendant by his counterclaim may join new parties to the action, who are in the position of defendants *quoad* the original defendant (though not *quoad* the plaintiff).[6] If both claim and counterclaim succeed the court will usually make one order as to damages.[7] There is a discretion as to costs and the court may either make one order as to costs (in which case the counterclaim is in effect treated as if it were a set-off) or two orders as to costs. In the latter case the defendant would be entitled to the costs of his successful counterclaim but would be liable for the costs of the plaintiff's claim, since a counterclaim is not a defence. In practice, where the claim and counterclaim arise out of the same transaction or series of transactions, for example, trading debts between the parties, the court will make just one order as to costs—in favour of the party who recovers the balance between the claim and counterclaim.[8]

For almost all purposes the counterclaiming defendant is in the same position as a plaintiff. He may obtain judgment in default of defence to his counterclaim[9] (though not in default of appearance except by third parties,[10] since appearance by the plaintiff is not required); he may also obtain judgment under Order 14 on his counterclaim.[11] In certain situations the counterclaiming

---

[1] The balance should be claimed by counterclaim: *Stooke* v. *Taylor* (1880), 5 Q.B.D. 569.
[2] *Richards* v. *James* (1848), 2 Exch. 471.
[3] O. 18, r. 18.
[4] O. 15, r. 2 (1); *Beddall* v. *Maitland* (1881), 17 Ch.D. 181.
[5] *Re Richardson*, [1933] W.N. 90; *Stumore* v. *Campbell & Co.*, [1892] 1 Q.B. 314.
[6] O. 15, r. 3 (1). There must, however, be a claim against the plaintiff as well; *Furness* v. *Booth* (1876), 4 Ch.D. 587. It is permissible that the liability of the plaintiff and of the third party be alternative: *Smith* v. *Buskell*, [1919] 2 K.B. 362.
[7] O. 15, r. 2 (4).
[8] *Provincial Bill Posting Co.* v. *Low Moor Iron Co.*, [1909] 2 K.B. 344; *Chell Engineering, Ltd.* v. *Unit Tool and Engineering Co., Ltd.*, [1950] 1 All E.R. 378; *Childs* v. *Gibson*, [1954] 2 All E.R. 243; [1954] 1 W.L.R. 809.
[9] O. 19, r. 8.
[10] O. 15, r. 3 (5).
[11] O. 14, r. 5.

defendant is in a better position than he would be as plaintiff. Of these the most important, in practice, arises where the defendant's cause of action has become statute-barred. Provided the plaintiff has issued his writ within the limitation period the defendant may counterclaim notwithstanding that his cause of action would, if he were the plaintiff, be statute-barred. The defendant cannot, however, counterclaim until he has been served with a statement of claim.[1]

3 Defence to counterclaim and reply

If the defendant has raised a counterclaim, the plaintiff must serve a defence to it, or the defendant will be entitled to judgment in default on his counterclaim. This pleading must be drafted in the same way as a defence, although the plaintiff cannot himself counterclaim since he is confined to the causes of action raised in his statement of claim.[2]

The plaintiff need not serve a reply to reaffirm the allegations in his statement of claim that the defendant has traversed. These are already in issue.[3] However he must serve a reply if he wishes to make admissions, rebut positive allegations in the defence or raise an objection in point of law in answer to a plea of confession and avoidance.

> "The reply is the proper place for meeting the defence by confession and avoidance."[4]

Thus where the defendant has pleaded fair comment or qualified privilege in an action for defamation, the plaintiff may rebut the defence by proving malice. This will be alleged in his reply.[5] If the defence of a statute of limitation is raised, the plaintiff, in his reply, may plead fraud or a written acknowledgement, which prevent time from running. The plaintiff cannot, however, raise a new cause of action in his reply since this constitutes a "departure" which is expressly forbidden by O. 18, r. 10.

A reply or a defence to counterclaim must be served within 14 days. If both are pleaded they must be incorporated in the same document.[6]

4 Subsequent pleadings

No pleading subsequent to a reply or a defence to counterclaim shall be served except with the leave of the court.[7] A rejoinder (by the defendant) may be necessary to rebut affirmative allegations in a defence to counterclaim. Surrejoinder (by the plaintiff), rebutter (by the defendant) and surrebutter (by the plaintiff) are virtually obsolete because of the rule prohibiting departures in pleading.

---

1 See *The Gniezno*, [1968] P. 418; [1967] 2 All E.R. 738.
2 This would amount to a "departure" in pleading, expressly prohibited by O. 18, r 10.
3 O. 18, r. 14 (1).
4 JAMES, L.J. in *Hall* v. *Eve* (1876), 4 Ch.D. 341, at p. 345.
5 O. 82, r. 3 (3).
6 O. 18, r. 3.
7 O. 18, r. 4.

C AMENDMENT OF WRIT AND PLEADINGS

1 Writ

Where there is some defect in the writ or in any pleading it can almost always be cured by amendment. Nevertheless the party at fault should act quickly so as to avoid increasing the extra costs which he will have to pay. The plaintiff may amend the writ[1] *once* without leave before the close of pleadings. An amended writ must be served on the defendant. The writ does not include any statement of claim indorsed upon it, since this is a pleading and not part of the writ. Amendments to the writ can be of a technical nature, for example, correction of a misspelling or an incorrect date; moreover the writ can with leave be amended under Order 20 to correct the name of a party, even if this has the effect of substituting a new party, if the court is satisfied that the mistake was a genuine one and not misleading as to the true identity of the party intended; similarly an amendment may be allowed which adds or substitutes a new cause of action provided it arises out of substantially the same facts as the original cause of action. Amendments to alter the parties to the action to add or substitute a new cause of action can be made without leave only before the writ has been served.[2] Leave may be granted to make these amendments even after the period of limitation current at the date of issue of the writ has expired, if the courts think it just. In this way a new statute-barred cause of action may be raised, or a party may be "brought in" by amendment at a time when he could no longer be sued in a fresh action.[3] Apart from the provisions of O. 20, new parties may be added by order of the court following an application by summons[4] but a new cause of action against a defendant can never be added. The proper procedure in this case is to issue a second writ and apply to have the actions consolidated. It will be appreciated, however, that in this case the Limitations Act comes into play since time will be deemed to have run up to the time of issue of the new writ.

2 Pleadings

Any party may amend his pleadings once without leave before the close of pleadings.[2] As long as the proposed amendment does not amount to pleading a completely new cause of action and causes no injustice to an opponent it is permissible. Thus a party will be allowed to withdraw an admission mistakenly made.[5] A plaintiff may be allowed to amend his statement of claim even where

---

[1] O. 20, r. 1 (1).

[2] O. 20, r. 1 (3).

[3] See *Rodriguez* v. *Parker*, [1967] 1 Q.B. 116; [1966] 2 All E.R. 349; *Mitchell* v. *Harris Engineering Co., Ltd.*, [1967] 2 Q.B. 703; [1967] 2 All E.R. 682; *Chatsworth Investments, Ltd.* v. *Cussins (Contractors), Ltd.*, [1969] 1 All E.R. 143; [1969] 1 W.L.R. 1; *Sterman* v. *E. W. and W. J. Moore*, [1970] 1 Q.B. 596; [1970] 1 All E.R. 581; cf. *Braniff* v. *Holland and Hannen and Cubitts (Southern), Ltd.*, [1969] 3 All E.R. 959; [1969] 1 W.L.R. 1533; *Brickfield Properties, Ltd.* v. *Newton*, [1971] 3 All E.R. 328; [1971] 1 W.L.R. 863.

[4] Under O. 15, rr. 6, 7. The court will not, however, grant an application so as to deprive the proposed defendant of a defence of limitation; therein lies the great advantage of adding a party under O. 20 rather than under O. 15 (where possible).

[5] *Hollis* v. *Burton*, [1892] 3 Ch. 226.

the original disclosed no cause of action. To adopt any other approach would be a regression to the formalism of pleading at common law. The court's attitude is well illustrated in the judgment of BOWEN, L.J. in *Cropper* v. *Smith*:[1]

> "I know of no kind of error or mistake which, if not fraudulent or intended to over-reach, the Court ought not to correct, if it can be done without injustice to the other party. Courts do not exist for the sake of discipline, but for the sake of deciding matters in controversy, and I do not regard such amendment as a matter of favour or grace. . . . It seems to me that as soon as it appears that the way in which a party has framed his case will not lead to a decision of the real matter in controversy, it is as much a matter of right on his part to have it corrected if it can be done without injustice, as anything else in the case is a matter of right."

The amended pleading must be served on the opponent who may himself serve an amended pleading to it within 14 days.[2] Alternatively he may allow his original pleading to stand, or he may apply to the master to disallow the amendment on the ground that it causes injustice.[3]

The writ and pleadings may be amended after the close of pleadings but only with leave.[4] The application is by summons, usually the summons for directions. Amendment may even be allowed at the trial if the judge is satisfied that no injustice is thereby caused.[5] If amendment is allowed it is almost always on terms that the party amending pays the costs thrown away in any event and if the amendment necessitates an adjournment of the trial he will usually be ordered to pay the costs thrown away by the adjournment.

D PARTICULARS

If a pleading is vague or too general the party on whom it is served may apply for particulars. The application should first be by letter, and the court will not usually make an order until there has been an application to the other side by letter. If particulars are not forthcoming application may be made by summons for an order for further and better particulars.[6] The functions of particulars are broadly twofold. First they prevent the party giving them from framing his case too widely, since at the trial he will be confined to his particulars as if they had been incorporated in his pleadings. Thus if he relies in his particulars on conduct which he alleges amounts to negligence, he cannot at the trial give evidence as to other conduct (unless he obtains leave to amend his particulars). Secondly the party who is served with particulars is thereby better acquainted with the case against him so that he will not be taken by surprise at the trial. Any particulars which ought to have been included in the pleadings may be ordered,[7] for example particulars of special damages. However particulars

---

[1] (1884), 26 Ch.D. 700, at pp. 710–711.

[2] O. 20, r. 3.

[3] O. 20, r. 4. The application is by summons and is usually made on the summons for directions.

[4] O. 20, r. 5. The court may even amend a pleading on its own motion; see *Nottage* v. *Jackson* (1883), 11 Q.B.D. 627.

[5] *Ives* v. *Brown*, [1919] 2 Ch. 314; but see *Esso Petroleum Co., Ltd.* v. *Southport Corporation*, [1956] A.C. 218; [1955] 3 All E.R. 864.

[6] O. 18, r. 12 (3), (6): *Milbank* v. *Milbank*, [1900] 1 Ch. 376.

[7] See pp. 263–265, *ante*.

cannot be ordered of matters which have not been specifically pleaded, nor can particulars be required of a simple traverse.[1] Particulars are most often sought in respect of the statement of claim.

Particulars cannot be required of any matter not pleaded. In this respect they differ from interrogatories which may, as we shall see, relate to any relevant matter whether pleaded or not.

E THE CLOSE OF PLEADINGS

The pleadings are deemed to be closed:

(*a*) at the expiration of 14 days after service of the reply or defence to counter-claim, or

(*b*) if neither a reply nor a defence to counterclaim is served, at the expiration of 14 days after service of the defence.[2]

Where the time for serving any of these pleadings is extended with leave, the close of pleadings is postponed until the expiry of such further time. The close of pleadings is important for three purposes:

(1) subsequent amendment of the writ and pleadings may only be made with leave;

(2) there is an implied joinder of issue on the pleading last served (unless the last pleading was a counterclaim); and

(3) the time is fixed within which discovery of documents must be made and the summons for directions taken out. These are the next stages in the action.

---

[1] *Weinberger* v. *Inglis*, [1918] 1 Ch. 133; see also *Chapple* v. *Electrical Trades Union*, [1961] 3 All E.R. 612; [1961] 1 W.L.R. 1290.
[2] O. 18, r. 20.

CHAPTER 19

Procedure from the Close of Pleadings to the Trial

A DISCOVERY AND INSPECTION OF DOCUMENTS

Discovery of documents is the procedure whereby a party discloses, to the court or to any other party, the relevant documents in the action that he has, or has had, in his possession, custody or power.

Documentary evidence plays an important part in nearly all civil cases. In an action for breach of contract, for example, the transactions between the parties may be contained entirely in letters which have passed between them. One party's letters may not be intelligible unless read in conjunction with letters in the possession of the other party. Accordingly a party will want, first, to have his opponent disclose which documents the latter has, or has had, in his possession (discovery), and, secondly, to inspect and take copies of those documents in his opponent's possession (inspection). This may be effected in two ways.

1 Discovery without order

Until 1964 discovery of documents was dependent upon the order of a master, which was made in most cases on the summons for directions. While discovery by order still exists, one of the major alterations in procedure effected by the 1962 Rules was the introduction of "automatic" discovery. Parties must now in any action commenced by writ, with certain exceptions, make discovery by exchanging lists within 14 days of the close of pleadings.[1] The lists are in a prescribed form[2] and annexed are two schedules, as follows:

SCHEDULE 1

Part 1

Relevant documents, listed numerically, which the party has in his possession, custody or power and which he does not object to produce.

---

[1] O. 24, r. 2. If any party does not comply he may be ordered to do so and may also be ordered to file an affidavit verifying his list: O. 24, r. 3 (2).
[2] O. 24, r. 5 (1).

Part 2

Relevant documents as above which he objects to produce.[1]

SCHEDULE 2

Relevant documents, listed as above, which have been, but at the date of service of the list are not, in the possession, custody or power of the party in question.[2]

Notice to inspect

A party serving a list of documents must also serve on his opponent a notice to inspect the documents in the list (other than those which he objects to produce) setting out a time within 7 days and place where the documents in Part 1 of the first schedule may be inspected.[3]

The right to inspect includes the right to take copies of the documents in question, although these will, as a matter of courtesy, be supplied on payment by the solicitors for the party in question.[4]

The foregoing provisions for automatic discovery do not apply to actions commenced by originating summons. There are certain other proceedings to which the procedure is not applicable; notably actions to which the Crown is a party, and actions arising out of an accident on land involving a vehicle, where the defendant must not make discovery unless ordered to do so.[5] In addition the court may, on the application of any party, made by summons, waive discovery by all or any of the parties or restrict discovery to certain classes of documents for disposing fairly of the action or for saving costs.[6]

2 Discovery by order

There are two important circumstances in which an order for discovery will be required. The first is where the action is one of those to which the above rule relating to automatic discovery is not applicable or where any party has failed to comply with that rule. In such a case there must be an application for an order for discovery of all relevant documents, if discovery is required. The second case arises where a party is dissatisfied with his opponent's list. He may then apply for discovery of particular documents.

A party who is served with a list of documents may believe that relevant documents which the maker of the list has, or has had, in his possession, custody or power are not included in his list. This may be due to a *bona fide* belief on the maker's part that the document in question is not relevant to the action, or to an omission, accidental or deliberate. In either case application may be made by summons to the master for an order for discovery of the documents in question. This application must be accompanied by an affidavit setting out the grounds for the deponent's belief and identifying the documents of which discovery is required. If the other party admits the existence of the documents in question but denies their relevance, the master will inspect them in order to decide whether they are in fact relevant. In addition that party may be required to

---

[1] The list must contain a sufficient statement of the grounds of the privilege claimed: O. 24, r. 5 (2).

[2] He must state what has become of them and who is presently in possession of them.

[3] O. 24, r. 9.

[4] *Ormerod, Grierson & Co.* v. *St. George's Ironworks*, [1905] 1 Ch. 505.

[5] O. 77. r. 12 (1); O. 24, r. 2 (2).

[6] O. 24, r. 2 (5).

make an affidavit stating whether or not any particular document is, or has at any time been, in his possession, custody or power and, if it no longer is, what has become of it.[1]

Finally, independent of the above provisions, any party may at any time require inspection of any document referred to in any other party's pleadings or affidavits.[2]

If any party fails to comply with an order for discovery the master may order his statement of claim to be struck out, if he is a plaintiff, or his defence to be struck out and judgment entered against him, if a defendant. In a case of extreme and wilful disobedience the offender may be committed for contempt of court.[3]

There is another issue which may be raised in connection with discovery. This arises where a party refuses to produce a document in his possession, custody or power.

3 Documents privileged from production

The only circumstance in which a party may refuse to produce a document is where that document is one of a class which the law recognises as privileged. The privilege which attaches to documents must be carefully distinguished from privilege in the law of defamation. Thus a document which attracts qualified privilege for the purposes of defamation, the minutes of a company meeting for example, is not necessarily privileged from discovery. The former rule is a rule of law, the latter a rule of evidence or procedure.

A party who wishes to claim privilege for a document cannot merely omit to include it in his list. He must include it in the second part of the first schedule to his list, together with a statement in the body of the list of the ground upon which he claims privilege for it. The principal classes of documents which the law recognises as being privileged from production are: documents which relate solely to the deponent's own case, incriminating documents, documents attracting legal professional privilege and documents whose production would be injurious to the public interest. These classes of evidential privilege are considered fully elsewhere in this work.[4]

4 Discovery and inspection against other persons

We have already examined the procedure introduced by the Administration of Justice Act 1970, whereby orders for discovery and inspection of documents against proposed parties may be made before the commencement of proceedings.[5]

Under section 32 (1) of the Administration of Justice Act 1970 there is, in addition, power, in actions for damages for death or personal injuries, to order a person who is not a party to the proceedings and who appears to be likely to have or have had in his possession, custody or power any documents which are relevant to an issue arising out of the action to disclose whether these documents

---

[1] O. 24, r. 7; *Astra-National Productions, Ltd.* v. *Neo-Art Productions, Ltd.*, [1928] W.N. 218.
[2] O. 24, r. 10.
[3] O. 24, r. 16.
[4] See pp. 477–479, 509–513, *post*.
[5] See p. 234, *ante*.

are in his possession, custody or power and to produce those which he has to the applicant.

This power is exercisable only after the commencement of proceedings, the application being by summons (which must be served on the person against whom the order is sought and on all parties to the action) supported by affidavit.[1] As stated above, the procedure is limited in its application to personal injuries litigation where it may be used, for example, by defendants to obtain a sight of the plaintiff's hospital notes or by plaintiffs to obtain copies of manufacturers' instructions for using and maintaining machines, reports by employers to the Factories Inspectorate and documents of that type.

B   INSPECTION OF PROPERTY

1   Inspection of property inter partes

The court has power, on the application of any party, to make an order for the detention, custody or preservation of any property which is the subject matter of the action or as to which any question may arise therein or for the inspection of any such property in the possession of a party to the action and, for the purpose of enabling such an order to be carried out, may authorise any person to enter a party's land or building.[2] The application is often made on the summons for directions but may, if need be, be made by summons at any stage of the proceedings. The procedure is widely used in personal injuries actions, usually to enable an expert engineer on behalf of the plaintiff to inspect the defendant's factory premises, but is not confined to such actions.

As has already been noted,[3] the Administration of Justice Act 1969, s. 21, extended the above provisions so as to enable orders to be made, in personal injuries actions, before the commencement of proceedings.

2   Orders against third persons

Analagous to the recently created power of the court to order discovery and inspection of documents against strangers to the proceedings is the power, also created by section 32 of the Administration of Justice Act 1970, to make orders for the inspection, photographing, preservation, custody or detention of property[4] which is not the property of, or in the possession of, any party to the proceedings but which is the subject matter of the proceedings or as to which any question arises in the proceedings; orders may also be made for the taking of samples of any such property and the carrying out of any experiment in relation thereto.

Application for such an order is by summons supported by affidavit. No

---

[1] O. 24, r. 7A.
[2] O. 29. There is no express power to order photographing (as there is in both s. 21 of the Administration of Justice Act 1969 and s. 32 of the Administration of Justice Act 1970) but this is obviously an oversight since inspection will often be worthless without a right to take photographs. It is anticipated that the rule will be changed in the near future.
[3] See p. 234, *ante*.
[4] "Property" includes any land, chattel or other corporeal property of any description: Administration of Justice Act 1970, s. 32 (4).

order will be made if it appears that compliance would result in the disclosure of information relating to a secret process, discovery or invention not in issue in the proceedings.[1]

C THIRD PARTY AND INTERPLEADER PROCEEDINGS

1 Third party proceedings

Irrespective of his liability to the plaintiff, the defendant may have a right to relief from a third party which relates to the original subject matter of the action or which is substantially the same as the relief or remedy claimed by the plaintiff.[2] Thus if the plaintiff is a lessor and sues the defendant lessee for breach of covenant, the defendant may be able to claim relief from a sub-lessee.[3] Usually the right claimed by the defendant is to an indemnity or a contribution. A right to indemnity may exist by contract, by statute[4] or by a rule of common law or equity. A common example is the right of an agent to be indemnified by his principal in respect of acts performed within the scope of his authority.[5] A contribution is, in effect, a partial indemnity. It arises where persons have expressly or by their conduct assumed an obligation jointly and one has been sued. The others, who may be joint trustees, joint debtors or joint tortfeasors,[6] for example, have a duty to contribute.

In any of the above cases the defendant may bring a separate action for the remedy sought against the third party. However he will save time and costs by issuing a third party notice. He may do this without leave before serving his defence and with leave thereafter.[7] The notice must contain particulars of the nature of the claim and the relief sought and must be served on the third party together with a copy of the statement of claim and all pleadings thus far served in the action.[8]

The effect of this procedure is to make the third party a defendant in relation to the original defendant. The action then proceeds between them as if the defendant had issued a writ against the third party in the ordinary way. Thus if the third party does not enter an appearance, the defendant is entitled to sign judgment in default. If his claim was for an indemnity the extent of this judgment will be the amount that the plaintiff recovers from the defendant.[9]

The third party may counterclaim against the defendant, but not against the plaintiff.[10] He can, however, interrogate the plaintiff. Alternatively the third

---

[1] O. 29, r. 7A (6).
[2] O. 16, r. 1. Until Rules made in 1929, a third party notice could only be issued for a contribution or indemnity. It now applies to a much wider range of proceedings by virtue of the wide provisions of the present rule.
[3] *Pontifex* v. *Foord* (1884), 12 Q.B.D. 152.
[4] Examples are: ss. 76, 77 of the Law of Property Act 1925, and Sch. 2 (implied covenants); Civil Aviation Act 1949, s. 40 (2).
[5] *Read* v. *Anderson* (1882), 10 Q.B.D. 108; *Johnson* v. *Kearley*, [1908] 2 K.B. 514.
[6] See Law Reform (Married Women and Tortfeasors) Act 1935, s. 6.
[7] O. 16, rr. 1, 2.
[8] O. 16, r. 3.
[9] O. 16, r. 5.
[10] *Barclays Bank, Ltd.* v. *Tom*, [1923] 1 K.B. 221.

party may join a fourth party and so on.[1] Although the third party does not, strictly speaking, stand in any relationship to the plaintiff the court is enabled by Order 16, rules 8 and 9 to determine any issue arising between the third party and the plaintiff. Third party proceedings are independent of the main action to the extent that they may continue to trial even after the issue between the plaintiff and defendant has been disposed of by final order.[2]

2   Stakeholder's interpleader

Although dealt with in this section, this procedure will, where appropriate, invariably arise at a far earlier stage of the proceedings than the close of pleadings.

It arises where a person is under a liability in respect of a debt or in respect of any money, goods or chattels and he is, or expects to be, sued by two or more rival claimants.[3] For example, an estate agent who is holding a purchaser's deposit or a repairer in possession of goods may find that there is a claim by a third party other than the depositor, such as the vendor or a hire purchase finance company. If he delivers the money or goods to the claimant who turns out not to have been entitled, he is liable to the rightful owner in the tort of conversion. If he wrongly withholds possession he is liable in detinue. In this situation he should interplead.

To do this he takes out an ordinary summons, if an action is pending, or an originating summons, if not, which he serves on all the rival claimants calling upon them to appear before a master or district registrar and specify their claims. The stakeholder, when he takes out the summons, must swear an affidavit stating that he claims no interest in the subject matter in dispute other than for charges or costs, that he does not collude with any of the claimants and that he is willing to pay or transfer the subject matter into court.[4] On the return day the court will, if the claimants appear, make an order in one of the following forms:[5]

(1)   that any claimant be made a defendant in a pending action in addition to, or in substitution for, the stakeholder;

(2)   that an issue between the claimants be stated and tried, directing which shall be plaintiff and which defendant;

(3)   that the issue be determined by the master if both parties consent, or one requests, or the question is solely one of law[6]. In this case appeal lies direct to the Court of Appeal;

(4)   that the proceedings be transferred to a county court if the subject matter or its value does not exceed £750.[7]

---

[1] O. 16, r. 9. The procedure between a third party and a fourth party is similar to the procedure as between the defendant and the third party.

[2] *Stott* v. *West Yorkshire Road Car Co., Ltd.*, [1971] 2 Q.B. 651; [1971] 3 All E.R. 534.

[3] O. 17, r. 1.

[4] O. 17, r. 3.

[5] O. 17, r. 5.

[6] The Court of Appeal has stated that the issue should not, however, be determined summarily if there is a serious claim to chattels of considerable value or there is a prospect of difficult questions of law arising; in such a case a proper trial of the claim should be ordered; *Fredericks and Pelhams Timber Buildings* v. *Wilkins (Read, Claimant)*, [1971] 3 All E.R. 545; [1971] 1 W.L.R. 1197.

[7] County Courts Act 1959, s. 68 as amended by Administration of Justice Act 1969, s. 2.

In addition the master may order the money or goods in issue to be paid or deposited in court pending the determination of the issue.[1] If the subject matter is money the stakeholder may deduct his charges and his taxed costs. Otherwise these will be paid after the determination of the issue.

D SECURITY FOR COSTS

As a rule no party can be required to deposit money as security for the costs of a pending action. This rule applies even if the party concerned is insolvent or even bankrupt.[2] However there are exceptions to this rule, as there are to most rules. In these exceptional cases the defendant may apply by summons, usually on the summons for directions, for an order that the plaintiff provide security for costs:

(*a*) where the plaintiff is ordinarily resident out of the jurisdiction.[3] However security will not be ordered on this ground if the plaintiff has substantial property within the jurisdiction out of which costs may be defrayed, since the basis of the exception is that the defendant, if successful, would not be able to enforce an order for his costs;[4]

(*b*) where the plaintiff is a nominal plaintiff suing for the benefit of a third party and there is reason to believe that he would be unable to pay the defendant's costs if ordered to do so;[5] a person suing in a representative capacity is not a nominal plaintiff;

(*c*) where the plaintiff has deliberately misstated his address on the writ, or has changed his address since the issue of the writ in order to evade the consequences of litigation;[6]

(*d*) where a plaintiff company may not be able to pay costs awarded against it.[7]

In addition, orders for the disclosure of documents at the inspection of property before the commencement of proceedings, or for the disclosure of documents or the inspection of property in relation to persons who are not parties to the proceedings, all of which orders may now be made in personal

---

[1] Under O. 17, r. 6, an order may be made for the sale of the goods in question. This is particularly useful where they are perishable; *Paquin* v. *Robinson* (1901), 85 L.T. 5.

[2] *Cowell* v. *Taylor* (1885), 31 Ch.D. 34; *Cook* v. *Whellock* (1890), 24 Q.B.D. 658; *Rhodes* v. *Dawson* (1886), 16 Q.B.D. 548.

[3] O. 23, r. 1 (1) (*a*). As to the meaning of the words "ordinarily resident", see *Levene* v. *Inland Revenue Commissioners.*, [1928] A.C. 217 and *Lysaght* v. *Inland Revenue Commissioners*, [1928] A.C. 234. The High Court may by issue of the prerogative writ *ne exeat regno* restrain a defendant from leaving the jurisdiction, subject to the conditions contained in the Debtors Act 1869, s. 6, of which the most important is that the defendant's absence will materially prejudice the plaintiff in prosecuting his action. The writ was last issued in *Lewis* v. *Lewis* (1893), 68 L.T. 198; see, generally, the judgment of MEGARRY, J. in *Felton* v. *Callis*, [1969] 1 Q.B. 200; [1968] 3 All E.R. 673.

[4] See *Kevorkian* v. *Burney*, [1937] 4 All E.R. 468.

[5] O. 23, r. 1 (1) (*b*). The next friend of a person under a disability is not a nominal plaintiff; *Fellows* v. *Barrett* (1830), 1 Keen. 119. An example of a nominal plaintiff is one who, before action, assigns to a third party any damages he may recover; see *Semler* v. *Murphy*, [1968] Ch. 183; [1967] 2 All E.R. 185.

[6] O. 23, r. 1 (1) (*c*), (*d*); O. 23, r. 1 (2); *Knight* v. *Ponsonby*, [1925] 1 K.B. 545.

[7] Companies Act 1948, s. 447.

injuries actions,[1] may be made conditional upon the applicant's giving security for costs.[2] However, in these cases, unlike the above cases, no application for security is made.

These are the only cases in which security for costs, as such, may be ordered. However it is as well to bear in mind that under Order 14 a defendant may be ordered to pay a sum into court as a condition of being granted leave to defend the action.[3]

A counterclaiming defendant may sometimes be ordered to give security for costs,[4] but, otherwise, security for costs cannot be ordered to be given by a defendant or anyone compelled to litigate.

Application for security should first be made by letter and then, if this fails, by summons. A party who has obtained an order that his opponent pay a fixed amount of money into court under this Order may apply by summons for further security to be given as the case proceeds and the bill of costs waxes more bulky.[5]

E INTERROGATORIES

Interrogatories are questions answerable on oath which any party may, with leave of the master, administer to his opponent.[6] The purpose of interrogatories is twofold; first to obtain admissions, and secondly to limit the scope of one's opponent's case. It may thus seem that answers to interrogatories are similar to particulars. In fact, they differ in several important respects.

(1) The scope of particulars is limited to matters raised in the pleadings. Thus particulars cannot be required of matters not pleaded. Interrogatories, on the other hand, may relate to any matter relevant to the action.[7] For example, in an action for defamation, a defendant cannot ask the plaintiff to give particulars of why the words complained of are untrue since it is no part of the plaintiff's case to allege or prove the falsity of the words in question. However, if the defendant pleads justification, he may administer interrogatories to the plaintiff the function of which is to elicit from the plaintiff how far the latter is prepared to admit that the words, or any part of them, are true.[8] Broadly speaking, any question which could be asked of a witness at the trial may be asked in the form

---

[1] Administration of Justice Act 1969, s. 21; Administration of Justice Act 1970, ss. 31, 32; see pp. 234, 277, *ante.*

[2] O. 24, r. 7A (5); O. 29, r. 7A (6). These rules were introduced by R.S.C. (Amendment No. 4) 1971 with effect from August 31, 1971.

[3] See p. 254, *ante.* Section 46 of the County Courts Act 1959 (transfer of action in tort to a county court unless the plaintiff provided security for costs) was abolished by the Administration of Justice Act 1969, s. 11.

[4] When his counterclaim is in the nature of a cross-action rather than a defence; see *Visco* v. *Minter,* [1969] P. 82; [1969] 2 All E.R. 714.

[5] It is common for the defendant's solicitors to prepare a skeleton bill of costs so that the master may estimate the proper amount of security. The usual amount ordered is two-thirds of the estimated costs: *Sturla* v. *Freccia,* [1877] W.N. 166; *Merton* v. *The Times Publishing Co.* (1931), 48 T.L.R. 34.

[6] O. 26, r. 1.

[7] O. 26, r. 1 (1) (a); *Nash* v. *Leyton,* [1911] 2 Ch. 71.

[8] *Marriott* v. *Chamberlain* (1886), 17 Q.B.D. 154; *Peter Walker & Son, Ltd.* v. *Hodgson,* [1909] 1 K.B. 239.

of an interrogatory, with the notable exception of questions as to the witness's credit or credibility.[1]

(2) Particulars cannot relate to evidence. Interrogatories are usually aimed at evidential matters, although they cannot extend to asking a party to disclose his means of proof or to name his witnesses.[2]

(3) An application for particulars may be made as soon as the pleading in question has been served. Interrogatories, however, will never be ordered before delivery of the defence (since that may contain admissions rendering them unnecessary) and will hardly ever be ordered before discovery of documents takes place (since an opponent's documents may contain the answers sought). In practice an application for leave to administer interrogatories should not be made before the hearing of the summons for directions.

(4) Particulars are not given on oath. Interrogatories must always be answered on affidavit (though parties often agree to accept answers by open letter, which answers can be put in at the trial in the same way as sworn answers).

(5) A party may apply for particulars by letter on his own initiative. Indeed he should do so. Interrogatories may only be administered by order of a master. The proper course is to apply to the master for leave to administer the proposed interrogatories. The master will only allow those which he "considers necessary either for disposing fairly of the cause or matter or for saving costs".[3] He will not allow irrelevant questions to be put, such as questions relating to the character of a party or witness; nor will the master allow interrogatories as to the contents of a document. Finally, the master will not allow "fishing" interrogatories; these are questions which are not asked in furtherance of a genuine inquiry, but in the hope that the answers which are given may lend support to a case which is insufficient as it stands.[4]

The interrogatories ordered must be answered on oath within the time prescribed by the master. The only ground upon which a party may refuse to answer is that of privilege. The privilege must be claimed on oath[5] and the grounds are the same as those for the privilege from production of documents. Other objections must be taken at the hearing of the summons at which the order for interrogatories is made or not at all. Answers to interrogatories are binding and the party administering them is in a position of advantage since he may put in evidence at the trial all *or any* of the answers. He cannot be compelled to put in any answer which does not favour his case.[6]

If a party's answers are evasive or ambiguous he may be ordered to make a further answer either on affidavit or by oral examination.[7] The final sanctions for failing to comply with an order for interrogatories are the same as for disobedience to any other interlocutory order. Thus the defaulter's statement of

---

[1] *Kennedy* v. *Dodson*, [1895] 1 Ch. 334.
[2] *Marriott* v. *Chamberlain (supra)*; *Knapp* v. *Harvey*, [1911] 2 K.B. 725.
[3] O. 26, r. 1 (3).
[4] See *Hooton* v. *Dalby*, [1907] 2 K.B. 18; *Pankhurst* v. *Hamilton* (1886), 2 T.L.R. 682.
[5] O. 26, r. 4; *Dalgleish* v. *Lowther*, [1899] 2 Q.B. 590.
[6] O. 26, r. 7. The court may, however, order an answer to be put in where it is so closely connected with another answer which has been put in evidence that the court considers that one ought not to be used without the other.
[7] O. 26, r. 5. The test is whether the answer is sufficient, not whether it is true; *Lyell* v. *Kennedy (No. 3)* (1884), 27 Ch.D. 1.

claim may be struck out if he is a plaintiff or his defence if a defendant. In an extreme case of wilful disobedience the offender may be committed for contempt of court.[1]

F THE SUMMONS FOR DIRECTIONS

The plaintiff must, within one month of the close of pleadings, take out a summons for directions returnable in not less than 14 days.[2] To do so he issues the summons, using the appropriate form, at the Central Office or a district registry, and serves it on all defendants to the action. If he does not do so the defendant has two courses open to him. He may apply to have the plaintiff's action dismissed for want of prosecution, or he may issue the summons himself and serve it on the plaintiff.[3] The plaintiff must issue a summons for directions in every action commenced by writ with a few exceptions, the chief of which are: cases where directions have already been given following an application for summary judgment under Order 14 or for a trial without pleadings under Order 18, r. 21, actions for an account and actions which have been referred to an official referee or transferred to the Commercial Court.[4]

The general functions of the summons for directions are summarised in Order 25, r. 1 (1), so that:

(a) all matters which must or can be dealt with on interlocutory applications and have not already been dealt with may so far as possible be dealt with, and

(b) such directions may be given as to the future course of the action as appear best adapted to secure the just, expeditious and economical disposal thereof.

The summons for directions has been described as a "stocktaking" of all the interlocutory matters in the action. It is possible for a party to issue a separate summons for each interlocutory application which he wishes to make, but to save time and expense it is generally prudent to await the summons for directions to apply for all the orders required.[5] The form on which the summons is issued sets out in outline matters on which directions may be given, leaving the parties to fill in their detailed requirements and also to add any other application for which the form does not provide (such as an order for the admission of a certified copy of notes of evidence taken in other proceedings). The applicant must delete the number[6] of any paragraph on the form which

---

[1] O. 26, r. 6.

[2] O. 25, r. 1 (1). In Admiralty actions the period is seven weeks and the summons will be returnable before a judge of the Admiralty Court; O. 75, r. 25; see p. 289, *post.* There is a *lacuna* in the Rules of the Supreme Court in that if no defence is served the close of pleadings never occurs and there is no provision for applying for directions; fortunately the High Court has an inherent power to give directions on application; *Austin* v. *Wildig*, [1969] 1 All E.R. 99; [1969] 1 W.L.R. 67.

[3] O. 25, r. 1 (4).

[4] The full list of exceptions is embodied in O. 25, r. 1 (2).

[5] There is a general rule that particulars will not be ordered before the summons for directions; nevertheless in exceptional cases, for example cases where the pleading is so vague that the other party cannot properly acertain the case against him, particulars may be waived: *Cyril Leonard & Co.* v. *Simo Securities Trust, Ltd.*, [1971] 3 All E.R. 1313; [1971] 1 W.L.R. 80.

[6] He must not, however, delete the text.

contains a matter on which he does not require directions. On the return day, and on adjourned hearings, the master will give directions for which the parties have applied and will also give directions of his own motion on certain matters, such as the mode and place of trial, whether or not the parties have applied for them.[1]

Matters dealt with on the summons

The standard form lists 29 matters upon which the parties may apply for directions, and leaves space for any others not listed. Certain matters which are, in fact, dealt with on the summons for directions, such as particulars of pleading, amendment of writ and pleadings, discovery and inspection of documents, security for costs and interrogatories have already been encountered.[2] It remains to consider the other principal matters which are dealt with at this important stage of the proceedings.

a   *Consolidation of actions*[3]

This is a procedure which enables a party to have separate issues tried together, whether or not they could have been joined on one writ.[4] It arises frequently in defamation actions where one plaintiff wishes to sue several defendants for separate publications of substantially the same defamatory matter.[5] The application to consolidate should be made as early as possible and will often be made before the summons for directions in which case a separate summons will be required.[6] The plaintiffs in a consolidated action must generally be represented by one firm of solicitors, so that, where more than one firm has been instructed, consolidation will be impossible unless the plaintiffs agree to be represented by one of the firms alone.[6]

A simple alternative to consolidation is for the master to order separate actions to be set down for trial consecutively in the same list, so that they will come before the same judge on the same day. The effect is to avoid the duplication of such expenses as witness fees.

b   *Evidence*

Order 38, r. 1. provides that:

> "subject to the provisions of these rules and of the Civil Evidence Act 1968 and any other enactment relating to evidence, any fact required to be proved at the trial of any action begun by writ by the evidence of witnesses shall be proved by the examination of the witnesses orally and in open court".

Nevertheless the rules provide facility for enabling and even compelling parties to reduce costs, particularly witness fees, by adopting alternative methods

---

[1] *Nagy* v. *Co-operative Press*, [1949] 2 K.B. 198; [1949] 1 All E.R. 1019.
[2] See pp. 272–284, *ante*.
[3] O. 4, r. 10.
[4] In fact cases are normally consolidated only where the parties could have been joined on one writ under O. 15, r. 4.
[5] See Defamation Act 1952, s. 13; *Stone* v. *Press Association*, [1897] 2 Q.B. 159; *Daws* v. *Daily Sketch*, [1960] 1 All E.R. 397; [1960] 1 W.L.R. 126.
[6] *Lewis* v. *Daily Telegraph (No. 2)*, [1964] 2 Q.B. 601; [1964] 1 All E.R. 705. This decision suggests that there is a power to "deconsolidate" consolidated actions.

of proof.[1] The most common method of reducing costs is by the use of admissions. A party need produce no proof of any matter admitted in his favour. Admissions on the pleadings may be express or implied from a failure to traverse.[2] Admissions may also be made in answer to interrogatories. A useful means of compelling an opponent to admit a fact is to serve him with a "notice to admit facts", calling upon him to admit the facts listed in the notice.[3] If he will not admit these facts and they are proved at the trial, unless the court otherwise orders, he will bear the costs of proof.[4] This is, of course, a powerful weapon but it must not be abused. A party should not be asked to admit the facts in issue or any inference of fact, such as negligence. He should only, in practice, be asked to admit facts of a formal nature or facts which can easily be proved against him if he does not admit them. Similar to such a notice is a "notice to admit documents", calling upon the party served to admit the authenticity of the documents listed, though not the truth of their contents.[5] The effect of failure to admit is, again, that the party who was served with the notice has to pay the costs of proving the documents at the trial, unless the court otherwise orders, which may involve an extra witness, such as a handwriting expert.[4]

Wide powers are conferred on the master by Order 38 as to the means of proof. Thus he may order evidence to be given at the trial by affidavit or in any other specified manner.[6] For example, he may order the date on which an important event occurred to be proved by production of a newspaper containing a report of the event. In addition he may restrict the number of medical or other expert witnesses who may be called at the trial.[7] The parties can usually agree a medical report, but if they cannot the master will often limit the parties to one or two medical experts each.

c Place of trial

The master sometimes exercises his power to transfer the action to another division of the High Court or to a county court.[8] In other cases he must direct where and in what manner the action is to be tried.[9] This must be the last matter upon which the master gives directions.[10] The place of trial will be either London or a centre at which the Lord Chancellor has directed sittings of the High Court to be held, pursuant to section 2 of the Courts Act 1971. No party, other than the Crown,[11] has a right to trial in London, and the place of trial will be fixed where it is most convenient for all parties having regard to such matters as the availability of witnesses. This will generally be London, if appearance was entered in London, or the centre for the district in the registry of which appearance was entered, though the place of entry of appearance is not

---

[1] Pursuant to the Judicature Act 1925, s. 99 (i) (i).
[2] O. 18, r. 13; see p. 250, *ante*.
[3] O. 27, r. 2.
[4] O. 62, r. 3.
[5] O. 27, r. 5.
[6] O. 38, rr. 1, 2.
[7] O. 38, r. 4.
[8] See p. 331, *post*.
[9] O. 33, r. 4.
[10] O. 25, r. 2 (4); *Southey-Roberts Estates, Ltd.* v. *Roe*, [1956] 2 All E.R. 829; [1956] 1 W.L.R. 946.
[11] O. 77, r. 13 (1).

conclusive since the jurisdiction of the High Court, unlike that of the county court, is in no way local.

d Mode of trial

If the master orders trial in London, he must fix the list in which the case is to be set down for trial. There are several such lists in the Queen's Bench Division, the most noteworthy being the Short Cause List, the Jury List, the Non-Jury List and the Commercial List. Cases which are to be tried without a jury and which are not likely to last more than two hours are set down in the Short-Cause List. Most actions are tried in the Non-Jury List by a judge sitting alone, or, occasionally, sitting with assessors. The importance of the jury in civil cases has declined rapidly since the Judicature Acts. Until then most civil actions were tried by a judge and jury. Trial by jury was substantially limited by section 6 of the Administration of Justice (Miscellaneous Provisions) Act 1933 which provides that the only cases in which either party has a right to a jury are cases where

(*a*) a charge of fraud against that party; or
(*b*) a claim for libel, slander, malicious prosecution or false imprisonment

is in issue unless in either case the trial requires any prolonged examination of documents or accounts or any scientific or local investigation which cannot conveniently be made with a jury.[1] In any other case the master has a discretion whether or not to order a jury. A conflict of authority on the scope of this discretion[2] was resolved by the Court of Appeal in the leading case of *Ward* v. *James*,[3] in which the Court of Appeal formulated the principle that, in the absence of special circumstances, it is a wrong exercise of the master's discretion to order a jury in an action based on a claim for damages for personal injuries. The fact that the injuries are exceptionally severe is not, apparently, a special circumstance to justify a jury. A jury may be ordered if there is likely to be a strong conflict of evidence, or if questions of honesty or dishonesty may arise.[4] The decision of the Court of Appeal in *Ward* v. *James*[5] is open to criticism as being rather of a legislative than of a judicial nature. Nevertheless if it is accepted that the function of the judiciary is to adapt the law to changing social aims and conditions, the decision appears entirely justifiable. Juries are told of no fixed scale of damages, and, being aware that the substantive defendants in personal injuries actions are frequently insurance companies,[6] are not constrained to limit the damages awarded. Accordingly, in some cases, awards far exceed what would constitute reasonable compensation to the plaintiff.[7]

---

1 The right must be claimed before the master first fixes the place and mode of trial. "Fraud", in this context, is limited to deceit: *Barclays Bank, Ltd.* v. *Cole*, [1967] 2 Q.B. 738; [1966] 3 All E.R. 948.
2 *Hope* v. *Great Western Rail Co.*, [1937] 2 K.B. 130; [1937] 1 All E.R. 625; *Hennell* v. *Ranaboldo*, [1963] 3 All E.R. 684; [1963] 1 W.L.R. 1391; *Sims* v. *William Howard & Son, Ltd.*, [1964] 2 Q.B. 409; [1964] 1 All E.R. 918.
3 [1966] 1 Q.B. 273; [1965] 1 All E.R. 563.
4 *Sims* v. *William Howard & Son, Ltd. (supra).*
5 [1966] 1 Q.B. 273, at p. 290–291; [1965] 1 All E.R. 563, at p. 570.
6 Though they must not, as a matter of practice, be told of this.
7 See, for example, *Warren* v. *King*, [1963] 3 All E.R. 521; [1964] 1 W.L.R. 1; *Morey* v. *Woodfield (No. 2)*, [1964] 1 Q.B. 1; [1963] 3 All E.R. 584.

These awards cannot usually be corrected on appeal, since the Court of Appeal cannot upset an award of damages on the ground only that it is too high, or, more rarely, too low.[1] The result is that the parties to a jury action have no way of estimating the likely damages, so that the plaintiff is reluctant to accept a reasonable sum in settlement and the defendant is prevented from making a payment into court. Where the trial is by a judge alone, however, awards must conform to a definite, though flexible, scale. If an award is out of scale the Court of Appeal feels no hesitation in adjusting the amount to bring it into line with awards in similar cases. In this way prospective litigants may more readily settle their actions and avoid the delay and expense of a High Court action.

Thus the law is that the discretion as to the mode of trial is a judicial rather than an absolute one, and that, in the absence of special circumstances, it is a wrong exercise of that discretion to order a jury in a personal injuries action.

The Commercial Court

A separate list is kept in London, Liverpool and Manchester to hear cases arising out of that branch of the law known as commercial law, whose origins are to be traced rather in commercial custom than in the common law. Insurance, banking, mercantile agency and the construction and enforcement of mercantile documents such as bills of lading, charterparties and negotiable instruments are the type of matter dealt with in the Commercial Court. The judges of the Commercial Court are such of the puisne judges of the High Court as the Lord Chancellor may from time to time nominate[2] and are usually judges of the Queen's Bench Division with special experience in commercial matters. Except by consent their powers are no greater than those of any other judge. However, procedure in the court is more flexible than the normal procedure. Thus the pleadings must be in the form of points of claim, defence, counterclaim, defence to counterclaim or reply and must be as brief as possible. Applications for particulars are not allowed unless essential. By consent the strict rules of evidence are relaxed. Thus evidence is admitted which would generally be excluded, and witness fees may be saved by deciding the case on documentary evidence alone.

A writ or originating summons issued out of London, Liverpool or Manchester may be marked in the top left hand corner, with the words "Commercial Court" and on the issue of the writ or summons so marked, the action will be entered immediately in the commercial list.[3] Actions may be transferred to the Commercial Court apart from this rule and, indeed, actions commenced

---

[1] See p. 342, *post*; but see observations of LORD DENNING, M.R. in *Ward* v. *James*, [1966] 1 Q.B. 273, at pp. 300–301; [1965] 1 All E.R. 563, at p. 575.

[2] Administration of Justice Act 1970, s. 3.

[3] O. 72, r. 4. As an alternative to the Commercial Court any party may apply for an order for trial before one of the Circuit judges nominated to try "official referees' business". The office of official referee was effectively abolished by the Courts Act 1971, s. 25 but by the same section such of the Circuit judges as the Lord Chancellor may from time to time nominate are to discharge the functions conferred by Rules of the Supreme Court or by any other provisions upon official referees, this jurisidiction being known as "official referees' business" and comprising (*inter alia*) the trial of cases involving prolonged examination of documents or accounts; also any issue of fact in an action may be referred by the court to one of the nominated judges for inquiry or report (O. 36, rr. 1, 2). Cases such as building disputes are often tried in this way.

in the Commercial Court under the rule may be removed from the list. Any party who seeks the removal of an action from the Commercial Court, when it has been set down in that list, must apply within 7 days of entering an appearance.[1]

Any party to an action in the Commercial Court may take out a summons for directions in the action before the close of pleadings. This is principally because the directions required may, in fact, relate to the framing of the pleadings.

The Admiralty Court

The Admiralty jurisdiction of the High Court, assigned to the Queen's Bench Division by the Administration of Justice Act 1970, is administered by the Admiralty Court, created by that Act as part of the Queen's Bench Division and consisting of such of the puisne judges of the High Court as the Lord Chancellor may from time to time nominate to be Admiralty Judges.[2] Procedure is governed by R.S.C. Order 75. There are special forms of writ for the commencement of proceedings and special rules of procedure, depending upon the type of Admiralty proceeding. To take but one example, in actions to enforce a claim for damage, loss of life or personal injury arising out of a collision between ships, each party must lodge a document known as a "preliminary act" which contains a statement of the material facts relating to the collision including such matters as the state of the weather, the course steered and speed of the ships, the lights on the ships, alterations in course, the angle of the ships at the moment of contact and what sound signals were given and heard. The preliminary acts are sealed and are not opened before the close of pleadings.[3]

It should be noted that the court has power to order any issue to be tried before, at or after the trial of the action and may order different issues to be tried separately.[4] Thus it appears that the master can order the assessment of damages, for example, to be postponed until after the trial on the issues of liability.[5] Under these provisions a preliminary point of law is often tried before the facts where this may effectively dispose of the action.[6]

Having dealt with all the interlocutory matters raised on the summons for directions including, finally, the mode and place of trial, the master will give an estimate of the length of trial, together with a provisional assessment of the substance, difficulty or public importance of the case.[7] He will then fix a period within which the plaintiff must set the action down for trial. When the

---

[1] O. 72, r. 6.

[2] Administration of Justice Act 1970, s. 2.

[3] O. 75, r. 18.

[4] O. 33, rr. 3, 4 (2).

[5] This power has been sparingly exercised; see observations of WINN, L.J. in *Stevens* v. *William Nash, Ltd.*, [1966] 3 All E.R. 156; [1966] 1 W.L.R. 1550, and in *Hawkins* v. *New Mendip Engineering, Ltd.*, [1966] 3 All E.R. 228; [1966] 1 W.L.R. 1341. One advantage of trying the issue of liability before damages is that a judgment on liability for damages to be assessed enables the plaintiff to apply for an interim payment; see p. 260, *ante*.

[6] See, for example: *Everett* v. *Ribbands*, [1952] 2 Q.B. 198; [1952] 1 All E.R. 832; *Carl-Zeiss-Stiftung* v. *Herbert Smith & Co.*, [1969] 1 Ch. 93; [1968] 2 All E.R. 1002.

[7] The assessment is as follows: "A"—cases of great substance or great difficulty or of public importance; "B"—cases of substance or difficulty; "C"—other cases: *Practice Direction (Summons for Directions)*, [1972] 1 All E.R. 288; [1972] 1 W.L.R. 3.

plaintiff has done so he must, within 24 hours, inform all the other parties.[1] The parties must then proceed to prepare their cases for trial.

G TRIAL

1 Preparation of evidence

At an early stage of the action the papers will have been sent to counsel. Counsel will normally settle the pleadings but, in any event, he will usually be instructed before the summons for directions so as to obtain his advice on interlocutory matters. Cases are won and lost in their preparation. Counsel will therefore wish to consider which applications should be made, whether the pleadings require amendment and similar matters.

The first consideration upon preparing an action for trial is on whom the burden of proof rests. The general rule is *quis affirmat debet probare*; thus where any allegation of fact is in issue the party who alleges that fact must prove it. The pleadings will disclose where the general burden lies. If an allegation in the statement of claim is admitted (expressly or impliedly) it need not be proved at all. If it is traversed then the burden rests on the plaintiff. If it is the subject of a plea in confession and avoidance, then the burden is on the defendant to prove the matters in avoidance. However, the burden may shift during the action by the effect of presumptions. If a presumption is raised in favour of a party, the effect is to shift the burden of disproving the matter presumed to his opponent.[2]

Having decided which matters he must prove, counsel will decide how he proposes to prove them. The two principal methods of proof are by witnesses and by documents.

a Witnesses

Counsel will name the witnesses whom he requires. There is no property in a witness, so that there is no objection to interviewing or calling any witness even if he has been served with a subpoena by an opponent. It is, of course, wrong to call a witness whose testimony is unlikely to support one's case, since a party cannot cross-examine a witness he has called, unless the court gives leave to treat the witness as hostile.[3] Also, to intimidate or otherwise tamper with a witness amounts to a contempt of court.[4]

Usually a witness will be prepared to attend voluntarily if he is tendered a reasonable fee. Where he will not, his attendance may be compelled by

---

[1] O. 34, r. 8. In addition, where the trial is set down for trial outside London, the plaintiff must, after giving to the defendant 7 days' notice of his intention so to do, lodge with the district registrar a certificate of readiness for trial containing certain particulars, notably whether the order made on the summons for directions has been complied with, and in particular whether medical or experts' reports have been submitted for agreement and, if so, whether they have been agreed (or if not how many medical or expert witnesses are to be called), whether plans and photographs have been agreed, an up-to-date estimate of the length of the trial and a statement that the plaintiff is ready and wishes the action to be brought on for trial: *Practice Direction (Trial out of London)* [1972] 1 All E.R. 287; [1972] 1 W.L.R. 5.

[2] See p. 484, *post*.   [3] See p. 507, *post*.

[4] *Chapman* v. *Honig*, [1963] 2 Q.B. 502; [1963] 2 All E.R. 513.

subpoena ad testificandum.[1] A witness who fails to comply may be committed for contempt of court. Where a witness will not, or may not, be able to attend the trial his testimony may, by order of the court, be taken before a special examiner.[2]

b Documents

Documentary evidence, especially in contract cases, frequently forms the basis of a party's case. Where he is in possession of the documents himself, he is in no difficulty. However the documents which are needed by a party may be in the possession of an opponent or of a third party. If they are in the possession of a third party, the proper course is to serve him with a *subpoena duces tecum*, i.e. "attend and bring the document with you". If the documents are in the possession of an opponent he should be served with a "notice to produce" the documents required. This does not have the effect of a subpoena, but if he does not produce the document, he cannot use the document himself and the party who served the notice may give secondary evidence of its contents.[3] In addition, if he has served a list of documents under Order 24 he is deemed to have been served with a notice to produce all the documents in his list.[4]

Formal proof of a document may be dispensed with if one's opponent is prepared to admit the authenticity of the documents in question. Accordingly, he should be served with a "notice to admit" these documents.[5] However, a party who has been served with a list of documents is deemed to admit the authenticity of every document in his list[6] unless he serves express notice of non-admission within 21 days after inspection.

Since automatic discovery now takes place in nearly all actions commenced by writ, it follows that express notices to produce and notices to admit documents will rarely be necessary.

Notices under the Civil Evidence Act 1968

Where it is desired to put in evidence at the trial, statements admissible under the provisions of the Civil Evidence Act 1968,[7] the party desiring to do so must within 21 days after setting down serve on every other party a notice containing prescribed particulars of (if the statement is oral) the time, place and circumstances in which the statement was made, the persons by whom and to whom it was made and the substance of the statement or, if material, the words used.[8] In the case of written statements admissible by virtue of the Act, the

---

[1] O. 38, r. 14. Where the witness is a prisoner an order may be obtained for his attendance by an application *ex parte* to a judge in chambers under the Criminal Procedure Act 1853, s. 9. Where he is in custody on civil process, his attendance is secured by writ of *habeas corpus ad testificandum* upon application *ex parte* on affidavit to a judge in chambers.

[2] O. 39. Where the witness is in another country a "letter of request" is issued to the judicial authorities of that country. A deposition taken under this Order may be put in evidence at the trial either by consent of the other side or on proof that the deponent is dead, outside the jurisdiction or unable from sickness or other infirmity to attend the trial (O. 38, r. 9).

[3] O. 27, r. 5 (4); *Sharpe* v. *Lamb* (1840), 11 Ad. & El. 805.

[4] O. 27, r. 4 (3).   [5] O. 27, r. 5 (1).

[6] O. 27, r. 4 (1).

[7] See pp. 533, 543, *post.*

[8] O. 38, r. 22 (1).

notice must annex a copy of the document in question as well as containing certain prescribed particulars relating to the circumstances of its compilation.[1]

If the party giving the notice alleges that the maker cannot be called as a witness at the trial because he is dead, beyond the seas, unfit by reason of his bodily or mental condition to attend as a witness, cannot be found or cannot reasonably be expected to have any recollection of matters relevant to the accuracy of his statement, the notice must contain a statement to this effect;[2] otherwise a party served with a notice may within 21 days serve a counter-notice requiring the maker of any statement to be called as a witness by the party who served the original notice, in which event if that person is not called as a witness, his statement is not admissible under the 1968 Act.[3]

When the evidence for each side has been prepared the parties must await trial. Neither party need serve any notice of the date of trial on his opponent. Accordingly (unless the case has been given a fixed date) all parties must watch carefully the lists. The Weeks' List is published on Mondays and contains the cases expected to be tried in that week. Each day there is published a Daily Cause List containing the actions to be heard that day and a Warned List consisting of actions likely to be tried on the following day. Thus neither side has any excuse if his case is not ready when the action comes on for trial. If one party fails to appear the trial may proceed in his absence.[4] However, if application is made within 7 days, a judgment obtained in the absence of a party may be set aside, generally on condition that he pay the costs thrown away.[5] Although adjournment is possible, last minute postponements are looked upon with disfavour by the judge in charge of the list and may result in the offending firm of solicitors being penalised personally with the extra costs incurred.[6]

2 Procedure at the trial

If the action is to be tried with a jury, a jury of 12 is sworn. The trial then begins.

a Right to begin

If damages are unliquidated or the burden of proving any single issue on the pleadings rests on the plaintiff, then the plaintiff begins. Thus the only case where the defendant has the right to begin is a case in which the plaintiff claims only liquidated damages and the defendant has not traversed any allegation in the statement of claim. The right to begin and the right to the last word are advantages which are probably exaggerated, especially in the absence of a jury.

---

[1] O. 38, rr. 22 (2), 23 (1), 24.

[2] O. 38, rr. 22 (3), 23 (2), 24 (3), 25. Any issue as to whether these conditions are satisfied in relation to the maker of a statement may be determined conclusively before the trial on an application by summons (O. 38, r. 27).

[3] O. 38, r. 26. The court has, however, discretion to admit statements under the Civil Evidence Act 1968 in cases where the proper notice was not served but it will not exercise this discretion in favour of a party who, for example, has deliberately not served a notice in order to retain the possibility of surprising an opponent; cf. *Ford* v. *Lewis*, [1971] 2 All E.R. 983; [1971] 1 W.L.R. 623.

[4] O. 35, r. 1.

[5] O. 35, r. 2. There can be an appeal against such a judgment, though this is rarely appropriate; *Armour* v. *Bate*, [1891] 2 Q.B. 233.

[6] O. 62, r. 8.

Counsel for the plaintiff opens his case stating the facts on which the plaintiff relies in the order in which they appear on the pleadings, which should be chronological order. He should not rely upon any fact which he is not permitted to prove, which means, of course, that he cannot allege any fact not pleaded, although he may, even at this late stage, be allowed to amend the pleadings. Neither counsel must disclose the existence of any interim payment, nor of any payment into court, unless the defendant has raised one of the two defences in which the payment is an essential element.[1] The plaintiff's witnesses are then called and sworn. They are examined and may be cross-examined and re-examined.[2] His documents, including answers to interrogatories which he wishes to put in, are not put in evidence. Finally counsel argues the propositions of law upon which he relies, citing to the court all relevant authorities on the point whether they support his own case or that of his opponent. If they tend to support his opponent's case, he must attempt to distinguish them from the present case on their facts. He cannot, however, ignore them, since this would infringe his duty to the court.

b Case for the defence

At the close of the plaintiff's case the defendant has the following courses open to him:

(1) He may submit "no case to answer". This is a submission that the plaintiff has failed to make out a *prima facie* case, or to establish the elements of a recognised cause of action. The submission is rare in a civil action since the objection will usually have been taken long before the trial. If it is made, the judge, before deciding, may require the defendant to "stand on his submission", which means that he can call no evidence if his submission fails, although this is not usual in jury actions.[3] Counsel for the plaintiff has a right to reply to the submission. If it succeeds, judgment is entered for the defendant. If it fails and the defendant has been put to his election, judgment is entered for the plaintiff.

(2) He may state that he intends to call no evidence, oral or documentary. Counsel for the plaintiff will then address the court followed by defence counsel, who thus obtains the right to the last word.[4]

(3) In most cases the defence will be a mixture of law and fact and the defendant will want to put in some evidence. In this event defence counsel may make an opening speech outlining his defence. His witnesses give their evidence in the same way as those of the plaintiff followed by the defendant's documents and legal submissions. He then makes a closing speech, following which counsel for the plaintiff has a right to make a closing speech in reply and may also be allowed to call rebutting evidence where the defendant has raised

---

[1] O. 22, r. 7; see p. 269, *ante*.

[2] See p. 506, *post*. It is a matter for the judge's discretion as to whether he allows other witnesses to remain in court while evidence is being given: *Moore* v. *Lambeth County Court Registrar*, [1969] 1 All E.R. 782; [1969] 1 W.L.R. 141.

[3] *Laurie* v. *Raglan Building Co., Ltd.*, [1942] 1 K.B. 152; [1941] All E.R. 332; *Young* v. *Rank*, [1950] 2 K.B. 510; [1950] 2 All E.R. 166; *Storey* v. *Storey*, [1961] P. 63; [1960] 3 All E.R. 279.

[4] O. 35, r. 7. This rule applies expressly to jury actions, but, in the Queen's Bench Division, applies in practice to non-jury actions as well; see *Weller* v. *O'Brien*, [1962] 3 All E.R. 65; [1962] 1 W.L.R. 885.

an affirmative defence. Where a party in his closing speech raises any fresh point of law, the other party is entitled to reply but only in relation to that point.

c Verdict and judgment

At the conclusion of all the evidence and the legal argument for both sides the judge sums up. He must direct the jury (if there is one) as to the issues in the case, stating on whom the burden of proving the individual issues rests, and outlining the evidence in support of those issues. He must also direct upon the standard of proof required from the party on whom the burden rests. He will direct on the law applicable to the issues of fact, for example, whether the words are capable of bearing the defamatory meaning alleged or whether the defendant owes the plaintiff a duty of care in negligence. He must leave the actual issues of fact and the assessment of damages to the jury. While he can suggest a conclusion of fact to the jury, the judge should not tell the jury of the limits within which an award of damages should fall, since this would amount to an attempt by the judge to assess damages. A modern tendency is for the judge to pose a series of questions to the jury calling for their decision on the facts and, if they find for the plaintiff on any issue, the amount of damages.[1]

Where the plaintiff has sought an equitable remedy as an alternative or in addition to damages, the grant of this remedy is in the discretion of the judge.

It remains for judgment to be entered in accordance with the verdict. A judgment crystallises the rights of the parties in respect of the subject matter of the action. Thus they are estopped from litigating the same issues of fact again.[2] Even if fresh damage becomes apparent the plaintiff cannot sue because his right is extinguished.[3] Counsel for the unsuccessful party may apply for a stay of execution pending an appeal. This may be granted on terms. After judgment on the issues of liability and damages[4] the judge may make an order as to costs.

---

[1] However where a jury delivers a general verdict, the judge is not then entitled to ask questions to ascertain the grounds for the verdict, *Arnold* v. *Jeffreys*, [1914] 1 K.B. 512; *Barnes* v. *Hill*, [1967] 1 Q.B. 579; [1967] 1 All E.R. 347.

[2] Clerical mistakes in judgments or orders, or errors arising therein from any accidental slip or omission, may at any time be corrected by the court on motion or summons without an appeal (O. 20, r. 11—the "slip rule").

[3] There is an exception to this rule; if special damage is an element in a cause of action, fresh special damage arising out of the same cause of action may be the basis of a second action: *Darley Main Colliery Co.* v. *Mitchell* (1886), 11 App. Cas. 127; *West Leigh Colliery Co.* v. *Tunnicliffe*, [1908] A.C. 27.

[4] There is power under the Law Reform (Miscellaneous Provisions) Act 1934 to award interest on debts or damages. This section has been amended by s. 22 of the Administration of Justice Act 1969 and now provides that, in the absence of special reasons, interest should be given on awards of damages exceeding £200 where those damages represent or include damages in respect of death or personal injury. The principles governing an award of interest were laid down by the Court of Appeal in *Jefford* v. *Gee*, [1970] 2 Q.B. 130; [1970] 1 All E.R. 1202.

CHAPTER 20

Originating Summons Procedure

A USES OF THE ORIGINATING SUMMONS

Although most actions in the Queen's Bench Division are commenced by writ, and many must be commenced in this way, the plaintiff may in some cases proceed by originating summons.[1] An originating summons is defined as "every summons other than a summons in a pending cause or matter".[2] The procedure is aptly named since it actually raises the point at issue in the first instance, thus dispensing with the need for pleadings. It is the proper method for making applications under certain statutes; for example, applications to approve the compromise of an action by an infant or patient, interpleader applications where an action is not pending and summary proceedings for possession of land occupied by trespassers.[3] In addition it is a streamlined method of obtaining the court's decision on a point of law or on the construction of a document or statute.

B ORIGINATING PROCEDURE

There are basically three forms of originating summons;[4] (1) originating summons between parties, appearance not required; (2) originating summons between parties, appearance required; (3) *ex parte* originating summons (this form is used mainly in the Chancery Division). The second form will almost always be the appropriate one in the Queen's Bench Division. The summons is issued in the same way as a writ, out of the Central Office or a district registry. It remains in force and is renewable in the same way as a writ

---

[1] See pp. 235–236, *ante*.

[2] O. 1, r. 4.

[3] O. 113. This Order was introduced to combat difficulties posed by "squatters" in cases in which it was not possible to identify by name the trespassers against whom an order was sought. The Order provides a swift and summary procedure whereby the plaintiff may proceed by *ex parte* originating summons on affidavit; an order for possession may then be made by a judge without the necessity for a trial and a writ of possession issued without leave.

[4] O. 7, r. 2. There are, in fact, four forms but the fourth is merely an alternative to (2) and is used for issue out of a district registry.

and must be served on the defendant as if it were a writ, leave being required to serve it outside the jurisdiction.

> "Every originating summons must include a statement of the questions on which the plaintiff seeks the determination or direction of the High Court or, as the case may be, a concise statement of the relief or remedy claimed in the proceedings begun by the originating summons with sufficient particulars to identify the cause or causes of action in respect of which the plaintiff claims that relief or remedy."[1]

Although an originating summons is not a pleading[2] it is in many ways similar to a statement of claim and it seems that the inherent jurisdiction of the court and under Order 18, r. 19 to strike out any pleading extends to an originating summons.[3]

After the time limited for entering an appearance, whether or not the defendant has in fact appeared, the plaintiff may obtain an appointment for the first hearing of the summons.[4] If he does not the defendant may himself obtain an appointment (cf. procedure on taking out a summons for directions). The party who obtains the appointment must give notice to every opponent who has entered an appearance at least 4 clear days before the return day.[5] Where the plaintiff proposes to adduce evidence in support of the summons at the first hearing, he must do so by affidavit and must serve a copy of this affidavit on every defendant who has been served with the summons at least 4 clear days before the hearing.[6] Any defendant who has entered an appearance may raise a counterclaim whether or not that counterclaim could have been commenced by originating summons had he been the plaintiff;[7] if the court cannot conveniently hear the counterclaim with the originating summons, it may order that it be struck out or tried separately.[8]

C DIRECTIONS OF THE COURT

The first hearing of the summons will usually be before a master who may adopt the following courses.

(1) If the liability of the defendant in respect of the claim is established, the master may make such order against him as the case may require. The issues raised are thus determined. However, if such an order is made against a defendant who does not appear at the hearing, it may subsequently be varied or revoked by the court on such terms as the court thinks just.[9]

(2) The master may order the proceedings to continue as if the action had been begun by writ (whether or not it could have been begun by writ), and may order that any affidavit shall stand as a pleading. In this event the master will treat the summons as if it were a summons for directions and will, accordingly,

---

[1] O. 7, r. 3 (1).
[2] *Lewis* v. *Packer*, [1960] 1 All E.R. 720; [1960] 1 W.L.R. 452.
[3] O. 18, r. 19 (3); *Punton* v. *Ministry of Pensions*, [1963] 1 All E.R. 275; [1963] 1 W.L.R. 186.
[4] O. 28, r. 2.
[5] O. 28, r. 3.
[6] O. 28, r. 3 (3).
[7] O. 28, r. 7 (1).
[8] O. 28, r. 7 (3).
[9] O. 28, r. 4 (1).

give directions on such matters as discovery of documents and the mode and place of trial.[1]

(3) The master may order the action to be transferred to the appropriate county court.

(4) Unless one of the above orders is made, the court will "give such directions as to the further conduct of the proceedings as it thinks best adapted to secure the just, expeditious and economical disposal thereof".[2] This includes most directions which would be given on the hearing of the summons for directions in an action commenced by writ. In particular the court must determine the mode and place of trial. This will usually be before a judge in open court, the evidence being given in most cases by affidavit. In addition the court is bound to consider at as early a stage as practicable whether there is or may be a dispute as to fact and whether the summons should be heard on oral evidence. The court may, if it thinks fit, order that no further evidence shall be filed and that the summons shall be heard on oral evidence or partly on oral evidence and partly on affidavit evidence, with or without cross-examination of the deponents as it may direct.[3]

---

[1] O. 28, r. 7. However an action based on an allegation of fraud (which must be commenced by writ; see p. 235, *ante*) cannot be continued as if commenced by writ; *Re 462 Green Lane, Ilford, Gooding* v. *Booland*, [1971] 1 All E.R. 315; [1971] 1 W.L.R. 138; cf. *Re Deadman, Smith* v. *Garland*, [1971] 2 All E.R. 101; [1971] 1 W.L.R. 426.

[2] O. 28, r. 4 (2).

[3] O. 28, r. 4 (3).

CHAPTER 21

Costs and the Enforcement of Judgments

A COSTS

1 Who must pay costs

There are two sets of costs. First there are the costs which each party will have to pay to his own solicitor. These must be paid irrespective of the outcome of the action and, subject to the Rules, depend upon the contract between solicitor and client. Secondly there are the costs which one side may be ordered to pay to his opponent. These must be assessed or "taxed" by the court and will very rarely cover the full amount that a party has to pay to his own solicitor. It follows that even a litigant who is completely successful will often have to pay some costs himself. These represent the difference between the amount he pays his solicitor and the amount he recovers from his opponent, and are sometimes described as "extra costs". If the judge makes no order as to costs each party pays his own costs. In most cases, however, the judge will order one side to pay all or a proportion of the costs of his opponent. At common law a successful litigant had a right to costs but this right has been virtually removed by legislation so that at the present day the award of costs is discretionary. It is not, of course, an absolute discretion and it is a wrong exercise of the discretion to deprive a party of his costs if he has been completely successful and guilty of no misconduct.[1] In addition there are statutory fetters on the exercise of this discretion, of which the following should be specially noted.[2]

a Costs should follow the event

Unless there are special factors present, a successful party may expect his costs from an unsuccessful opponent. Nevertheless there is clearly a power to deprive a successful party of his costs on the ground that he has conducted the litigation

---

[1] *Donald Campbell & Co., Ltd.* v. *Pollak*, [1927] A.C. 732. See remarks of VISCOUNT CAVE, L.C., at pp. 811, 812.

[2] Though mention may also be made of the Slander of Women Act 1891, s. 1 and the Rent Act 1968, s. 105 (4).

dishonestly or recovered only a small part of his claim.[1] In an extreme case a successful plaintiff may have to pay the costs of the defendant.[2] There is jurisdiction to order a successful defendant to pay costs but this jurisdiction is only exercisable in the most exceptional circumstances.[3]

There has been a considerable volume of litigation as to what is "the event" in an action.[4] In a simple action involving one plaintiff, one defendant and a single issue, no difficulty arises; the event is judgment on that issue. However, where there are several parties or several issues the situation is more complex.

Several parties—Where a plaintiff properly joins several defendants and succeeds against some but fails against others, the court may, in its discretion, order the costs of a successful defendant to be paid directly or indirectly by an unsuccessful defendant.[5] Conversely, where one defendant is sued by several plaintiffs, some of whom succeed and some of whom fail, the defendant should make a special application for the extra costs he has incurred through the presence of an unsuccessful plaintiff.[6]

Several causes of action—Where several causes of action are tried together the court will, if the issues are severable, order the costs of them to be taxed separately.[7] The effect is that the plaintiff will recover the costs of the causes of action upon which he succeeds, and the defendant will be awarded the costs of the others. However this method of taxation is not possible where the several causes of action arise out of the same transaction. In such cases the judge may order that the whole of the successful plaintiff's costs be taxed, but that he shall recover only a fixed proportion of the taxed costs from the defendant.[8]

Costs of interlocutory proceedings—There will be various interlocutory applications made by each party throughout the action. There are two possibilities with respect to the costs of these applications. The court may make a special order as to the costs of the individual application upon making or refusing an interlocutory order.[9] Alternatively the court may order that the costs of the application be "costs in the cause" which means that the party who is eventually successful will recover the costs of the application. A modification of the latter order is "plaintiff's costs in cause" or "defendant's costs in cause", the effect of which is that if the plaintiff, in the former case, or the defendant, in the latter, is eventually successful, he will be awarded his costs of the interlocutory application in question, whereas if he is ultimately unsuccessful, each

---

[1] *Barnes* v. *Maltby* (1889), 5 T.L.R. 207; *O'Connor* v. *Star Newspaper Co., Ltd.* (1893), 68 L.T. 146.

[2] *London Welsh Estates, Ltd.* v. *Phillip* (1931), 100 L.J.K.B. 449.

[3] *Knight* v. *Clifton*, [1971] Ch. 700; [1971] 2 All E.R. 378. There was no such power prior to the Judicature Act 1890 (now Judicature Act 1925, s. 50 (1)). An order against a successful defendant was made in *Ottway* v. *Jones*, [1955] 2 All E.R. 585; [1955] 1 W.L.R. 706.

[4] See *Reid, Hewitt & Co.* v. *Joseph*, [1918] A.C. 717.

[5] *Bullock* v. *L.G.O. Co.*, [1907] 1 K.B. 264; *Sanderson* v. *Blyth Theatre Co.*, [1903] 2 K.B. 533.

[6] *Keen* v. *Towler* (1924), 41 T.L.R. 86.

[7] As to what is an "issue", see *Howell* v. *Dering*, [1915] 1 K.B. 54, at. p. 63; *Reid, Hewitt & Co.* v. *Joseph*, [1918] A.C. 717. Any item of costs attributable to more than one issue will be divided between the issues.

[8] O. 62, r. 9 (4); *Cinema Press, Ltd.* v. *Pictures and Pleasures, Ltd.*, [1945] K.B. 356; [1945] 1 All E.R. 440.

[9] O. 62, r. 4. In this case the court is treating an interlocutory order as an "event" within r. 3.

party pays his own costs of the interlocutory application. This type of order is the usual one on, for example, an application for an interlocutory injunction; if an interlocutory injunction is granted, the usual order is "plaintiff's costs in cause", and if it is refused, the usual order is "defendant's costs in cause". On a summons for directions the normal order is "costs in cause", on the basis that there has to be a summons, irrespective of what orders are made on the summons.

b Payment into court

It has been noted that a payment into court (unless it is an element in a substantive defence) can affect only costs and not liability or damages. The effect is that if the successful plaintiff recovers no more than the amount paid in, in respect of one or more causes of action, he will be ordered to pay the defendant's costs of those causes of action from the date of payment in. He will still be entitled to his costs to the date of payment in, though these are often small consolation by comparison.[1]

c County Courts Act 1959, s. 47 (as amended)

This is the most important of the statutory fetters on the judge's discretion as to costs. The purpose of the section is to encourage parties to conduct their litigation in the county court rather than the High Court wherever possible. The section provides that where an action founded on contract or tort is commenced in the High Court which is within the jurisdiction of the county court:[2]

(1) if the plaintiff recovers less than £100, he will be entitled to no costs whatever;

(2) if the plaintiff recovers £100 or more but less than £500[3] he will be entitled to costs on the appropriate county court scale only,

unless in either case the judge is satisfied that there was reasonable ground for supposing the amount recoverable in respect of the plaintiff's claim to be in excess of the county court maximum, or the defendant objected to the transfer of the action to the county court.

Because of this provision a party must hesitate before commencing a High Court action where the sum in dispute is within the county court limits. If in doubt a safer course is to commence proceedings in the county court and then apply to have them transferred to the High Court.

This section does not operate if the plaintiff recovers any relief other than damages, such as an injunction.[4] Nor does the section apply to counterclaims, since a defendant has no control over the court in which an action is commenced. Where the section does apply, however, it should be carefully borne in mind when advising a plaintiff whether to proceed in the High Court or in a county court, since the wrong choice may well cost the plaintiff the fruits of his action.

---

[1] O. 62, r. 5 (6); *Hultquist v. Universal Pattern and Precision Engineering Co., Ltd.*, [1960] 2 Q.B. 467; [1960] 2 All E.R. 266.

[2] As to which see pp. 313–315, *post*.

[3] The figures were raised to £100 and £500 by the Administration of Justice Act 1969, s. 4.

[4] *Keates v. Woodward*, [1902] 1 K.B. 532. Nor does it apply where an award in excess of the limits is reduced by reason of the plaintiff's contributory negligence.

Having considered the question of which side must pay costs, the judge must decide what is to be the basis of taxation, for this will determine how much of an opponent's costs the loser will have to pay.

2 The taxation of costs

a Bases of taxation

It was stated at the beginning of this chapter that there are two sets of costs; costs as between a solicitor and his own client, and costs as between the parties. The bases upon which these bills are taxed differ.

Regarding costs between a solicitor and his own client, each party must pay his own solicitor's costs as a contractual debt.[1] Very often the client will simply pay the bill presented to him without knowing or wishing to know of his right to have it taxed. He has, however, a right to have the bill taxed. In this case the bill will be taxed on a "solicitor and own client" basis. This means that "all costs are to be allowed except in so far as they are unreasonable in amount or have been unreasonably incurred."[2] All costs incurred with the express or implied approval of the client are deemed to be reasonable.[3] The result is that the client must pay his solicitor all costs unless they are both unauthorised and certified by the taxing master to be unreasonable, in which case the solicitor will have to pay them personally.

There is one exception to this principle. Where a litigant is legally aided, his solicitor recovers from the Fund his disbursements and 90 *per cent* of his profit costs taxed on a "common fund" basis.[4] This is far less than the complete indemnity which a "solicitor and own client" taxation provides. There is allowed, on this basis, a reasonable sum in respect of all costs reasonably incurred or incurred with the prior approval of the Area Committee. Reasonableness, both as to items and as to amount, depends upon all the circumstances of the case, such as its length, the sum involved and the complexity and novelty of the issues raised.

As to the costs between the parties, the court has jurisdiction to award a fixed sum by way of costs to be paid by a party to his opponent.[5] In any other case the costs must be taxed. There are now three possible bases of taxation which may be ordered:

(1) party and party;
(2) common fund;
(3) solicitor and own client.

---

[1] A lay litigant appearing in person is not entitled to remuneration for the time and labour expended in the preparation of his case, though a solicitor acting in person is so entitled: *Buckland* v. *Watts*, [1970] 1 Q.B. 27; [1969] 2 All E.R. 985.

[2] O. 62, r. 29 (1); see pp. 210–211, *ante*.

[3] O. 62, r. 29 (2). By r. 29 (3) any costs which are of an unusual nature, and such that they would not be allowed on a "party and party" taxation, shall be presumed, until the contrary is shown, to have been unreasonably incurred, unless the solicitor told his client before they were incurred that they might not be so allowed: *Cavendish* v. *Strutt*, [1904] 1 Ch. 524.

[4] Legal Aid and Advice Act 1949, Sched. 3; Legal Aid (General) Regulations 1971, reg. 22 (10). Counsel is awarded 90 *per cent* of his fees.

[5] O. 62, r. 9 (4) (b). This must not exceed the amount a party would have to pay if the costs were taxed: *Willmott* v. *Barker* (1881), 17 Ch.D. 772.

(1) "Party and party" is the usual basis of taxation between the parties and it is also the least generous to the party in whose favour the order is made. On this basis are allowed "all such costs as were necessary or proper for the attainment of justice or for enforcing or defending the rights of the party whose costs are being taxed".[1] The taxing master must decide not only which items are reasonable, but also what is a reasonable amount in respect of each item. As to items allowable the master will not allow costs which may be termed luxuries, or costs thrown away by neglect or excessive caution.[2] As to scale the taxing master will have regard to Order 62, Appendix 2, in which certain items carry fixed costs while others are discretionary as to amount. Where an item is discretionary Part X of Appendix 2 lists factors to which the master must have regard. These include the complexity and novelty of the questions involved, the skill, specialised knowledge and responsibility required by the solicitor or counsel, the amount involved and similar considerations. Thus it was recently held that a brief fee of 500 gns. for leading counsel and two thirds thereof for junior counsel, with refreshers of 100 gns. per day and two thirds was reasonable in a novel and difficult Chancery action, and therefore allowable on a party and party taxation.[3]

(2) Where a party has conducted his litigation scandalously or fraudulently he may, as a penalty, be ordered to pay costs on a "common fund" basis. Where this is so a reasonable amount will be allowed to his opponent for all costs reasonably incurred.[4] This is more generous than a party and party taxation both as to amount and as to items allowable,[5] although it does not amount to a complete indemnity.

It must be noted that this basis of taxation does not apply by reason only of one of the parties being legally aided. Where a party is awarded his costs out of the Legal Aid Fund under the Legal Aid Act 1964 the basis of taxation will usually be party and party,[6] although the Fund pays the assisted litigant's costs on a common fund basis.

(3) The "solicitor and own client" basis of taxation applies between each party and his own solicitor. However, the court rarely has jurisdiction to order a party to pay his opponent's costs on this basis except by consent, as a term of a settlement of the action. Accordingly a party who is awarded costs must still pay the difference between a solicitor and own client taxation, which is the basis of his personal liability, and a party and party taxation, which he receives from his opponent. The extent of this liability for extra costs will

---

[1] O. 62, r. 28 (2).

[2] *Smith* v. *Buller* (1875), L.R. 19 Eq. 473, at p. 475; the costs of taking a shorthand note and supplying transcripts thereof are not usually allowed on a party and party taxation (*Re Blyth* (1882), 10 Q.B.D. 207).

[3] *Simpson's Motor Sales (London), Ltd.* v. *Hendon Corporation*, [1964] 3 All E.R. 833; [1965] 1 W.L.R. 112.

[4] O. 62, r. 28 (3), (4). *Gibbs* v. *Gibbs*, [1952] p. 332; [1952] 1 All E.R. 942; *Reed* v. *Gray*, [1952] Ch. 337; [1952] 1 All E.R. 241. However where the taxing master believes the full value of the work done to have been allowed on a party and party taxation, he cannot allow any further costs on a common fund taxation (*Lyon* v. *Lyon*, [1953] P. 1; [1952] 2 All E.R. 831).

[5] E.g., the cost of taking a shorthand note may be allowed on a common fund taxation where it would not be allowed on a party and party taxation (*Re De Nicols*, [1906] W.N. 192).

[6] Legal Aid Act 1964, s. 1 (6); see p. 228, *ante*.

depend upon the degree of extravagance which he has authorised in the conduct of his case.

b Review of taxation

Any party who is dissatisfied with a taxation of a bill of costs may apply in writing to the same taxing master for a review of his decision. The application must be made within 14 days and must set out the disputed items and a summary of the grounds of objection.[1] The taxing master will then review his taxation of those items and certify his grounds and reasons for allowing, disallowing or altering the amount of disputed items.[2] If still dissatisfied either party may apply within 14 days by summons to a judge in chambers for an order for a further review. The judge may review the taxation himself or refer it to another taxing master.[3]

B ENFORCEMENT OF JUDGMENTS

1 Judgments for the payment of money

a Enforcement in the High Court

The judgment creditor's rights in respect of which he brought the action are extinguished by the judgment. In their place he has a judgment debt. He will wish to enforce this debt which may consist of an award of damages and taxed costs, in addition to which may be included interest at $7\frac{1}{2}$ *per cent per annum* from the date of judgment.[4] The judgment creditor may proceed to enforce the judgment[5] by any of the following five methods prescribed by Order 45, rule 1:

    (i) writ of *fieri facias*;
    (ii) garnishee proceedings;
    (iii) a charging order;
    (iv) the appointment of a receiver;
    (v) writ of sequestration.

Writ of fieri facias (*fi.-fa.*)—This is directed to the sheriff of the county in which is situated the property which it is proposed to seize. Where the debtor has property in more than one county concurrent writs may be issued.[6] The writ commands the sheriff to cause to be made (*fieri facias*) in the name of Her Majesty out of the debtor's chattels a sum sufficient to satisfy the judgment debt and interest together with the costs of execution, unless the judgment is for

---

[1] O. 62, r. 33.

[2] O. 62, r. 34; see *Re Fraser, Leach* v. *Public Trustee*, [1958] 1 All E.R. 26; [1958] 1 W.L.R. 6.

[3] O. 62, r. 35.

[4] Judgments Act 1838, ss. 17, 18 as amended by Judgments Act 1838 (Judgment Debts (Rate of Interest) Order 1971, made under Administration of Justice Act 1970, s. 44.

[5] A stay of execution, for example pending trial of a counterclaim or appeal, is often ordered by the court. However, although this operates to stay execution by *fi.-fa.* (*infra*) it does not prevent the judgment creditor proceeding by one or more of the other methods of enforcement since these do not constitute "execution"; they are alternatives to execution: *Berliner Industriebank Aktiengesellschaft* v. *Jost*, [1971] 2 Q.B. 463; [1971] 2 All E.R. 1513. The Court of Appeal pointed out the need for some modification of the normal form of order.

[6] O. 47, r. 2.

less than £100 and does not include an order for costs. The sheriff may enter the judgment debtor's land (although he may not effect a forcible entry)[1] or the land of a third party if the debtor's goods are to be found thereon. He may seize and sell chattels, choses in action such as banknotes or cheques, promissory notes and a lease belonging to the judgment debtor, which he may assign. He cannot, however, seize property which is exempt from execution. This comprises freehold interests in land, equitable interests in land or chattels, fixtures attached to land, wearing apparel, bedding and tools and implements of trade to a total value of £50[2] and goods belonging to a third party. The latter provision operates to exempt property which is subject to a hire purchase agreement.

• A writ of execution may be issued within the six years following the judgment or order, or later with leave.[3] It may be executed within 12 months of issue on any day not excepting Sunday.[4] There are several other cases in which leave is required, notably where the writ is to be executed against the property of a partner in a firm where the judgment is against the firm,[5] against any person not a party to the original proceedings such as an assignee and against persons represented in a representative action.[6]

It is not unusual for a sheriff to find that goods which he has seized or is about to seize in execution are claimed by a third party such as a hire purchase finance company. His proper course of action in such a situation is to interplead. To do this he issues an interpleader summons serving it on the execution creditor and the claimant.[7] All three parties attend before the master on the return day. The master may try the issue himself, direct an issue to be stated and tried or otherwise deal with the summons as he might deal with a stakeholder's interpleader summons.[8]

The sheriff must make arrangements for the sale of the property seized in execution. Such sale should normally be by public auction and should not take place on the judgment debtor's premises.[9] In practice the sheriff himself takes no part in enforcement and a local auctioneer, acting as a sheriff's officer, usually takes possession of the goods and arranges the auction, or they are left in the possession of the judgment debtor subject to periodic inspection by the sheriff's officers. This arrangement is termed "walking possession" of the goods. In practice the judgment debtor will invariably pay the debt if he can to avoid a sale of his property. Comparatively few sales take place because the court may stay execution on application if the applicant is unable from any cause to pay the money.[10]

Garnishee proceedings—The purpose of these proceedings is to enable the judgment creditor to have assigned to him the benefit of any debt owed by a

---

[1] *Semayne's Case* (1604), 5 Co. Rep. 91.
[2] Small Debts Act 1845, s. 8 (as amended.)
[3] O. 46, r. 2 (1) (*a*).
[4] The Sunday Observance Act 1677 having been repealed by the Statute Law (Repeals) Act 1969.
[5] O. 81, r. 5 (4).
[6] O. 15, r. 12 (3); p. 240, *ante.*
[7] O. 17, r. 1 (1) (*b*).
[8] See p. 280, *ante.*
[9] O. 47, r. 6; *Watson* v. *Murray & Co.*, [1955] 2 Q.B. 1; [1955] 1 All E.R. 350.
[10] O. 47, r. 1 (1) (*b*).

third party (the garnishee) to the judgment debtor. A garnishee order will only issue in respect of a legal debt presently owing to the judgment debtor. A common object of garnishee proceedings is a credit balance at the judgment debtor's bank.[1] Earnings may be garnished but only where the right to them has accrued, so that future earnings cannot be garnished. There is, in fact, no way of seizing or intercepting the judgment debtor's future earnings in the Queen's Bench Division.[2]

The judgment debtor may be required to attend before a master to submit to an oral examination as to what debts are owing to him and as to what property or means, if any, he has of satisfying the judgment.[3] When these matters have been ascertained, by examination or otherwise, the judgment creditor may apply *ex parte* on affidavit for an order nisi which is served on the garnishee personally and, unless the court otherwise directs, on the judgment debtor.[4] This order calls upon the garnishee either to pay the debt, or so much of it as may be sufficient to satisfy the balance of the judgment debt, to the judgment creditor or show cause for not so doing. If the garnishee fails to comply or show cause the order is made absolute and execution may issue against the garnishee to the extent of his obligation, which is, in effect, assigned to the execution creditor.[5] If the garnishee disputes liability to pay the debt claimed to be due from him the[6] master may determine the question at issue summarily or determine the manner in which it shall be tried, no consent being required to trial before a master.[7]

Where money is standing to the credit of the judgment debtor in court, garnishee proceedings cannot be taken in respect of that money but the judgment creditor can apply by summons for an order for the payment out of all or any part of such money. This summons must be served on the judgment debtor at least 7 days before the return day.[8]

Charging order—The judgment creditor may apply *ex parte* on affidavit for an order imposing a charge on (1) land or an interest in land; (2) securities; (3) money standing to the credit of the judgment debtor in court. In addition the judgment creditor may apply by summons to the court for an order charging a partnership interest.

(1) If he discovers that the judgment debtor has land or an interest in land within the jurisdiction, the judgment creditor may apply for an order creating a

---

[1] *Rogers v. Whitely*, [1892] A.C. 118. A savings account at a post office savings bank may not be garnished: Administration of Justice Act 1956, s. 38 (2); a debt which is not assignable, such as state pension, alimony or the pay of a member of the armed forces, cannot be attached.

[2] *Mapleson v. Sears* (1911), 105 L.T. 639. Future earnings may be attached in respect of a maintenance order under the Attachment of Earnings Act 1971, s. 1. Attachment of earnings orders may be obtained in respect of judgment debts only by transferring the judgment to a county court; see p. 325, *post*.

[3] O. 48, r. 1.

[4] O. 49, r. 3 (1). The immediate effect of the order is to bind the debt specified in the order from the moment of service of the order.

[5] O. 49, r. 4. The order absolute may be enforced in the same manner as any other order for the payment of money.

[6] He may, for example, allege a counterclaim against the judgment debtor: *Hale v. Victoria Plumbing Co., Ltd., and En-Tout-Cas, Co., Ltd.*, [1966] 2 Q.B. 746; [1966] 2 All E.R. 672.

[7] O. 49, r. 5.

[8] O. 49, r. 9.

charge over the land or over the interest in the land.[1] An order nisi is made in
the first instance specifying the time and place for further consideration of the
matter and imposing the charge until that time.   Unless the judgment debtor
pays the debt or shows cause at that time the order will be made absolute.   The
charge so created is a general equitable charge and the judgment creditor should
register it in the Land Charges Registry under the provisions of the Land
Charges Act 1925.   There are two important advantages of registration; a
purchaser takes the land subject to the charge (registration amounting to notice)
and priority is obtained over subsequent chargees.   A land charge may be
enforced by an order for sale in the Chancery Division.[2]

(2) If the judgment debtor has government stock or stock or shares in any
registered company these cannot be seized in execution of a writ of *fi.-fa.*
because a share certificate is not a negotiable instrument.   It is simply evidence of
obligations owed by the company which has issued it to the person named in the
certificate.   The judgment creditor's proper course is to apply for an order nisi
creating a charge over the shares.[3]   The effect of such an order is that no subsequent disposition by the judgment debtor is valid as against the judgment
creditor.   Unless the judgment debtor shows cause the charging order is made
absolute.   There is no provision for registering a charge on securities corresponding to the registration of land charges.   The judgment creditor, to prevent
a disposition of the securities by the judgment debtor, must serve on the company in which the shares are held a "stop notice".   The effect is that the company
on whom the notice is served must not register a transfer of the shares without
serving notice on the judgment creditor, who may apply to the Chancery
Division for an order prohibiting the transfer.[4]   After the expiration of six
months from the charging order nisi the judgment creditor may proceed to
realise his charge by an order for sale obtainable in the Chancery Division.

(3) By the 1965 Rules a new power was conferred upon the court to impose
a charge on any money in court in which the judgment debtor has a beneficial
interest.[5] This might occur, for example, where the judgment debtor has made
a payment into court as security for costs.   The court may make a "stop order"
prohibiting any dealing with the whole or any part of the funds in question.
Application for such an order is by summons in the cause or matter relating to
the funds in court or, if there is no such cause or matter, by originating summons.[6]   The summons must be served on every person whose interest may be
affected by the order and on the Accountant General.   The judgment creditor

---

[1] O. 50, r. 1.   This was introduced by the Administration of Justice Act 1956, s. 35 (1)
to replace the old writ of *elegit*. If the land is owned by the judgment debtor jointly with
some other person (his wife, for example) his interest is, of course, an interest in the
proceeds of sale under the express or statutory trust for sale and is not, therefore, "an
interest in land" and cannot be made the subject of a charging order; *Irani Finance, Ltd.*
v. *Singh*, [1971] Ch. 59; [1970] 3 All E.R. 199. However, distinguish cases in which the
judgment is obtained against *both* of the joint owners, in which case (since they own the
legal estate as well as the beneficial interests under the trust for sale) a charging order may
be made: *National Westminister Bank, Ltd.* v. *Allen*, [1971] 2 Q.B. 718; [1971] 3 All
E.R. 201.
[2] O. 31, r. 1.
[3] O. 50, r. 2.
[4] O. 50, r. 15.
[5] O. 50, r. 8.
[6] O. 50, r. 10.

may enforce his charge by applying by summons for an order for payment out of the money or so much of it as is sufficient to satisfy his charge.[1]

(4) In relation to partnership property the sheriff cannot levy execution upon property belonging to a partnership in which the debtor is a partner (unless the judgment is against the firm). Nonetheless the judgment creditor may apply by summons to the master for an order charging the partner's interest in the partnership property.[2] The jurisdiction to create such a charge derives from section 23 of the Partnership Act 1890. The creation of a charge on a partnership interest gives the other partners the option of purchasing the interest charged.[3] Failing this the judgment creditor may apply by summons for the appointment of a receiver who will receive on behalf of the judgment creditor money accruing from the debtor's interest in the partnership.[4]

Appointment of a receiver by way of equitable execution.[5]—This is a method of enforcement directed at the interception of certain classes of income and profits before they reach the debtor so that he does not have the opportunity of disposing of them to the detriment of the judgment creditor. The judgment creditor may apply by summons or motion to the court to appoint some person as a receiver to receive income such as rents or profits in respect of any interest in land, legal or equitable, or of any interest in chattels which could not be reached by a writ of *fi.-fa.*[6] It should be stressed, however, that a receiver cannot be appointed to receive the judgment debtor's future earnings of employment for, as stated earlier, there is no direct means of attaching earnings in the Queen's Bench Division.

Before appointing a receiver the court will consider whether the probable costs of the appointment are justified by the amount claimed and the amount likely to be recovered by the receiver, and may direct an enquiry on these matters before making an appointment.[7] The general powers and duties of receivers appointed by the court are contained in Order 30. The receiver is usually required to provide a guarantee as security for what he receives as receiver or, if the amount for which the security is given does not exceed £1,000, an undertaking.[8] The receiver is allowed a proper remuneration which is fixed by the court. His obligation is to submit accounts to the court for approval as and when ordered to do so and to pay into court the amounts shown by his accounts to be due.[9]

Prior to 1971, committal for contempt of court was an indirect means of enforcing a judgment debt. However section 11 of the Administration of Justice Act 1970, limited the jurisidiction of the High Court to commit to prison in respect of non-payment of a debt due under a judgment or order to

---

[1] O. 49, r. 9.

[2] O. 81, r. 10.

[3] Partnership Act 1890, s. 23 (3).

[4] O. 51, r. 3; O. 30; *infra.*

[5] O. 51, r. 3. The expression "equitable execution" is explained by the fact that this method of enforcement originated in the Court of Chancery. It is, however, misleading since it is not confined to equitable interests, nor is it a method of execution. It is a method of enforcement alternative to execution: see *Re Shepherd* (1889), 43 Ch.D. 131, at p. 137.

[6] Administration of Justice Act 1956, s. 36; *Morgan* v. *Hunt,* [1914] 2 K.B. 188.

[7] O. 51, r. 1.

[8] O. 30, r. 2.

[9] O. 30, rr. 3–5.

cases of default in respect of maintenance orders. Since these orders are invariably made in the Family Division, committal in the Queen's Bench Division for non-payment of a debt is effectively abolished (though, as will be seen, it remains a sanction for failure to comply with orders other than orders for the payment of money).

There remains, however, one process of contempt in respect of failure to pay judgment debts—the procedure by writ of sequestration.

Writ of sequestration[1]—In cases of contempt of court a committal order is sometimes accompanied by a writ of sequestration. The two have much in common in that they are both indirect methods of enforcement being in the nature of punitive measures. As indicated above, although committal to prison in respect of a judgment debt (other than a maintenance order) has been abolished, a writ of sequestration may still issue in respect of continuous failure to comply with an order for the payment of money, although the procedure is very rarely used in such cases, save occasionally against corporate bodies. A writ of sequestration may issue in any case in which a person refuses or neglects to do an act within a specified time or disobeys an order requiring him to abstain from doing some act.[1] The writ commissions not less than four persons to enter upon and take possession of all the real and personal estate of the judgment debtor and to keep the same under sequestration until the debtor complies with the judgment. The procedure on application is by notice of motion for leave to issue the writ stating the grounds of the application and accompanied by an affidavit in support.[2] The application must be heard in open court.[3]

A writ of sequestration is a practical alternative to committal where the judgment debtor is a corporation and the writ may issue, with leave, against the property of any director or other officer of the body.

b Other methods of enforcing judgments for the payment of money

County court enforcement—A judgment of the High Court for the payment of money may be enforced in a county court as if it were a judgment of the county court.[4] This is done by registering the judgment in the county court for the district where the debtor resides. There are two methods of enforcement available in county courts which are not available in the Queen's Bench Division—judgment summonses and attachment of earnings orders. The primary advantage of the judgment summons, as opposed to the power of the High Court to require a debtor to attend an examination as to his means under Order 48, rule 1, is that the county court has power to make an order for payment by instalments in the first instance. Secondly, an attachment of earnings order may now be obtained, under the provisions of the Attachment of Earnings Act 1971, in a county court in respect of a High Court judgment debt. Both of these methods of enforcement are extremely practical in relation to debtors

---

[1] O. 45, r. 5.
[2] O. 46, r. 5.
[3] Except in the special cases set out in O. 52, r. 6 where the application may be heard in private, notably where the case involves the wardship, adoption, guardianship, custody or maintenance of infants, proceedings relating to mental patients, cases where in secret process, discovery of inventions is involved or where it appears to the court that in the interests of the administration of justice or for reasons of national security the application should be heard in private.
[4] Administration of Justice Act 1956, s. 39; County Courts Act 1959, s. 139.

who have insufficient assets to satisfy the judgment but who have earnings out of which the debt, or at least part of it, might be recoverable.[1]

Bankruptcy—Where the debtor's total debts amount to at least £50 the judgment creditor may serve upon him a bankruptcy notice calling upon him to pay the judgment debt within seven days. Failure to comply by the judgment debtor constitutes an "act of bankruptcy" and the judgment creditor may proceed to institute bankruptcy proceedings.[2] Bankruptcy proceedings are, in general, an unsatisfactory method of enforcement though the mere threat of bankruptcy proceedings may be a sufficient sanction where the judgment debtor is a person, such as a solicitor, whose livelihood cannot survive bankruptcy.

2 Judgments and orders other than for the payment of money

a *Judgments for possession of land*[3]

A judgment or order for the giving of possession of land may be enforced by any one or more of the following three methods:

(1) *Writ of possession*—This is the direct method of enforcement. It directs the sheriff to enter the land and cause the plaintiff to have possession of it. The writ cannot be issued without leave,[4] application for which is *ex parte* on affidavit, and leave cannot be granted unless it is shown that every person in actual possession of the whole or any part of the land has received sufficient notice of the proceedings to enable him to apply to the court for any relief to which he may be entitled, such as relief against forfeiture.[5] In practice judgments or orders for the possession of land are always enforced in this way.

(2) *Order of committal*; and (3) *writ of sequestration* are, in theory at least, indirect methods of enforcement but are almost never employed in this context. The procedure on application for leave to issue a writ of sequestration has already been noted; committal procedure is considered below.

b *Judgments for delivery of goods*[6]

The appropriate writ of execution for a judgment for the delivery of goods depends upon whether or not the judgment contains an alternative provision for payment of the assessed value of the goods.

Writ of specific delivery—This is the appropriate writ where the judgment orders the delivery of specific goods without an alternative provision for the payment of their assessed value. It directs the sheriff to seize the goods described in the writ and deliver them to the plaintiff.

Writ of delivery—This is appropriate where the judgment orders the delivery of goods with an alternative provision for payment of their assessed

---

[1] For details of procedure see p. 325, *post*.
[2] Bankruptcy Act 1914, s. 1 (1) (*a*).
[3] O. 45, r. 3.
[4] Except where the judgment or order was given or made in a mortgage action (O. 45, r. 3 (2)) or where the order was made in summary proceedings for possession of land against trespassers following the issue of an originating summons under Order 113 (O. 113, r. 7); as to this procedure, see p. 295, *ante*.
[5] O. 45, r. 3 (3).
[6] O. 45, r. 4.

value. The writ directs the sheriff to seize the goods described and deliver them to the plaintiff and, if he cannot obtain the goods, to levy execution upon the goods and chattels of the defendant to an extent sufficient to realise the assessed value of the goods. If the alternative course is adopted the writ has the same effect as a writ of *fi.-fa.*

Whether a writ of delivery or a writ of specific delivery is issued the sheriff is authorised to enforce by execution the payment of any money ordered to be paid by way of damages or costs by the judgment or order which is to be enforced by the writ together with the costs of execution and interest. *Order of committal* and *writ of sequestration* are theoretically available as indirect methods of enforcement but, as in the case of orders for the possession of land, their use is generally inappropriate in this context.

c   Judgments to do or abstain from doing any act

Where the judgment or order requires the defendant to perform any act other than the payment of money or the delivery of goods or land or requires him to abstain from doing any act, it is enforceable only by: (1) *order of committal*; and (2) *writ of sequestration*.

The order to which these rules apply may have been, for example, an injunction (mandatory or prohibitory), an order to deliver an account, an order to produce a document or an order to answer an interrogatory.

Procedure by writ of sequestration has already been noted. In cases of contempt a writ of sequestration is an appropriate method of enforcement against a corporate body and is often joined with a committal order in respect of the officers of the corporate body.[1]

Committal orders—A committal order is an order committing a person to prison for contempt of court. An order may be made where a person required by a judgment or order to do an act within a time specified in the judgment or order refuses or neglects to do it within that time,[2] or a person disobeys a judgment or order requiring him to abstain from doing an act. A master or registrar has no power to make a committal order. The order is made by a judge following a motion in open court.[3] Notice of motion must have been served on the person sought to be committed together with a copy of the affidavit which must support the application. Personal service is generally required.[4] Committal may be either for a fixed period or for an indefinite term in which case it will last until the court deems that the contemnor has "purged his contempt" and releases him, generally on his undertaking to perform (or abstain from repeating, as the case may be) the act in respect of which he was committed.

It was formerly held that a person might not be committed for a mere neglect

---

[1] See, for example, *Worthington* v. *Ad Lib Club, Ltd.*, [1965] Ch. 236; [1964] 3 All E.R. 674.

[2] Save where the act is the payment of money, in which case (except in the case of maintenance orders) there is no power of committal (Administration of Justice Act 1970, s. 11); see p. 307, *ante.*

[3] Except in the cases set out in O. 52, r. 6 in which the court may sit in private; see p. 308 (n), *ante.*

[4] O. 52, r. 4.

as opposed to a "wilful and contumacious disobedience of a court order".[1] However in *Knight* v. *Clifton*[2] the Court of Appeal rejected this principle and asserted that in proceedings for committal for breach of an order of the court there is no need to prove that the conduct in question was wilful or contumacious; when an injunction prohibits an act, the performance of that act is a contempt irrespective of questions of intention unless otherwise stated on the face of the order.

---

[1] See, for example, *Worthington* v. *Ad Lib Club, Ltd.*, [1965] Ch. 236; [1964] 3 All E.R. 674.

[2] [1971] Ch. 700; [1971] 2 All E.R. 378, disapproving *Worthington* v. *Ad Lib Club, Ltd.* (*supra*); see also *Re Mileage Conference of Tyre Manufacturers' Agreement*, [1966] 2 All E.R. 849; [1966] 1 W.L.R. 1137 in which breach of an undertaking was held to be contempt where the persons concerned had taken all reasonable care to avoid a breach.

CHAPTER 22

Procedure in County Courts

A CONSTITUTION AND JURISDICTION OF COUNTY COURTS

1 Origins and constitution

It will be recalled that one of the principal deficiencies of the English legal system, until the reforms of the nineteenth century, was the lack of a system of courts to deal with civil actions involving only a small amount of money.[1] As a result, the modern county courts were established by the County Courts Act 1846. The upper limit of the new courts' jurisdiction was originally fixed at £20 but this figure has been progressively increased and presently stands at £750 in most cases. The jurisdiction of the county courts is now principally contained in the County Courts Act 1959 (as amended). Procedure in the county courts is regulated by the County Court Rules made by a Rule Committee under powers conferred by the Act.[2] The rules presently in force are the County Court Rules 1936 (as amended). These and other rules relating to county court practice and procedure are to be found in the County Court Practice (the "Green Book") which, although not an official publication, is accepted as authoritative in the same way as the White Book is accepted in the Supreme Court.

England and Wales is divided into some 400 districts each having its own county court. These courts are, for administrative convenience, grouped into 63 circuits with one or more judges presiding over each circuit. Each court has a sitting at least once a month.[3]

a Judges of county courts

The office of county court judge, as such, was abolished by the Courts Act 1971 and on the date on which that Act came into operation, January 1st, 1972, all

---

[1] See p. 55, ante.

[2] Section 102. In any case not expressly provided for in the Act or Rules, the principles of High Court procedure apply; see *Williamson* v. *Rider*, [1963] 1 Q.B. 89; [1962] 2 All E.R. 268.

[3] Section 2 of the County Courts Act 1846 provided that these matters might be determined by the Lord Chancellor by statutory instrument. These are contained in the County Courts District Order 1949, as amended (*S.I.* 1949 No. 2058).

existing county court judges automatically became Circuit judges.[1] Although every Circuit judge is, by virtue of his office, enabled to sit in any county court the Lord Chancellor is bound to assign one or more Circuit judges to each county court district.[2]

b Registrars

These are appointed by the Lord Chancellor and must be solicitors of at least 7 years' standing.[3] The county court registrar exercises both an administrative and a judicial function. In his administrative capacity he maintains the court records, arranges for the issue and service of summonses, accounts for money paid into court and exercises a large number of similar functions. In practice he delegates much of this work to subordinate court officers, notably the clerks and bailiffs. The scope of his judicial function is narrower than that of the judge. He deals with interlocutory matters and the taxation of costs. With leave of the judge of the court he has the full jurisdiction of the judge in any action where the defendant does not appear at the hearing, or where the claim is admitted. He may also try actions, unless the parties object, where the claim does not exceed £75 and any other action with the consent of the parties.[4]

2 Jurisdiction

Because county courts are the creation of statute, their jurisdiction derives entirely from statute. The general jurisdiction of the county court is to be found in the County Courts Act 1959, as amended. Nevertheless extensive jurisdiction is conferred upon the county court by other statutes. This latter jurisdiction is usually concurrent with the High Court or magistrates' courts although in a few cases it is exclusive to the county court.[5]

a Jurisdiction under the County Courts Act 1959

The jurisdiction of the county court under the 1959 Act may be classified as follows.

(1) *Actions founded on contract or tort* where the debt, demand or damage claimed does not exceed £750, except actions for defamation.[6] The plaintiff may not divide his cause of action so as to bring separate actions on the same facts claiming less than £750 in each. He can, however, abandon his right to recover any damages in excess of £750.[7] In an action for detinue for the return of specific goods the county court has jurisdiction if the value of the goods claimed does not exceed £750. Where the plaintiff's claim is for an injunction

---

1 Courts Act 1971, s. 16; Sch. 2; as to the position of Circuit judges, see p. 168, *ante*.
2 *Ibid.*, s. 20. In addition every judge of the Court of Appeal, every judge of the High Court and every Recorder (though at the time of writing the provision to this effect is not yet in operation) is capable of sitting as a county court judge if he consents so to do and may be required, under s. 20 (3), so to act on such occasions as the Lord Chancellor considers desirable. It is difficult to envisage any judge of the Court of Appeal or High Court sitting as a county court judge.
3 County Courts Act 1959, s. 21 (1).
4 C.C.R., O. 23. The amount was raised from £30 to £75 by the Administration of Justice Act 1969, s. 9.
5 For example, under the Rent Act 1968 and the Race Relations Act 1968.
6 County Courts Act 1959, s. 39 (1) as amended by the Administration of Justice Act 1969, ss. 1, 2, which raised the limit from £500 to £750.
7 *Ibid.*, s. 41 (1).

or a declaration the court has not, in the absence of agreement between the parties, jurisdiction to try the action unless there is also a claim for damages not exceeding £750. Accordingly if the plaintiff seeks, for example, an injunction to compel the defendant to abate a nuisance, he must claim damages, even if only nominal, to give the county court jurisdiction.

Section 42 of the Act enables the parties to confer jurisdiction on a particular county court in any action which, if commenced in the High Court, would have been assigned to the Queen's Bench Division. This section operates to extend the jurisdiction of a particular county court to any action in contract or tort, including such actions as libel and slander, up to any amount. The parties must agree to this increased jurisdiction by memorandum signed by the parties or their solicitors.

(2) *Actions for the recovery of land* or where the title to any hereditament or right over land is in question, where the net annual value for rating does not exceed £400.[1]

(3) *Equity proceedings* where the sum involved does not exceed £5,000, or more by written memorandum signed by the parties or their solicitors, and then only where the proceedings fall within certain specified categories. These categories are set out in section 52 of the Act and include: the administration of estates of deceased persons, the declaration and execution of trusts, the foreclosure and redemption of mortgages,[2] the rectification or cancellation of deeds, the maintenance and advancement out of trust funds of infants and proceedings for relief against fraud or mistake. These categories cannot be extended even if both parties are willing to extend them.

(4) *Admiralty proceedings*, but only in certain specified proceedings and only in county courts which have been appointed by the Lord Chancellor to exercise jurisdiction in admiralty matters.[3] All these courts, with the exception of the Mayor's and City of London Court, are on or near the coast. The admiralty proceedings in question are set out in sections 1 and 2 of the Administration of Justice Act 1956. They include claims for damage to a ship or for damage to or loss of goods carried by sea, towage and pilotage disputes. The limit of jurisdiction is in each case £1,000 (or £3,500 in salvage claims), but this limit can be increased by memorandum of agreement, although the extent of the proceedings over which the county court has jurisdiction cannot be so increased.

(5) *Contentious probate proceedings* where there is an application for a grant or revocation of probate or letters of administration, where the net value of the estate at the time of death was less than £1,000. The applicant must swear an affidavit containing the value of the estate and also the place of abode of the deceased, since only the county court for that district has jurisdiction.[4]

---

[1] County Courts Act 1959, ss. 48 (1), (2), 51, as amended by the County Courts (Jurisdiction) Act 1963, s. 1 (1). The title to land may come in question in an action which is not for the recovery of the land but only for damages, for example in trespass, where the defendant sets up his title as a defence. The value for rating is determined by reference to the valuation list in force at the time that the proceedings are commenced (s. 200 (1)).

[2] Mortgage proceedings outside the financial limit may nevertheless be within the county court jurisdiction if there is a claim for the recovery of land having a net annual value for rating not exceeding £400; see *West Penwith R.D.C.* v. *Gunnell*, [1968] 2 All E.R. 1005; [1968], 1 W.L.R. 1153.

[3] County Courts Act 1959, ss. 55, 56.

[4] *Ibid.*, s. 62.

(6) *Set-off and counterclaim.* Where there is a counterclaim, or set-off and counterclaim, which involves a claim outside the jurisdiction of the county court, such as a claim in respect of libel or a claim in tort for more than £750, the Act expressly provides that the county court shall have jurisdiction to hear and determine the whole proceedings, notwithstanding.[1] However, in such a case, any party may apply to the High Court for an order that the proceedings be transferred in whole or in part to the High Court.[2] The master may then order the whole proceedings to be determined in the High Court, or in a county court, or that the counterclaim, or set-off and counterclaim, be transferred to the High Court leaving the plaintiff's claim to be determined in the county court.

b Jurisdiction under other statutes

Apart from the County Courts Act 1959, there are more than 150 statutes which confer jurisdiction in certain matters either on the county courts generally, or upon particular county courts. Of these mention may be made of the Rent Act 1968 and the Hire-Purchase Act 1965 both of which are fertile sources of county court litigation. Special attention should be drawn to the Matrimonial Causes Act 1967 which conferred jurisdiction upon those county courts nominated by the Lord Chancellor as "divorce county courts" to hear undefended matrimonial causes.[3]

B PROCEDURE IN THE COUNTY COURT

1 Ordinary actions

a Choice of county court

Unlike that of the High Court, the jurisdiction of county courts is local. This means that the plaintiff must usually commence proceedings:

(1) in the court for the district in which the defendant or one of the defendants resides or carries on business; or

(2) in the court for the district where the cause of action arose wholly or in part.[4]

If the plaintiff commences proceedings in any other county court the judge of that court may transfer the proceedings to a court which does have jurisdiction, order them to be struck out, or allow them to continue in his court.[5]

b Parties

The County Court Rules regulating the choice and joinder of parties are parallel to the provisions of the Rules of the Supreme Court. Thus two or more persons may be joined as plaintiffs or defendants if their rights or liabilities arise out of

---

[1] *Ibid.*, s. 65 (3); *Hardwicke* v. *Gilroy*, [1944] K.B. 460; [1944] 1 All E.R. 521.
[2] *Ibid.*, s. 65 (1), (2).
[3] See p. 329, *post*, for a brief outline of procedure under the Matrimonial Causes Rules 1971.
[4] O. 2, r. 1 (1). Oddly enough the matrimonial jurisdiction of divorce county courts is not local; a petition may be filed in any divorce county court (Matrimonial Causes Rules, 1971, r. 12 (1)).
[5] O. 16, r. 4.

the same transaction or series of transactions and, if separate actions were brought, any common question of law or fact would arise.[1]

Parties to whom special rules of procedure apply in the High Court, such as partners, companies and persons under disability, are in a similar position in the county court. An infant must generally, as in the High Court, sue by his "next friend" who must file an undertaking to be responsible for costs.[2] However, an infant may sue in his own name for a sum not exceeding £750 due to him for wages or piece work or for work as a servant.[3]

c Issue and service of the summons

The plaintiff or his solicitor commences an ordinary action by filing in the court office a request for the summons (formerly called a praecipe) setting out the names, addresses and descriptions of all parties and the nature and amount of the claim. He must also file particulars of claim and the sum claimed with a copy for each defendant. Upon filing these documents the registrar issues to the plaintiff a plaint note containing the title of the action, the reference number of the plaint and a date and time for the return day. He also prepares, from the plaintiff's request, and issues a summons to which are annexed the particulars of claim. The summons and particulars are then served on every defendant at least 21 clear days before the return day.[4] The defendant is also served with forms of admission, defence and counterclaim.

A county court summons may be served by the plaintiff or his agent, in which case he must within 3 days of service file an affidavit of service,[5] but it is usually served by the county court bailiff. For this reason the rules relating to service are less stringent than those applicable in the High Court. The summons may be served by delivering it to the defendant personally, by leaving it at his residence or place of business, or by ordinary prepaid post by leave of the registrar or if the plaintiff so requests.[6] The defendant's solicitor may accept service on the defendant's behalf, in which case he must indorse on the bailiff's copy summons a statement to this effect. Substituted service may be ordered by the registrar following application by the plaintiff on affidavit. A summons may not be served out of the jurisdiction without leave of the judge. The circumstances in which leave may be granted are similar (though not identical) to those contained in Order 11, rule 1 of the Rules of the Supreme Court.[7]

d Defence

A defendant who is served with a summons has open to him the following courses of action.[8]

---

[1] O. 5, r. 1.

[2] O. 11.

[3] County Courts Act 1959, s. 80 (as amended).

[4] O. 8, r. 8 (4).

[5] O. 8, r. 2.

[6] O. 8, r. 8 (2). Service by post is deemed to be effected at the time at which the letter would be delivered in the ordinary course of post (Interpretation Act 1889, s. 26). Consequently service may be deemed to be validly effected even though the defendant never actually receives the summons. The defendant's remedy is to apply to set aside judgment, though this is a matter of discretion rather than of right; see *Cooper* v. *Scott-Farnell*, [1969] 1 All E.R. 178; [1969] 1 W.L.R. 120.

[7] O. 8, r. 41.

[8] O. 9.

(1) He may within 14 days of service pay into court the whole or any part of the claim together with costs on a fixed scale.[1] If the whole sum claimed is paid in, proceedings will be stayed. If a lesser sum is paid in the plaintiff will be notified by the registrar of this payment. If he accepts the sum he must, within 7 days of receiving notice, himself deliver or send notice of acceptance to the registrar and to every defendant. The action will then be stayed and the defendant will not be liable for any further costs. If the plaintiff does not accept the payment the action proceeds but, as in the High Court, if the plaintiff recovers less or no more than the amount paid in he will normally be held liable for all costs subsequent to the date of payment in.

(2) Where the defendant admits the whole or any part of the claim but desires time to pay he may, within 14 days, file the form of admission attached to the summons and state how he proposes to pay the admitted sum, for example by fixed instalments. The registrar sends notice of this admission to the plaintiff who must, within 8 days, inform the registrar whether or not he accepts the offer. If he does accept, the registrar will enter judgment accordingly. If he does not accept, the registrar must inform the defendant whereupon the action proceeds.[2]

(3) If the defendant denies liability or wishes to plead a set-off or counterclaim he must, within 14 days, file the forms of defence and counterclaim if appropriate. The registrar will serve copies of these upon the plaintiff.[3]

(4) The defendant may appear on the return day without having filed a defence and dispute the plaintiff's claim. However he will be ordered to pay any extra costs incurred by his failure to file a defence.[4]

e Pre-trial review and other interlocutory proceedings

In the case of an ordinary action (other than an action for recovery of land) the return day on the summons will be, unless the court otherwise directs, a day fixed for the preliminary consideration of the action by the registrar, known as a "pre-trial review".[5] The pre-trial review is analogous to the summons for directions in High Court actions[6] and the registrar is enjoined to "consider the course of the proceedings and give all such directions as appear to him necessary or desirable for securing the just, expeditious and economical disposal of the action".[7] In particular the registrar must endeavour to secure that the parties make all such admissions and agreements as ought reasonably to be made by them and may record in the order any admission or agreement so made or any refusal to make any admission or agreement. Evidence on the pre-trial review may be given by affidavit. If the defendant does not appear on the pre-trial review and has not delivered an admission or defence, the registrar may, if he thinks fit, enter judgment for the plaintiff; if the defendant does not appear on the pre-trial review and has delivered a defence, the plaintiff may proceed to

---

[1] O. 11, r. 7.
[2] O. 9, r. 1.
[3] O. 9, r. 4.
[4] O. 9, r. 4 (4). The Court may, in addition, make an order debarring the defendant from defending altogether (O. 9, r. 4 (8); O. 13, r. 3 (2)).
[5] O. 6, r. 3 (3), added by the County Court (New Procedure) Rules 1971 with effect from 1st March 1972.
[6] See p. 284, *ante.*
[7] O. 21, r. 1.

prove his case (generally by affidavit) and may ask for judgment in the same way as if the defendant had not appeared at the trial.

Every party must apply on the pre-trial review for any interlocutory order which he seeks and if he does not and makes a subsequent interlocutory application, he will usually have to pay the extra costs incurred. Interlocutory orders are, in practice, required rather less frequently than in High Court actions.

The interlocutory orders which the county court has power to make are similar to the orders which may be made in the High Court, the following being frequently encountered—third party proceedings,[1] further and better particulars of claim,[2] discovery and inspection of documents, interrogatories[3] and amendment of claim and defence.[4]   After giving all necessary directions the registrar must, if the action remains to be tried, fix a day for the trial and give notice thereof to every party.[5]

The pre-trial review operates, therefore, both as a summons for directions in actions which are destined to proceed to trial and as a means of the plaintiff obtaining judgment (either by default or by proving his case, as above) in other cases, without the need of a proper trial in open court.

f   Premature determination of proceedings

A high proportion of actions never come to trial because they are prematurely determined by agreement, by the defendant admitting liability, by the plaintiff discontinuing his claim, or by a judgment or order given or made on a pre-trial review.

If the parties arrive at a settlement, the plaintiff must give notice of this to the registrar who notes it in the minute book. The action is thus determined. However the consent of the court is required to a settlement of an action by or on behalf of a person under disability.[6]   Some actions are brought solely for obtaining the court's sanction for a settlement which has already been reached. The particulars of claim in such an action contain only an outline of the claim, the terms of the proposed settlement and a request for the court's approval, which will be given in chambers by the judge or registrar.[7]   The judge or registrar will direct how the money is to be dealt with; in the case of an infant the money is usually paid into court and invested or applied for his benefit until he attains his majority, when he can demand payment of the capital.[8]

Where the parties cannot reach a settlement the defendant may pay money into court at any time before judgment.[9]   The registrar sends to the plaintiff notice of this payment. If the plaintiff takes the money out of court proceedings are stayed and the plaintiff may tax and sign judgment for his costs. If the plaintiff does not accept the amount paid in, the effect is similar to that of a pay-

---

[1] O. 12.
[2] O. 7, r. 9.
[3] O. 14.
[4] O. 15.
[5] O. 21, r. 9.
[6] O. 5, r. 19.
[7] O. 5, r. 19 (2).
[8] *Re Embleton*, [1947] K.B. 142; [1946] 2 All E.R. 542.
[9] O. 11, r. 1. His payment is not deemed to be made with an admission of liability so that the defendant need not accompany the payment with a notice denying liability.

ment into court in the High Court. Thus, except where the payment accompanies a plea of tender before action, the court must not be told of its existence until all questions of liability and damage have been decided.[1] If the damages recovered by the plaintiff are no greater than the amount paid in, the plaintiff will usually, as in the High Court, be ordered to pay the whole costs of the action subsequent to the date of payment in.

The plaintiff may, at any time before trial, discontinue his action by giving notice in the prescribed form to the registrar and to the defendant, who will be entitled to his costs incurred before receiving notice of discontinuance.[2]

g Trial

Unless it is settled or discontinued or disposed of at the pre-trial review the action comes on for trial on the day fixed. If the plaintiff does not appear when the case is called his action will be struck out and he will have to apply to have it reinstated at another time. If the defendant does not appear the trial may proceed in his absence and judgment may be entered against him. The trial will be before the registrar, the judge or, very rarely, the judge and a jury. In busy county courts there is a judge's court and a registrar's court. It is then usually the practice to set down actions where the claim is less than £75 and actions where the defendant is not expected to appear in the registrar's list, other actions being set down in the judge's list. The county court jury is obsolescent. No party has a right to claim trial with a jury unless there is in issue a charge of fraud against him or claim in respect of libel, slander, malicious prosecution or false imprisonment unless the trial requires any prolonged examination of documents or accounts or any scientific or local investigation which cannot conveniently be made with a jury.[3] In any other case he may be granted a jury, 8 in number. In fact actions which would be heard by a jury are usually heard in the High Court. The conduct of the trial is similar to that in the High Court. Solicitors, however, have a right of audience in the county court and frequently appear. Also, if the action is not determined in one day, the registrar must fix another date to continue the hearing which will not necessarily be the next day.

If the defendant admits the plaintiff's claim or does not appear judgment will be entered for the plaintiff. Where this judgment is for the payment of money the court may order the sum to be paid forthwith or within a specified time, or may order payment by fixed instalments.[4]

If the plaintiff does not succeed in proving his case the court may either give judgment for the defendant or non-suit the plaintiff. The non-suit has long been abolished in the High Court but still exists in the county court. It differs from a judgment for the defendant in that it does not decide the case affirmatively against the plaintiff, so that he is not estopped from bringing a subsequent action on the same facts. However a second action may be stayed until the

---

[1] O. 11, r. 15. The rule is not mandatory and breach does not *ipso facto* necessitate a new trial: *Millensted* v. *Grosvenor House (Park Lane), Ltd.*, [1937] 1 K.B. 717; [1937] 1 All E.R. 736.

[2] O. 18, r. 1.

[3] County Courts Act 1959, s. 94 (as amended). The application for an order for trial by jury must be made not less than 10 clear days before the return day: O. 13, r. 14.

[4] County Courts Act 1959, s. 99.

plaintiff has complied with an order for costs made against him in the former action.[1]

2 Default actions

Where the plaintiff claims only a debt or liquidated demand he must (subject to exceptions noted below) proceed by default action rather than ordinary action.[2] The essential feature of this procedure is that if the defendant fails to take appropriate steps the plaintiff is entitled to enter judgment in default without the need for a trial.

A default action cannot be commenced to recover unliquidated damages. It follows, therefore, that it cannot, as a rule, be used in an action in tort. However, by way of exception, it is expressly provided by Order 49, rule 5 that a claim for the cost of repairs to a vehicle in respect of damage alleged to have been sustained in an accident on land due to the defendant's negligence is, unless the court otherwise orders, to be treated as a liquidated demand. In addition, the following actions for a debt or liquidated demand must, exceptionally, be commenced by ordinary rather than default summons, that is to say actions brought:

(1) against a person under disability;
(2) by a moneylender for debt or interest;
(3) to recover money secured by mortgage or charge;
(4) on a claim arising out of a hire-purchase agreement unless the claim is only for arrears of instalments; or
(5) to recover interest accruing after the commencement of the action.[2]

A default action is commenced in the same way as an ordinary action, except that a special form of request must be used. The registrar issues a default summons which is served on the defendant in the same way as an ordinary summons. It may, however, be noted that a default summons contains no date for the return day. Particulars of claim and forms of defence, counterclaim and admission are sent to the defendant with the summons. The course the action now follows depends upon the defendant.

If the defendant, within 14 days of service inclusive of the day of service, delivers at the court office a defence or counterclaim the registrar must fix a date for the hearing or, if he thinks fit, a day for a pre-trial review (in which event there will be a pre-trial review in the same way as in an ordinary action followed, if the action is not disposed of at the pre-trial review, by a hearing on a date fixed by registrar), and give 14 clear days' notice thereof to the parties. He must also deliver to the plaintiff a copy of the defence or counterclaim.[3]

If the defendant, within the same period, delivers an admission of the whole or any part of the claim containing a request for time to pay, without a

---

[1] O. 23, r. 3. At any time before the facts are found the plaintiff has an absolute right to elect to be non-suited; thereafter the court has a discretion: *Clack* v. *Arthurs Engineering, Ltd.*, [1959] 2 Q.B. 211; [1959] 2 All E.R. 503.

[2] O. 6, r. 2 (1). The rule was amended to its present form by the County Court (New Procedure) Rules 1971. The rule does not apply to Admiralty actions or "rent actions", as to which see *infra*.

[3] O. 10, r. 3.

counterclaim, the registrar must send notice of this to the plaintiff.[1] Within 8 days of receiving this notice the plaintiff must inform the registrar whether or not he accepts the amount admitted to be due and the proposals for payment, which may be by instalments. If the plaintiff does file notice of acceptance judgment will be entered accordingly without requiring the parties to appear. The defendant will be notified of this so that his offer in effect becomes a judgment debt payable in the time and manner proposed. If the plaintiff files notice of non-acceptance the registrar fixes a date for "disposal," which may take place in chambers, giving the parties 8 clear days' notice thereof. If the plaintiff fails to file notice of non-acceptance within 12 months of the date of service of the summons the action will be struck out.[2]

If the defendant does not within 14 days of service deliver a defence, counterclaim or admission or pay the amount claimed with costs into court, the plaintiff may, on proof of service of the summons, sign judgment in default. Herein lies the advantage of default procedure. The plaintiff signs judgment by producing the plaint note and filing the appropriate request with the registrar, whereupon judgment will be entered for the claim and costs.

As in the High Court, the defendant may have a default judgment set aside if he can explain his default and show that he has a triable defence, but he will have to pay the extra costs occasioned by his default.

Where proceedings which ought to have been brought by ordinary action are brought by default action or *vice versa*, the court may either strike out the proceedings or order them to continue in accordance with the procedure prescribed for an ordinary action.[3]

3 Rent actions

Much of the time of the average county court is taken up by landlords' actions for the recovery of premises and arrears of rent from tenants. Indeed the jurisdiction of county courts in actions for the recovery of possession of unfurnished dwellings which are within the rateable value limits of the Rent Act 1968 is virtually exclusive.

A new summary procedure for the recovery of arrears of rent from a tenant or former tenant who is still in occupation of the demised premises was introduced as from the 1st March 1972.[4] The action, known as a "rent action" is commenced by the filing of a special form of request for a summons in the court for the district in which the land is situated. The summons fixes a return day for the hearing, there being no pre-trial review, and must be served on the defendant not less than 7 clear days before the return day. There is no provision for the defendant to serve a defence or counterclaim and the usual forms of admission, defence and counterclaim are not sent to the defendant; nor is there any provision for his making an admission and a written request for time to pay. The form of summons simply requires the defendant to pay into court the whole of the claim (or such part as he admits) or to attend court on the return day, failing which judgment may be given in his absence.

---

[1] O. 10, r. 4.
[2] O. 10, r. 7.
[3] O. 6, r. 7 (3).
[4] By the County Court (New Procedure) Rules 1971.

4   Matters

Where, subject to any Act or Rule, the object of proceedings is to obtain relief against any person or to compel any person to do or abstain from doing any act, the proper method of proceeding is by action, the procedure for which has been described above. Proceedings in the county court which do not fall into this category are described as "matters" and are commenced by originating application unless any Act or Rule requires that they be commenced otherwise.[1]

An originating application may be likened to an originating summons in the High Court. It is appropriate where the applicant seeks an order of the court which does not amount to a claim for relief from another person. Thus the person who seeks an adoption order, a declaration of legitimacy, or an order under the Landlord and Tenant Acts will commence proceedings by originating application. Notice of the application must be served on the proper respondent; for example, an application for a declaration of legitimacy must be served on the Attorney-General and all persons whose interests might be affected by the declaration. If the respondent wishes to resist the application he must file an answer, following which there will be a hearing before the judge or registrar. Since there is no plaint, but only an application, the parties are described not as "plaintiff" and "defendant" but as "applicant" and "respondent".

5   Costs in the county court

The position as to costs between a party and his own solicitor has already been considered in connection with High Court litigation. As between the parties, the court has a judicial discretion over costs,[2] but as a rule the successful party will recover his costs from his opponent, as in the High Court.

a   Scales of costs

The essential distinction between High Court and county court costs is that the latter are fixed in amount by reference to scales according to the sum claimed or recovered in the action or, where the claim is not only a money claim, according to the discretion of the court.

For the regulation of solicitors' charges and disbursements, other than court fees, there are five scales of costs:

Exceeding £5 but not exceeding £20	Lower Scale
Exceeding £20 but not exceeding £50	Scale 1
Exceeding £50 but not exceeding £200	Scale 2
Exceeding £200 but not exceeding £500	Scale 3
Exceeding £500	Scale 4[3]

If the plaintiff succeeds the scale is determined by the amount for which he recovers judgment. If the plaintiff fails the scale is determined by the amount of the plaintiff's claim. The court has a discretion to award costs on a higher or lower scale than the one applicable in certain cases, notably if the judge certifies that a difficult question of law or fact is involved.[3] Where the claim is less than £20 the court cannot allow any solicitors' charges unless the judge

---

[1] O. 6, r. 4 (1). Other possible methods of commencing proceedings include petition, appeal and arbitration.

[2] O. 47, r. 1.

[3] O. 47, r. 5.

certifies that a difficult question of law or fact is involved,[1] though, provided the sum exceeds £5, there may be allowed in respect of solicitors' charges, the fixed costs stated on the summons together with the costs of enforcing any judgment or order otherwise than by warrant of execution.[2] No fee for counsel can be awarded where the defendant, in an action for money alone, files no defence and does not appear at the hearing, unless the judge issues a certificate for counsel at the trial.[3] The judge has no power to award a fixed sum by way of costs (except on the lower scale or by consent), although he may direct the registrar to allow or disallow any specific item on taxation.[4]

b   Assessment of costs

Certain items are fixed in amount. For example, when a summons is issued in an action where the only relief claimed is a sum of money liquidated or unliquidated, the court fee and the charges of the plaintiff's solicitor for the issue of the summons are fixed and are entered on the summons. Accordingly, if the defendant within 14 days of service pays the sum claimed and costs into court, or pays in a lesser sum with an admission of liability which the plaintiff accepts in satisfaction, the defendant is generally liable for no further costs beyond those stated on the summons. This may, of course, cause hardship to a plaintiff who has already incurred expense, for example by obtaining a medical report or by having particulars of claim settled by counsel. Where costs are on the Lower Scale they must be assessed at a lump sum.[5] In other cases the costs will be taxed according to the appropriate scale; the basis of taxation within the scale is similar to that applicable in the High Court so that taxation will almost always be on a "party and party" basis.[6] The registrar may fix and allow costs without taxation if the successful party so requests. Otherwise they must be taxed unless the parties agree an amount of costs in lieu of taxation.[7]

c   Taxation of costs

The registrar is the taxing officer of the court. The successful party must, within 14 days of the order for costs, lodge a bill of costs with the registrar and obtain an appointment for taxation. He must serve a copy of this bill on his opponent and give him not less than one clear day's notice of the appointment.[8] On taxation the registrar will allow, in accordance with the scale, a reasonable amount for each item incurred. The judge may, at the trial, expressly authorise the registrar to allow an amount in respect of certain items, such as counsel's fee, in excess of the scale maximum. In this event the registrar may allow such sum as he considers reasonable in respect of these items. Where an item is not provided for in the scales the registrar may or may not in his discretion make

---

[1] O. 47, rr. 13, 15.
[2] O. 47, rr. 5 (4), 13.
[3] O. 47, r. 20.
[4] O. 47, r. 17.
[5] The maximum figure on the Lower Scale is £8 in addition to court fees, witness allowances and £0.50 in respect of service of process by a solicitor (O. 47, r. 37 (3), Appendix E). It follows that Lower Scale litigation is extremely unremunerative for all concerned.
[6] O. 47, r. 38; see p. 302, *ante*.
[7] O. 47, r. 37.
[8] O. 47, r. 38 (1).

an allowance in respect of it. The registrar certifies the total amount due on taxation in his *allocatur* which is endorsed on the bill.

d   Review of taxation[1]

Any party not satisfied with a taxation may apply to the registrar to review his taxation; the application must set out the disputed items and the grounds of objection. The registrar will then certify in writing his reasons for allowing or disallowing the disputed items. If dissatisfied with this review, any party may apply to the judge for a review. The judge then has the equivalent powers of the registrar in his review. He cannot upset the discretion of the registrar unless the exercise of this discretion was based upon a wrong principle of law.[2] There is a further appeal to the Court of Appeal if a question of legal principle is involved.[3]

6   Execution and enforcement of judgments

a   Judgments for the payment of money

Where the judgment or order directs the payment of money, the methods of enforcing the judgment are similar to those available in the High Court, i.e. execution against the debtor's personal property, garnishee proceedings, appointment of a receiver, creation of a charge over the debtor's land, shares or partnership interest, and bankruptcy proceedings. Furthermore the important jurisdiction to make attachment of earnings orders under the Attachment of Earnings Act 1971, which in the High Court is limited to the enforcement of maintenance orders, is, in county courts, exercisable in respect of maintenance orders, judgment debts of £5 or more and administration orders.[4]

Finally mention may be made of the judgment summons. This was, until recently, a widely used procedure to enforce both county court and High Court judgments. However, as noted below, the drastic curtailment of the power to commit to prison for default in paying civil debts in favour of the power to make attachment of earnings orders has rendered judgment summonses inappropriate in all but a very few cases.

Execution—Execution is effected by warrant of execution issued to the county court bailiff which is in the nature of a writ of fieri facias.[5] The warrant directs the bailiff to execute upon the debtor's personal property for the judgment debt, costs and interest. The rules relating to property which is exempt from execution, method of execution and interpleader proceedings are similar to those in the High Court. A judgment creditor seeking the issue of a warrant of execution must file the appropriate praecipe in the court office. A notice is usually sent to the defendant telling him that a warrant has been issued and that if he pays the debt there will be no need to execute the warrant. This often

---

[1] O. 47, r. 42.
[2] *White* v. *Altrincham U.D.C.*, [1936] 2 K.B. 138; [1936] 1 All E.R. 923.
[3] *Goodman* v. *Blake* (1887), 19 Q.B.D. 77.
[4] Attachment of Earnings Act 1971, s. 1 (2); see p. 325, *post*. Under the same section, magistrates' courts have power to make attachment of earnings orders in respect of maintenance orders, fines and analogous impositions and legal aid contributions; accordingly the use of attachment of earnings orders to enforce ordinary judgment debts is confined to county courts.
[5] County Courts Act 1959, s. 120.

results in the warrant being paid out. As an alternative the plaintiff may agree to suspend the warrant on condition that the debt and costs are paid within a specified time or by instalments.[1] In fact most warrants are paid out or suspended in this way and only in a small proportion of cases does the warrant have to be executed. The warrant, once issued, remains in force for one year from the date of issue. The bailiff seizes sufficient goods to satisfy the warrant and either deposits them in a proper place, such as a warehouse or auction room, or takes "walking possession" of them. There will then be a sale of such goods as are sufficient to satisfy the judgment debt including costs. In order that the bailiff does not sell too much, he will have the goods "appraised", usually by a local auctioneer who also deals with the storage and sale of the goods. The sale is usually by public auction following advertisement and, where the execution is for a sum exceeding £20, must be by public auction unless the court directs otherwise.[2] If there are several warrants against the same debtor and it appears that the goods seized will not satisfy them all they take priority in accordance with their date of issue.[3] Priority is determined in the same way as between a warrant of execution and a writ of fi-fa from the High Court.[4]

The jurisdiction of the county courts is local. This rule applies to the county courts' jurisdiction over the execution of warrants. Thus where the debtor has property outside the jurisdiction of the county court from which the warrant against him was issued, the warrant must be sent to the registrar of the county court for that district, called the "foreign court", for execution.[5]

A judgment obtained in the High Court for the payment of money, whatever the sum, may be executed in the county court.[6] The execution creditor must file in the court for the district where execution is to be levied a praecipe together with an office copy of the judgment or order to be enforced.

Attachment of earnings—Prior to 1970, attachment of earnings orders could only be made in matrimonial causes under the provisions of the Maintenance Orders Act 1958. Following recommendations of the Payne Committee[7] the procedure was extended by the Administration of Justice Act 1970 to judgment debts generally in virtual substitution for the powers of committal to prison under the Debtors Act 1869, though, as noted below, the power of committal was retained in a few cases. The relevant provisions of the 1970 Act were repealed and consolidated by the Attachment of Earnings Act 1971.

An application for an attachment of earnings order may be made by the person entitled to the benefit of the judgment or order, where the relevant order is an administration order[8] by any of the creditors scheduled to the order or (where the application is for an order to secure maintenance payments) by the judgment debtor himself.[9] The application is generally to the court for the district in which the debtor resides and must be served, in the same manner as an

---

[1] If a suspended warrant has taken effect, there is no power to suspend it further: *Moore* v. *Lambeth County Court Registrar*, [1969] 1 All E.R. 782; [1969] 1 W.L.R. 141.
[2] County Courts Act 1959, s. 132.
[3] *Ibid,*, s. 120.
[4] *Ibid.*, s. 134.
[5] *Ibid.*, s. 138.
[6] *Ibid.*, s. 139.
[7] Cmnd. 3909 of 1969.
[8] *Infra.*
[9] Attachment of Earnings Act 1971, s. 3 (1).

ordinary summons, not less than 21 clear days before the return day. The debtor must then, within 14 days of service, complete and return a form containing full details of his employment, pay and income, financial liabilities and proposals for payment of the debt,[1] which proposals are notified to the applicant. The registrar may by notice require any person appearing to have the debtor in his employment to supply particulars of the debtor's earnings.

The application is heard by the registrar who may hear it in chambers, evidence being given by affidavit. If the debtor does not attend, the registrar may adjourn the hearing and notify the debtor of the date of the adjourned hearing; if the debtor then fails to attend or attends but refuses to give evidence, he may be imprisoned by the judge for up to 14 days.

An attachment of earnings order may be made in respect of any sums payable by way of wages or salary or by way of pension.[2]   The order requires the debtor's employer to make periodical deductions from the debtor's earnings and to pay them to the collecting officer of the court; the order specifies the "normal deduction rate" and the "protected earnings rate", the latter being the amount which the court decides the debtor must retain out of his earnings in any event.[3]   It is the duty of both debtor and employer to notify the court of changes in the debtor's employment. As long as an attachment of earnings order is in force, no execution for the recovery of the judgment debt may issue without the leave of the court.[4]

There was for some time a general opposition to the concept of attachment of earnings orders on the ground that a debtor might be prejudiced in his employment by his employer's knowledge that he was a debtor. This opposition has been overcome, no doubt as a result of acknowledgment of the fact that debt is not the social disgrace which it was in Victorian times and as a result of the expense and futility of keeping debtors in prison, though the power to imprison certain classes of recalcitrant debtors, notably husbands who will not maintain their wives and families, has been retained and is enforceable by judgment summons.

Judgment summons—This is a method of enforcing a judgment for the payment of money in that it enables the court to ascertain the debtor's means, to order payment of the debt by instalments (where the debt is a High Court debt it is not likely that the debtor will have had an opportunity to pay by instalments) and, as a final sanction, to imprison the debtor.

Imprisonment for civil debt as such was abolished by the Debtors Act 1869, section 4. However there remained a few cases under that Act in which a defaulting judgment debtor might be committed to prison. These are contained in section 5 of the Act which empowers any court to commit to prison for a term not exceeding six weeks or until payment of the sum due any person who defaults in paying a debt, or instalment of a debt, due from him under any order of that or any other competent court. This power can only be

---

[1] Attachment of Earnings Act 1971, s. 14; O. 25, r. 81: Form 404. Failure to comply with this or other requirements under the Act is an offence punishable as a contempt of court with imprisonment for not more than 14 days (*ibid.*, s. 23).

[2] *Ibid.*, s. 24. Certain classes of payment are excluded, notably the pay of members of the forces, social security payments, disablement or disability pensions and seamen's wages.

[3] *Ibid.*, s. 6. There is provision for variation and discharge or orders in sections 9–11 of the Act.

[4] *Ibid.*, s. 8.

exercised by a judge who must be satisfied that the defaulter has, or has had, since the date of the judgment against him, the means to pay. It does not, therefore, render a defaulter liable to imprisonment where he simply has not the means to pay. His conduct must be in the nature of a contempt.[1] However the power to commit under Section 5 of the Debtors Act was severely curtailed by the Administration of Justice Act 1970, and the power is now exercisable by county courts only in respect of High Court or county court maintenance orders and orders for the payment of certain debts of a public nature such as income tax and national insurance contributions.[2]

Imprisonment does not extinguish the debt, although the debtor cannot be committed twice in respect of the same debt (though he can be committed separately in respect of separate instalments of the same debt). Since the 1970 Act, imprisonment in respect of civil debt is extremely rare and the judgment summons is of far less practical importance than formerly. Furthermore on a judgment summons the court has power, instead of making a committal order, to make an attachment of earnings order.[3]

The plaintiff must file the appropriate praecipe in the office of the county court for the district where the debtor resides or carries on business, together with the plaint note. Where the judgment in question is not a county court judgment he must also produce an office copy of the judgment or order, an affidavit verifying the amount due and a copy of the sheriff's return to any writ of execution issued in the High Court.[4] The county court will then issue a judgment summons which is served on the defendant not less than 10 clear days before the day fixed for the hearing.[5]

At the hearing there will be an enquiry into the debtor's means. The judgment creditor may give evidence, orally or by affidavit, as to the debtor's means and the debtor will also be required to undergo a sworn examination as to his means. If he does not appear at the hearing the judge may adjourn the hearing and order the defendant to attend the adjourned hearing. This order must be served personally on the defendant not less than 5 clear days before the date fixed for the adjourned hearing.[6] If he does not attend then the judge may commit him to prison for not more than 14 days.[7]

If the judge is satisfied that the debtor has had the means to pay the debt but has not done so he may commit the defendant to prison for a term not exceeding six weeks. In fact the judge usually makes an order for payment by instalments if this has not already been done. If the judgment summons was issued in respect of a default on an instalment the judge will more readily make a committal order but even then it will usually be suspended provided that debt is paid within a specified time.

Administration orders—The great advantage of attachment of earnings orders is that they provide a means of intercepting the earnings of judgment debtors and thereby ensuring, so far as possible, that the debtor with insufficient assets to

---

[1] *Re Edgcome*, [1902] 2 K.B. 403.
[2] Administration of Justice Act 1970, s. 11, Sch. 4.
[3] Attachment of Earnings Act 1971, s. 3 (4), (6).
[4] O. 25, rr. 33, 37.
[5] O. 25, r. 40.
[6] O. 25, r. 43.
[7] County Courts Act 1959, s. 144.

justify execution process pays his debts, albeit slowly. By the nature of things it is often the case that a judgment debtor has outstanding against him not one but several judgment debts. In such a case there is provision in the Attachment of Earnings Act 1971[1] for the making of a "consolidated attachment order" which is an attachment of earnings order for the payment of two or more judgment debts.

An alternative procedure in the case of insolvent judgment debtors lies in the power of county courts to make administration orders. An administration order is·an order providing for the administration of the debtor's estate by the court. The court may make such an order, under section 148 of the County Courts Act 1959 (as amended) on the application of a debtor whose total debts do not exceed £500 and who is unable to pay forthwith the amount of a judgment obtained against him in a county court. The court also has an independent power under section 4 of the Attachment of Earnings Act 1971 to make an administration order on an application for an attachment of earnings order to secure payment of a judgment debt if of the opinion that the case is one in which all the debtor's liabilities should be dealt with together; if of opinion that it may be such a case the court may order the debtor to furnish to the court a list of all his creditors and the amounts which he owes to them and if it appears that his total indebtedness does not exceed £500 the court may make an administration order. An application for an administration order under the County Courts Act and an order that a debtor furnish a list of his creditors under the Attachment of Earnings Act procedure are acts of bankruptcy for the purposes of the Bankruptcy Act 1914.[2]

Where an administration order has been made, any creditor, on proof of his debt before the registrar, is entitled to be scheduled as a creditor of the debtor for the amount of his proof.[3] Where the debtor applies for an order, he must state in his request whether he proposes to pay his creditors in full or whether he proposes to pay a composition and, in either case, the amount of the instalments by which he proposes to pay.[4] Any person who becomes a creditor after the date of the order may be scheduled as a creditor but payment to him is deferred until those who were creditors before the making of the order have been paid.

The effect of an administration order is that no creditor has any remedy against the person or property of the debtor in respect of any debt which the debtor has notified to the court or which has been scheduled to the order except with leave of the court.[5] Furthermore no creditor whose name is included in the schedule may, without the leave of the county court, present or join in a bankruptcy petition unless his name was notified to the county court by the debtor, he is a creditor, for a sum exceeding £100 and the petition is

---

[1] S. 17. Application for a consolidated attachment order may be made by the debtor or by any person who has obtained or is entitled to apply for an attachment of earnings order or, in certain circumstances, the court may make such an order of its own motion. Payments made under the order are divided *pro rata* among the creditors (O. 25, r. 90).

[2] Administration of Justice Act 1965, s. 21; Attachment of Earnings Act 1971, s. 4 (3).

[3] County Courts Act 1959, s. 149.

[4] Administration Order Rules 1936, r. 3. The court is not bound by the debtor's proposals and may make an order for the payment of the debtor's debts to a greater or less extent, or by greater or smaller instalments (*ibid*).

[5] County Courts Act 1959, s. 150.

presented within 28 days of the creditor receiving notice that his name has been notified to the court.[1]

The court will, under the order, administer the debtor's estate and distribute his assets and instalments paid by him *pro rata* among his creditors. As has been noted, an administration order may itself be enforced by an attachment of earnings order.

b Other judgments

Warrants of delivery and possession—A judgment for the recovery of land or for the delivery of possession of land may be enforced by warrant of possession which corresponds to the writ of possession available in the High Court.[2]

Similarly, a judgment for the delivery of specific goods is enforced by warrant of delivery. There are different forms of warrant of delivery which enable the bailiff either to execute upon the defendant's goods to the value of the chattel, as if the warrant were a warrant of execution, or to seize the specific chattel which is the subject matter of the warrant.[3]

Attachment—The power of county courts to attach a person for contempt of court may be compared with the power of committal in the High Court. Thus where a person has failed to comply with any order of the court, he may be attached. A copy of the order in question must be served on the defendant personally, warning him of the consequences of his disobedience. If the defendant still fails to comply with the order he will be required to attend the court and show cause why he should not be committed to prison. If he does not show cause, the judge may order a warrant of attachment to issue for his arrest and imprisonment.[4] He will remain in prison until he has purged his contempt.

There are various other penal sanctions available to the county court. Thus a person who assaults an officer of the court in the execution of his duty or commits a contempt in the face of the court is liable to a fine of up to £50 (in the case of an assault) or £20 (in other cases) or, in either case, imprisonment for a period not exceeding one month.[5]

C MATRIMONIAL CAUSES PROCEDURE

A matrimonial cause is commenced by filing a petition in any divorce county court. The form of petition is prescribed by the Matrimonial Causes Rules 1971; in addition to various formal matters the petition must contain the names of the parties, details of the marriage, the names of all children of the family, particulars of previous proceedings between the parties and details of grounds upon which relief is sought. In a divorce suit the petition must state that "the said marriage has broken down irretrievably" and must then allege which of the five facts set out in section 2 of the Divorce Reform Act 1969 the petitioner relies upon as proof of breakdown. The petition concludes with a prayer for the relief sought, which, in the case of divorce, is "that the said marriage may be

---

[1] Administration of Justice Act 1965, s. 20 (3).
[2] O. 25, r. 71.
[3] O. 25, rr. 74, 75.
[4] O. 25, rr. 67, 68.
[5] County Courts Act 1959, ss. 30, 157. Appeal lies under the Administration of Justice Act. 1960, s. 13.

dissolved", including any claim for a financial provision, costs or custody of children of the family.

The petitioner must file copies of the petition for each person to be served and their names and addresses are annexed to the petition. With the petition the petitioner must file a written statement containing details of the present and proposed arrangements for the residence, education, financial provision and access of all children of the family under 16.[1] In addition, where a solicitor is acting for a petitioner for divorce or judicial separation a certificate as to whether or not he has discussed with the petitioner the possibility of a reconciliation must be filed with the petition. Unless the petitioner otherwise requests the petition, together with forms of Notice of Proceedings and Acknowledgment of Service, is served by post through the court. There is no entry of appearance although a party may, within 8 days of service, give "notice of intention to defend." Within 21 days of the time limited for giving notice of intention to defend the respondent may file an answer. If an answer to the petition is filed the proceedings become defended and *must* then be transferred to the High Court (Family Division). The answer contains the respondent's defence to the allegations in the petition, together with any claim for relief which the respondent wishes to make. If an answer is filed the petitioner has 14 days in which to file a reply. The following interlocutory proceedings are similar to those in the Queen's Bench Division and may include such matters as particulars of pleading, discovery of documents and interrogatories. These are closed by the registrar giving "directions for trial"[2] whereupon the case is set down in the High Court (if defended) or a divorce county court (if undefended). The trial is similar to the trial of any other civil action and takes place before a judge who deals with the relief sought and ancillary matters such as custody, costs and maintenance.

D TRANSFER OF PROCEEDINGS

1 From one county court to another

It must be remembered that the jurisdiction of the county courts is local, so that the plaintiff is restricted in his choice of venue. This must generally be in the court for the district in which the defendant or one of the defendants resides or carries on business, or where the cause of action wholly or in part arose. Where proceedings are commenced in the wrong county court, the judge of that court may transfer them to the court in which they ought to have been commenced.[3]

Where an action is commenced in the proper court it may still, in two cases, be transferred to another county court. First, the judge may transfer the proceedings to another court if he is satisfied that they can more conveniently or fairly be tried in that court. Secondly, where an action has been commenced in a county court against a defendant who does not reside or carry on business within the district of that court, the latter may apply *ex parte* in writing for an

---

[1] And those minor children over 16 who are receiving instruction at an educational establishment or undergoing training for a trade, profession or vocation: Matrimonial Causes Rules 1971, r. 8 (2); Form 4.

[2] M.C.R. 1971, r. 33; cf. the summons for directions in the Queen's Bench Division; see p. 284, *ante.*

[3] See p. 315, *ante.*

order transferring the proceedings to the county court for the district in which he does reside or carry on business.[1]

Finally, a judgment summons can only be issed in the county court for the district in which the defendant resides or carries on business. Thus where the action in which the judgment was obtained took place in some other court, proceedings must be transferred to the court having jurisdiction to issue the judgment summons. The action is then transferred for all purposes to the latter court, so that money paid by the defendant must be paid to the court from which the judgment summons issued.[2]

2 From a county court to the High Court

Proceedings may be transferred from the county court in which they were commenced to the High Court in the following circumstances (*inter alia*):[3]

(1) where the action is for damages in contract or tort and the plaintiff applies for transfer on the ground that the amount recoverable is likely to exceed £750;[4]

(2) on the defendant's application in an action in contract or tort, where the sum claimed is over £100, the judge certifies that an important question of law or fact is involved and the defendant gives security for High Court costs and damages of such amount as the registrar may determine;[5]

(3) where the action is for the recovery of land and the title to land with a net annual value for rating of over £400 would be affected;[6]

(4) where the action is one in which the county court has no jurisdiction, including a counterclaim, or set-off and counterclaim, in respect of matters outside the county court's jurisdiction.[7]

The procedure in the High Court on transferred actions is governed by R.S.C. Order 78. The master must give all directions as to the future conduct of the proceedings as he would on a summons for directions.

3 From the High Court to a county court

The following are the more important cases in which actions may be transferred from the High Court to a county court:

(1) where the claim is founded on contract or tort and the amount claimed or remaining in dispute does not exceed £750.[8] The application is by summons to a master, who may transfer the action either to a county court which would have had jurisdiction if the action had been commenced in the county court, or to any county court which is most convenient to the parties. The county court judge is bound to try the case and cannot question the order for

---

[1] O. 16, r. 1. The defendant is expressly notified of this right on the summons (County Courts Forms, Form 18 (1)). There is power, under the Matrimonial Causes Rules 1971, r. 32 (2) to transfer a matrimonial cause from one divorce county court to another.

[2] O. 25, r. 48.

[3] The Matrimonial Causes Rules 1971 contain various provisions for transfer of matrimonial causes to the High Court, the most important being r. 18 (5) under which a matrimonial cause which becomes defended must be so transferred.

[4] *Ibid.*, s. 43.

[5] *Ibid.*, s. 44 as amended by the Administration of Justice Act 1969, s. 3.

[6] *Ibid.*, s. 49 as amended by the County Courts (Jurisdiction) Act 1963.

[7] *Ibid.*, ss. 65, 66.

[8] *Ibid.*, s. 45 (as amended).

transfer; he can, however, transfer it back to the High Court under his own powers.   After transfer the county court has exclusive jurisdiction over the action and deals with costs incurred in the High Court prior to transfer unless they are provided for in the order for transfer;[1]

(2)   interpleader proceedings where the subject matter of the dispute does not exceed £750 in amount or estimated value;[2]

(3)   certain actions for the recovery of land by a landlord where the net annual value for rating does not exceed £400;[3]

(4)   where a matrimonial cause, having been transferred to the High Court, subsequently becomes undefended.[4]

[1] County Courts Act 1959, s. 77; O. 16, rr. 10–15.
[2] *Ibid.*, s. 68.
[3] *Ibid.*, s. 50.
[4] Matrimonial Causes Rules 1971, r. 27.

CHAPTER 23

Civil Appeals

A RIGHTS OF APPEAL

There is no common law right of appeal from a superior court. It was established in *Darlow* v. *Shuttleworth*[1] that the common law jurisdiction of the Court of King's Bench to hear proceedings in error from the inferior courts of local jurisdiction was transferred by the Judicature Acts to the divisional court of the Queen's Bench Division. However since this right of appeal is confined to situations in which proceedings in error might have been brought at common law and since the local courts have ceased to function[2] common law rights of appeal are virtually obsolete. Apart from this all rights of appeal are statutory. The basic rights of appeal in the Supreme Court derive from the Judicature Acts although numerous statutes create particular rights of appeal in special cases.

1 Appeal to the Court of Appeal: Civil Division

The fulcrum of the system of civil appeals is the civil division of the Court of Appeal. In a number of cases the Court of Appeal hears appeals directly from the decision of the court below. In other cases the appeal lies to the High Court in the first instance and then to the Court of Appeal.

Appeal lies to the Court of Appeal, unless the parties agree to exclude their right of appeal, against any judgment or order of the High Court subject to any contrary provision in the Judicature Act 1925 or the Rules of the Supreme Court. The Court also has jurisdiction to entertain every motion for a new trial or to set aside a verdict, finding or judgment in any cause or matter tried in the High Court.[3] By section 13 of the Administration of Justice Act 1960 appeal lies to the Court of Appeal from any order or decision of a judge of the High Court in the exercise of jurisdiction to punish for contempt of court.

Appeals from county courts lie, subject to the conditions set out in sections

---

[1] [1902] 1 K.B. 721.
[2] See p. 5, *ante*.
[3] Judicature Act 1925, ss. 27 (1), 30. Where the House of Lords grants leave to appeal direct from the High Court to the House, appeal to the Court of Appeal is excluded (Administration of Justice Act 1969, s. 13 (2)).

108–110 of the County Courts Act 1959, to the Court of Appeal[1] with the single exception of appeals from orders in bankruptcy matters which lie in the first instance to a divisional court of the Chancery Division and thence with special leave to the Court of Appeal.[2]

The Court of Appeal also has jurisdiction to hear appeals from the National Industrial Relations Court,[3] the Restrictive Practices Court,[4] the Lands Tribunal[5] and certain other statutory tribunals and from Commercial Judges sitting as arbitrators or umpires under Section 4 of the Administration of Justice Act 1970.

Leave to appeal

As a general rule appeal lies to the Court of Appeal as of right but in certain cases leave is required. The more important cases in which leave is required are:

(1) from the determination of an appeal by a divisional court of the High Court;[6] leave may be given either by the divisional court or by the Court of Appeal;

(2) from a consent order or an order which is solely an order as to costs which by law are left to the discretion of the court;[7]

(3) from an interlocutory order or judgment made or given by a judge (with certain exceptions, notably where the liberty of the subject or the custody of infants is involved or where an injunction or the appointment of a receiver has been granted or refused);[8]

(4) from the decision of a county court judge, and only with leave of the county court judge, in most actions where the claim does not exceed £20 except where the action is for the recovery of land, or the title to any hereditament is in question or the relief sought includes an injunction.[9]

Right of appeal excluded

Although section 27 of the Judicature Act 1925 confers a general right of appeal

---

1 Administration of Justice (Appeals) Act 1934, s. 2. Prior to this Act county court appeals lay to the divisional court of the Queen's Bench Division.

2 Bankruptcy Act 1914, s. 108.

3 But only on a point of law (Industrial Relations Act 1971, s. 99; Sch. 3, para. 29); see p. 173, *ante.*

4 Restrictive Trade Practices Act 1956, Sched. 1, para. 7, 8.

5 Lands Tribunal Act 1949, s. 3 (4). Appeal from tribunals is by case stated on a point of law. The procedure is governed by R. S. C. (Revision) 1965, O. 61.

6 Judicature Act 1925, s. 31 (1) (*f*). Leave may be granted by the House of Lords for an appeal direct to the House from the divisional court (Administration of Justice Act 1969, s. 12 (2) (*c*)). See also Tribunals and Inquiries Act 1971, s. 13 (4) as to appeals under that Act.

7 Judicature Act 1925, s. 31 (1) (*h*). Where there are genuine grounds of appeal in addition to an appeal against an order as to costs the appeal is not as to costs only even if all the other grounds of appeal are unsuccessful: *Wheeler* v. *Somerfield,* [1966] 2 Q.B. 94; [1966] 2 All E.R. 305.

8 Judicature Act 1925, s. 31 (1) (*i*). Whether an order is final or interlocutory depends on the nature of the application to the court rather than the nature of the order made. Thus, for example, the refusal of a county court judge to order a new trial is an interlocutory order as is an order dismissing an action for want of prosecution (see p. 251, *ante*) even though the practical effect may be final in that the action is at an end; the test stated above was laid down by the Court of Appeal in *Salter Rex & Co.* v. *Ghosh,* [1971] 2 All E.R. 865; [1971] 3 W.L.R. 31.

9 County Courts Act 1959, s. 108.

from the High Court to the Court of Appeal there are certain cases specified in the 1925 Act and in the Rules in which the right of appeal is excluded. Of these the most important are:

(1) from any judgment of the High Court in any criminal cause or matter.[1] In fact it is not true to say that these appeals do not lie to the Court of Appeal; they do not lie to the civil division of the Court of Appeal but they generally do lie to the criminal division with the notable exception of appeals from the divisional court of the Queen's Bench Division which lie, under the Administration of Justice Act 1960, direct to the House of Lords;[2]

(2) from an order of a judge giving unconditional leave to defend an action; [3]

(3) from a decision which is provided by any statute to be final, or where a statute provides that there shall be no appeal without leave and leave is not granted;[4]

(4) from an order absolute for dissolution or nullity of marriage provided that the party wishing to appeal had time and opportunity to appeal from the decree nisi;[5]

(5) from any judgment, order or decision of a Circuit judge in the course of official referees' business except as provided in Order 58, rule 5.[6]

To the above list of cases (which is not exhaustive) in which the right of appeal to the Court of Appeal is excluded by the Judicature Act 1925 and the Rules there should be added the restrictions on appeals from county courts on questions of fact; these are contained in sections 109[7] and 110 of the County Courts Act 1959. These sections confer a right of appeal (*inter alia*) on any question of fact in actions of contract or tort and admiralty actions where the sum involved exceeds a prescribed figure, generally £200.

2 Appeals from masters and registrars

The general rule is that an appeal lies as of right from any order of a Queen's Bench Division master to a judge in chambers.[8] In certain exceptional cases, set out in Order 58, rule 2, appeal lies from a master direct to the Court of Appeal. The most important of these circumstances are appeals from any judgment,

---

[1] Judicature Act 1925, s. 31 (1) (*a*). [2] See p. 444, *post.*
[3] Judicature Act 1925, s. 31 (1) (*c*).
[4] *Ibid.*, s. 31 (1) (d); *Lane* v. *Esdaile*, [1891] A.C. 210. Statutes under which an appeal to the High Court is final are listed in O. 94, r. 6.
[5] Judicature Act 1925, s. 31 (1) (*e*).
[6] Under O. 58, r. 5 (1) an appeal lies (a) from a decision of an official referee on a point of law; and (b) from a decision of an official referee on a question of fact relevant to a charge of fraud or breach of professional duty. There is, in addition, a right to appeal against a committal order made by an official referee under the Administration of Justice Act 1960, s. 13. Apart from these cases the decision of an official referee cannot be called in question "by appeal or otherwise" (O. 58, r. 5 (2)). By section 25 of the Courts Act 1971 (which abolished the office of official referee) jurisdiction formerly conferred by rules of court or otherwise upon official referees is conferred upon such Circuit judges as the Lord Chancellor may from time to time nominate and is known as "official referees' business". Any reference (for example, in Order 58) to an official referee is to be construed as a reference to a Circuit judge discharging the functions of an official referee.
[7] As amended by the County Courts (Jurisdiction) Act 1963, s. 2.
[8] O. 58, r. 1. Likewise, appeal from any order of a district registrar (O. 58, r. 4).

order or decision (other than an interlocutory judgment, order or decision)
given or made:

(*a*)　on the hearing or determination of any issue tried before the master or
referred to him;[1]

(*b*)　on an assessment of damages; or

(*c*)　on the hearing or determination of any interpleader or garnishee proceedings.

3　Appeal to the House of Lords

In civil matters appeal lies from the civil division of the Court of Appeal to the
House of Lords only with leave of the Court of Appeal or of the House of
Lords.[2]　There is no requirement that the appeal be based on a point of law,
though almost always appeal to the House of Lords is based upon a point of law
rather than on an issue of fact or an award of damages.　Although leave is the
only prerequisite for appealing, no appeal lies from the decision of the Court of
Appeal where any statute expresses the decision of the Court of Appeal to be
final.　Thus, for example, section 27 of the Judicature Act 1925 limits the jurisdiction of the House of Lords to hear appeals from decisions of the Court of
Appeal in matrimonial causes to appeals on questions of law and appeals from
the grant or reference of a decree of dissolution or nullity or of a declaration of
legitimacy.　Similarly the decision of the Court is final on any appeal from a
county court in probate proceedings[3] and from the determination by a
divisional court of the Chancery Division of a bankruptcy appeal from a county
court.[4]

The Administration of Justice Act 1969, Part II now provides for a "leap-frog"
appeal direct from the High Court to the House of Lords subject to the grant of
a certificate by the trial judge and of leave by the House of Lords in any case in
which appeal lies to the Court of Appeal (with or without leave).[5]

B　PROCEDURE FOR APPEALING TO THE COURT OF APPEAL

Appeal is by notice of motion in respect of the whole or any part of the judgment or order in respect of which the appeal is brought.　This notice must
set out the grounds of appeal shortly but with sufficient particularity to enable
the respondent to ascertain exactly what issues are being raised against him.
Thus, merely to complain that the trial judge misdirected the jury would be

---

[1] An appeal from the decision of a registrar of the Family Division on the hearing of an
application under section 17 of the Married Women's Property Act 1882, also lies direct
to the Court of Appeal; O. 58, r. 2 (2) (*a*).

[2] Administration of Justice (Appeals) Act 1934, s. 1.

[3] County Courts Act 1959, s. 114.　　　　　[4] Bankruptcy Act 1914, s. 108 (2) (*a*).

[5] See p. 333, *ante*; the principal conditions precedent to the grant of a certificate are (1)
the consent of all parties, and (2) that the case involves a point of law of general public
importance either relating to the construction of an enactment or being a point on which
the judge was bound by precedent.　*Todd* v. *Davison*, [1971] 1 All E.R. 994; [1971]
2 W.L.R. 898 appears to have been the first "leap-frog" appeal heard by the House of
Lords; the case concerned the construction of the words "in the custody of a parent" in
section 22 (2) (*b*) of the Limitations Act 1939 (as amended), and the decision of the trial
judge was affirmed.

inadequate; the particular nature of the misdirection must be specified. The notice must also contain a statement of the order for which the appellant is applying to the court, and the list in which he proposes to set down the appeal. The notice must be served on all parties interested in the appeal and upon such other persons as the Court of Appeal may direct.[1] Notice of appeal must normally be served within 6 weeks[2] of the date upon which judgment in the court below was signed or entered, though this time may be extended either by the Court of Appeal or, if application is made before the time expires, by the court below. Having served the notice of appeal, the appellant must within 7 days apply to set down the appeal. To do so he produces an office copy of the judgment or order appealed from, together with two copies of his notice of appeal, one of which must bear the appropriate judicature fee stamp.[3] The appeal is then set down in the appropriate list to await hearing. The appeal is likely to come on in most cases about three months after the case has been set down.

Appeals must be heard by at least three judges of the Court, unless the parties consent or the appeal is from an interlocutory judgment or order.[4]

Except in the case of applications for a new trial or to set aside a verdict, appeal is "by way of rehearing". That is to say the Court hears full legal argument from both sides and may substitute its own judgment for that of the court below. However it is not a complete rehearing, as it is in the Crown Court, since the Court does not, in practice, hear again the testimony of the trial witnesses, but merely sees transcripts of their evidence.[5]

In addition the appellant is normally confined to the points of law which he raised in the court below. He may in certain circumstances, discussed below, be allowed to take new points on appeal but he cannot, except with leave of the Court of Appeal, rely on any grounds of appeal or apply for any relief not specified in his notice of appeal.[6]

Cross-appeal

A respondent who, not having appealed from the decision of the court below, seeks to have the judgment or order of the court below either varied or affirmed on other grounds need not enter a separate notice of appeal. His proper course is to serve on the appellant, and on any other party directly affected, a "respondent's notice" specifying the grounds of his contention and any alteration in the judgment or order which he requests. Thus, for example, if the appellant is appealing against a finding as to his liability the respondent may, by his notice, appeal against his award of damages. A respondent's notice must be served within 21 days of service of the notice of appeal, or 7 days in the case of an interlocutory appeal, and the respondent must, within 2 days after service of the notice, file two copies of the notice.[7]

---

[1] O. 59, r. 3. Appeals from tribunals to the Court of Appeal are by case stated, the procedure being governed by O. 61.

[2] 14 days in the case of appeal from an interlocutory order; 21 days in winding-up and bankruptcy matters: O. 59, r. 4.

[3] O. 59, r. 5.

[4] Under the Domestic and Appellate Proceedings (Restriction of Publicity) Act 1968, s. 1 appeals in the Court of Appeal (and High Court) may be heard in private if the court below would have had power to sit in private.

[5] O. 59, r. 12.   [6] O. 59, r. 3 (3).   [7] O. 59, r. 6.

C POWERS OF THE COURT OF APPEAL

The Court of Appeal has all the powers, authority and jurisdiction of the High
Court in any matter before it[1] and all the powers and duties as to amendment
and otherwise of the High Court including the power under Order 36 to refer
any question or issue of fact for trial before, or inquiry and report by, a Circuit
judge discharging the functions of an official referee.[2] The Court has power to
examine trial witnesses though it rarely does so, being content in most cases
to rely upon the judge's note or a transcript of the official shorthand note.
It has power to receive further evidence orally, by affidavit or by deposition
taken before an examiner but, where there was a trial or hearing on the merits,
the Court of Appeal will not admit further evidence (other than evidence as to
matters which have occurred since the trial) except on special grounds.[3] In
Ladd v. *Marshall*[4] DENNING, L.J. (as he then was), prescribed the following three
conditions for the reception of fresh evidence in the Court of Appeal:[5]

> "First, it must be shown that the evidence could not have been obtained with reason-
> able diligence for use at the trial; secondly, the evidence must be such that, if given,
> it would probably have an important influence on the result of the case, though it
> need not be decisive; thirdly, the evidence must be such as is presumably to be
> believed, or, in other words, it must be apparently credible though it need not be
> incontrovertible."[6]

This statement was approved by the House of Lords in *Skone* v. *Skone*[7]
where the evidence consisted of a bundle of love letters written by the co-
respondent in a divorce suit to the wife which tended to prove adultery between
them. The trial judge had dismissed the husband's petition and accepted the
co-respondent's evidence to the effect that adultery had not taken place. It was
argued that these letters (which were in the possession of the wife) could have
been obtained by seeking discovery of documents from the wife. The House of
Lords rejected this argument on the basis that the husband had no reason to
suspect the existence of such letters, that the letters, if genuine, falsified the
judge's finding to such an extent that it would be unjust to leave matters where
they were and, furthermore, that there was a strong *prima facie* case of deception
of the court.

It must be emphasised that these rigorous conditions need not be satisfied in
respect of evidence of matters occurring after the trial. Evidence will be

---

[1] Judicature Act 1925, s. 27. These powers are both statutory and inherent. Thus the
Court of Appeal may strike out a notice of appeal in the same way as the High Court may
strike out a statement of claim either under O. 18, r. 19 or in exercise of its inherent
power: *Aviagents, Ltd.* v. *Balstravest Investments, Ltd.*, [1966] 1 All E. R. 450; [1966] 1
W. L. R. 150.

[2] O. 59, r. 10 (1); Courts Act 1971, s. 25 (3).

[3] O. 59, r. 10 (2).

[4] [1954] 3 All E.R. 745; [1954] 1 W.L.R. 1489; applied in *Roe* v. *Robert McGregor & Son,
Ltd.*, [1968] 2 All E.R. 686; [1968] 1 W.L.R. 925.

[5] [1954] 3 All E. R. 745, at p. 748; [1954] 1 W. L. R. 489, at p. 1491.

[6] Compare the somewhat wider provisions for the reception of fresh evidence in the criminal division of the Court of Appeal; see p. 428, *post*.

[7] [1971] 2 All E.R. 582; [1971] 1 W.L.R. 812.

admitted of matters occurring after the trial where the basis on which the trial judge gave his decision has been clearly falsified by subsequent events.[1]

Since appeal to the Court of Appeal is "by way of rehearing" the Court of Appeal has full power to make any order which should have been made in the court below[2] and to substitute its own order as to liability, quantum or costs for that of the court below. In addition the Court of Appeal is not confined to the points raised in the notice of appeal or respondent's notice. It may, though it rarely does, take any point of law or fact so far as is necessary to ensure the determination on the merits of the real question in issue between the parties. Should the Court of Appeal wish to decide an issue of fact which has not been pleaded, an extremely infrequent contingency, it may allow the pleadings to be amended.[3]

The Court has power to order an appellant to give security for the costs of an appeal in any case in which he could be required to give security for costs under Order 23[4] and, in addition, in "special circumstances"[5] generally where the appellant would be unable to pay the costs of the appeal if unsuccessful. Although an appeal does not operate as a stay of execution the Court of Appeal has power to order a stay of execution though it will only do so if there is some good reason, since it inclines against depriving a person of the fruits of his litigation. If a stay of execution is ordered on an appeal from the High Court, interest is allowed on the judgment debt unless there is an express order to the contrary.[6]

In addition to the powers of the Court of Appeal listed above there is an extremely important power which the High Court does not possess. This is the power to order a new trial, the exercise of which is considered in detail below.

D THE APPROACH OF THE COURT OF APPEAL TO THE DETERMINATION OF APPEALS

1 Appeal on a point of law

Most appeals to the Court of Appeal are based on a point of law. It has already been stated that, notwithstanding the general power of the Court of Appeal to take a point not raised therein, the Court usually confines itself to the points raised in the notice of appeal or respondent's notice. Furthermore there is a general rule that a party cannot take on appeal a point which he did not take in the court below.[7] To this rule there are two important exceptions. The first

---

[1] *Mulholland* v. *Mitchell*, [1971] A.C. 666; [1971] 1 All E.R. 307. Where the fresh evidence becomes available to a party during the trial he must adduce it then and there, even though this may necessitate an adjournment. He must not disregard it and thereafter found an application for a new trial upon the fresh evidence: *Cowling* v. *Matbro, Ltd.*, [1969] 2 All E.R. 664; [1969] 1 W.L.R. 598.

[2] O. 59, r. 10 (3).

[3] See *Bell* v. *Lever Brothers, Ltd.*, [1932] A.C. 161, at p. 216.

[4] See p. 281, *ante.*

[5] O. 59, r. 10 (5).

[6] O. 59, r. 13.

[7] The rule is not, however, invariable so that where all the findings of fact upon which the application of the point of law depends were made by the trial judge, the Court of Appeal may allow the point to be taken: *Donaghey* v. *P. O'Brien & Co.*, [1966]

occurs where the point of law was expressly reserved in the court below. This might occur where the court below was not free to consider the point because it was bound by precedent on that point, whereas the Court of Appeal might be free to reconsider the precedent in question. Secondly, the Court of Appeal will allow a point to be taken, and indeed will take the point itself, where not to do so would result in an abuse of the court's process. Thus the illegality of a contract may be raised on appeal even though the point was overlooked in the court below. The rule against taking new points on appeal is particularly strong in relation to appeals from county courts since section 108 of the County Courts Act 1959 expressly provides that the appeal is from "the determination or direction of the judge in point of law".[1] Nevertheless, despite this statutory provision, it was held by the Court of Appeal in *Snell* v. *Unity Finance, Ltd.*[2] that the illegality of a contract could be raised on appeal even though the point had not been taken in the county court. Apart from this, if there is a substantial error of law in a county court action or matter the fact that the point was not taken at the trial and, therefore, cannot be raised on appeal to the Court of Appeal does not mean that the error must stand since the party aggrieved may apply to the county court judge for a new trial under Order 37 of the County Court Rules. If the judge refuses to order a new trial appeal lies to the Court of Appeal from this refusal.[3]

It should be noted, finally, that even in the case of a county court appeal the respondent may, by his notice, seek to support the judgment of the court below on another ground which may be a point of law not taken at the trial.

2 Appeal against a finding of fact

Since the appeal is by way of rehearing the Court of Appeal has power to substitute its own finding of fact, direct or inferential, for that of the trial judge or jury. There are, however, three restrictions upon this general power to upset findings of fact made at the trial. First, the Court of Appeal in practice confines itself to issues of fact raised in the notice of appeal or respondent's notice. Secondly, the Court of Appeal cannot make a finding in relation to a fact not pleaded, although it can give leave to amend the pleadings.[4] Finally, the Court does not as a rule upset direct findings of fact, whether they were made by a judge or by a jury. The reason for this is that, as stated earlier, the Court of Appeal does not have the advantage, which the judge and jury had, of seeing the trial witnesses and observing their demeanour.[5] Consequently the jurisdiction

---

2 All E.R. 822; [1966] 1 W. L.R. 1170 (affirmed on this point, though reversed on another ground, *sub. nom. Donaghey* v. *Boulton and Paul, Ltd.,* [1968] A.C. 1; [1967] 2 All E.R. 1014); cf. *Wilson* v. *Liverpool City Council,* [1971] 1 All E.R. 628; [1971] 1 W.L.R. 302.

[1] See *Smith* v. *Baker* [1891] A.C. 325.

[2] [1964] 2 Q.B. 203; [1963] 3 All E.R. 50; cf. *Oscroft* v. *Benabo,* [1967] 2 All E.R. 548; [1967] 1 W.L.R. 1087.

[3] *Handley* v. *London, Edinburgh and Glasgow Insurance Co.,* [1902] 1 K.B. 350. The appeal is an interlocutory appeal: *Salter Rex & Co.* v. *Ghosh,* [1971] 2 Q.B. 597; [1971] 2 All E.R. 865.

[4] See *Bell* v. *Lever Brothers, Ltd.,* [1932] A.C. 161.

[5] The Court of Appeal feels no such inhibition when the evidence at the trial was given by written statement or deposition; see *Gallie* v. *Lee,* [1969] 1 All E.R. 1062, at p. 1079; [1969] 2 W.L.R. 901 at p. 921 (affirmed [1971] A.C. 1004; [1970] 3 All E.R. 961).

exercised by the Court of Appeal in relation to findings of fact is confined to inferential findings of fact. The Court has power to substitute its own inference from the facts as found for that of the trial judge or jury and will not hesitate to do so. Thus, for example, in one case the Court of Appeal reduced a plaintiff's award of damages by half on the basis of his contributory negligence even though there had been no finding of contributory negligence at the trial.[1] Contributory negligence, like negligence, is an inference of fact to be drawn from the facts as found. Where a jury has returned a general verdict it is impossible to distinguish direct findings of fact from inferential findings and, indeed, the jury cannot be asked, after they have returned a general verdict, to state what their direct findings of fact were.[2] The Court of Appeal, therefore, can only upset the general verdict of a jury if it cannot be supported by the evidence or is a verdict which no reasonable men could have reached.[3]

3 Appeal against the exercise of a discretion

In many circumstances the judge has a discretion as to whether, and in what manner, to exercise his powers. Commonly encountered instances of judicial discretion are the discretion as to costs and the discretion as to the mode of trial, in particular in relation to the question of whether or not to order jury trial. However, no discretion is absolute[4] and there may be a successful appeal to the Court of Appeal in relation to the exercise of a judicial discretion if the appellant can show that the judge exercised his discretion under a mistake of law,[5] or under a misapprehension as to the facts, or that he took into account irrelevant matters or failed to have regard to matters which he ought to have taken into account[6] or that he failed to exercise his discretion at all.[5] If the judge gives no reasons, or insufficient reasons for the exercise of his discretion, the court may infer that he has gone wrong in one respect or another.[7] The burden of proof is on the party who alleges that the discretion was wrongly exercised.

4 Appeal against an award of damages

The approach adopted by the Court of Appeal when determining an appeal against an award of damages differs according to whether the award was made by a jury or by a judge sitting alone. Where unliquidated damages are claimed, the Court will not interfere with the award of a jury unless the damages awarded are so large or, more rarely, so small that no jury could reasonably have given

---

[1] *Hicks v. British Transport Commission*, [1958] 2 All E.R. 39; [1958] 1 W.L.R. 493; see also *Benmax v. Austin Motor Co., Ltd.*, [1955] A.C. 370; [1955] 1 All E.R. 326; *Qualcast (Wolverhampton), Ltd. v. Haynes*, [1959] A.C. 743; [1959] 2 All E.R. 38.

[2] *Barnes v. Hill* [1967] 1 Q.B. 579; [1967] 1 All E.R. 347.

[3] *Mechanical and General Inventions Co., Ltd. v. Austin*, [1935] A.C. 347.

[4] R.S.C. (Revision) 1962, O. 36, r. 1 described the discretion as to the mode of trial as an "absolute one" but the Court of Appeal in *Ward v. James*, [1966] 1 Q.B. 273, at p. 293; [1965] 1 All E. R. 563, at p. 568 stated that the word "absolute" either added nothing or, if it did, was *ultra vires*. R.S.C. (Revision) 1965, O. 33 omits the reference to an "absolute" discretion.

[5] *Evans v. Bartlam*, [1937] A.C. 473; [1937] 2 All E.R. 646.

[6] *Ward v. James*, [1966] 1 Q.B. 273; [1965] 1 All E.R. 563.

[7] *Ward v. James (supra)*; In re *A debtor (No. 12 of 1970)*, [1971] 1 All E.R. 504; [1971] 1 W.L.R. 261 (affirmed [1971] 2 All E.R. 1494; [1971] 1 W.L.R. 1212).

them.[1] The reason for this is that the assessment of damages is historically the province of the jury in any case. Thus juries know of no fixed scale of damages comparable to that applied by judges, and the law does not consider it desirable that they should be made aware of any such scale.[2] In the matter of damages; "the views of juries may form a valuable corrective to the views of judges".[3] However a new trial may be ordered if it appears to the court either that the jury took into account irrelevant factors or failed to consider matters which it ought to have considered and in consequence awarded damages which were excessive or inadequate. The case of *Lewis* v. *Daily Telegraph, Ltd.*[4] provides a recent example. In that case two national newspapers published on the same day paragraphs alleged to be defamatory of the plaintiffs. The jury in the first action awarded the plaintiffs a total of £100,000; in the second action two days later in which there were factors which a jury might be entitled to take into account as aggravating damages, a different jury awarded the plaintiffs a further £117,000. New trials of both actions were ordered on the ground (*inter alia*) that the damages in each case were excessive. The House of Lords, affirming the decision of the Court of Appeal, stated that in such a case, pursuant to section 12 of the Defamation Act 1952, each jury should be directed to consider how far the damage suffered can reasonably be attributed solely to the libel with which they are concerned, and how far it ought to be regarded as the joint result of the two libels, bearing in mind that the plaintiff ought not to be compensated twice for the same loss.

Where the award of damages appealed against was made by a judge sitting alone the Court of Appeal will not hesitate to interfere with the assessment, not only on the ground that the judge applied a wrong principle of law in making the assessment, but also on the ground that the award is out of scale with awards in similar cases. There is, of course, no prescribed scale of damages in any type of action but, nevertheless, there is a certain degree of parity in awards in respect of similar types of damage particularly in actions for damages for personal injuries.[5] In such cases the Court of Appeal will not make small adjustments to the sum awarded though it will make a substantial adjustment if that is found necessary. In practice the Court will rarely interfere unless an adjustment of at least 20 or 25 *per cent* is envisaged. It is this diversity of approach to awards of damages made by judges and juries respectively that has led to the virtual disappearance of jury trial in personal injuries actions.[6]

---

[1] *Johnston* v. *G. W. Railway*, [1904] 2 K.B. 250. The award must be an "entirely erroneous" estimate: *Banbury* v. *Bank of Montreal*, [1918] A.C. 626, at p. 694. The principle was reaffirmed by the House of Lords in *Cassell & Co., Ltd.* v. *Broome*, [1972] 1 All E.R. 801; [1972] 9 W.L.R. 645 where the House, by a bare majority, upheld an award of £40,000 for libel although unanimous in regarding the sum as excessive.

[2] The desirability of not informing juries of awards of damages in comparable cases was reiterated by LORD DENNING, M.R. in *Ward* v. *James*, [1966] 1 Q.B. 273; [1965] 1 All E.R. 563.

[3] *Per* MORRIS, L.J. in *Scott* v. *Musial*, [1959] 2 Q.B. 429; [1959] 3 All E.R. 193.

[4] [1964] A.C. 234; [1963] 2 All E.R. 151.

[5] See observations of LORD DENNING, M.R. on scales of damages in personal injuries actions in *Ward* v. *James*, [1966] 1 Q. B. 273, at pp. 296 *et seq.*; [1965] 1 All E. R. 563, at pp. 572 *et seq.* For an illustration of the tendency to standardise damages see *Bastow* v. *Bagley & Co., Ltd.*, [1961] 3 All E.R. 1101; [1961] 1 W.L.R. 1494. See also *Brown* v. *Thompson*, [1968] 2 All E.R. 708; [1968] 1 W.L.R. 1003.

[6] See p. 287, *ante.*

5 Exercise of the power to order a new trial

The Court of Appeal has power under Order 59, rule 11 to order a new trial. It may exercise this power on an appeal from a judge and jury or from a judge alone just as it can on a motion for a new trial following a trial with a jury.[1] A new trial may be ordered on any one issue without disturbing the finding of the court below on any other issue. Thus the Court of Appeal may order a new trial on the issue of damages while affirming the decision on the question of liability. Indeed if the only ground of application is the amount of damages the Court should limit the new trial to that issue and leave the findings as to liability undisturbed.[2] If there is a new trial that trial is completely independent of the first trial. The mode of trial need not be the same, no estoppels arise as a result of the first trial and the parties may raise new points and may contest issues left uncontested at the first trial. The costs of the first trial are sometimes ordered to await the outcome of the new trial though, as a rule, the successful applicant ought to be allowed the costs of his application.[3]

There are several grounds upon which a new trial may be ordered of which the more important are set out below.

a Misdirection

The judge has a duty to provide the jury with an adequate direction as to what are the issues to be decided, what is the law applicable to those issues and what is the effect in law of the evidence received. If this is not done there is a misdirection. The expression "misdirection" includes a failure to direct at all.[4]

b Improper admission or rejection of evidence

c Wrongful withdrawal of a question from the jury

It is expressly provided by Order 59, rule 11 (2) that a new trial shall not be ordered on any of the above three grounds "unless in the opinion of the Court of Appeal some substantial wrong or miscarriage has been thereby occasioned".[5] There will not have been an operative miscarriage of justice unless the appellant has lost a chance of success which was fairly open to him. The burden is on the party supporting the verdict to show that, on the evidence, there has been no miscarriage of justice.

d Perverse jury verdict

The Court of Appeal is slow to order a new trial on this ground and there is a heavy burden on the applicant. He must show not merely that the verdict is one which reasonable men *ought* not to have reached but that it is one which no jury of reasonable men, properly directed, *could* have found upon the evidence. This may occur either because there was no evidence at all in support of a material fact or because such evidence as there was could not reasonably be believed.

---

[1] Judicature Act 1925, s. 30. Compare the very limited power of the criminal division of the Court of Appeal to order a new trial ; see p. 428, *post*.

[2] *Tolley* v. *Fry & Sons, Ltd.*, [1931] A.C. 333, at p. 341.

[3] *Hamilton* v. *Seal*, [1904] 2 K.B. 262; cf. *Bray* v. *Ford*, [1896] A.C. 44.

[4] *Hobbs* v. *Tinling*, [1929] 2 K.B. 1.

[5] Compare the wording of the proviso to s. 2 (1) of the Criminal Appeal Act 1968; see p. 425, *post*.

e Jury verdict as to damages

The limited circumstances in which the Court of Appeal is prepared to upset a jury verdict as to damages have already been noted.[1] Where the Court of Appeal does decide that damages awarded by a jury are excessive or inadequate it has no power to substitute its own award without the consent of all parties concerned although it may increase or reduce an award in respect of any distinct head of damages erroneously included in or excluded from the sum awarded, with consent of the party who will be adversely affected by the increase or reduction.[2]

f Discovery of fresh evidence

The principles upon which the Court of Appeal acts when considering applications for a new trial on the ground of the discovery of fresh evidence are similar to those applicable where the Court is asked to receive fresh evidence on the hearing of an appeal.[3]

A common example of fresh evidence which will justify a new trial is the discovery that one of the trial witnesses gave false evidence.[4]

g Misconduct or other irregularity at the trial

A new trial may be ordered on the ground of misconduct on the part of the judge, the jury, counsel, court officers or other persons, provided that the misconduct in question prevented either party from having a fair trial. It is not sufficient that either judge or jury expressed a strong opinion in favour of one party during the trial. However new trials have been ordered where the verdict of the jury was reached by drawing lots,[5] where the jury expressed a strong opinion in favour of the plaintiff before hearing the defendant's evidence,[6] where the court was misled by counsel[7] and where the judge's constant interruptions prevented one side from conducting an effective cross-examination.[8]

h Surprise

The applicant for a new trial on the ground of surprise must swear an affidavit setting out the facts on which he relies. He may allege, for example, that the action came on for trial unexpectedly when his witnesses were not available or that his opponent was allowed to present his case in a way for which the applicant was not prepared. Thus where, in a personal injuries action, the plaintiff at the end of the trial confronted the defendants with, and succeeded on, a case based on allegations which had not been pleaded and which the defendants had not come to the trial prepared to meet, a new trial was ordered.[9] The

---

[1] See p. 342, *ante.*
[2] O. 59, r. 11 (4).
[3] See p. 338, *ante.*
[4] *Piotrowska* v. *Piotrowski*, [1958] 2 All E.R. 729 n.; [1958] 1 W.L.R. 797. A new trial was ordered in *Skone* v. *Skone*, [1971] 2 All E.R. 582; [1971] 1 W.L.R. 812; see p. 338, *ante.*
[5] *Harvey* v. *Hewitt* (1840), 8 Dowl. 598.
[6] *Allum* v. *Boultbee* (1854), 9 Exch. 738.
[7] *Meek* v. *Fleming*, [1961] 2 Q.B. 366; [1961] 3 All E.R. 148.
[8] *Jones* v. *National Coal Board*, [1957] 2 Q.B. 55; [1957] 2 All E.R. 155.
[9] *Lloyde* v. *West Midlands Gas Board*, [1971] 2 All E.R. 1240; [1971] 1 W.L.R. 749.

application will only succeed if the surprise has occasioned a substantial miscarriage of justice.

i Judgment obtained by fraud

There are alternative methods of challenging a judgment obtained by fraud. The first is by a motion for a new trial. Alternatively, and this is the usual procedure, the party affected may bring an action to have the judgment set aside. In either case the party has the burden of particularising and proving the fraud alleged.[1]

---

[1] *Hip Foong Hong* v. *H. Neotia & Co.*, [1918] A.C. 888.

PART V

Criminal Procedure

SUMMARY

CHAPTER 24

Preliminary Considerations and Alternative Methods of Trial

A CLASSIFICATION OF OFFENCES

For the purpose of criminal procedure all offences fall into one of three classes:

(1) *Indictable offences.* These are offences triable by judge and jury. The trial is usually preceded by a hearing in the magistrates' court; this is not a trial, but merely an enquiry[1] to see if the evidence against the defendant is sufficient to put him on trial. If so, he is committed to the court of trial, which will be the Crown Court; otherwise, he is discharged. The magistrates' court may commit for trial without considering the strength of the case against the defendant if, as often happens, it is accepted on his behalf as sufficient to put him on trial.

(2) *Summary offences.* These are offences triable in the magistrates' court, without a jury. Statute creates these offences and declares the mode of trial. This will be an actual determination of the case and not merely a preliminary enquiry.

(3) *Offences triable summarily or on indictment*, colloquially known as "hybrid" offences. Statute creates these offences also and provides that they may be tried summarily or on indictment. A person charged with one of these offences is brought in the first instance before a magistrates' court, where a special procedure determines the mode of trial of the particular charge.

This classification is of great importance, for our whole system of criminal courts is based on it. It is, however, of comparatively recent origin. At common law the only mode of trial, apart from the ordeal, was trial before judge and jury; in the modern classification, all offences were indictable. In most cases there was a preliminary enquiry, not always of the same character as at present. Even

---

[1] Commonly known as a "preliminary enquiry" or, more generally, "committal proceedings".

today, no offence is either summary or "hybrid" unless some statute declares it to be so.

> "All breaches of the public law punishable by fine or imprisonment are indictable unless a statute either expressly or by implication[1] excludes the liability of the offender to be indicted. Originally all offences were indictable, and it was not till about the fifteenth century that statutes began to be passed which excluded the liability of the offender to be indicted."[2]

In the past hundred years in particular:

> "The policy of the legislature [has] moved towards a more minute regulation of social life by the creation of many non-indictable offences carrying a relatively light punishment.[3] . . ."

A statute creating a summary offence will first define the offence and then state that the offence is punishable "on summary conviction" with a particular penalty, indicating thereby that the offence is a summary one. Similarly, in the case of hybrid offences, the statute will first define the offence and then state that it is punishable "on conviction on indictment" with a particular penalty and "on summary conviction" with a particular (lesser) penalty.[4] Summary offences are now very numerous; "hybrid" offences are fewer in number but are generally more serious.

Even here it may be noted that while an indictable offence is one which is primarily triable before judge and jury and a summary offence is one which is primarily triable in the magistrates' court, in neither case is the offence always so tried. Thus the majority of indictable offences may be tried summarily, and indeed a high proportion of those which may be tried summarily are so tried; conversely a summary offence may in certain circumstances be tried on indictment. Both these exceptions are discussed more fully below;[5] yet it is very important to note that in each case the offence retains its essential and original quality of being an indictable or summary offence, as the case may be; it is the mode of trial which is varied.[6] This is illustrated by the definitions contained in section 125 of the Magistrates' Courts Act, 1952. A summary offence is defined as:

> "an offence which, if committed by an adult, is triable by a magistrates' court . . . except an offence triable by a magistrates' court with the consent of the accused under section nineteen of this Act . . ." [relating to summary trial of an indictable offence].

---

[1] I.e. even if the actual word "summary" is not used, or there is no express reference to summary trial.

[2] Sir Valentine Holmes, K.C., *arguendo*, in *Hastings and Folkestone Glassworks* v. *Kalson*, [1949] 1 K.B. 214, at p. 216. For the actual decision in this case, see p. 351, *post.*

[3] Kenny, *Outlines of Criminal Law* (19th Edn.), p. 46. The courts have gone far in holding that such offences are complete without proof of *mens rea*. It was natural to entrust their enforcement to magistrates, since no other authority covered the whole country; also procedure in the magistrates' court was speedy and inexpensive.

[4] A recent example of a hybrid offence is "applying a false trade description" under the Trade Descriptions Act 1968.

[5] See pp. 351–365, *post.*

[6] Thus it is customary to speak of "summary trial of an indictable offence" and "trial on indictment of a summary offence".

An indictable offence is defined as:

"an offence which, if committed by an adult, is triable on indictment (whether or not it is also triable by a magistrates' court)[1] except an offence otherwise triable only by a magistrates' court which under section twenty-five of this Act [relating to trial on indictment of a summary offence] . . . is required to be tried on indictment . . .".

Both these definitions are expressed to be for the purposes of the Magistrates' Courts Act, but they are of general validity.[2] Thus by section 104 of the Magistrates' Courts Act there is a time limit on the prosecution of summary offences, but this has no application to an indictable offence tried summarily; again magistrates have a somewhat wider jurisdiction[3] when conducting a preliminary enquiry into an indictable offence than they have when conducting the trial of a summary offence, and they have this wider jurisdiction[3] when an indictable offence is tried summarily.

An indictable offence charged against an adult can only be tried summarily if the defendant gives his consent, in addition to certain other conditions. However any indictable offence except "homicide" charged either against a child (a person under the age of fourteen) or a young person (fourteen or over but under seventeen) must normally be tried summarily.[4] Thus the age of the defendant may determine the mode of trial.

Similarly, a hybrid offence is one which is both indictable and summary, whatever the mode of trying any particular charge of such an offence. Thus in *Hastings and Folkestone Glassworks* v. *Kalson*[5] articles of association of a company provided that a director could be disqualified on being convicted of "an indictable offence".[6] The Court of Appeal held that he could be disqualified on being convicted of a hybrid offence, even one which in the particular case had been tried summarily.

"An 'indictable offence' without any qualifying context can mean nothing else but an offence in respect of which an indictment would lie . . . it is none the less 'indictable' because, if the prosecution chose, it could proceed in respect of it summarily. . . . The measure of gravity is to be sought, in my opinion, in what can happen to persons guilty of that class of offence, not what does happen."[7]

B ALTERNATIVE METHODS OF TRIAL

1 Summary trial of an indictable offence

a *Introduction*

It has already been seen that the essential and original quality of an indictable offence is that it is triable before judge and jury at the Crown Court.   If

---

[1] For the significance of this phrase, see the discussion of *Hastings and Folkestone Glassworks* v. *Kalson* (*infra*).

[2] The general definition may be modified in the context of a particular Act of Parliament: see Costs in Criminal Cases Act 1952, s. 13 (2).

[3] As to the place where the alleged offence was committed: see p. 380, *post*.

[4] Children and Young Persons Act 1969, s. 6 (1): see pp. 356–357, *post*.

[5] [1949] 1 K.B. 214; [1948] 2 All E.R. 1013.

[6] With the exception of an offence "under the Road Traffic Act 1930, or any statutory provision in lieu or modification thereof".

[7] ASQUITH, L.J., at [1949] 1 K.B. at pp. 220, 221; [1948] 2 All E.R. at pp. 1016, 1017. See also *R.* v. *Fussell*, [1951] 2 All E.R. 761, making the same point in respect of the hybrid offence of taking and driving away a motor vehicle.

therefore the magistrates before whom such a case is brought for preliminary enquiry purport to try it themselves, such a "trial" will on principle be a complete nullity; even if the defendant has been "sentenced" he may later be committed for trial, and properly tried. The plea of *autrefois convict* will not be open to him since he was never in peril at the first hearing.[1] Thus in *R. v. West*[2] the magistrates purported to try a charge of being accessory after the fact to larceny.[3] Under the provisions of the Magistrates' Courts Act, presently to be considered, such a charge had to be tried on indictment. The Court of Criminal Appeal held that the whole proceedings before the magistrates were a nullity and that the same magistrates could afterwards commit the defendant for trial on precisely the same charge.

In a number of cases, however, statute gives magistrates the power actually themselves to try an indictable offence. Such jurisdiction was first given in the case of young offenders, and seems to have been inspired by the same motives of humanity and convenience (since indictable offences vary in gravity) as governed the establishment of proper juvenile courts. It was not until 1879 that the Summary Jurisdiction Act of that year gave a certain right to try indictable offences in the case of adults (persons aged 17 or over). Since then the list of indictable offences which may be tried summarily has steadily been enlarged, and a further considerable extension was made by the Criminal Justice Administration Act 1962.[4] Many offences under the Theft Act 1968 may be tried summarily. This no doubt indicates a faith by Parliament in the magistrates' courts. The actual working of the relevant provisions shows a faith by the public in the courts or at least an absence of suspicion, since, although it is fundamental that no-one, other than a child, can be tried summarily for an indictable offence unless he consents, a very large proportion of indictable offences which can be tried summarily are so tried. Another consideration, no doubt, is a desire in many defendants to have the charge hanging over them disposed of as quickly and cheaply as possible. In the case of experienced criminals this may be combined with a hope of less severe punishment than would otherwise be their fate;[5] this hope may be nugatory because of certain provisions as to penalty, considered below.[6]

Before the conditions governing summary trial of an indictable offence are considered it must be stressed once again that the offence remains an indictable one; it is only the mode of trial which is varied. Thus the geographical jurisdiction to try an indictable offence summarily is as for the preliminary enquiry, since the defendant was technically brought before the court for that purpose however likely, in fact, that the charge would be tried summarily.[7]

---

[1] See p. 405, *post*.

[2] [1964] 1 Q.B. 15; [1962] 2 All E.R. 624.

[3] "Accessories after the fact" and "larceny" have been abolished by the Criminal Law Act 1967 and the Theft Act 1968, respectively, but this does not affect the rule stated in the text.

[4] See also Criminal Justice Act 1967, s. 27, making a further extension in the case of certain offences under the Forgery Act 1913.

[5] "Most accused persons are guilty of some offence (although it may happen that the offence charged is not the most appropriate accusation) and know that a conviction by the Magistrates' Court is likely to result in lighter punishment than a conviction on trial on indictment": Jackson, *The Machinery of Justice in England* (5th Edn.), pp. 112, 113.

[6] See pp. 357–360, *post*.

[7] See p. 351, *ante* and p. 380, *post*.

Again the time limit laid down in section 104 of the Magistrates' Courts Act 1952 has no application to summary trial of an indictable offence. Conversely, in such a trial the magistrates have no general power to sit in closed court; they only have this power when they are holding a preliminary enquiry, with a view to committal for trial.

b Conditions in which an adult may be tried summarily for an indictable offence: Magistrates' Courts Act 1952, section 19

In the case of an adult there are four conditions for summary trial of an indictable offence:

(1) The defendant must appear or be brought before a magistrates' court charged with one of those indictable offences which as a pure matter of law may be tried summarily; it is not of course every indictable offence which may be so tried. The main list of offences so triable is to be found in the First Schedule to the Magistrates' Courts Act 1952, and the offences are therefore called "First Schedule" offences; however, as stated above,[1] this list has been considerably extended by the Criminal Justice Administration Act 1962 and other Acts. Among indictable offences which may be tried summarily are: unlawful wounding (but not wounding "with intent") assault occasioning actual bodily harm, indecent assault, theft, burglary (in certain circumstances), obtaining property by deception, obtaining a pecuniary advantage by deception, handling (unless the offence antecedent to the handling was committed outside the United Kingdom), attempt or incitement to commit one of the offences in the Schedule, attempt to commit a hybrid offence, and incitement to commit a summary offence. It will be seen from this list that all but the very gravest indictable offences may be tried summarily; yet merely because a particular charge can be tried summarily does not of course oblige the magistrates to try it; this matter is discussed more fully below.[2] There have been persistent efforts in Parliament to make infanticide an offence which may be tried summarily, because of the peculiar need for speedy disposal of this charge.

(2) At some stage during the enquiry into the indictable offence charged the justices must proceed with a view to summary trial, that is, make the decision that they are prepared to try the case summarily and proceed accordingly, subject to the other conditions for summary trial being satisfied. Thus they may and often should proceed some way with the preliminary enquiry, and consider the evidence, before making up their minds whether to try the case summarily. However the Act[3] expressly provides that they can only make this decison if they are satisfied, having regard to any representations made in the presence of the defendant by the prosecutor, and by the defendant, and to the nature of the case, that their own powers of punishment under the section would be adequate and that the circumstances do not make the offence one of serious character and do not for other reasons require trial on indictment. The exact meaning of this is perhaps somewhat obscure; the expression "would be adequate" appears to mean "would be adequate if the defendant were found guilty and if he were found not to have a bad record justifying committal for sentence", since, as will

---

[1] See p. 352, *ante.*
[2] See p. 354, *post.*
[3] Section 19 (2).

be seen,[1] if he is found guilty he may be committed for sentence to the Crown Court and considerably greater punishment there inflicted on him than the magistrates have power to impose. The expression "punishment" cannot refer to committal for sentence since that is not a punishment.[2]

Of course, merely because the magistrates decide that they are prepared to try the case summarily does not mean that it will be tried summarily, since the defendant must consent. Again LORD GODDARD repeatedly emphasised during the period that he was Lord Chief Justice that:

"... the fact that justices have power to try cases is no reason why they should necessarily do so. When a case is of a serious character ... it ought to go to trial on indictment. It is not merely a question of sentence; it may be that when the case does go for trial the court of trial will think it necessary only to impose a nominal sentence or even bind over. That is not the point; serious cases ought to be dealt with by superior courts."[3]

Severer condemnation still was reserved for magistrates who, at the express request of both the prosecution and the defence, reduced a charge of wounding with intent (which is not triable summarily) to one of unlawful wounding (which is),[4] presumably with the object of holding the summary trial which was in fact held.

"Here is a case in which a man's life has been seriously imperilled and if he had died ... the accused would have been charged with murder. It was never intended that ... justices should deal with such a case. ... For justices to exercise jurisdiction under that section by treating a case of this sort as nothing much more than common assault is a most extraordinary state of affairs. Justices should remember that they have to deal with matters of this sort judicially, and, although they must take into account what the prosecution and the defence say with regard to whether or not it is a proper case for the charge to be reduced, they are not bound to assent to dealing with the case summarily because the prosecution want to get the matter dealt with there and then."[5]

Again, in a case[6] where a number of serious charges against two defendants had been summarily dealt with at the express request of the prosecution, LORD PARKER, C.J., said:[7]

"This court is quite unable to understand how ... the prosecution invited the magistrates' court ... to deal summarily with the indictable offences. ... No doubt it is convenient in the interests of expedition, and possibly in order to obtain a plea of

---

[1] See pp. 357–360, *post.*

[2] *R. v. Bullock,* [1964] 1 Q.B. 481; [1963] 3 All E.R. 506; see p. 441, *post.*

[3] *R. v. Norfolk Justices, Ex parte Director of Public Prosecutions,* [1950] 2 K.B. 558, at p. 567; [1950] 2 All E.R. 42, at p. 44–45.

[4] See p. 353, *ante.*

[5] *R. v. Bodmin Justices, Ex parte McEwen,* [1947] K.B. 321, at pp. 324–325; [1947] 1 All E.R. 109, at p. 111.

[6] *R. v. Coe,* [1969] 1 All E.R. 65; [1968] 1 W.L.R. 1950, C.A. One only of the defendants was committed for sentence, and the Court of Appeal was considering his application for leave to appeal against sentence; for a further point arising from the case, see p. 359, *post.*

[7] [1969] 1 All E.R. at p. 67; [1968] 1 W.L.R. at p. 1953. See also the remarks of the Divisional Court in *R. v. King's Lynn Justices, Ex parte Carter,* [1969] 1 Q.B. 488, at p. 494; [1968] 3 All E.R. 858, at pp. 859–860. The court consisted of the same judges as in *R. v. Coe.* For a further point arising from the case, see p. 358, *post.*

guilty,[1] for the prosecution to invite the magistrates' court to deal with indictable offences summarily. But there is something more involved than convenience and expedition. Above all there is the proper administration of criminal justice to be considered, questions such as the protection of society and the stamping out of this sort of criminal enterprise if it is possible. . . . The court would like to observe that while in their view the prosecution was at fault . . . that is no excuse for the magistrates' court. Their duty in the case of indictable offences is to begin to enquire into the matter as examining justices, and only to deal with the case summarily if the matter can be brought fairly and squarely within section 19 (2) of the Magistrates Courts Act 1952."

(3) The court must then cause the charge to be written down, if this has not already been done, and read to the defendant. The court must then tell the defendant that he may, if he consents, be tried summarily instead of by a jury; they must also tell him what is meant by summary trial, "if the court thinks it desirable for his information".[2] It is one of the hazards of the magistrates' system that, particularly in a small community, the magistrates and hardened offenders may know each other of old; thus, the court may not think it "desirable for his information". The court must also explain to him that if, having elected for summary trial, he pleads or is found guilty and the magistrates, on obtaining information as to his character and antecedents, consider their own powers of sentence insufficient, they may commit him for sentence. Failure to give this warning will make any subsequent conviction and committal bad;[3] the defendant will not have been in peril from the moment that the warning should have been given but was not, and a fresh charge may be brought against him.

(4) The court must then ask the defendant whether he consents to summary trial. The consent of the prosecutor is not required except in a case involving the "property or affairs" of the Queen or a public body; but the Director of Public Prosecutions must consent if the prosecution is being carried on by him.[4]

If the defendant does not consent the court can only hold or continue the preliminary enquiry. Normally, as already seen, he will consent. If the necessary consent or consents are given the procedure will be as for summary trial. If the court has already begun proceedings as a preliminary enquiry, any oral evidence already given before the court shall be deemed to have been given in and for the purpose of the summary trial;[5] where, however, the defendant pleads not guilty the court must recall for cross-examination any witness who has already given evidence, unless not required by either side for that purpose.[6] The reason for this is that at a preliminary enquiry the defence will usually be reserved completely, or at any rate hardly pressed, and cross-examination of the

---

[1] This is an interesting reference to "plea-bargaining", i.e. the defendant pleading guilty in exchange for the prosecution dropping another charge or agreeing to summary trial. The process has been critically considered by the Court of Appeal with particular reference to the judge suggesting such an arrangement: *R. v. Turner*, [1970] 2 Q.B. 321; [1970] 2 All E.R. 281.

[2] Magistrates' Courts Act 1952, s. 19 (3), as amended.

[3] *R. v. Kent Justices, Ex parte Machin*, [1952] 2 Q.B. 355; [1952] 1 All E.R. 1123.

[4] Magistrates' Courts Act 1952, s. 19 (7).

[5] *Ibid.*, s. 23.

[6] Magistrates' Courts Rules 1968, r. 19.

same witness may differ very much according to whether proceedings are to be regarded as the preliminary enquiry or the trial proper. If the witness was cross-examined as for the former but then proceedings became the latter, grave injustice might be caused to the defendant unless there was a power to recall for full cross-examination. Once the court has begun to try an information for an indictable offence summarily it can change back to the preliminary enquiry at any time before the conclusion of the case for the prosecution.[1] "Begun to try" in this context appears to mean "begun to hear evidence".[2]

c Finding and sentence

If the defendant pleads or is found guilty the magistrates will proceed to the question of sentence in the usual way. Their powers are limited generally to a maximum of six months' imprisonment or £400 fine in the case of each indictable offence tried summarily; if, however, two or more sentences for indictable offences are ordered to run consecutively, the aggregate of these and any other sentences imposed by the court may exceed six months but must not generally exceed twelve months.[3] For this or other reasons the justices may decide to exercise their power to commit the defendant to the Crown Court for sentence; this is dealt with below.[4] It is expressly provided that where the court dismisses the information the dismissal "shall have the same effect as an acquittal on indictment".[5]

d Summary trial of children and young persons: Children and Young Persons Act 1969, s. 6

Section 4 of the Children and Young Persons Act 1969 imposes a complete ban on prosecution of a child for any offence except "homicide" and section 5 imposes considerable limitations on prosecution of a young person, subject to the same exception. Criminal proceedings will be replaced in each case by "care proceedings" under section 1 and succeeding sections of the Act. These important provisions have yet to be brought into force and in the meantime the law is as follows. Whenever a child or young person appears before a magistrates' court charged with any indictable offence he must be tried summarily. Exceptionally a young person may be committed for trial if charged with any offence for which the punishment in the case of an adult is fourteen years' imprisonment or more, not being an offence for which the penalty is fixed by law. A young person may also be committed for trial if charged jointly (with any offence) with an adult, and the court considers it necessary in the interests of justice to commit them both for trial. "Homicide" is not of course a single offence but comprises all offences of unlawful homicide.[6] If the court finds the child or young person guilty it may exercise the same powers as it could have

---

[1] Criminal Justice Administration Act 1962, s. 13.
[2] *R. v. Ibrahim* (1957), 122 J.P. 119.
[3] Magistrates' Courts Act 1952, s. 19 (6) and s. 108 (2); Criminal Justice Act 1967, s. 43.
[4] See p. 357, *post.*
[5] Magistrates' Courts Act 1952, s. 22.
[6] The effect of these provisions is that the normal rules as to trial on indictment of a summary offence and trial of a hybrid offence are excluded in the case of children and young persons: see pp. 363 and 366, *post.* Certain difficulties formerly arose in the procedure for committing a child or young person for trial, where committal is legally possible; see p. 383, *post.*

exercised if the defendant had been found guilty of an offence carrying, in the case of an adult, three months' imprisonment or more; since the defendant is not an adult the court cannot impose imprisonment at all but may instead exercise various other powers, such as sending him to a detention centre. Alternatively, the court may impose a fine not exceeding £50. There is no power to commit for sentence.

2 Committal for sentence

In seven cases a defendant may be tried in the magistrates' court but committed to the Crown Court, to be sentenced or otherwise dealt with. The case then becomes:

> ". . . a sort of composite case in which power is given to one court to convict and to another to give judgment; and until the judgment is given the hearing of the case is not complete".[1]

Although the seven cases vary in detail, there are basically three objects of committal for sentence, namely to ensure that (a) a defendant receives greater punishment than a magistrates' court has power to inflict, if thought to deserve it, (b) the same court which made an order for probation or conditional discharge should deal with its breach and (c) generally, there should be uniformity in sentencing.

The seven cases are as follows:

a Following trial of an adult in the magistrates' court for an indictable offence or for a "hybrid" offence tried summarily other than at the prosecution request

It has already been noted that if a magistrates' court tries an adult for an indictable offence and convicts him, but considers that, having regard to the defendant's character and antecedents, greater punishment should be inflicted than the justices have power to impose, they may commit the defendant to the Crown Court for sentence.

This power, which is contained in section 29 of the Magistrates' Courts Act 1952, also exists in relation to "hybrid" offences tried summarily other than at the request of the prosecution. This is dealt with more fully below.[2] The magistrates' court is not limited to considering the actual past record of the defendant, but may also take into account the general circumstances of the offender and also of the offence, since:

> "'character' in my opinion relates to something more than the fact that a person has been previously convicted, and the word 'antecedents' is as wide as can be conceived."[3]

Neither need there be any offences to be taken into consideration. In *R. v. King's Lynn Justices, Ex parte Carter*,[4] the defendants, all of previous good

---

[1] Lord Goddard, C.J. in *R. v. Norfolk Justices*, [1950] 2 K.B. 558, at p. 568; [1950] 2 All E.R. 42, at p. 46.
[2] See p. 367, *post.*
[3] Lord Goddard, C.J. in *R. v. Vallett*, [1951] 1 All E.R. 231, at pp. 231–232.
[4] [1969] 1 Q.B. 488; [1968] 3 All E.R. 858.

character, pleaded guilty in the magistrates' court to larceny as servants of goods to the value of nearly £3,500. The prosecution alleged an organised conspiracy to steal over a long period, although the defendants denied this. All three defendants were committed for sentence, and the Queen's Bench Divisional Court held that the committals were lawful, in spite of the absence of previous convictions or offences to be taken into consideration, assuming the magistrates to have accepted the prosecution allegation of a conspiracy.

> "As I see it . . . the expression 'character and antecedents' being as wide as it possibly can be, justices are entitled to take into consideration in deciding whether or not to commit . . . matters revealed in the course of the case connected with the offence charged which reflect in any way on the defendant's character."[1]

The court also (i) criticised the magistrates for trying the case summarily, or at any rate not proceeding at first with the preliminary enquiry, and examining the facts, before deciding whether to try summarily; they had started summary trial at once[2]; (ii) pointed out that where the court did make proper enquiry into the circumstances of the offence, and then decided to try summarily, they could not rely on those circumstances again to justify committal for sentence, on their own, but had to find fresh circumstances (e.g. offences to be taken into consideration).[3]

Although magistrates have had the power to try indictable offences summarily for nearly a hundred years, they have had the power to commit for sentence only since the passing of the Criminal Justice Act 1948.[4] Without this power magistrates might be in a considerable dilemma. They could hardly decide whether to deal with a case summarily without knowing of the defendant's record, since otherwise a person with a very long record might accept their offer of summary trial and in effect escape with the magistrates' power of punishment; at the same time, if they did enquire about the defendant's record and found him to have some previous convictions, yet not so many as to rule out summary trial, they would start proceedings with the gravely prejudicial knowledge of the defendant's previous convictions. As it is they need not, and indeed ought not, to enquire into the defendant's previous record before deciding whether to try the case summarily, since they can be confident that if the defendant is convicted by them, but requires greater punishment than they can impose, he will receive it, through the medium of committal for sentence.

Committal will normally be to the most convenient location of the Crown Court. In selecting this the justices must have regard to directions given by the

---

[1] LORD PARKER, C.J., [1969] 1 Q.B. at p. 497; [1968] 3 All E.R. at p. 862.
[2] See *ante*, p. 354.
[3] For an illustration of the latter point, see *R.* v. *Tower Bridge Magistrates, Ex parte Osman*, [1971] 1 All E.R. 1018; [1971] 1 W.L.R. 1109. On point (i) see the remarks of BRIDGE, J. at pp. 1021 and 1112 of the respective reports.
[4] In *R.* v. *Sheridan*, [1937] 1 K.B. 223; [1936] 2 All E.R. 833, the magistrates tried the defendant summarily for an indictable offence and convicted him. Then, on hearing of his bad record, they purported to commit him for *trial* at Quarter Sessions. There his plea of autrefois convict was overruled, but the Court of Criminal Appeal held the plea to be good. This and other cases led to the reform in the 1948 Act, although it may be that the actual reasoning in *R.* v. *Sheridan* cannot be supported having regard to the decision of the House of Lords in *S. (An Infant)* v. *Manchester City Recorder*, [1971] A.C. 481; [1969] 3 All E.R. 1230.

presiding judge or judges of the Circuit.[1]   Committal may be in custody or on bail,[2] but the Court of Appeal had indicated that:

". . . the cases must be rare when magistrates' courts can properly commit for [sentence] on bail because the whole purpose of the committal is to have the man sent to prison, and have him sent to prison for a longer period than the magistrates' court could impose."[3]

However, the defendant may give notice of appeal against conviction[4] and may then, *qua* appellant, be released on bail, although, where a possibly severe sentence awaits him, bail will only be granted "with extreme care, and only in really exceptional cases".[5]   There is no appeal against the order of committal as such;[6] if the defendant thinks that the committal was bad in law, for example because he was not warned that he might be committed, he should apply to a divisional court of the Queen's Bench Division for an order of certiorari or prohibition; the Crown Court will not, of course, sentence him until the result of his application is known, since the order of committal may be held to be a nullity.   On such an application the divisional court can only hear argument as to the legality of the committal and cannot entertain any suggestion that the committal was too harsh a step to take having regard to the facts; this is an argument to be addressed (although not in so many words) to the Crown Court when the defendant appears there for sentence.

On such appearance, procedure is as if the defendant had been committed for trial to the Crown Court and had pleaded guilty to the charge.   No actual plea will be taken, since that stage of the trial is concluded, but otherwise the position is as if the defendant had pleaded guilty at the Crown Court itself.   Thus notices required to be served three days before the "trial" may be served three days before the hearing at the Crown Court,[7] and, if the defendant has been granted bail, but fails to surrender, the Crown Court may issue a bench warrant, since a court trying the defendant for an indictable offence would certainly have such power.[8]   It might then be thought that the Crown Court could allow the defendant to withdraw his plea of guilty (if such was tendered), in the magistrates' court, before he was sentenced, and it is now clear from *R. v. Mutford and Lothingland Justices, Ex parte Harber*[9], following the

---

[1] *Practice Note*, reported at [1971] 3 All E.R. 829; [1971] 1 W.L.R. 1535, paras. 6–9. The Note contains Directions given by the Lord Chief Justice as to distribution of Crown Court business, see p. 170, *ante*.   There may be transfer from one location of the Crown Court to another: Directions, paragraph 14.   See also p. 387, *post*.

[2] Criminal Justice Act 1967, s. 20.

[3] *R. v. Coe*, [1969] 1 All E.R. 65, at p. 68; [1968] 1 W.L.R. 1950, at p. 1954; see p. 354, *ante*.

[4] See p. 440 *post*.

[5] *Re Whitehouse*, [1951] 1 K.B. 673, at p. 675; [1951] 1 All E.R. 353, at p. 354.

[6] *R. v. London Sessions, Ex parte Rogers*, [1951] 2 K.B. 74; [1951] 1 All E.R. 343.

[7] *R. v. Grant*, [1951] 1 K.B. 500; [1951] 1 All E.R. 28.

[8] *R. v. Lloyd-Jones, Ex parte Thomas*, [1958] 3 All E.R. 425; [1958] 1 W.L.R. 1110.   Both this case and *R. v. Grant* were of course decided before the Courts Act 1971, but are presumably still good law.   Apparent power to issue a bench warrant is expressly conferred by the Courts Act 1971, s. 13 (4) (*a*).

[9] [1971] 2 Q.B. 291; [1971] 1 All E.R. 81.   In the *Mutford* case the committal was under s. 28 (below) but it was accepted that the position was the same under s. 29.   The Crown Court can only take into consideration what took place in the magistrates' court: *R. v. Marylebone Justices, Ex parte Westminister City Council*, [1971] 1 All E.R. 1025; [1971] 1 W.L.R. 567.

decision of the House of Lords in *S. (An Infant)* v. *Manchester City Recorder*,[1] that this would be permissible. The Crown Court certainly has such a power when trying a case on indictment.[2]

At the hearing there should be formal identification by the police of the defendant as the person who appeared at the magistrates' court and was committed; if there is no police officer present who can give this information, the defendant may, it seems, be asked whether he was the person who appeared and was committed. The Crown Court will enquire into the circumstances of the case as it would following a plea of guilty before itself; prosecuting counsel will give the court an outline of the facts, and the defendant's antecedents, and defending counsel (or solicitor) will address the court in mitigation. The Crown Court can then pass any sentence up to the maximum which the particular indictable offence carries. The position as to appeal itself against this sentence is considered below.[3]

If the defendant appeals against conviction, as well as being committed for sentence, the Crown Court will of course hear his appeal first, since, if this succeeds, there will be no cause to sentence him. This is logical but leads to the undesirable result that the court may hear his appeal against conviction with knowledge that he has been committed for sentence on the basis of his "character and antecedents". This phrase is now widely interpreted,[4] but may include previous convictions.[4]

b   With a recommendation for Borstal training: Magistrates' Courts Act 1952, s. 28

Magistrates have no power to commit a person to Borstal training. The reason appears to be that a sentence of Borstal training will certainly result in the defendant being deprived of his liberty for six months, since this is the minimum period allowed by statute for a period of Borstal training; it is presumably thought undesirable that magistrates should have the power to send to Borstal for what must be this period at least, when their maximum power of imprisonment is normally for six months. Therefore, when the magistrates have before them a defendant who (i) is within the Borstal age group, that is 15[5] or over but under 21, and is in other respects eligible legally for a sentence of Borstal training, his age being taken as on the day of conviction;[6] (ii) appears to be a suitable person for a sentence of Borstal training; and (iii) has been convicted by the court of an offence punishable on summary conviction with imprisonment, the court may commit him in custody or on bail to the Crown Court for sentence. The words "with a view to a Borstal sentence" do not appear in section 28 but only in the marginal note; nevertheless the purpose of committal is clear. The general rules as to committal, already noted in connection with section 29, apply here also. Procedure at the hearing will be as described in respect of section 29, above; however an important limitation is that in the odd case

---

[1] [1971] A.C. 481; [1969] 3 All E.R. 1230.
[2] See p. 404, *post*.
[3] See p. 422, *post*.
[4] See p. 357, *ante*, and *R.* v. *Dorset Quarter Sessions, Ex parte O'Brien*, [1956] 1 Q.B. 452n; [1956] 1 All E.R. 449.
[5] The Children and Young Persons Act 1969, s. 7 (1) raises this age qualification to 17, but the provision is not yet in force.
[6] *R.* v. *Baxter*, [1969] 3 All E.R. 1290n; [1970] 1 W.L.R. 13.

where the Crown Court does not send the defendant to Borstal the court can only deal with him in any way in which the magistrates' court could have done. For this reason, in cases where a defendant could equally be committed under section 28 or 29, committal should normally be under section 29. The Crown Court will then have wider powers.[1]

c Committal under the Criminal Justice Act 1948:[2] *probation and conditional discharge*

If a defendant has been put on probation, or given a conditional discharge, by the Crown Court, and is subsequently convicted by a magistrates' court of an offence committed during the period of probation or of conditional discharge, the magistrates' court may commit him in custody or on bail, until he can be brought before the court by which the order was made.[3] The process is analogous to those already discussed, although the defendant is not committed directly to the Crown Court and is committed to be dealt with for the original offence only.

d Committal under the Criminal Justice Act 1967:[4] *suspended sentences*

Where the defendant has been convicted by the magistrates' court of an offence (i) punishable with imprisonment and (ii) committed during the operational period of a suspended sentence passed by the Crown Court the magistrates' court may commit him, in custody or on bail, to the Crown Court.[3] If it does not commit him, it must at least notify the conviction to the court which originally imposed the sentence.

e Committal under the Criminal Justice Act 1967:[5] *prisoners on licence*

Where a person released on licence from the Parole Board is convicted by a magistrates' court of an offence punishable on indictment with imprisonment, the court may commit him for sentence to the Crown Court, in custody or on bail. That court may revoke the licence.

f Committal under the Mental Health Act 1959[6]

A magistrates' court may make an order under the Mental Health Act 1959 committing the defendant, if he is fourteen or over, to a hospital, but it cannot at the same time make an order restricting the defendant's discharge for a fixed number of years. If, therefore, the court considers that a hospital order is appropriate but that it must in the particular case be accompanied by restrictions on release, the magistrates' court may, instead of making a hospital or any other order, commit the defendant to the Crown Court to be dealt with. Committal must be in custody; if, however, the magistrates' court is satisfied that arrangements have been made by a hospital to receive the defendant in the event of the

---

[1] *R. v. Dangerfield*, [1959] 3 All E.R. 88, at p. 90; [1960] 1 W.L.R. 269, at pp. 272–273.

[2] Section 8 (4).

[3] Committal must normally be to the Crown Court where the order was made or sentence passed: *Practice Note*, [1971] 3 All E.R. 829; [1971] 1 W.L.R. 1535, para. 6. This is in accordance with the terms of the sections, as originally passed.

[4] Section 41 (2).

[5] Section 62 (6), (7).

[6] Section 67.

Crown Court making a hospital order, the court may itself direct the defendant to be admitted to that hospital and to be detained there, pending determination of the case by the Crown Court. The Crown Court may make a hospital order, with or without restrictions, or it may deal with the defendant in any way in which the magistrates' court could have done.

g Incorrigible rogues

A person deemed to be an "incorrigible rogue", within the meaning of section 5 of the Vagrancy Act 1824, for one of the various causes there specified, may be committed to the "house of correction"—that is, in custody or on bail to the Crown Court for sentence. The Crown Court may impose up to a year's imprisonment. A person is deemed to be a rogue within section 5 if, *inter alia*, he breaks or escapes out of a place of legal confinement before the expiry of his sentence or if he is apprehended as a rogue and vagabond and violently resists the constable "or other peace officer" so arresting him.

It is not of course for every offence that the defendant can be committed for sentence. Thus, under section 29 of the Magistrates' Courts Act 1952, the offence must be an indictable one tried summarily; under section 28 the offence must be punishable on summary conviction with imprisonment, and so on. Thus the defendant may be convicted of two or more offences, and prima facie liable to be committed in respect of only one. Now, however, for the sake of uniformity, where a defendant is committed for sentence under any of the seven cases, except section 67 of the Mental Health Act 1959, in respect of an offence, he may also be committed in respect of a second offence tried with the first.[1] The second offence must however be punishable with imprisonment, or attract disqualification from driving; alternatively the defendant must have been previously sentenced by a magistrates' court to a suspended sentence. Where there is a committal in respect of the "second offence", the Crown Court can only deal with the defendant as the magistrates could have done; subject to this, they have all duties and powers of sentence transferred to them, except that the magistrates' court may impose an order of interim disqualification from driving, pending the defendant's appearance at the higher court.

3 Trial on indictment of a summary offence: Magistrates' Courts Act 1952, section 25

a Introduction

It has already been seen that a summary offence is one which possesses the original and essential quality of being triable by a magistrates' court. If, therefore, the magistrates purport to commit for trial a person charged with a summary offence, both the committal and any "trial" based upon it are complete nullities and the magistrates may themselves try the case at a later date; no plea of *autrefois convict* or *autrefois acquit* will be open to the defendant since he will not previously have been in peril.[2] It will be seen that this situation is precisely the converse of that which arose in *R. v. West*,[3] where magistrates purported to

---

1 Criminal Justice Act 1967, s. 56.
2 *Bannister* v. *Clarke*, [1920] 3 K.B. 598; see p. 405, *post*.
3 [1964] 1 Q.B. 15; [1962] 2 All E.R. 624; see p. 352, *ante*.

try summarily an offence that was only indictable; the result in each case was the same, namely that the hearing before the magistrates was held to be a nullity.

Where, however, a person who has attained the age of seventeen[1] is charged before a magistrates' court with a summary offence for which he is liable, or would if he were an adult be liable, to more than three months imprisonment, he may claim to be tried by a jury. This is the general rule laid down by section 25 of the Magistrates' Courts Act 1952. There are two qualifications to this rule: first, certain other statutes give the right to trial by jury for a summary offence, subject in some of the cases to conditions contained in that Act. Thus the Explosives Act 1875 gives the defendant the right to claim trial by jury for any summary offence contained in that Act for which the penalty exceeds £100, and the Witnesses (Public Inquiries) Protection Act 1892 gives either the prosecutor or the defendant the right to claim trial by jury for the summary offence, created by that Act, of intimidating a witness; secondly, there are certain exceptions to the general rule contained in the Magistrates' Courts Act; that is to say, there are cases in which although the penalty for a summary offence exceeds three months imprisonment, the defendant nevertheless has no right to trial by jury for that offence. One such offence is "an assault"; there are, of course, numerous offences of assault, some of which are not summary at all, but where an offence in which there is the element of assault is at the same time a summary offence carrying more than three months' imprisonment there is no right to trial by jury in respect of it. One such offence of assault is an assault on the police.[2] Again, certain sexual offences contained in sections 30, 31 and, in part, 32 of the Sexual Offences Act 1956 are subject to the same prohibition. All these offences are in fact "hybrid" offences; in so far as they are summary offences they carry a maximum penalty of more than three months' imprisonment and the defendant would normally have a right to trial by jury if that right were not expressly taken away by statute. Neither is there any right to trial by jury where the defendant is liable to imprisonment for more than three months, but only in default of payment of a fine, or for disobeying an order to enter into a recognisance.

b Procedure

Where the defendant has the right to trial by jury for a summary offence, under the Magistrates' Courts or any other Act, the procedure will be as follows. It is essential that the defendant appears *in person*;[3] even if he appears by counsel or solicitor, so that he is then not "absent" by virtue of section 99[4] of the Magistrates' Courts Act, he must appear in person before his right is effective. If he does appear personally he must be informed that he has the right to trial by jury; this must, of course, be done before the defendant is asked to plead since, if he elects for trial by jury, no plea will be taken.[3] He must also be told, "if the court thinks it desirable for [his] information", what is the meaning of being

---

[1] See pp. 356–357, *ante*.
[2] *R. v. Woolwich Justices, Ex parte Toohey*, [1967] 2 A.C. 1; [1966] 2 All E.R. 429.
[3] Magistrates' Courts Act 1952, s. 25 (2).
[4] Which deals generally with "absence" and "presence" in a criminal trial.

tried summarily.[1] He is then asked whether he wishes to be tried by jury instead of being tried summarily.[2] It is essential that this question be put to the defendant personally even if he has a solicitor who has already advised him as to his rights, or if he declares that he wishes to plead guilty and have the case disposed of before the magistrates or if he must know perfectly well from previous experience that he has the right to trial by jury (the magistrates being aware of this from their previous experience of him). His solicitor or counsel is however entitled to answer the question on his behalf and in his presence.

> "I think it would be wrong to fritter away the protection which the section intends to give to accused persons. It intends to give them protection in the broadest and most generous way by providing that the option of trial shall be put before any accused person before the charge is gone into. The protection is possibly even more necessary where he intends to plead guilty. He might plead guilty because, though he had no great confidence in the tribunal before which he appeared, he thought that by pleading guilty he might get a lighter sentence; whilst, if he knew he had a right to be tried by a jury, he would prefer to avail himself of that right. I think it is immaterial whether in fact he knows that he has the right or not; he ought to be informed of it by the court."[3]

Further, although there is now no exact form of words, the question must be put in the form "Do you wish to be tried by a jury?" and not "Do you wish to be tried here?"; the defendant must be told specifically that he has a right to be tried by jury. "If a man has a right to be tried by A, he is not told of that right by being asked if he wishes to be tried by B."[4] Failure to observe these rules as to the information to be given to the defendant will mean that the whole of the subsequent proceedings will be a nullity;

> "The justices have only power to deal with cases summarily if they are given power by statute to do so,[5] and if some provision in the statute is not complied with, it follows that the justices have no jurisdiction to hear and determine."[6]

It may be that the defendant has the right to be tried by jury only if he has previously been convicted of a like offence. Thus, the offence may be punishable with three months' imprisonment on a first conviction and six months' imprisonment on a second or subsequent conviction. If this is the case, the defendant must be given the necessary information in the form that he may have the right to be tried by jury, if he has the necessary qualifying conviction.[7] If he declines trial by jury in any event the court is spared the embarrassment which may result from enquiring into his record; if, on the other hand, he says that if he has the right to trial by jury he wishes to exercise it, then the court has no option but to enquire into his record to see if he qualifies. However the

---

[1] Magistrates' Courts Act 1952, s. 25 (3).
[2] *R. v. Kettering Justices, Ex parte Patmore,* [1968] 3 All E.R. 167; [1968] 1 W.L.R. 1436.
[3] WRIGHT, J. in *R. v. Cockshott,* [1898] 1 Q.B. 582, at p. 586: "the case with which one always starts in considering this matter:" LORD PARKER, C.J. in *R. v. Kettering Justices, Ex parte Patmore, supra* at pp. 168 and 1439.
[4] DONOVAN, J. (as he then was) in *R. v. Salisbury and Amesbury Justices, Ex parte Greatbatch,* [1954] 2 Q.B. 142, at p. 148; [1954] 2 All E.R. 326, at p, 329.
[5] See p. 350, *ante.*
[6] LORD GODDARD, C.J. in *Stefani v. John,* [1948] 1 K.B. 158, at p. 161; [1947] 2 All E.R. 615, at p. 617.
[7] Magistrates' Courts Act 1952, s. 25 (4).

court must confine its enquiries as far as possible "to matters necessary for determining whether he has a previous conviction giving him that right".[1] Presumably the court need do no more than enquire from the police whether the defendant has the specific conviction necessary; the only difficulty that might arise would be if the court found that the defendant had the necessary conviction and this fact were quoted in newspaper reports of the case. Since the conviction will necessarily be for "a like offence" there is even greater risk of prejudice than usual. The restrictions on reporting committal proceedings[2] would not apply, since proceedings would not have reached that stage.

The right of election is the defendant's own and neither the prosecutor nor the court can deny him trial by jury if he elects for it. The motives will perhaps be somewhat different from those which impel summary trial of an indictable offence; the defendant may be anxious to have the preliminary sight of the prosecution's evidence which the preliminary enquiry will give him, or he may simply think—almost certainly rightly—that his chances of acquittal are better before a jury.

> "Of course, nearly every accused person who is given the chance of being tried summarily takes it, unless he is charged with being under the influence of drink, when he always goes to quarter sessions if he can and, for some reason, nearly always gets acquitted, but that is the fault of juries and not of the law."[3]

If the defendant elects to go for trial the justices will hold a preliminary enquiry and (assuming there is sufficient evidence) commit the defendant for trial;[4] indeed the Magistrates' Courts Act provides that after the election the court must deal with the information "in all respects as if it were for an offence punishable on conviction on indictment only; and the offence, whether or not indictable otherwise than by virtue of any such claim, shall as respects the accused be deemed to be an indictable offence".[5] This sub-section deals with the proceedings before the magistrates; it does not deal with the hearing at the court of trial, still less does it turn into an indictable offence what is and remains a summary offence, whichever court tries it.[6] Different considerations apply where the defendant has the right to elect for trial, and does elect for trial, in the case of a "hybrid" offence; this matter is discussed below.[7] The basic rule is that the Crown Court has no power to impose a sentence of greater severity than the magistrates could have imposed.[6] Thus the defendant does not expose himself to a risk of greater sentence by electing to be tried on indictment for a summary offence.[8]

---

1 Magistrates' Courts Rules 1968, r. 21.
2 See pp. 389–390, *post.*
3 LORD GODDARD, C.J., in *R. v. Salisbury and Amesbury Justices Ex parte Greatbatch,* [1954] 2 Q.B. 142, at p. 146. The Road Safety Act 1967 has somewhat altered this position.
4 Committal must normally be on bail: Criminal Justice Act 1967, s. 18 (3) and see p. 388, *post.* As to what charges may be included in the indictment against the defendant at the trial, see pp. 391–392, *post.*
5 Magistrates' Courts Act 1952, s. 25 (6).
6 *R. v. Furlong,* [1962] 2 Q.B. 161; [1962] 1 All E.R. 656.
7 *R. v. Gibbs,* [1965] 2 Q.B. 281; [1964] 3 All E.R. 776; see p. 368, *post.*
8 But he does risk other counts being added; see *R. v. Nisbet,* [1972] 1 Q.B. 37; [1971] 3 All E.R. 307; see p. 392, *post.*

4 "Hybrid" offences: Magistrates' Courts Act 1952, section 18

A "hybrid" offence is an offence which by the terms of the statute creating it is at the same time both indictable and summary. Parliament has created hybrid offences for the same reasons as apply in the case of the alternative procedures, already discussed, namely to adapt procedure so far as possible to the seriousness of the offence. In the case of a hybrid offence, only the prosecutor will know the full circumstances of the alleged offence and the defendant's record; therefore, as will be seen, his option determines the mode of trial. Examples of hybrid offences are: dangerous driving, driving under the influence of drink or drugs, driving while disqualified and driving with excess alcohol in the blood. Of course, a single charge of a hybrid offence can only be dealt with in one way, either on indictment or summarily; the procedure used to determine the mode of trial of the particular charge is as follows. The magistrates' court will have jurisdiction to enquire into the case merely if the defendant appears or is brought before the court; in other words the jurisdiction is in the first instance as for the preliminary enquiry.[1] When the defendant appears the magistrates must treat the offence as indictable and must therefore proceed with the preliminary enquiry unless (i) the defendant is a young person or child;[2] or (ii) the prosecutor before any evidence is called requests summary trial and the court both has jurisdiction to try the information summarily and agrees to do so.[3] In so far as it is a summary offence the magistrates may have no jurisdiction to try it at all; thus the offence may have been committed outside the time limit laid down in section 104 of the Magistrates' Courts Act.[4] In this case the magistrates only have jurisdiction over the offence in so far as it is indictable and this in turn means that they must hold a preliminary enquiry; they cannot deal with the case in any other way since the provisions already discussed relating to summary trial of an indictable offence have no application to hybrid offences.

As stated, the prosecutor's application for the case to be heard summarily must be made before any evidence is called. If the defendant fails to appear in answer to the information, the application may be made in his absence.[5] It has been held that: ". . . the application can be made either expressly or by conduct which inevitably leads to the inference that it is being made",[6] that is by the prosecutor opening his case and calling witnesses, but this is perhaps surprising in view of the plain words of section 18 (1) and:

> "It would perhaps be better in such case for the clerk to say to the prosecutor 'Are you asking for summary trial?' when he could say 'Yes' or 'No'."[7]

If the magistrates accede to the prosecutor's request (as they normally will, unless there are circumstances of special gravity in the case) they will proceed to the trial of the summary offence before them; the prosecutor's election has made it no longer material that the offence is also indictable. However it may

---

[1] See p. 380, *post*.
[2] For definitions of these terms, and for the mode of trial of charges against young persons or children, see pp. 351, 357, *ante*.
[3] Magistrates' Courts Act 1952, s. 18 (1).
[4] See p. 433, *post*.
[5] Magistrates' Courts Act 1952, s. 18 (2).
[6] DEVLIN, J. (as he then was), in *Ex parte Rigby*, [1958] 3 All E.R. 30 at p. 32; [1958] 1 W.L.R. 843, at p. 845.
[7] LORD GODDARD, C.J. in *James* v. *Bowkett*, [1952] 2 All E.R. 320, at p. 321.

be that the offence, as a summary offence, carries more than three months' imprisonment; in this case the defendant has the option to have the case tried on indictment, on the principles already discussed.[1] The order of proceedings in such a case will therefore be: (1) the prosecutor elects summary trial; (2) the court agrees thereto; (3) before taking the defendant's plea the court informs him that he has a right to be tried by jury for this summary offence and asks him whether he elects jury trial. Of course, he is only asked to elect where the offence, as a summary offence, carries more than three months' imprisonment.

If both the prosecutor and the defendant (where he has the right to trial by jury) elect summary trial the plea will be taken and the trial will proceed in the normal way. If the defendant is convicted the justices have no power to commit him to the Crown Court for sentence, a matter which they will no doubt bear in mind when deciding whether to accept the prosecutor's request for summary trial in the first place.[2] A committal to the Crown Court in these circumstances is a nullity and can be quashed by certiorari; the position is as if the court had convicted the defendant and then given no decision at all on sentence but merely adjourned; they must therefore finish the case by passing sentence.[3]

It may be, however, that the magistrates at first refuse the prosecutor's request for summary trial (bearing in mind the strictures of LORD GODDARD, C.J. and LORD PARKER, C.J. quoted on pp. 354–355, *ante*), or that no application is made at all, but thereafter the case appears not to be so serious as was first thought. In that case the court, having regard to any representations made in the presence of the defendant by the prosecutor and by the defendant himself, and to the nature of the case, may proceed to try the case summarily.[4] If the prosecution is being carried on by the Director of Public Prosecutions he must consent to this course. The court will then cause the charge to be written down, if this has not already been done, and read to the defendant. The defendant now stands charged with a summary offence and if it carries more than three months' imprisonment he must be told of his right to be tried by jury and may elect for trial by jury. In practice this situation will probably not arise, since before proceeding to try the case summarily the justices must have regard, as has been noted, to any representations made by the defendant; if he informs the court that even if the court proceeds to summary trial he will claim trial by jury the justices will not waste time by making any move to try the case summarily. If the magistrates do proceed to try the case summarily and either the defendant has no right to trial by jury (since the offence as a summary offence does not carry more than three months' imprisonment) or he chooses not to exercise his right, the defendant's plea will be taken and the trial will proceed. If the defendant is found guilty he may be committed to the Crown Court for sentence under section 29 of the 1952 Act, and the court must warn him of the power of committal before proceeding to try the case summarily. It is perhaps strange

---

[1] See p. 363, *ante*.
[2] Magistrates' Courts Act 1952, s. 18 (1) and 29.
[3] *R. v. Norfolk Justices, Ex parte Director of Public Prosecutions*, [1950] 2 K.B. 558; [1950] 2 All E.R. 42, and *R. v. Gwyn Jones*, [1969] 2 Q.B. 33; [1969] 1 All E.R. 325. The Court of Appeal has no power to quash any "sentence" passed by the Crown Court; it is the "committal" which must be quashed.
[4] Magistrates' Courts Act 1952, s. 18 (3).

that the justices have no power to commit to the Crown Court if they both begin and continue to the end with summary trial, but section 18 of the 1952 Act is quite clear.

Conversely, even if the court has begun to try the information summarily it may at any time before the close of the prosecution case discontinue summary trial and proceed as examining justices.[1] In the first of the two "change-over" cases evidence given is deemed to have been given in and for the purposes of the summary trial;[2] in the second, it seems that the witnesses must be recalled for their evidence to be taken in the form of depositions, but there is no authority for this.

It appears that the right to elect trial by jury for a hybrid offence punishable with more than three months' imprisonment on a summary conviction is a dubious advantage. The reason for this is that if the defendant is convicted there is a "conviction on indictment" so that the court of trial may legitimately impose any sentence which the statute creating the offence provides for a conviction on indictment, even though this exceeds the maximum which the magistrates could have imposed if the defendant had been content to have the case tried summarily. Nor is there any provision for warning the defendant of this hazard. The result is that the defendant may unwittingly increase his potential sentence by electing for trial by jury since, it will be recalled, if he were tried summarily at the prosecution request, the magistrates would have no power to commit him to the Crown Court for sentence under section 29 and would be confined to imposing the maximum provided on "summary conviction". This hazard was disclosed by the Court of Criminal Appeal in the case of *R. v. Gibbs.*[3] The defendant was charged before justices with driving while disqualified contrary to section 110 of the Road Traffic Act 1960 as amended by the Road Traffic Act 1962, an offence for which he was liable "(i) on summary conviction to imprisonment for a term not exceeding six months ... and (ii) ... on conviction on indictment to imprisonment for a term not exceeding twelve months". The prosecution desired the case to be tried summarily but the defendant exercised his right under section 25 (1) of the Magistrates' Courts Act 1952 to elect to be tried by jury. He pleaded guilty at Quarter Sessions and was sentenced to nine months' imprisonment.[4] The Court of Criminal Appeal held that the sentence was valid since there had been a "conviction on indictment", the words of the statute being clear and unambiguous.

The defendant in *R. v. Gibbs* relied heavily upon the principle in *R. v. Furlong*[5] to the effect that section 25 (1) was purely procedural and did not justify Quarter Sessions imposing a greater sentence than the magistrates could have

---

[1] Magistrates' Courts Act 1952, s. 18 (5).
[2] *Ibid.*, s. 23.
[3] [1965] 2 Q.B. 281; [1964] 3 All E.R. 776.
[4] See pp. 365 and 366, *ante.* It is difficult to see why the defendant exercised his right but then pleaded guilty. Normally the right would be exercised with a view to a plea of not guilty, in the hope of acquittal by a jury.
[5] [1962] 2 Q.B. 161; [1962] 1 All E.R. 656; see p. 365, *ante. R. v. Gibbs* was followed in *R. v. Roe,* [1967] 1 All E.R. 492; [1967] 1 W.L.R. 634. *R. v. Roe* also deals with a separate point, as to what charges may be included in the indictment, on which it was approved; in *R. v. Nisbet,* [1972] 1 Q.B. 37; [1971] 3 All E.R. 307; see pp. 391–392, *post.*

imposed. The distinction between the two cases is, however, a simple one; Furlong was convicted of a summary offence; Gibbs of a "hybrid" offence. An additional factor of interest in the two cases is that the offence charged in both cases was driving while disqualified contrary to section 110 of the Road Traffic Act 1960. However, unfortunately for Gibbs, Parliament had amended section 110, which was initially a summary offence, so as to make it a hybrid offence.[1]

---

[1] Road Traffic Act 1962, Sch. 1, Part I (6). The need for this amendment had been pointed out by the Court of Criminal Appeal in *Furlong's* case.

CHAPTER 25

Trial of an Indictable ·Offence

A COMPELLING THE APPEARANCE OF THE DEFENDANT: PROCESS

A person accused or suspected of having committed an indictable offence may be brought before the court in one of three ways:

(i) by summons; this is a document, sent to or served on, the defendant, ordering him to appear in court;

(ii) by warrant for his arrest; this is an order to the police, or in certain circumstances to private persons, to arrest the defendant and bring him before the court;

A summons and a warrant are generally known as "process".

(iii) by arrest without warrant, where permitted by law.

Each of these will be considered in turn.

1 Information

Both a summons and a warrant are obtained by the laying of information before a magistrate.

> "An information is nothing more than what the word imports, namely the statement by which the magistrate is informed of the offence for which the summons or warrant is required. . . ."[1]

It is not necessary for the person requiring the issue of process to attend to lay the information personally; it may be laid by his counsel or solicitor or other person authorised for the purpose.[2] In theory process could be applied for and granted at any time or place; however:

> "In most well regulated courts an application for a summons or warrant is not made in open court, but must be made at a time when the court is not sitting as such."[3]

It is, of course, fundamental that any person[4] may lay information—not only a police officer—unless there is a specific rule to the contrary in the case of the

---

[1] HUDDLESTON, B., in *R.* v. *Hughes* (1879), 4 Q.B.D. 614, at p. 633.
[2] Magistrates' Courts Rules 1968, r. 1 (1).
[3] *Stone's Justices' Manual* (101st Edn.), p. 40.
[4] On the subject of prosecutions by private persons, see Jackson, *Machinery of Justice in England* (5th Edn.), pp. 128–9, and Edwards, *Law Officers of the Crown*, especially chapter 16.

particular offence alleged. To take two examples, proceedings under section 6 of the Race Relations Act 1965, prohibiting incitement to racial hatred, can only be instituted by or with the consent of the Attorney-General,[1] and proceedings under section 4 of the Criminal Law Act 1967, which provides penalties for assisting offenders, can only be instituted by or with the consent of the Director of Public Prosecutions.[1] Where consent or authority is required for the issue of process, the magistrate before whom information is laid should see that the consent or authority is produced before issuing process.[2]

In general there is no time limit on the prosecution of an indictable offence. *Kenny* records four cases in which convictions of murder were obtained 35, 30, 23 and 19 years after the actual murders.[3] In some cases Parliament has for reasons of policy imposed a time limit; thus a prosecution for unlawful sexual intercourse with a girl under sixteen may not be commenced more than twelve months after the commission of the offence.[4] It seems that a prosecution is commenced when information is laid,[5] or (presumably) at the moment of arrest, where the defendant is arrested without warrant.

An information is sufficient in form if it describes the specific offence alleged in ordinary language. Technical terms should be avoided as far as possible. It is not necessary to set out in the information all the elements of the offence, and in particular it is not necessary to "specify or negative" any exemption or general defence;[6] however the information should give such particulars as may be necessary for explaining the nature of the charge and where the offence charged is statutory there should be a reference to the relevant section of the Act.[7] Further, a magistrates' court must not proceed to the trial of an information which charges more than one offence; such an information must be amended, so as to charge one offence only, before the commencement of the trial.[8]

An information may normally be in any form; if, however, a warrant is sought in the first instance the information should be in writing and substantiated on oath.[9]

Failure to conform to these rules will not necessarily mean that the issue of process is invalid (with possible liability in false imprisonment) since section 100 of the Magistrates' Courts Act provides that:

---

[1] Failure to obtain consent appears to make proceedings a nullity: *R. v. Angel*, [1968] 2 All E.R. 607n; [1968] 1 W.L.R. 669.

[2] *Price v. Humphries*, [1958] 2 Q.B. 353, at p. 357; [1958] 2 All E.R. 725, at p. 727. Considerable limitations on the power to issue process in the case of young offenders are contained in section 5 of the Children and Young Persons Act 1969. Only a "qualified informant" i.e. a police officer, a children's officer or the N.S.P.C.C. may obtain process. These provisions are not yet in force.

[3] *Kenny's Outlines of Criminal Law* (19th Edn. 1966), p. 547. See also the singular case of *Collins*, convicted of manslaughter 21 years after the event: *The Times*, October 8, 1971.

[4] Sexual Offences Act 1956, s. 37, and Sched. II (10) (*b*). The cases are set out in *Archbold* (37th Edn.) paras. 152–162.

[5] *R. v. Wakely*, [1920] 1 K.B. 688.

[6] Magistrates' Courts Rules 1968, r. 1 (3). Compare the rule that a statement of claim in a civil action must not anticipate the defence.

[7] *Ibid.*, r. 83.

[8] *Ibid.*, r. 12 (1). See p. 434, *post*.

[9] Magistrates' Courts Act 1952, s. 1 (1).

"No objection shall be allowed to any information . . . or to any summons or warrant . . . for any defect in it in substance or in form, or for any variance between it and the evidence adduced on behalf of the prosecutor."[1]

The section indicates that:

"technical objections to informations are not to prevail, even though they touch the substance of the charge. There have been, however, many decisions under that section which show that the section does not operate to prevent an objection being effective where the error alleged is fundamental. . . ."[2]

It is a question of fact and degree in each case whether the error is indeed fundamental. Thus it was held in *Meek* v. *Powell*[3] that where an information charges an offence under a statute which has been repealed this is a fundamental defect which cannot be cured by section 100, but only by amendment or dismissal of the summons. Equally, section 100 cannot "save" an information that is bad because it does not charge any offence at all,[4] or, presumably, one that is bad for duplicity.[5] Again, in *Wright* v. *Nicholson*[6] the appellant had been convicted on an information alleging that the offence charged had been committed on August 17. On appeal to Quarter Sessions the victim simply said "in August". It was held that at that stage there ought to have been an amendment of the information, and then, to avoid injustice, an adjournment of the hearing, since the appellant indicated that he could establish an alibi for the whole of August. Even apart from section 100, it is well settled at common law that: "where a person is before justices who have jurisdiction to try the case they need not inquire how he came there, but may try it."[7] Thus in *R.* v. *Hughes*[8] the defendant made a wilfully false statement on oath at the trial of a person who had been brought before the court by illegal process. It was held that this latter fact did not affect the defendant's liability for perjury.

If and when the defendant is committed for trial he is entitled to a sight of the information, if it is sworn; before committal, and seemingly in any case where the information is not sworn, the defendant's only right is to apply for particulars of the charge to be given. This may be done at any time, application being in the first instance to the prosecutor, although application may be made to the magistrates' court for an order if particulars are refused or those given are thought to be insufficient.[9]

---

[1] If, however, the variance between a summons or a warrant and the evidence adduced is such that the defendant has been misled, the court must, on the application of the defendant, adjourn the hearing.

[2] HUMPHREYS, J. in *Atterton* v. *Browne*, [1945] K.B. 122, at p. 127, dealing with a section of the Summary Jurisdiction Act 1848 in similar terms to s. 100.

[3] [1952] 1 K.B. 164; [1952] 1 All E.R. 347. *Quaere* whether the defendant could waive the irregularity. See also *Hunter* v. *Coombs*, [1962] 1 All E.R. 904; [1962] 1 W.L.R. 573.

[4] *Garman* v. *Plaice*, [1969] 1 All E.R. 62, at p. 64; [1969] 1 W.L.R. 19, at p. 23.

[5] For the meaning of this, see p. 434, *post*.

[6] [1970] 1 All E.R. 12; [1970] 1 W.L.R. 142.

[7] LORD COLERIDGE, C.J. in *Dixon* v. *Wells* (1890), 25 Q.B.D. 249, at p. 255.

[8] (1879), 4 Q.B.D. 614.

[9] *R.* v. *Aylesbury Justices, Ex parte Wisbey*, [1965] 1 All E.R. 602; [1965] 1 W.L.R. 339 (a case arising out of the great train robbery trial). It was held that the defendant was entitled to particulars of an information charging perjury on a particular day in the trial, since it did not state what piece of evidence was alleged to be false.

2 Conditions for issue of process

Before issuing process a magistrate must be satisfied of two matters: (1) that as a matter of law he has jurisdiction to issue process; and (2) that in the particular case there is sufficient evidence against the person named in the information to justify the issue of process. As to jurisdiction, section 1 (2) of the Magistrates' Courts Act provides that a justice of the peace[1] for any county or borough may, on information being laid before him, issue a summons or a warrant in the following cases.

(*a*) If the offence[2] was committed or is suspected to have been committed within the county or borough.[3]

(*b*) If it appears to the magistrate issuing process necessary or expedient, with a view to the better administration of justice, that the person charged should be tried jointly with, or in the same place as, some other person who is charged with an offence, and who is in custody, or is being or is to be proceeded against, within the county or borough.[4]

The effect of this provision is shown by the decision of the Court of Criminal Appeal in *R. v. Blandford, R. v. Freestone*[5] In that case property had been stolen, and received in Montgomeryshire. The two defendants had received other property, stolen in the same incident from the same prosecutors; however they had received their share in the county borough of Southampton and the county of Stafford respectively. The court held that they had been validly summoned to appear in Montgomeryshire to answer the charge of receiving.

> "[the provision] operates although the persons are not to be tried jointly. It is enough if some other person is charged with an offence ... connected with the offence in which the summons has been issued against the other defendant. ... The fact that persons resident within that jurisdiction are being charged with offences so similar or closely connected that the witnesses for the prosecution or some of them will be the same in both cases may ... be a good reason for the justice exercising the discretion [to issue process] vested in him by the section. Further ... where there are offences which are so similar or closely connected, uniformity in the treatment of the accused persons may be desirable."[6]

However the court went on to point out that a magistrate must bear in mind the interests of the defendant before issuing process under this subsection, since the defendant might be caused great difficulty and expense in preparing his defence and procuring the attendance of witnesses.[6]

(*c*) If the person charged resides or is believed to reside in the county or borough.[7]

(*d*) If under any enactment a magistrates' court for the county or borough has

---

[1] Section 1 and certain other sections of the Magistrates' Courts Act use the term "justice of the peace", which is synonymous with "magistrate".

[2] By Magistrates' Courts Act 1952, s. 126 (6), except where the context otherwise requires references in the Act to an offence include references to an alleged offence.

[3] *Ibid.*, s. 1 (2) (*a*).

[4] *Ibid.*, s. 1 (2) (*b*).

[5] [1955] 1 All E.R. 681; [1955] 1 W.L.R. 331.

[6] *R. v. Blandford, R. v. Freestone*, [1955] 1 All E.R. 681, at pp. 683, 684; [1955] 1 W.L.R. 331, at pp. 334, 335.

[7] Magistrates' Courts Act 1952, s. 1 (2) (*c*).

jurisdiction to try the offence.[1] Jurisdiction to try is dealt with at pp. 432–433, but here it may be noted that by section 28 of the Criminal Justice Act 1967 summary offences may be tried at the same magistrates' court provided that the court has jurisdiction to try one of them. Thus, if the court has jurisdiction to try offence A, it may also try offences B and C, committed by the same defendant which otherwise it would not have jurisdiction to try. It follows that it may issue process in respect of B and C.

It will be seen that a magistrate is concerned generally with offences committed in, or persons resident in, that county or borough for which he is a magistrate.[2] However section 3 of the 1952 Act lays down certain rules which enable a common-sense view to be taken of whether an offence is committed "within" the county or borough. Thus an offence committed on or within 500 yards of the boundary between two local jurisdictions may be regarded as having been committed in either jurisdiction, as may an offence begun in one jurisdiction and completed in another. Again where an offence has been committed on a vehicle engaged on a journey through two or more local jurisdictions, the offence may be treated for the purpose of section 1 as having been committed in any of them.

Further authority to issue process is to be found in section 27 of the Criminal Justice Administration Act 1914, which provides that a warrant (but not a summons) may be issued in any case where common law or statute gives a right of arrest without warrant. These cases are considered below.[3]

As to the point of sufficiency of evidence, namely (2) above, it is in the magistrates' judicial discretion whether he issues process; there is however some authority for saying that if he refused to hear an application for process at all or if he refused to issue process, in spite of being satisfied both as to jurisdiction and as to the evidence in the case, because of "extraneous and extra-judicial" matters, then in either case mandamus would lie to order him to issue process.[4] Assuming, however, that he has decided to issue process, he must then consider whether to issue a summons or a warrant. Subject to certain exceptions,[5] this too is a matter for his discretion.

3 Summons

"A summons is a citation proceeding upon an information . . . laid before the magistrate who issues the summons, and conveying to the person cited the fact that the magistrate is satisfied that there is a *prima facie* case against him."[6]

A summons must state shortly the matter of the information and then set out the time and place at which the defendant is required by the summons to appear.

---

[1] Magistrates' Courts Act 1952, s. 1 (2) (*d*).
[2] This "local" jurisdiction contrasts sharply with the jurisdiction of the Crown Court under the Courts Act 1971.
[3] See pp. 376–380, *post*.
[4] *R. v. Adamson* (1875), 1 Q.B.D. 201. The persons against whom process was sought had broken up a meeting addressed by Dr. Kenealy, the defender of the Tichborne Claimant, and the extraneous and extra-judicial matter was the magistrate's own opinion of the Tichborne case, then recent and highly controversial. See also *R. v. Metropolitan Police Commissioner, ex parte Blackburn*, [1968] 2 Q.B. 118; [1968] 1 All E.R. 763, an attempt to secure more sustained enforcement of the then gaming laws.
[5] See p. 376, *post*.
[6] MATHEW, J. in *Dixon v. Wells* (1890), 25 Q.B.D. 249, at p. 257.

A single summons may be issued in respect of several informations, but must state the matter of each information separately and has effect as several summonses, one for each information.[1] In all cases the summons must either be signed by the magistrate issuing it[2] or must state his name, with the signature of the clerk of the court to authenticate it in either event. The summons must then be served on the defendant; this may be effected by: (1) delivering it to him; (2) leaving it for him with some person at his last known or usual place of abode; or (3) sending it by registered or recorded delivery letter addressed to him at his last known or usual place of abode.[3] If a person summoned for an indictable or hybrid offence fails to appear at the trial, service of the summons by methods (2) or (3) above must not be treated as proved unless it is first shown that the summons came to the defendant's knowledge; for this purpose, however, a letter or other communication purporting to be written by or on behalf of the defendant and giving rise to the reasonable inference that the summons came to his knowledge shall be admissible as evidence of that fact.[4] This limitation does not apply to a summary offence,[5] but it is now provided[6] that where a summons has been issued under section 1 of the Act of 1952, and the court has begun to try the information to which the summons relates, the defendant may at any time during or after the hearing make a statutory declaration[7] that he did not know of the summons until a date specified by him. Thereafter the information remains valid (with the result that subsequent proceedings will not be barred by lapse of time),[8] but all subsequent proceedings are void. There may be a fresh trial but not before any of the same magistrates.[9] A summons remains in force even though the magistrate who issued it ceases for any reason to be a magistrate[10] and with certain exceptions (for example under the Road Traffic Act 1960) it may be served at any time after issue.

4 Warrant[11]

A warrant, unlike a summons, is an order for the arrest of the defendant. It is addressed to the officers of the police area in which the warrant is issued and such other persons as are named in the warrant, and directs them to arrest a particular person. That person must be mentioned by name or otherwise described;[12] general warrants, i.e. warrants which do not name the person to be arrested, have been held to be illegal at common law ever since a series of famous cases[13] in the eighteenth century.

---

1 Magistrates' Courts Rules 1968, r. 81 (2) and (3).
2 *Ibid.*, r. 81 (1). Magistrates' Courts Act 1952, s. 100 and Rules, r. 83, pp. 372 and 371, *ante*, apply to a summons.
3 *Ibid.*, r. 82 (1).
4 *Ibid.*, r. 82 (2).
5 *Ibid.*, r. 82 (2).
6 Under s. 24 of the Criminal Justice Act 1967.
7 With liability for perjury if it is false.
8 Under s. 104 of the Magistrates' Courts Act: see p. 433, *post*.
9 Criminal Justice Act 1967, s. 24 (6).
10 Magistrates' Courts Act 1952, s. 101 : *quaere* as to the death of the person laying information.
11 Strictly called "a warrant of arrest" there being various other types of warrant, such as a search warrant.
12 Magistrates' Courts Rules 1968, r. 79 (2).
13 Notably *Money* v. *Leach* (1765), 3 Burr. 1742.

A warrant must contain a statement of the offence charged in the information and, like a summons, must be signed by the magistrate issuing it.[1]

A warrant may be executed (i.e. the arrest effected) anywhere in England and Wales, at any time,[2] by any person to whom the warrant is directed or by any police officer acting within his police area;[3] an officer making the arrest need not have the warrant in his possession at the time but must show it to the defendant as soon as is practicable, if the defendant demands to see it.[4] This duty is equivalent to the duty imposed on a person making an arrest without warrant to inform the defendant of the reason for his arrest. In the unlikely event of a warrant being addressed to a private person he could of course make the arrest, but by the terms of section 102 would actually have to have the warrant in his possession as well as having to show it on demand.

When a magistrate issues a warrant he may at the same time endorse it with a direction that the person named in the warrant shall, on arrest, be released on bail, on such terms as may be specified in the endorsement. The warrant is then said to be "backed for bail", and the officer in charge of the police station to which the defendant is taken after arrest must release him once he has complied with the conditions specified in the endorsement.[5] Special provisions apply in relation to the execution of warrants in Scotland and Ireland.[6]

As stated above,[7] the magistrate's discretion as to whether to issue a summons or a warrant is now limited, by section 24 (2) of the Criminal Justice Act 1967. No warrant may be issued against a person who is seventeen or over, unless the offence is indictable[8] or punishable with imprisonment, or unless the defendant's address is not "sufficiently established" for a summons to be served on him. Even before the Act a magistrate would not normally issue a warrant unless he was satisfied that a summons would be ineffectual to secure the defendant's presence.

5   Arrest without warrant

Finally, the defendant may be arrested without warrant. Until recently the law placed police officers and private persons in equal difficulties. A police constable might have had to "decide at a moment's notice a point that has puzzled the appellate courts several times"[9] while a private person's powers were "so limited and illogical that he is well advised not to try arresting anyone".[10]

---

[1] Magistrates' Courts Rules 1968, rr. 79 (2), 78; Magistrates' Courts Act 1952, ss. 100, 101 and Rules, r. 83, (*ante*, pp. 372 and 371, and *supra*) apply to a warrant.

[2] Until withdrawn: Magistrates' Courts Act, 1952, s. 102 (1).

[3] *Ibid.*, s. 102 (2).

[4] *Ibid.*, s. 102 (4). This is reasonable from the point of view of the police (since there may be many police seeking to make the arrest, but only one warrant) and also for the purpose of protecting the liberty of the subject.

[5] Magistrates' Courts Act 1952, s. 93.

[6] For Eire, see the Backing of Warrants (Republic of Ireland) Act 1965 which resolves the difficulties revealed by the decision of the House of Lords in *Metropolitan Police Commissioner* v. *Hammond*, [1965] A.C. 810; [1964] 2 All E.R. 722. As regards Scotland, an alternative, more expeditious procedure is provided by the Criminal Justice (Scotland) Act 1963, s. 39 (2).

[7] See p. 374, *ante.*

[8] As defined by 125 of the 1952 Act; see p. 350, *ante.*

[9] Winfield and Jolowicz on *Tort* (9th Edn. 1971), p. 40.

[10] Jackson, *op. cit.*, p. 141.

Now, however, the law has been greatly simplified[1] by the Criminal Law Act 1967. The Act created a new category of offence (called an "arrestable offence") for which arrest without warrant[2] is permissible. An arrestable offence is any offence for which a person not previously convicted may by statute be sentenced to five years' imprisonment or more, any offence for which the penalty is fixed by law, and attempt to commit any of the offences in these two categories.[3] The Criminal Law Revision Committee, on whose report[4] the Act is based, took as its criterion for selecting these offences "the seriousness of the offence and the possible danger of leaving the offender at large, including the risk of the offence being repeated".[5]

Where an offence is arrestable (1) any person may arrest without warrant anyone who is, or is reasonably suspected by the person arresting to be, in the act of committing the offence; (2) any person may arrest without warrant any person whom he reasonably believes to have committed such an offence, or who is in fact guilty of it (reasonably suspected or not). If it is later discovered that no offence was committed by anyone (if for example a taking apparently amounting to theft is discovered to be innocent[6]) a police officer can escape liability for false imprisonment by proving reasonable cause to believe that an arrestable offence had been committed. A private person will however be liable.[7] This rule previously governed the lawfulness of arrest in the case of felonies; it has been criticised,[8] but survived examination by the Criminal Law Revision Committee and is likely to remain law for a considerable time. If the rule discourages arrest by private persons it may perhaps be justified; (3) a police officer may arrest without warrant anyone who is, or whom he reasonably suspects to be, about to commit an arrestable offence.[9]

For the purpose of exercising a right of arrest conferred by section 2, a police officer may enter any place (by force if need be) and search it.[10] More generally section 3 provides that a person may use such force as is reasonable in the circumstances in the prevention of crime, or in effecting or assisting in the lawful arrest of offenders or suspected offenders or persons unlawfully at large. The section replaces the common law rules on the subject.

Additionally, a large number of statutes now authorise arrest without warrant

---

[1] As one of the surprisingly large number of consequences flowing from the abolition of the distinction between felonies and misdemeanours.

[2] Called by the Act "summary arrest". The concept of an "arrestable offence" is used in sections 4 and 5 of the Act, which replace the old law as to accessories after the fact to felony and misprision of felony.

[3] Section 2 (1). Therefore, theft and many offences under the Theft Act are arrestable.

[4] Seventh report (Cmnd. 2659 of 1965).

[5] Paragraph 8.

[6] Thus a person shopping in a store may be arrested by a store detective for alleged shoplifting. At the trial the defendant may raise some defence going to show that although he or she took the articles, that taking was (legally) innocent; thus he may suggest that he picked the goods up and later forgot to pay for them. If the defendant is acquitted the store detective and, vicariously, the store will have no defence to an action for false imprisonment.

[7] *Walters* v. *W.H. Smith & Son, Ltd.*, [1914] 1 K.B. 595.

[8] As one respect "in which the common law has become fossilized": DIPLOCK, L.J. (as he then was) in *Dallison* v. *Caffery*, [1965] 1 Q.B. 348, at p. 370; [1964] 2 All E.R. 610, at p. 619.

[9] Criminal Law Act 1967, s. 2 (2)–(5).

[10] *Ibid.*, s. 2 (6).

in the case of individual offences.[1] For example, it is permissible to arrest a
person found committing any indictable offence by night.[2] Where a statute
authorises arrest, it is a question of construction of the particular statute as to
whether the defendant in an action for false imprisonment, arising out of an
arrest purportedly made under the Act, must show that the offence was actually
committed by the plaintiff, or whether there is a wider right to arrest if the
person arrested was apparently committing the offence in question. There is no
general rule, one way or the other, which can be applied to all such statutes.[3] In
Wiltshire v. *Barrett*[4] the Court of Appeal had to consider section 6 (4) of the Road
Traffic Act 1960, which permits a police officer to arrest without warrant "a
person committing" an offence under section 6 (driving while under the
influence of drink or drugs). The Court held that the power of arrest extended
to a person apparently committing the offence.

> ". . . This statute is concerned with the safety of all of Her Majesty's subjects who use
> the roads in this country. It is of the first importance that any person who is unfit to
> drive through drink should not be allowed to drive on the road, and that the police
> should have power to stop him from driving any further. The most effective way
> to do it is by arresting him then and there. The police have to act at once, on the
> facts as they appear on the spot: and they should be justified by the facts as they
> appear to them at the time and not on any *ex post facto* analysis of the situation."[5]

The courts, and in particular the House of Lords,[6] have laid down certain
rules governing the procedure in all cases of arrest without warrant. Every
person arresting another without a warrant must inform that other of the
reason for his arrest, or at least the facts said to constitute a crime on his part; he
need not tell him the exact charge, which may in any event be difficult or impossible to determine until after full examination of the facts. Neither need he even
give the information as to the facts of the case

> "if the arrested man is caught red-handed, and the crime is patent to high Heaven.
> Nor, obviously, is explanation a necessary prelude to arrest when it is important to
> secure a possibly violent criminal."[7]

Further, the utmost duty resting on the person making the arrest is to do what
is reasonable in the circumstances, in discharge of his obligations; thus an
arrest was held to be lawful where the defendant was unaware, because of
total deafness and inability to lip-read, that he was being arrested but the police
officer was likewise unaware of his disability and went through the motions of
arrest as for a person not under disability.[8] It seems also that an initially unlawful arrest may be "cured" by the supply of further information at a later stage.[9]

---

[1] The Criminal Law Act does not affect the power to arrest in these cases: s. 2 (7), and the
offences are not strictly "arrestable".
[2] Prevention of Offences Act 1851, s. 11.
[3] See *Barnard* v. *Gorman*, [1941] A.C. 378; [1941] 3 All E.R. 45.
[4] [1966] 1 Q.B. 312; [1965] 2 All E.R. 271.
[5] [1966] 1 Q.B. 312, at p. 321; [1965] 2 All E.R. 271, at p. 274, *per* LORD DENNING, M.R.
[6] In *Christie* v. *Leachinsky*, [1947] A.C. 573; [1947] 1 All E.R. 567.
[7] LORD SIMONDS in *Christie* v. *Leachinsky*, [1947] A.C. 573, at p. 593; [1947] 1 All E.R.
567, at p. 575.
[8] *Wheatley* v. *Lodge*, [1971] 1 All E.R. 173; [1971] 1 W.L.R. 29.
[9] *R.* v. *Kulynycz*, [1971] 1 Q.B. 367; [1970] 3 All E.R. 881.

Subject to these limitations, failure to give the defendant the reason for his arrest, or giving him a false reason (even if in fact there is a lawful ground for his arrest, of which the police do not inform him[1]) makes the arrest unlawful.

"Is citizen A bound to submit unresistingly to arrest by citizen B in ignorance of the charge made against him? I think, my Lords, that cannot be the law of England. Blind, unquestioning obedience is the law of tyrants and of slaves: it does not yet flourish on English soil."[2]

On the other hand LORD SIMONDS expressly sanctioned[3] "holding charges", i.e. minor charges made pending investigation of a major one, provided, of course, that there is reasonable belief in the minor charge.

A private person arresting without a warrant must hand the person arrested to the police or to a magistrate as soon as reasonably practicable; he will not, however, be liable in false imprisonment if he holds the person arrested for a reasonable time in order to consider the position.[4] A police officer has greater latitude:

"He can do what is reasonable to investigate the matter, and to see whether the suspicions are supported or not by further evidence. He can . . . take the person suspected to his own house to see whether any of the stolen property is there; . . . he can take the person suspected to the place where he says that he was working, for there he may find persons to confirm or refute his alibi.[5] . . ."

When a person is taken into custody without a warrant a police officer not below the rank of inspector, or the police officer in charge of the station, whatever his rank, may grant bail; further, if it will not be practicable to bring the defendant before a magistrates' court within 24 hours the officer must enquire into the case and is obliged to grant bail unless the offence appears to him to be a serious one.[6] The defendant may also be bailed to appear at the police station for further enquiry.[7] If detained in custody, he must be brought before a magistrates' court as soon as practicable.[8] At the other end of the scale it may become apparent that the defendant has not in fact committed any offence; in this case he may be released without formality, and there is no obligation to take him before any court.[9]

In this way, it will be seen that English law gives substantial protection to a person arrested without warrant, both in requiring him to be brought before a court within a reasonable time or released on bail, and in requiring that he be given particulars of what is alleged against him. The second part of the ruling in *Dallison* v. *Caffery* may be open to criticism in that it offends against the plain words of section 38 (4). The defendant can only be in custody while the police

---

1 As in *Christie's* case itself.
2 *Christie* v. *Leachinsky*, [1947] A.C. 573, at p. 591; [1947] 1 All E.R. 567, at p. 575, *per* LORD SIMONDS. It is perhaps instructive to compare the same judge's speech in *Shaw* v. *Director of Public Prosecutions*, [1962] A.C. 220; [1961] 2 All E.R. 446; see pp. 64–65, *ante*.
3 *Christie* v. *Leachinsky*, [1947] A.C. 573, at p. 593; [1947] 1 All E. R. 567, at p. 575, and see the speech of LORD DU PARCQ, at pp. 604 and 577 of the respective reports.
4 *John Lewis* v. *Tims*, [1952] A.C. 676; [1952] 1 All E.R. 1203.
5 LORD DENNING, M.R. in *Dallison* v. *Caffery*, [1965] 1 Q.B. 348, at p. 367; [1964] 2 All E.R. 610, at p. 617 (where the defendant police officer had done both these things).
6 Magistrates' Courts Act 1952, s. 38 (1).
7 *Ibid.*, s. 38 (2).
8 *Ibid.*, s. 38 (4).
9 *Wiltshire* v. *Barrett*, [1966] 1 Q.B. 312; [1965] 2 All E.R. 271; *ante*, p. 378.

officer is making his further enquiries; either a person is under arrest or he is completely free, and contrary to what is often thought and said there is no half-way-house of "arrest on suspicion".[1] Yet the Court of Appeal in *Dallison* v. *Caffery* evidently contemplated some little delay while the further enquiries were made, whereas the plain words of section 38 (4) are "as soon as practicable".

B PRELIMINARY ENQUIRY: COMMITTAL

1 Introduction

The next stage of the trial of an indictable offence will be the preliminary enquiry before justices. The police are rarely, if ever, ready to proceed on the defendant's first appearance before the magistrates' court; usually the defendant will be remanded. Remand may be in custody or on bail with or without sureties,[2] and subject to such conditions if any as are thought to be likely to result in his appearance or to be necessary in the interests of justice or for the prevention of crime.[3] Unless the accused is released on bail the period of remand cannot exceed eight clear days.[4] As regards jurisdiction, the magistrates' court at the preliminary enquiry has jurisdiction over any offence committed by a person who appears or is brought before the court, whether or not the offence alleged was committed in the county or borough for which the magistrates' court acts.[5] It will be seen that these words are wide enough to cover all the cases set out above[6] in which a magistrate may issue process in the case of an indictable offence; thus the jurisdiction of the single magistrate issuing process and the magistrates' court sitting for the purpose of the preliminary enquiry are made co-extensive. It has been noted[7] that magistrates also possess this very wide jurisdiction in a number of other cases (although not for the trial of a summary offence). A single lay magistrate may sit for the purpose of commital proceedings.[8]

Great changes in the form of committal proceedings were made by the Criminal Justice Act 1967. In all committal proceedings prior to the Act prosecution witnesses had to give evidence orally, and the magistrates had to go through the motions of satisfying themselves that there was sufficient evidence to put the defendant on trial by jury, although no-one, least of all the defendant,

---

[1] See the remarks of DEVLIN, J. (as he then was) in *R.* v. *Roberts* (1953), unreported on this point, quoted in Street, *The Law of Torts* (4th Edn.), pp. 91–92. For another point arising from the case, see p. 402, *post*.

[2] Magistrates' Courts Act 1952, s. 105 (1).

[3] Criminal Justice Act 1967, s. 21 (1). Conditions may now be imposed when anyone is released on bail, but the court has no power to order the defendant to find sureties in respect of the condition; *ibid.*, s. 21 (2).

[4] Magistrates' Courts Act 1952, s. 105 (4). Even in this case, both the defendant and the prosecutor must consent to the longer period of remand.

[5] *Ibid.*, s. 2 (3). The rules as to offences committed on boundaries or on journeys apply: see p. 374, *ante*.

[6] *Ante*, p. 373.

[7] *Ante* p. 351.

[8] Magistrates' Courts Act 1952, s. 4 (1).

questioned this.[1] The result was a great waste of time in many cases, especially long ones. Further, it was expressly provided that magistrates were not bound to sit in open court at the preliminary enquiry. Whether they should do so was the subject of much controversy. There are certain obvious arguments both in favour of publicity and against it; thus it may be argued that the general public (including the twelve jurors who will try the accused if there is a committal for trial) may be improperly prejudiced by evidence given at proceedings which are not the trial of the accused and at which the defence side of the case is very rarely heard. On the other hand there are undoubted arguments in favour of courts generally being open to the public; thus there are a number of examples[2] of persons, having read of the preliminary enquiry, coming forward with evidence for the defence. The matter received considerable attention at the trial of Dr. Adams for murder in 1957; the trial judge, DEVLIN, J. (as he then was), stating that he was speaking with the authority of the then Lord Chief Justice (LORD GODDARD), said that it would have been far better if the preliminary proceedings in that case had been held in private. Dr. Adams's case was a somewhat extreme one since the preliminary proceedings and the trial itself received a quite exceptional amount of publicity and at the preliminary enquiry there was a reference to the deaths of certain other of Dr. Adams's patients, besides the patient of whose murder he was eventually charged at the trial; no further mention was made of these patients and no evidence in respect of them was led at the trial, but there was obviously a grave risk of prejudice. The remarks of DEVLIN, J. were not apparently intended to be of general application; nevertheless, following the case, a committee was set up, under the chairmanship of LORD TUCKER, to consider the matter. In 1958 the committee reported[3] that in their opinion no details of the preliminary enquiry should be made public beyond the name of the accused and the charge, until the accused had been committed for trial or discharged by the magistrates.

2 Procedure

a Committal under the 1967 Act

This change, desirable or not, could hardly be put into effect until there was a complete reform of committal proceedings, designed to save time in the type of case mentioned above, but to preserve the existing advantages of committal proceedings, namely to give the defendant fair notice of the evidence against him and a chance to defeat a weak case at an early stage. This reform was brought about by the 1967 Act. It is now open to the court to commit for trial "without consideration of the evidence"[4] if *all* the evidence before it consists of written statements in the form required by the Act. Provided that all conditions are satisfied, the statements are admissible in committal proceedings to the same

---

[1] It is outside the scope of this work to consider the merits of having committal proceedings at all. For a full discussion, see Napley, *Law and Practice under the Criminal Justice Act*, pp. 14–19.

[2] Set out in the Tucker Report, *infra*, paragraphs 45–49. The committee was sceptical about the value of committal proceedings for this purpose.

[3] Cmnd. 479 of 1958.

[4] For the significance of this phrase (taken from the marginal note to section 1), see p. 382, *post.*

extent that oral evidence to the same effect, by the makers of statements, would be. Such statements will normally be of the prosecution witnesses, the defence not revealing its case at this early stage. The statements must be signed with a declaration that the statement is true to the best of the maker's knowledge or belief; before it is tendered to the court a copy must be given to all other parties (i.e., normally by the prosecution to the defence), none of whom must object to the statement being tendered to the court.[1] Normally, the prosecution will have ascertained in advance that there will be no objection, and would not use the procedure otherwise. They will also inform the court that all their evidence is in the form of written statements, copies of which have been given to the defence.

Thus far, statements having been tendered to the defence without objection, the court must cause the charge to be written down and read to the defendant if not already done, and then may itself receive the statements and commit for trial, at once, on the statements, without any consideration of the strength of the prosecution evidence contained in them, or even reading them.[2] The court will however consider the statements and will therefore depart from this procedure if counsel or a solicitor for the defendant or any of the defendants submits that they contain insufficient evidence to put his client on trial by jury,[3] and, not unnaturally, does not and cannot commit under this procedure if the defendant wishes to give evidence himself or call witnesses.[4] In any event, every statement must be authenticated by a signature from one of the magistrates, but signature of a single certificate now suffices. By this certificate he is treated as signing each statement individually.[5]

This shortened procedure is commonly called a "section 1 committal" or "short committal" or "committal for trial without consideration of the evidence".[6] It does however seem necessary to consider it for certain questions other than testing its strength—such as determining whether the defendant should be released on bail, and to what court he should be committed. The section 1 procedure may not be used if the defendant is not legally represented;[7] even though defendant A is legally represented, if defendant B is not the procedure may not be used in the case of either. This is a most important limitation.

The magistrates do not have to use the procedure; it is optional, and either the court or any party may require any witness to attend and give evidence in person.[8]

It was formerly held[9] that where the defendant, although under seventeen,

---

[1] Criminal Justice Act 1967, s. 2 (2). Service on the solicitor for the defendant suffices, but where there is more than one defendant, there must be one copy of the statements for each defendant: *R. v. Bott: R. v. Baker*, [1968] 1 All E.R. 1119; [1968] 1 W.L.R. 583.
[2] Magistrates' Courts Rules 1968, r. 3 (1)–(3).
[3] Criminal Justice Act 1967, s. 1 (1) (*b*).
[4] Magistrates' Courts Rules 1968, r. 3 (2).
[5] Criminal Justice Act 1967, s. 7.
[6] See p. 381, *ante.*
[7] Criminal Justice Act 1967, s. 1 (1) (*a*).
[8] *Ibid.*, s. 2 (4).
[9] *R. v. Coleshill Justices Ex parte Davies*, [1971] 3 All E.R. 929; [1971] 1 W.L.R. 1684; and see *R. v. L. and W.*, [1971] Crim. L.R. 481. In the latter case the judge held that, though not expressly prohibited, it was contrary to the spirit of the Children and Young Persons Act 1969 to use the voluntary bill procedure (for which see p. 393, *post*). *Quaere* whether this point will remain good in the light of Clause 31, *infra.*

was liable to be committed for trial under section 6 (1) of the Children and Young Persons Act 1969,[1] it was not possible to use the section 1 procedure. The reason was that section 6 (1) used the phrase ". . . if [the court] is of opinion that there is sufficient evidence to put the accused on trial" and this was construed to exclude section 1. However, clause 31 of the Criminal Justice Bill presently before Parliament permits use of the procedure.

b. *"Old-style" committal*

If it is not possible to use the section 1 procedure the court can only proceed with what is now called an "old-style committal", although this too is now somewhat altered. On appearing, the defendant is not of course asked to plead, since this is not the trial of the charge against him; indeed it may well not be until a later stage in the enquiry (as will be seen) that any specific charge is recorded in writing. In accordance with the general provisions of section 99 of the Magistrates' Courts Act 1952 either party may be represented by counsel or solicitor; if represented, the defendant would normally be deemed to be present if in fact physically absent, but in the particular case of the preliminary enquiry section 4 (3) of the 1952 Act provides that evidence before examining justices must be given in the presence of the accused. The prosecutor may make an opening speech, outlining for the benefit of the justices the facts against the accused; it is a matter for his discretion whether he does so. He will then call his evidence, which may consist of witnesses giving evidence orally or of written statements.[2] If witnesses give evidence orally their evidence must be given on oath, subject to any enactment or rule of law permitting or authorising the reception of unsworn evidence.[3] They will first be examined in chief by the prosecutor; they will then be subject to cross-examination on behalf of the defence and, if cross-examined, to re-examination on behalf of the prosecution. As each witness for the prosecution gives his or her evidence it will be recorded either by the clerk to the justices or by one of the clerk's assistants; then, as soon as possible after the examination of the witness is concluded, the whole record of that witness's evidence must be read over to him in the presence and hearing of the defendant.[4] After making any corrections that are necessary the witness must sign the document.[4] The record of the witness's evidence is called a deposition; as will be seen,[5] depositions are documents of considerable importance in the general process of the trial of an indictable offence. A deposition must be authenticated in the same way as a written statement, by signature of a magistrate, but again signature of a single certificate suffices.[6]

It is also open to the prosecution to tender written statements, in exactly the same form as those used under the section 1 procedure. Again, copies must be given to each of the defendants before they are tendered to the court and none of the defendants must object to their use. The court or any party has power to require the attendance of the maker. This procedure is very useful in the case of a witness, such as the owner of the property in many cases of theft or handling,

---

[1] See pp. 356–357, *ante.*
[2] See *infra.*
[3] Magistrates' Courts Act 1952, s. 78.
[4] Magistrates' Courts Rules 1968, r. 4 (2).
[5] See p. 391, *post.*
[6] Magistrates' Courts Rules, r. 4 (3), and see p. 382, *ante.*

whose evidence is not disputed by anyone but is necessary for the prosecution to prove their case. The statement must be read aloud unless the court otherwise directs, and the court may direct that an "account" be given of any part not read aloud.[1]

After the whole of the evidence of the prosecution has been given the defence may submit that there is no case to answer, either on the charge brought against the accused (assuming that a specific charge has been formulated at this stage; as noted above,[2] this is not necessarily so) or generally. In other words it may be submitted either that the charge brought should be reduced to a lesser charge (murder to manslaughter for example) or that the accused should be discharged altogether as being completely innocent of any crime. Such a submission is only likely to succeed in the clearest of cases, since, it will be recalled,[3] the magistrates are not concerned at this stage to assess the actual guilt or innocence of the defendant; their only duty is to decide whether there is sufficient evidence against the accused to put him on trial for any indictable offence. In rare cases the magistrates themselves (no doubt advised by their clerk; this being a case in which he could take the initiative in advising them) may take the same point on behalf of a defendant. If no submission of "no case" is made, or if it is rejected, the magistrates must cause the charge to be written down, if this has not already been done, and then read out to the defendant and its nature explained to him in ordinary language.[4] Then, before the defendant is allowed to say anything in answer to the charge the court must administer to him the statutory caution,[5] which is as follows:

> "You will have an opportunity to give evidence on oath before us and to call witnesses. But first I am going to ask you whether you wish to say anything in answer to the charge. You need not say anything unless you wish to do so; and you have nothing to hope from any promise, and nothing to fear from any threat, that may have been held out to induce you to make any admission or confession of guilt. Anything you say will be taken down and may be given in evidence at your trial. Do you wish to say anything in answer to the charge?"

Although the rule says that "words to that effect" may be used in place of the actual words of the caution, it is customary for these exact words to be used. It is one example of the English tradition of fair treatment of the defendant that, although he may be willing and anxious to admit his guilt once the charge has been read over to him and its nature explained, he will not be allowed to do so until the statutory caution has been put to him. It will be noted that although the defendant is told that anything he says may be given in evidence at his trial it will not necessarily be given in evidence against him.[6]

Whatever the defendant says in answer to the charge, once the statutory caution is complete, must be taken down in writing, read over to him and signed by one of the examining justices and also by the defendant if he so wishes.[7] This statement may then be given in evidence at the trial of the defendant

---

[1] Criminal Justice Act 1967, s. 2 (5).
[2] See p. 383, *ante.*
[3] See p. 349, *ante.*
[4] Magistrates' Courts Rules 1968, r. 4 (6).
[5] *Ibid.,* r. 4 (7).
[6] Cf. the position under the Judges' Rules; see p. 538, *post.*
[7] Magistrates' Courts Rules 1968, r. 4 (8).

(assuming that he is committed for trial) without the need for further proof. The only limitation on this procedure is that laid down by the Court of Criminal Appeal in *R.* v. *Morry*.[1] In that case the defendant was given the statutory caution in the form stated above; he then made a speech of some three hours' duration, "defending himself as an advocate". Only part of what he said was in fact transmitted to the court of trial. It was held by the Court of Criminal Appeal that: (1) the magistrates' signature was conclusive as to the contents of the statement and that no evidence could be called at the trial to prove that the whole statement was not transmitted; and (2) (in effect the reason for (1)):

> "The procedure under s. 12 was never intended to apply to a man making an oration as an advocate on his own behalf. That is not the time at which all the arguments should be put."[2]

The defendant was not handicapped for he could make the same statement to the judge and jury at his trial; in the particular case the defendant had signed not merely the end of his statement but each individual sheet of it "so that a more unmeritorious objection can scarcely be conceived".[2]

Once the defendant has made such answer as he wishes to the statutory caution, the court must further give him an opportunity to give evidence himself, and to call witnesses.[3] It will be remembered that this is not the trial of the defendant and further that the magistrates have no power to change their mind in the sense of refusing to commit for trial at all. If a submission of no case is made and rejected there must be a committal on some charge. Therefore it may do the defendant no good, and indeed positive harm, tactically, to give evidence and thereby reveal his case at this stage, especially if there is no question of being committed on a lesser charge. There have been many comments from judges on the desirability of evidence being called for the defence as early as possible, but in spite of this the defendant frequently "reserves his defence".[4] If defence evidence is called at this stage, the procedure is as follows. It is unusual for the defendant's solicitor or counsel to make an opening speech, but he may do so, in his discretion; except in one case, set out below, he has only one chance to address the court and as a matter of tactics he will usually take it after his evidence and not before. Defence evidence will then be called. Any evidence, whether that of the defendant himself or any of his witnesses, will be reproduced in the form of depositions, or may be by written statement, in exactly the same way as the evidence of prosecution witnesses. The only exception is that a witness "merely"[5] as to the accused's character will not have his evidence taken in the form of a deposition, in the rather unlikely event of such a witness being called at the preliminary enquiry. It has been said that "Good character may tend to prove the innocence of the accused, and, if so, his deposition must be taken . . ."[6] However it may be difficult in a

---

[1] [1946] K.B. 153; [1945] 2 All E.R. 632. The court was concerned with section 12 (2) and (4) of the Criminal Justice Act 1925 which is in similar terms to rule 4 (7) and (8).

[2] HILBERY, J., in *R.* v. *Morry*, [1946] K.B. 153, at pp. 155, 156; [1945] 2 All E.R. 632, at p. 634.

[3] Magistrates' Courts Rules 1968, r. 4 (10).

[4] See the cases cited in *Stone's Justices Manual* (103rd Edn.), p. 3925 (v). It is commonly (but strictly inaccurately) also stated that he "pleads not guilty".

[5] Magistrates' Courts Rules 1968, r. 4 (2).

[6] *Stone, op. cit.* p. 3923 (m).

particular case to decide whether evidence as to character does in fact exculpate the defendant until the evidence has already been given, by which time it will be too late to take a deposition if such is found to be necessary.

As to speeches, defending counsel or solicitor may, as a rule, make one speech on behalf of his client (as already noted). If however (1) the defendant himself gives evidence, (2) witnesses are called on his behalf, and (3) the court gives leave, he may address the court both before and after the defence evidence; but in this case the prosecutor will have the right to reply. His reply will be heard immediately after the evidence for the defence is concluded; then will come the second speech for the defence.[1]

3   Committal for trial

On committal for trial, four questions arise: (1) what should the charge be; (2) to which location of the Crown Court should the defendant be committed; (3) should the defendant be committed in custody or on bail and (4) should there be an "alibi warning"? Each of these questions will be considered in turn.

a   Charges

In an old-style committal it is for the justices to consider, on all the evidence, what charge is appropriate, the only limitation being that it must be properly founded on evidence appearing in the depositions. As seen,[2] their power to dismiss the charge completely only arises at the end of the prosecution evidence.

There is no power to reduce the charge on a section 1 committal; therefore, if such a committal is to be used, the prosecution may be wise to bring charges in the alternative. As already seen,[1] so long as the section 1 procedure is used, no question of dismissing the charge arises.

b   Court of trial

The Crown Court is a single court but sits in a number of different locations. These are described as first-tier, second-tier and third-tier centres. First-tier centres deal with both civil and criminal cases and are visited by High Court and Circuit judges; second-tier centres deal with criminal cases only but are visited by both High Court and Circuit judges, while third-tier centres deal with criminal cases only and are visited only by Circuit judges. Each circuit contains a number of each type of centre. Thus, for example, on the new, combined Midland and Oxford Circuit, Birmingham and Stafford are first-tier centres, Leicester and Worcester are second-tier centres and Coventry and Wolverhampton are third-tier centres. Offences in turn are divided into four classes,[3] each containing a number of offences. Offences in Class 1 must be tried by a High Court Judge; examples are murder and any offence for which a person may be sentenced to death. Offences in Class 2 must be tried by a High

---

[1] Magistrates' Courts Rules 1968, r. 4 (11).
[2] *Ante*, p. 385.
[3] By the Directions set out in *Practice Note*, [1971] 3 All E.R. 829; [1971] 1 W.L.R. 1535, para. 1; see p. 170, *ante*.

Court Judge unless a presiding judge of the Circuit releases any particular case for trial by a Circuit judge or Recorder; examples are manslaughter, abortion and rape. Offences in Class 3 are normally to be tried by a High Court judge, but may be tried by a Circuit judge or Recorder; these are all indictable offences not falling within any other Class. Offences in Class 4 will normally be tried by a Circuit Judge or Recorder,[1] although they may also be tried by a High Court judge; examples are causing death by dangerous driving, robbery, wounding with intent, all indictable offences which may be tried summarily,[2] all summary offences which may be tried on indictment[3] (when so tried) and all "hybrid" offences (when tried on indictment).[4]

Therefore, when a magistrates' court commits for trial a person charged with any offence within Classes 1–3,[5] it must specify, as the place of trial, the location of the Crown Court where a High Court judge regularly sits. In the case of an offence in Class 4 the magistrates' court must simply specify the most convenient location of the Crown Court. If, however, the magistrates think that an offence[6] although within Class 4 should be tried by a High Court judge, they should commit as for an offence in Classes 1–3, giving their reasons in a notice included with the papers sent to the Crown Court. The Directions specify a number of reasons which "should influence the justices in favour of trial by a High Court judge", for example that widespread public concern is involved, the case involves violence of a serious nature, the accused holds a public position or is a professional or other person owing a duty to the public, or a novel or difficult issue of law is likely to be involved. In selecting the most convenient location of the Crown Court, the magistrates should have regard to (i) the convenience of the defence, the prosecution and the witnesses, (ii) the expediting of the trial and (iii) the location or locations designated by a presiding judge of the Circuit in question as being the "normal" location or locations for committal.[7]

The Crown Court has jurisdiction to alter the location of any trial on indictment, whether previously fixed by itself or the magistrates.[8] A corresponding power, vested in the High Court by the Administration of Justice Act 1938, was sometimes used where there was such strong bias against the defendant that there was little chance of finding an impartial jury to try him.[9]

It is now expressly provided that the trial of a person committed to the Crown Court must begin not later than eight weeks from the date of his committal,

---

[1] By paragraph 13 of the Directions, proceedings listed for hearing by a Circuit judge or Recorder are suitable for allocation to a court comprising Justices of the Peace.

[2] See p. 351, *ante*.

[3] See p. 362, *ante*.

[4] See p. 366, *ante*.

[5] Even if there is one or more further offences within Class 4 and not of a type suitable to be tried by a High Court judge.

[6] Even if there is one or more other offences, within Class 4, and not of a type suitable to be tried by a High Court judge.

[7] Directions, paras. 2–5 and Courts Act 1971, s. 7 (1) (*a*) and (*b*).

[8] Courts Act 1971, s. 7 (2).

[9] Since jurors at that time had to come from the locality. See however, Jackson, *Machinery of Justice in England* (5th Edn.), p. 115 for an account of removal of a trial because of local bias against the prosecution. There had already been one trial, at which the jury disagreed.

unless the Crown Court itself otherwise orders.[1] It must not begin sooner than fourteen days from committal, unless both the prosecution and the defence consent.[1] The trial is deemed to begin when the defendant is arraigned.[2]

c   Bail

The magistrates must consider whether to release the defendant on bail, or to commit in custody. Generally, the matter is in their discretion, except that (a) a person charged with treason can only be admitted to bail by order of a High Court judge or the Home Secretary[3], (b) where the charge is a summary offence, on which the defendant or the prosecutor has a right to, and has chosen, trial by jury, committal must be on bail, except in specified circumstances.[4] The Court of Criminal Appeal has said[5] that the magistrates not only can but must enquire into the previous record of the defendant at this stage if not earlier, since if the defendant has a bad record this is a matter which they must consider before granting bail. It is obviously very undesirable that any record of the convictions should appear in any newspaper;[6] "arrangements as to bail" may still be published in the press (see below) but it is open to question whether this includes discussion of previous convictions. Where a magistrates' court commits a person for trial for any offence, but does not release him on bail, he has a right of appeal to a High Court judge; if he is not legally represented he must be expressly told of the right.[7] The court must also give him written notice stating the reason for refusal, in any event if he is not represented or at the request of his counsel or solicitor if he is.[7]

d   Alibi warning

Finally, there will be the question of what is commonly called "the alibi warning". At his trial the defendant will not be allowed to adduce evidence in support of an alibi—except with leave of the court—unless he has given to the prosecutor particulars of the alibi within seven days from the end of the committal proceedings.[8] Therefore, if there is any question at the trial as to the time or place of an alleged offence, this must be resolved on the material available to the defendant, namely the charges and the depositions.[9] Notice

---

[1] Courts Act 1971, s. 7 (4) (*a*), (*b*) and Crown Court Rules 1971 (S.I. 1971/1292), r. 19. Delay in hearing cases, especially of defendants on bail, was one of the main criticisms of the old system of Assizes and Quarter Sessions.

[2] Courts Act 1971, s. 7 (4) (ii); for "arraignment" see p. 400, *post*.

[3] Magistrates' Courts Act 1952, s. 8.

[4] Criminal Justice Act 1967, s. 18 (3)–(5).

[5] In *R.* v. *Armstrong*, [1951] 2 All E.R. 219.

[6] Even if they do, it seems that this affords the defendant no valid ground of appeal: *R.* v. *Armstrong* (*supra*).

[7] Criminal Justice Act 1967, s. 18 (7), (8). It will be recalled that the section 1 committal procedure cannot be used if any defendant is not represented.

[8] *Ibid.*, s. 11. For the definition of "evidence in support of an alibi", and for the position at the trial, see p. 412, *post*.

[9] *R.* v. *Lewis*, [1969] 2 Q.B. 1; [1969] 1 All E.R. 79. The court stated this "with confidence", but said, "It will no doubt be proved in future that there are many difficulties in

may of course be given before the committal proceedings, or during them; if it has not been given up to then, the warning must contain the name and address of the prosecutor, on whom notice may be served.

If the court of trial is satisfied that the warning is not given, evidence in support of an alibi may be called without leave.[1] In practice the warning may be inappropriate, because there is obviously no question of a defence of alibi; the clerk to the justices may confirm this by reference to the defendant's counsel or solicitor, and then not give the warning.[2]

4 Publicity

It would have been inappropriate to reform committal proceedings without solving the vexed question of publicity. By section 3 of the 1967 Act, it is generally unlawful to publish any report of committal proceedings, apart from various formal matters such as the court, the names of the justices, defendants and advocates, a summary of the charges and the decision as to whether or not to commit. The evidence, called by either side, may not be published until the end of the trial,[3] if the defendant is committed, or the end of committal proceedings, if he is not. Reforms such as these have often been urged, but attacked by the press on the ground of "secrecy of justice"; yet of course none of the restrictions apply to the trial proper. Further it is open to the defendants or any one of them to apply, and the court must then order that the restriction is not to apply.[4] Where charges against different defendants are so interconnected as to be the result of one set of committal proceedings, there must be full publicity for the whole proceedings even if only one defendant applies for it.[5] The same applies if there is only one defendant and several charges, but one set of committal proceedings.[6] Where committal proceedings are adjourned, the court must on the adjourned hearing state that an order lifting the ban was made at the earlier hearing, if that was the case.[7]

All the above applies to publicity in the press, and on radio and television. As regards admission of the public to committal proceedings, the Act expressly states that examining justices must sit in public unless (a) statute directs to the contrary or (b) the magistrates consider that the ends of justice would not be served by them sitting in open court, as regards the whole or any part of the committal proceedings.[8] It remains to be seen how (b) is interpreted. Thus, the position under the 1952 Act is reversed, and publicity is encouraged as

---

section 11"; for some of these, see p. 412, *post*. The prosecutor should send a copy of any notice received by him to the court of trial, to assist in estimating the length of the trial: *Practice Direction*, [1969] 1 All E.R. 1042; [1969] 1 W.L.R. 603.

[1] Criminal Justice Act 1967, s. 11 (3).
[2] Magistrates' Courts Rules 1968, r. 4 (9).
[3] By which time it will have been superseded by evidence given at the trial and will be of no general interest.
[4] Criminal Justice Act 1967, s. 3 (2).
[5] *R. v. Russell, Ex parte Beaverbrook Newspapers, Ltd.,* [1969] 1 Q.B. 342; [1968] 3 All E. R. 695.
[6] *R. v. Bow St. Magistrate, Ex parte Kray,* [1969] 1 Q.B. 473; [1968] 3 All E.R. 872; and see *R. v. Blackpool Justices, Ex parte Beaverbrook Newspapers, Ltd.,* [1972] 1 All E.R. 388; [1972] 1 W.L.R. 95.
[7] Magistrates' Courts Rules 1968, r. 3 (3).
[8] Criminal Justice Act 1967, s. 6.

regards the attendance of members of the public in court, but not as regards reports to a wider public in the press and on television. Further, where the defendant is committed, or discharged after decision not to commit, there must be published on that day or the next, in a part of the magistrates' court to which the public have access, certain details such as the defendant's name and address, the charge or charges and (if there is a committal) the court of trial.[1]

5 Securing the attendance of witnesses

Formerly, on committal for trial, most, if not all, witnesses giving evidence at the preliminary enquiry would have been bound over in a certain sum to appear at the court of trial and give evidence. A new scheme was created by the Criminal Procedure (Attendance of Witnesses) Act 1965; it applies to all witnesses giving evidence before the magistrates except the defendant and any witness of his merely as to character. As soon as possible after the witness has signed his deposition[2] he must be handed a document called a witness order, commanding him to appear at the court of trial. No sum of money is liable to be forfeited if the witness fails to appear, but disobedience to a witness order is contempt of the trial court and as such is punishable summarily by imprisonment for a period not exceeding three months or by other penalty imposed by the court of trial, unless the witness can satisfy the court that he had "just excuse" for failure to attend.[3]

If, however, the magistrates consider that the evidence of a particular witness at the trial is unlikely to be disputed or even required they may make in the case of that witness a conditional witness order, which requires him to attend at the court of trial only if notice is given to him to do so. Even if a full order has been made in the case of a particular witness, the court may subsequently direct that it be treated as a conditional witness order.[4] Either side may procure the attendance of such a witness by giving notice to the clerk to the justices at any time before the opening of the sittings of the trial court and to the clerk of the trial court thereafter.[5] On committing the defendant for trial the court must inform him of his right to require the attendance at the trial of a witness in respect of whom a conditional witness order has been made, and the necessary steps which he must take.[6]

The depositions and a number of other documents will be forwarded to the trial court by the clerk to the justices.[7] The person having custody of the depositions (the clerk to the justices before committal; the clerk of the trial court thereafter) must supply to the defendant copies of the depositions and a copy of the list of witnesses in respect of whom witness orders have been made, if and when he makes application to see them.[8] The defendant's right to see the information has already been noted.[9] The general importance of the depositions

---

[1] Criminal Justice Act 1967, s. 4. It is not stated how long the notice must be displayed.
[2] A term which includes in this context statements tendered for the purpose of section 1 committal proceedings.
[3] Act of 1965, s. 3.
[4] See generally Magistrates' Courts Rules 1968, r. 5, and Act of 1965, s. 1 (2).
[5] Magistrates' Courts Rules 1968, r. 6 (1). The other party must be informed.
[6] Act of 1965, s. 1 (3).
[7] See generally, Magistrates' Courts Rules 1968, r. 10.
[8] *Ibid.*, r. 11.
[9] See p. 372, *ante.*

is that, subject to a notice of additional evidence being served, what is in the depositions will be the evidence called against the defendant at the trial; the indictment can only be drawn from material appearing in the depositions, prosecuting counsel at the trial must confine himself in his opening speech to what appears in them and any departure from a deposition is regarded as an appropriate subject for cross-examination of a witness.

C PREFERMENT OF BILL

1 Introduction

"A bill of indictment is a written or printed accusation of crime made at the suit of the Crown against one or more persons."[1] There is an important difference between a bill of indictment and an indictment proper. A bill of indictment may be preferred by any person[2] against any other person before the Crown Court;[3] however a bill of indictment is of no legal validity in itself. It only becomes a legal document when it is turned into an indictment proper by being signed by the appropriate officer of the court, who in turn can only sign the draft bill if he is satisfied that one of four things has happened: (1) either the person charged has been committed for trial by examining justices; this is naturally the most common; (2) the "voluntary bill" procedure has been followed; (3) the bill is preferred pursuant to an order made under section 9 of the Perjury Act 1911; or (4) the bill is preferred by direction of the Court of Appeal.[3] The three latter contingencies are considered below.[4] If one of these four is satisfied, the judge of the court may direct the appropriate officer to sign the bill, either on his own motion or on the application of the prosecution.[3] After it has been signed, the proper officer must on request supply to the defendant a copy free of charge.[5]

Where the bill is preferred on the authority of a committal for trial it may charge any offence which appears on the depositions, or statements, in addition to or in place of the offence or offences for which he was committed, subject to the normal rules as to joinder of offences.[6] It is immaterial that the "added" offences involve a higher penalty than the original charge or charges. This rule does not in any way destroy what has already been described as one of the main purposes or advantages of the preliminary enquiry, namely to give the defendant fair notice of the case against him, since he will necessarily have knowledge of the facts alleged to constitute the offence, if not of the precise charge based on those facts. However, there are obvious possibilities of injustice, and the Court of Appeal has said[7] that whenever it is decided to bring such "fresh" charges, the police ought to see the defendant and warn him of

---

1 Archbold, *Pleading, Evidence and Practice in Criminal Cases* (37th Edn.), para. 1.
2 Except in those cases where a private person has no right to institute proceedings: see p. 371, *ante*.
3 Administration of Justice (Miscellaneous Provisions) Act 1933, s. 2 (1), (2), as amended.
4 See pp. 392–394, *post*.
5 Indictment Rules 1971, r. 10 (1).
6 Administration of Justice (Miscellaneous Provisions) Act 1933, s. 2 (2) (i). For the rules as to joinder, see p. 396, *post*.
7 In *R. v. Dickson*, [1969] 1 All E.R. 729; [1969] 1 W.L.R. 405, where the defendant's solicitors had six days' notice of "fresh" charges.

the charges under caution, so that he may make a statement in answer if he wishes.

The whole of the indictment may consist of such "substitute" charge or charges. If the defendant considers that one or more of such charges does not fairly arise out of the facts in the depositions he may move to quash the indictment. It is then for the trial judge to rule on the sufficiency of the indictment. "The question in its nature is one of legal objection to the indictment, and is appropriate matter for a motion to quash it."[1]

Where however the defendant was committed for trial in respect of two offences which had been repealed by statute, it was held that he was never lawfully committed at all, and it was immaterial that the third count of the indictment was in respect of an offence which both existed and was disclosed by the depositions.[2]

It cannot be denied that there is a certain risk of hardship to the defendant in this procedure, since he may go to trouble and expense to defeat a particular charge at the stage of committal proceedings, only to find (on the assumption that he is committed for trial in respect of other matters) that the same charge appears in the indictment.

"...We think it right to say that... it is an undesirable practice and can easily in some cases work hardship on defendants, and the right to prefer in the indictment charges which the magistrate has rejected is one which ought to be very carefully regarded."[3]

It was formerly held[4] that the power ought not to be exercised where the defendant could elect and had elected to be tried on indictment in respect of a summary offence. This was doubted in *R. v. Roe*[5] (*obiter*, since the court was concerned with a hybrid offence) and not followed in *R. v. Nisbet*,[6] where the defendant was originally charged with one offence, could and did elect trial, and then faced added charges. This is subject to the paramount requirement that the new charges must be founded on facts or evidence disclosed in the depositions or statements, and subject to the inherent jurisdiction of the court to prevent unfairness. The court "explained" *R. v. Phillips* on this ground. In *R. v. Nisbet* there was no unfairness; the appellant having elected trial in respect of the single, original, charge, it was reasonable to suppose that he would also have elected in respect of the added charges had they been put to him in the magistrates' court.

2 Voluntary bills

The voluntary bill procedure must now be considered. The essence of the procedure is that the prosecution apply to a judge for leave to prefer a bill of indictment against the accused; the judge in his discretion grants or refuses[7] leave,

---

[1] HILBERY, J. in *R. v. Morry*, [1946] K.B. 153, at p. 157; [1945] 2 All E.R. 632, at p. 636.
[2] *R. v. Lamb*, [1969] 1 All E.R. 45; [1968] 1 W.L.R. 1946.
[3] FINNEMORE, J. in *R. v. Dawson*; *R. v. Wenlock*, [1960] 1 All E.R. 558, at p. 562; [1960] 1 W.L.R. 163, at p. 168.
[4] In *R. v. Phillips*, [1953] 2 Q.B. 14; [1953] 1 All E.R. 968.
[5] See p. 368, *ante*.
[6] [1971] 1 Q.B. 37; [1971] 3 All E.R. 307.
[7] See, for example, *In Re Roberts*, [1967] 1 W.L.R. 47. The exercise of the judge's discretion is not open to review: *R. v. Rothfield*, [1937] 4 All E.R. 320.

with the result that if leave is granted the bill is preferred forthwith and there is no need for any committal proceedings. At the same time the defendant loses the advantage of knowing in advance the substance of the case against him; indeed the applicant himself does not have to attend unless directed by the judge to do so, and even if he does attend the hearing is not in open court.[1] Regular use of the voluntary bill procedure could therefore lead to hardship, and, there are indications in the rules that the procedure[2] is to be regarded as a somewhat exceptional one.

All applications must be accompanied by the proposed bill of indictment and, unless the application is being made by or on behalf of the Director of Public Prosecutions, an affidavit by the applicant that the statements contained in his application are true to the best of his knowledge, information and belief. It has been held[3] to be sufficient compliance with these rules if the proposed indictment is actually before the judge at the time when he deals with the application. There must also be the depositions, where appropriate, and the statements of witnesses proposed to be called for the prosecution, in so far as their evidence does not appear from the depositions. The application must also state whether there has been any previous application for a voluntary bill, whether there have been any committal proceedings and the result in each case. Most applications for a voluntary bill are made after the magistrates have refused to commit. Where there have been no committal proceedings, the application must state why the present procedure is being used; again, if the defendant has been committed for trial the application must contain a statement as to the reason why it is being made. There might, of course, be perfectly good reasons; thus the voluntary bill procedure is obviously much quicker than proceedings by way of preliminary enquiry, and it might be thought desirable to use it if certain co-defendants had already been committed for trial and were awaiting trial. By the voluntary bill procedure, considerable delay and hardship to them might be avoided. Nevertheless the requirement that the bill must state specifically why the present procedure is being used instead of committal proceedings (if such is the case) shows that indiscriminate use of the procedure is to be avoided.

3 Perjury Act 1911

Section 9 of the Perjury Act provides that where a judge (including a justice of the peace) is of opinion that any person has committed perjury in proceedings before him he may order the prosecution of that person for perjury and may commit him in custody or on bail to take his trial. This procedure, which is a combination of the voluntary bill procedure and committal for trial by examining justices, is now rarely used; even in the clearest cases the judge will normally send the papers to the Director of Public Prosecutions for him to consider the matter and take proceedings if thought fit, rather than take the initiative himself.

---

[1] Although it seems that judgment may be given in open court: *Re Roberts (supra)*.
[2] Laid down in the Indictments (Procedure) Rules 1933.
[3] In *R. v. Rothfield*, [1937] 4 All E.R. 320.

4 Criminal Appeal Act 1968

Section 8 of this Act provides that, where the Court of Appeal orders a new trial under the Act, that trial is to be on a fresh indictment preferred by the direction of the Court of Appeal.

D INDICTMENT

1 Form and contents

The rules as to the form of indictments are now contained in the Indictments Act 1915 and the Indictment Rules 1971. The Act in particular effected a much needed simplification in the law, the previous rules being technical to the point of absurdity. At present, drafting of the indictment is primarily the responsibility of the appropriate officer of the court, but in cases where more than ordinary care may be requisite in framing the indictment, it is often drawn by counsel. In *R* v. *Martin*[1] the Court of Criminal Appeal said that counsel should be instructed "in all cases of difficulty".

An indictment is in three parts: introductory matters, statement of offence and particulars of offence. The introductory matters are twofold, first the court of trial and secondly the name of the defendant, appearing in the form:

THE QUEEN v. [Defendant] . . . charged as follows:—

As regards the statement of offence and particulars of offence, the Rules now provide[2] that every indictment must contain, and need not contain more than, a statement of the specific offence with which the defendant is charged, describing the offence shortly, together with such particulars as are necessary to give reasonable information as to the nature of the charge. Where, however, the offence is created by statute, there must be a reference to the statute and to the relevant section, and all the essential elements of the offence must be disclosed in the particulars, unless the defendant is not prejudiced or embarrassed by failure to describe any such element.[3] The repealed Rules contained elaborate provisions as to descriptions;[4] these are now superfluous.

2 Joinder: Separate Trials

Hitherto the indictment has been considered as charging one offence only. However, within certain limits, a single indictment may charge more than one offence, or be drawn in respect of more than one defendant, or both. The rules relating to joinder (the technical term used) of offenders or offences must therefore now be considered. So far as joinder of offenders is concerned, the basic rule is that where two or more persons join in the commission of an offence, all or any number of them may be jointly indicted for that offence, or each may be indicted separately. In the latter case there would be no power in

---

[1] [1962] 1 Q.B. 221; [1961] 2 All E.R. 747.

[2] Indictment Rules, r. 5 (1). Cf. the rules for the contents of an information; see p. 371, *ante*. Rule 5 further provides for a form of indictment for individual offences to be approved by the Lord Chief Justice.

[3] *Ibid.*, r. 6. It is not necessary for the indictment to specify or negative any exception, exemption, excuse, proviso or qualification. There is again an analogy with the rules for the contents of an information.

[4] For details, see the earlier editions of this work.

any court to order "consolidation" of the indictments, however desirable this might seem from the point of view of saving time and expense.[1] However, joinder is now very common. None of the Indictment Rules deal specifically with joinder of offenders (as distinct from offences) and the matter depends upon decisions of the courts, particularly of the Court of Criminal Appeal. The latest formulation of the rule on this subject is as follows:[2]

"As a general rule it is, of course, no more proper to have tried by the same jury offenders on charges of committing individual offences that have nothing to do with each other than it is to try before the same jury offences committed by the same person that have nothing to do with each other. Where, however, the matters which constitute the individual offences of the several offenders are upon the available evidence so related, whether in time or by other factors, that the interests of justice are best served by their being tried together, then they can properly be the subject of counts in one indictment and can ... be tried together. Such a rule, of course, includes cases where there is evidence that several offenders acted in concert but is not limited to such cases."

The court stressed that:

"... It is the interests of justice as a whole that must be the governing factor and ... amongst those interests are those of the accused."

This formulation will no doubt govern the practice of the courts for a considerable time to come. The question of joinder of offenders requires careful consideration, since where two persons are charged jointly they must be acquitted if it is shown that each committed an offence independently.[3] If this may happen, it is in the prosecution's interest to bring separate indictments.

If these rules are broken, the indictment is bad and may properly be made the subject of a motion to quash.[4] Even if the indictment is good on the face of it, it is essentially a matter for the discretion of the court whether several offenders can properly be tried together at the same time.

"The discretion, no doubt, must be exercised judicially, that is, not capriciously. The judge must consider the interests of justice as well as the interests of the prisoners."[5]

Further there is no rule that where the defence of one co-accused is to blame the other for the crime a separate trial must be ordered, although that is obviously a matter which the trial judge will take into consideration.[6] Separate trials might also be ordered where prejudice would result from a joint trial; thus evidence might be admissible against one co-defendant but not against another, or one of

---

[1] *Crane* v. *Director of Public Prosecutions*, [1921] 2 A.C. 299.

[2] *R.* v. *Assim*, [1966] 2 Q.B. 249, at pp. 261–262; [1966] 2 All E.R. 881, at pp. 887–888.

[3] *R.* v. *Scaramanga*, [1963] 2 Q.B. 807; [1963] 2 All E.R. 852. See also *R.* v. *Parker*, [1969] 2 All E.R. 15; [1969] 2 Q.B. 248, and *R.* v. *Merriman*, [1971] 2 Q.B. 310; [1971] 2 All E.R. 1424. In the last case the Court of Appeal, while following the two earlier decisions, commented unfavourably on the state of the law and gave leave to appeal to the House of Lords. The appeal has still to be heard.
    The position is of course different if the co-defendant is acquitted; there is then no question of the other defendant being found guilty of a second offence and no need for evidence that he acted jointly: *R.* v. *Rowlands*, [1972] 1 All E.R. 306; [1972] 2 W.L.R. 39.

[4] As to which, see p. 407, *post.*

[5] Lord Goddard, C.J. in *R.* v. *Grondkowski*; *R.* v. *Malinowski*, [1946] K.B. 369, at p. 372.

[6] See, among many cases, *R.* v. *Bywaters* (1922), 17 Cr. App. Rep. 660.

the co-defendants might already have been convicted in respect of substantially similar offences.

"The real test after all, which must be applied by a court of criminal appeal on a matter which is essentially one of discretion is, has the exercise of the discretion resulted in a miscarriage of justice?"[1]

So far as joinder of offences is concerned, the basic rule is to be found in rule 9 of the 1971 Rules:

"Charges for any offences may be joined in the same indictment if those charges are founded on the same facts or form or are a part of a series of offences of the same or a similar character."

It is a matter of fact and degree in each case as to whether this rule is satisfied. Thus it has been held[2] that there should not be included in the same indictment one count charging rape and another count charging indecent assault on another woman at another time; wholly disconnected and dissimilar offences ought not to be joined in the same indictment even against the same accused. Again, one and the same incident should not be made the subject of distinct charges,[3] because "hereafter it may appear to those not familiar with the circumstances that two entirely separate offences were committed".[4] Thus, one incident should not be the subject of separate charges of buggery and indecent assault.[3] In contrast, the House of Lords[5] held that two charges were properly joined in the same indictment where the defendant was charged first with attempted larceny from a public house and secondly with robbery, following a fracas, in another public house in the same area 15 days later. Although the offences were not founded on the same facts, two could make a series, and the offences had the same essential ingredient of theft or attempted theft in a public house. It used to be the rule[6] that no other offence should be charged in any indictment alleging murder or manslaughter, the charge of murder being regarded as too serious a matter to be complicated by having alternative counts inserted in the indictment. This rule was progressively abrogated by the Homicide Act 1957 which allowed two murders to be joined in one indictment and, later, by the decision of the House of Lords in *Connelly* v. *Director of Public Prosecutions*[7] and a *Practice Direction*[8] consequent thereon. There is now no special rule as regards murder or manslaughter.

If the rules as to joinder of offences are infringed the indictment again is bad and is liable to be quashed. Even on the assumption that joinder is legally permissible, the judge may in his discretion order one or more counts to be tried separately from the rest of the indictment, on the ground that the defendant would be prejudiced or embarrassed by the joinder. Thus, separate trials may

---

[1] LORD GODDARD, C.J. in *R.* v. *Grondkowski (supra)*, at p. 374.
[2] *R.* v. *Muir* (1938), 26 Cr. App. Rep. 164.
[3] *R.* v. *Harris*, [1969] 2 All E.R. 599; [1969] 1 W.L.R. 745.
[4] *R.* v. *Harris*, [1969] 2 All E.R., at p. 599; [1969] 1 W.L.R., at p. 746.
[5] In *Ludlow* v. *Metropolitan Police Commissioner*, [1971] A.C. 29; [1970] 1 All E.R. 567. The House was considering the appropriate provision of the 1915 Rules, which was materially the same as Rule 9. See also *R.* v. *Kray*, [1970] 1 Q.B. 125; [1969] 3 All E.R. 941.
[6] Laid down in *R.* v. *Jones*, [1918] 1 K.B. 416. There was also the possibility of a compromise verdict in a murder case.
[7] [1964] A.C. 1254; [1964] 2 All E. R. 401; see p. 407, *post*.
[8] [1964] 3 All E.R. 509; [1964] 1 W.L.R. 1244.

be ordered where evidence is admissible on one count but not on another, or where even if such evidence is technically admissible on both or all counts its prejudicial value on one count far exceeds its probative value. Thus in a case in which the defendant had been tried on an indictment containing no less than forty counts of obtaining or attempting to obtain by false pretences HAWKINS, J. observed:[1]

> "Though not illegal, it is hardly fair to put a man upon his trial on such an indictment for it is almost impossible that he should not be grievously prejudiced as regards each one of the charges by the evidence which is given on the others. In such a case it would not be unreasonable for the defendant to make an application that each count or set of counts should be taken separately."

The sentiment was echoed by a Lord Chief Justice:

> "The risk, the danger, the logical fallacy is indeed quite manifest. . . . It is so easy to derive from a series of unsatisfactory accusations, if there are enough of them, an accusation which at least appears satisfactory. It is so easy to collect from a mass of ingredients, not one of which is sufficient, a totality which will appear to contain what is missing."[2]

Alternatively, the offences may be numerous and complicated, or difficult to disentangle, so that a joint trial would cause confusion, and embarrassment to the defence.[3] Conversely, it may be very material (though not conclusive) in favour of a joint trial that evidence given in support of one count is admissible, to prove system, on other counts.[4] The test is essentially one of prejudice to the defendant, and the Court of Appeal will not interfere with the judge's discretion unless it can see that justice has not been done or unless compelled to do so by some overwhelming fact. Even if the judge gives a bad reason, the Court of Appeal will not interfere if satisfied that there was a good reason.[5]

Where two or more offences are joined in one indictment each one must be alleged in a separate count or paragraph of the indictment.[6] Well before the passing of the Indictments Act this rule was uniform and well established. Where an indictment contravenes this rule it is said to be bad for duplicity. Thus in *R. v. Molloy*[7] the defendant was charged in an indictment, the particulars of which stated that in a certain place and at a certain time he "stole, or with intent to steal, ripped and severed or broke" certain articles. The indictment was clearly bad for duplicity since, under the relevant Act, the Larceny Act 1916, stealing and ripping with intent to steal were distinct offences; they should therefore have been put in separate counts of the indictment and separate pleas taken in respect of each. Similarly in *R. v. Nicholls*[8] the defendant

---

[1] *R. v. King*, [1897] 1 Q.B. 214, at p. 216.

[2] LORD HEWART, C.J. in *R. v. Bailey*, [1924] 2 K.B. 300, at p. 305.

[3] Cf. *Ludlow's* case (*supra*), at pp. 41 and 576 of the respective Reports. See also *R. v. Fitzpatrick*, [1962] 3 All E.R. 840; [1963] 1 W.L.R. 7.

[4] *R. v. Flack*, [1969] 2 All E.R. 784; [1969] 1 W.L.R. 937; and see *R. v. Sims*, [1946] K.B. 531; [1946] 1 All E.R. 697; see p. 460, *post*.

[5] *Ibid.*

[6] Indictment Rules 1971, r. 4 (2). Each count is equivalent to a separate indictment (for one consequence of this, see p. 400, *post*). Counts must be numbered consecutively: r. 4 (3).

[7] [1921] 2 K.B. 364.

[8] [1960] 2 All E.R. 449; [1960] 1 W.L.R. 658. In *Jones v. Freeman*, [1970] 1 All E.R. 1117; [1970] 1 W.L.R. 659 the Queen's Bench Divisional Court indicated that handling under section 22 of the Theft Act was only one offence but that the different methods of handling, described in the section, should be alleged in separate counts.

was charged on an indictment of which the statement of offence and particulars of offence were as follows:

> *Statement of offence*: warehousebreaking contrary to sections 26(1) and 27(2) of the Larceny Act 1916. *Particulars of offence*: the defendant on a particular named day "broke and entered a warehouse with intent to steal therein and stole therein . . .".

This indictment again was bad for duplicity, since both the statement of offence and the particulars of offence contained two separate offences, warehousebreaking with intent to steal and warehousebreaking and stealing. The matter was not a mere technicality, since the first offence carried a maximum of seven years' imprisonment and the second a maximum of fourteen.

There are exceptions or apparent exceptions to this rule. Where an offence created by statute is defined as doing or not doing different acts in the alternative, or in any one of different capacities or with any one of different intentions, or where some part of the offence is stated in the alternative, the indictment may follow the statute and charge the offence in a single count[1] Thus it was held under the old law (and would presumably still be held today) that a single count in an indictment may charge driving while under the influence of a drink or a drug; the words of the relevant section in the Road Traffic Act charge a single offence, namely driving while incapable of having proper control, whether that incapacity is caused by drink or drugs.[2]

Again, s. 1 (1) of the Children and Young Persons Act 1933 makes it an offence wilfully to assault, ill-treat, neglect, abandon or expose a child. It has been held that the section describes in detail various forms of cruelty to a child, and that if the indictment selects one out of the five verbs it is immaterial that the conduct proved might be more aptly described by one of the others. Therefore a count in the indictment may properly charge more than one or even presumably all five forms of cruelty.[3]

It has even been held[4] that a count in an indictment may charge causing death by driving a motor car at a speed and in a manner dangerous to the public having regard to all the circumstances, the offence being defined by the Road Traffic Act 1960, section 1 as causing death

> ". . . by the driving of a motor vehicle on a road recklessly, or at a speed or in a manner which is dangerous to the public, having regard to all the circumstances of the case".

Similarly, by long standing practice of the courts if not by any express statutory authority, a single count in an indictment could charge burglary and larceny under the Larceny Act 1916; equally a single count could charge any of the housebreaking offences and larceny. Practice under the Theft Act 1968 appears to be similar.

3   Objecting to the indictment: amendment

If the defendant desires to object to the validity of the indictment he should do so before he is arraigned. The Court of Appeal does not readily hear objec-

---

[1] Indictment Rules 1971, r. 7.
[2] *Thomson* v. *Knights*, [1947] K.B. 336; [1947] 1 All E.R. 112. See also *R.* v. *Inman*, [1967] 1 Q.B. 140; [1966] 3 All E.R. 414, and see p. 371, *ante*; p. 434, *post*.
[3] *R.* v. *Hayles*, [1969] 1 Q.B. 364; [1969] 1 All E.R. 34.
[4] *R.* v. *Clow*, [1965] 1 Q.B. 598; [1963] 2 All E.R. 216.

tions to the validity of an indictment where the objection was not taken at the trial, although failure to take it is not insuperable. When objection is taken the court may (unless it rules against the objection altogether) either quash the indictment or amend it. Quashing the indictment may arise from causes other than formal defects in it and will be considered below.[1] As to amendment section 5 (1) of the 1915 Act provides:

"Where before trial, or at any stage of a trial, it appears to the court that the indictment is defective, the court shall make such order for the amendment of the indictment as the court thinks necessary to meet the circumstances of the case, unless, having regard to the merits of the case, the required amendments cannot be made without injustice. . . ."

Since amendment of the indictment includes the addition of a new count, the court's powers would appear to be very wide;

"In our opinion, any alteration in matters of description, and probably in many other respects, may be made in order to meet the evidence in the case so long as the amendment causes no injustice to the accused person."[2]

Thus in *R. v. Pople*[3] the defendants were charged with obtaining certain quantities of cash by false pretences (under the Larceny Act 1916). At the close of the prosecution case, and because of the state of the prosecution evidence, the prosecution were permitted to amend the indictment by the substitution of cheques for the amounts in question instead of cash as originally alleged. It was held that in substance the charge was unaltered and that the amendment was properly made. Again in *R. v. Hall*[4] a charge of stealing 3 pictures was amended to stealing 8, there being evidence of stealing 8 on the depositions. The court applied what had been said in *R. v. Martin*, that

"An indictment which charges offences which are not disclosed in the depositions and fails to charge an offence which is lacks the most essential quality of an indictment."[5]

At the other end of the scale it is very doubtful whether, once the defendant has been arraigned and has pleaded, any new count can be added by way of amendment since the defendant will not have pleaded to it and injustice would almost certainly be caused.[5] A new count may be added before the defendant is arraigned, and even after arraignment a count can be amended to any extent short of charging a completely new offence; the question is one of degree depending on the facts of the particular case.[6]

Application for amendment may be made by either side and at any time. Since counsel for the prosecution has general responsibility for the correctness of the indictment he should not open his case without being satisfied on the point and should make any necessary application for amendment before the

---

[1] See p. 407, *post*.
[2] Humphreys, J. in *R. v. Pople*, [1951] 1 K.B. 53, at p. 57; *sub. nom. R. v. Smith*, [1950] 2 All E.R. 679, at p. 681.
[3] *Supra*.
[4] [1968] 2 Q.B. 788; [1968] 2 All E.R. 1009.
[5] *Per curiam* in *R. v. Martin*, [1962] 1 Q.B. 221; [1961] 2 All E.R. 747.
[6] It seems that an amendment on an immaterial matter can be made at or after verdict: *R. v. Dossi* (1918), 87 L.J.K.B. 1024. Compare the position which arose in *Wright* v. *Nicholson*, *ante*, p. 372.

defendant is arraigned, having inspected the indictment for the purpose. Defending counsel should also inspect, in his own client's interests. Amendment may be made by the judge of his own motion, but before doing so he should give both sides the opportunity of commenting on the proposed amendment.[1]

E ARRAIGNMENT AND PLEAS

1 Attendance of the accused

The general course of the trial of an indictable offence will now be considered. On the day fixed for the trial to begin the defendant, if he has been detained in custody, will be brought from the prison or remand centre where he has been detained and lodged in the cells beneath the dock. If he has been on bail he must surrender to his bail and will then be placed in the cells to await his trial. It may be that the defendant has been on trial and does not appear, in which case by a long established procedure for which there is surprisingly little apparent authority, the court of trial may issue a warrant, called a "bench warrant," for the arrest of the defendant; this is a more summary procedure and will not normally be used unless the arrest of the defendant is a matter of urgency. It seems that any court seised of a criminal case has power to issue a bench warrant: "One would think that the position is that every court would have inherent power to do so. . . ."[2]

Still further powers are provided by section 23 of the Criminal Justice Act 1967, by which a constable may arrest without warrant any person admitted to bail, if (*inter alia*) he has reasonable grounds for believing that the person is unlikely to appear at the time and place required.

2 Arraignment

Assuming that the defendant has appeared at, or has been brought to, the court, the first formal step in his trial will be the arraignment. The defendant will be brought from the cells into the dock and the proper officer will first ask him his name. Assuming that he is the person named in the indictment he will then be asked to plead. The indictment will be read to him (omitting only the introductory matters) and he will be asked to plead to it; further, where the indictment contains more than one count, each should be put to the defendant separately and he should be asked to plead separately.[3] The reason is that

"... Every count in an indictment is equivalent to a separate indictment; the prisoner can be tried on one or all of the counts. The verdicts have to be taken separately, and the right practice is that he should be asked to plead to each count as each count is read to him."[4]

---

[1] *R. v. West*, [1948] 1 K.B. 709, at p. 717; [1948] 1 All E.R. 718, at p. 721.
[2] LORD PARKER, C.J. in *R. v. Lloyd-Jones, Ex parte Thomas*, [1958] 3 All E. R. 425, at p. 426; [1958] 1 W.L.R. 1110, at p. 1111. For the apparent powers of the Crown Court, see p. 359, *ante*.
[3] *R. v. Boyle*, [1954] 2 Q.B. 292; [1954] 2 All E.R. 721; see p. 397, *ante*.
[4] LORD GODDARD, C.J. in *R. v. Boyle*, [1954] 2 Q.B. 292, at p. 296; [1954] 2 All E.R. 721, p. 722.

Unfitness to plead

On arraignment the defendant may, of course, simply say nothing. If this occurs, the first question is whether the defendant is mute of malice, that is to say, able to speak but refusing to do so, or whether he is mute by visitation of God, that is to say, temporarily or permanently unable to speak. If there is any doubt a jury must be sworn to try the issue. Witnesses may be called on either side and counsel may address the jury; the judge will then sum up the case to the jury, who will retire if necessary and then give a verdict.[1] If the finding is that the defendant is mute of malice the court may then order the proper officer of the court to enter a plea of not guilty on behalf of the defendant (assuming that he still declines to speak);[2] the trial will then proceed as if the defendant had himself pleaded not guilty. If, however, the finding is that the defendant is mute by visitation of God, the defendant may yet be perfectly well able to defend himself, and a plea of not guilty should be entered by the court and the trial should proceed in the ordinary way. However there may well be some question of whether the defendant is fit to plead, the test for which is whether he is fit to understand proceedings and make his defence.[3] The procedure to be followed is now contained in section 4 of the Criminal Procedure (Insanity) Act 1964. A jury must be sworn to try the issue. It may be the same jury which has just found the defendant mute by visitation of God, although it seems that evidence given on the first trial within a trial, as to the defendant's muteness, must be led in full again on the question of unfitness. Again, evidence may be called by either side and speeches will be made; the judge will direct the jury, who will return a verdict.[4] If the finding is that the defendant is unfit to plead the trial does not proceed, but the defendant is not free to go; he is liable to be detained in hospital. If the finding is one of fitness to plead, the defendant will then be called upon to plead to the indictment; if he still declines to answer, a plea of not guilty may be entered on his behalf, as in the case of a person mute of malice.[5]

It is important to note the precise relationship between the issue of whether the defendant is mute of malice or mute by visitation of God, and the issue of unfitness to plead. If a defendant refuses or cannot answer on the indictment being put to him, the criminal court must necessarily enquire as to the cause for his not replying. It by no means follows that there will be a further enquiry as to unfitness; for instance the defendant may be found mute of malice, which of itself does not raise any question of unfitness. Even if he is found mute by visitation of God this may be for some reason which involves no question of unfitness to plead. Conversely, the question of unfitness may arise even though there is no doubt whatever about the defendant's ability and willingness to speak, as in the case of *R. v. Podola.*[6] The question of unfitness may be raised by either side, or the judge himself may raise it;[7] it must normally be deter-

---

[1] Not necessarily unanimous: see pp. 413–414, *post.*
[2] Criminal Law Act 1967, s. 6 (1) (c).
[3] Not whether he is able to defend himself properly and well: *R. v. Robertson*, [1968] 3 All E.R. 557; [1968] 1 W.L.R. 1767.
[4] Again not necessarily unanimous, see pp. 413–414, *post.*
[5] Criminal Law Act 1967, s. 6 (1) (c).
[6] [1960] 1 Q.B. 325; [1959] 3 All E.R. 418.
[7] *R. v. Dashwood*, [1943] K.B. 1; [1942] 2 All E.R. 586; and see *R. v. McCarthy*, [1967] 1 Q.B. 68; [1966] 1 All E.R. 447.

mined as soon as it is raised,[1] but the court may postpone the issue until any time up to the opening of the case for the defence if it considers it expedient to do so and in the interests of the defendant. If, before the question falls to be determined, the jury return a verdict of acquittal on the count or each of the counts on which the accused is being tried, the question is not determined.[2] This change in procedure, effected[3] by the 1964 Act, gives the defendant the opportunity of submitting "no case to answer" at the close of the prosecution case and obtaining an acquittal without putting in issue his state of mind.

The court should have regard to the facts of the case; if there are reasonable chances of the prosecution case being successfully challenged, so that the defence is not called on, it is clearly in the defendant's interest to have the issue postponed. The court should also consider the supposed disability and whether the defendant would have to be confined, in the public interest, whatever the result of the trial.[4] Thus in *R. v. Burles*[5] the defendant had been charged with manslaughter of a fellow inmate in a hospital. He was severely subnormal and unable to communicate except with those who knew him well. The Crown admitted that there was insufficient evidence to convict. The Court of Appeal held that this was a clear case where the issue of unfitness should have been postponed.

3 Pleas

Assuming that all questions of fitness to plead have been disposed of adversely to the defendant, in the sense that the trial on the substantive issues must go on, the possible pleas open to the defendant are as follows:

a Plea of guilty

On the assumption that the plea covers the whole indictment counsel briefed for the prosecution will give a brief outline of the facts[6] and then call the police officer in charge of the case to give the antecedent history of the defendant, in the form of a sheet setting out the defendant's home and educational background, previous jobs, criminal record and anything else thought to be relevant. He may be cross-examined by defending counsel. There is then a plea in mitigation made by counsel for the defence, sometimes supported by witnesses (very rarely the defendant). The defendant will then usually be given the opportunity of saying something himself to the court, after which sentence will be passed. If there are two defendants, one of whom is pleading guilty and the other not guilty, the one pleading guilty should not normally be sentenced until the trial

---

[1] Criminal Procedure (Insanity) Act 1964, s. 4 (3).

[2] Act of 1964, s. 4 (2).

[3] Following the procedure devised for the occasion by DEVLIN, J. (as he then was), in *R. v. Roberts*, [1954] 2 Q.B. 329, [1953] 2 All E.R. 340—a notable example of "judicial valour".

[4] *R. v. Webb*, [1969] 2 Q.B. 278; [1969] 2 All E.R. 626.

[5] [1970] 2 Q.B. 191; [1970] 1 All E.R. 642.

[6] In somewhat fuller detail where committal has been under the Criminal Justice Act. Where the defendant pleads guilty to murder, the only possible sentence is life imprisonment, and nothing said in court can affect it. Nevertheless the prosecution should still state the facts, which otherwise would never be publicly revealed on the assumption that committal was under the Act: *Practice Direction*, [1968] 2 All E.R. 144; [1968] 1 W.L.R. 529.

of the other defendant is concluded; he should only be sentenced immediately if he is to give evidence against his co-defendant.[1] It is customary for the normal rules of evidence to be relaxed at proceedings following a plea of guilty. Thus in a case where normal "antecedent" evidence had been given LORD GODDARD, C.J. said:[2]

> "That evidence would be quite properly admissible . . . after verdict. What happens after verdict is very different from what happens before verdict. After verdict, there is no longer an issue between the Crown and the prisoner. The issue has been determined by the verdict of the jury and there is no more room for evidence except to inform the mind of the court as to what the prisoner's previous history has been for the purpose of enabling the court . . . to assess the proper sentence."

b Plea of not guilty

It should be noted that this is not necessarily a positive assertion that the defendant is innocent but merely a request or a challenge to the prosecution to prove the case against him. The trial will then proceed in the manner to be described.

As to pleas of guilty and not guilty generally, certain observations may be made. First, the defendant may plead guilty to one count in the indictment but not guilty to another, or even admit part of an offence contained in a single count but not the rest of the offence.[3] He may also plead not guilty to the offence charged but guilty to some other offence of which he may lawfully be convicted by way of alternative verdict;[4] thus he may plead not guilty to murder but guilty to manslaughter. The whole question of alternative verdicts is now regulated by section 6 (3) of the Criminal Law Act 1967. This enables the jury to acquit of the offence charged, but to convict of another offence which the court has jurisdiction to try and which is expressly or impliedly alleged in the indictment. The section only applies to a trial on indictment, and not to treason, or murder (which is dealt with by s. 6 (2)). Where another offence is expressly alleged there is no difficulty, but the courts are in the process of working out what amounts to an implied allegation. It has been held that an allegation of rape or unlawful sexual intercourse implies an allegation of indecent assault,[5] but that unlawful sexual intercourse is not a possible alternative verdict on a charge of rape.[6] Where nothing appears on the depositions which can be said to reduce the crime charged to the lesser offence of which the defendant wishes to plead guilty it is the duty of counsel for the Crown to present the offence charged in the indictment, leaving it to the jury "in the exercise of their undoubted prerogative" to return a verdict of guilty of the lesser offence.[7] Even if counsel for the Crown indicates willingness to accept the plea the judge may insist on the defendant being tried for the offence charged, since his plea of guilty to the lesser offence will only rank as a conviction

---

[1] *R. v. Payne*, [1950] 1 All E.R. 102.
[2] *R. v. Butterwasser*, [1948] 1 K.B. 4, at p. 8; [1947] 2 All E.R. 415, at pp. 416–417.
[3] See *Machent* v. *Quinn*, [1970] 2 All E.R. 255, *post*, p. 415.
[4] Criminal Law Act 1967, s. 6 (1) (*b*).
[5] *R. v. Mochan*, [1969] 1 W.L.R. 1331; *R. v. McCormack*, [1969] 2 Q.B. 442; [1969] 3 All E.R. 371.
[6] *R. v. Fisher*, [1969] 2 Q.B. 114; [1969] 1 All E.R. 265; see also *R. v. Woods*, [1969] 1 Q.B. 447; [1968] 3 All E.R. 709, dealing with the Larceny Act 1916.
[7] *R. v. Soanes*, [1948] 1 All E.R. 289.

when he is sentenced.[1] Secondly, the defendant may change his plea once the trial has started but in this case the appropriate verdict must be returned by the jury which will have been sworn to try the case;[2] it may seem a formality that if the defendant changes his plea, for example, from not guilty to guilty the foreman of the jury should be required to stand up and say that the defendant is guilty but ". . . once a prisoner is in charge of a jury he can only be either convicted or discharged by the verdict of the jury".[3] Thirdly, whether the plea is guilty or not guilty it must always come from the defendant himself. This is important since pressure of various sorts may have been brought to bear on the defendant to plead guilty;[4] the requirement that he must personally plead is a safeguard at least against the grosser type of intimidation. Finally, in certain circumstances a plea of guilty may be withdrawn and a plea of not guilty entered.

> "The question . . . is entirely a matter for the trial judge. If the court came to the conclusion that there was a question of mistake or misunderstanding, or that it would be desirable on any ground that the prisoner should be allowed to join issue, no doubt the court would allow him to do it. For example, it has been known for a prisoner charged with receiving stolen goods to acknowledge that he received them, and to plead guilty, adding 'but I did not know that they were stolen'. In such a case, the trial judge might well allow the prisoner to change his plea. . . ."[5]

However a plea of guilty cannot in any circumstances be withdrawn after the defendant has been sentenced.[6]

Where on being arraigned the defendant pleads not guilty and the prosecution propose to offer no evidence against him, the presiding judge may order a verdict of not guilty to be recorded without the defendant being given in charge to a jury.[7]

c Autrefois acquit *and* autrefois convict

These two are by far the most important of a number of so-called "special pleas in bar" which can be raised by the defendant when the indictment is put to him. The substance of the pleas in bar is that there is some reason why the court should not proceed to try the defendant, which should be made the subject of immediate enquiry, so that if the reason is found to be a valid one the defendant should be released and further proceedings stayed.[8] The general principle of the two pleas of *autrefois acquit* and *autrefois convict* is that the same person should not be put in jeopardy twice for the same offence founded on the same facts—not, it may be noted at once, merely for the same facts. The two pleas were exten-

---

[1] *R. v. Cole*, [1965] 2 Q.B. 388; [1965] 2 All E.R. 29.
[2] *R. v. Heyes*, [1951] 1 K.B. 29; [1950] 2 All E.R. 587.
[3] LORD GODDARD, C.J. in *R. v. Heyes*, [1951] 1 K.B. 29, at p. 30; [1950] 2 All E. R. 587, at p. 588.
[4] See *R. v. Turner (No.* 1), [1970] 2 Q.B. 321; [1970] 2 All E.R. 281; see p. 355, *ante.*
[5] *R. v. McNally*, [1954] 2 All E.R. 372; [1954] 1 W.L.R. 933, at p. 934. See *R. v. Ingleson, post*, p. 422, and *S. (An Infant)* v. *Manchester City Recorder*, [1971] A.C. 481; [1969] 3 All E.R. 1230, and p. 360, *ante.*
[6] *R. v. McNally, supra*, disapproving *R. v. Blakemore* (1948), 33 Cr. App. Rep. 49.
[7] Criminal Justice Act 1967, s. 17. This is in contrast with the situation in *R. v. Heyes* (*supra*) where the trial had already proceeded some way.
[8] See the remarks of LORD GODDARD, C.J. in *R. v. Chairman, County of London Quarter Sessions, Ex parte Downes*, [1954] 1 Q.B. 1, at pp. 5–6; [1953] 2 All E. R. 750, at p. 751.

sively considered by the House of Lords in *Connelly* v. *Director of Public Prosecution*.[1]

"Principle and authority establish: (1) that a man cannot be tried for a crime in respect of which he has previously been convicted or acquitted; (2) that a man cannot be tried for a crime in respect of which he could on some previous indictment have been convicted; (3) that the same rule applies if the crime in respect of which he is being charged is in effect the same, or is substantially the same as either the principal or a different crime in respect of which he has been acquitted or could have been convicted or has been convicted; (4) that one test as to whether the rule applies is whether the evidence which is necessary to support the second indictment, or whether the facts which constitute the second offence, would have been sufficient to procure a legal conviction upon the first indictment either as to the offence charged or as to an offence of which, on the indictment, the accused could have been found guilty; (5) that this test must be subject to the proviso that the offence charged in the second indictment had in fact been committed at the time of the first charge; thus if there is an assault and a prosecution and a conviction in respect of it there is no bar to a charge of murder if the assaulted person later dies; (6) that on a plea of *autrefois acquit* or *autrefois convict* a man is not restricted to a comparison between the later indictment and some previous indictment or to the records of the court, but that he may prove by evidence all such questions as to the identity of persons, dates and facts as are necessary to enable him to show that he is being charged with an offence which is either the same, or is substantially the same, as one in respect of which he has been acquitted or convicted or as one in respect of which he could have been convicted; (7) that what has to be considered is whether the crime or offence charged in the later indictment is the same or is in effect or is substantially the same as the crime charged (or in respect of which there could have been a conviction) in a former indictment and that it is immaterial that the facts under examination or the witnesses being called in the later proceedings are the same as those in some earlier proceedings; (8) that apart from circumstances under which there may be a plea of *autrefois acquit*, a man may be able to show that a matter has been decided by a court competent to decide it, so that the principle of *res judicata* applies; (9) that, apart from cases where indictments are preferred and where pleas in bar may therefore be entered, the fundamental principle applies that a man is not to be prosecuted twice for the same crime."[2]

These nine propositions must be regarded as settling for some considerable time to come the law as to both *autrefois acquit* and *autrefois convict*. Some comment may now be offered on them. It is very well settled that neither plea applies unless the previous conviction or acquittal was before a court with jurisdiction to try both the offence and the defendant. Thus in *R.* v. *Hogan*; *R.* v. *Tompkins*[3] the two appellants, who had escaped from prison, had been recaptured and sentenced by a "court" of visiting justices to certain loss of privileges. They were subsequently charged on indictment with a number of offences, among them prison breach and escape from prison. It was held that the court was in no way concerned with the proceedings before the visiting justices, which were a mere matter of the internal running of the prison. In fact the trial judge struck out the count charging prison breach on hearing that the appellants had been dealt with under prison rules, but the Court of Criminal Appeal held that this was unnecessary as a matter of law, although sensible from the point of view of the sentence ultimately to be passed on the defendants.

---

[1] [1964] A.C. 1254; [1964] 2 All E.R. 401.
[2] Lord Morris, [1964] A.C. 1254, at pp. 1305, *et seq.*; [1964] 2 All E.R. 401, at p. 412.
[3] [1960] 2 Q.B. 513; [1960] 3 All E.R. 149.

Again in *Lewis* v. *Mogan*[1] the respondent, a seaman, had neglected his duties and had been punished summarily by the master of his ship to the extent of forfeiting a day's pay. He was subsequently charged before a magistrates' court with being absent from duty without leave, contrary to the then existing Defence (General) Regulations 1939. The justices upheld a plea of *autrefois convict*, but the divisional court of the King's Bench Division held that this was incorrect:

> "the master of the ship in dealing with the respondent was not in any way acting as a court of competent jurisdiction.... He was acting in a domestic way...."[2]

In addition the previous proceedings must actually have resulted in a verdict of guilty or not guilty; mere disagreement or discharge of the jury is not enough. When the criminal division of the Court of Appeal quashes a conviction it is required by statute to direct that a verdict of acquittal be entered;[3] this therefore is sufficient (indeed it was the case in *Connelly's* case itself).

Apart from these two preliminary points the court, in assessing a plea of *autrefois convict* or *autrefois acquit*, must now address itself closely to the principles laid down in *Connelly's* case, with reference to the facts before the court. Vital to the operation of the doctrine is the whole rule as to alternative verdict offences.[4] As has already been noted a defendant on being charged with certain crimes may plead, or be found, guilty of certain other crimes and not guilty of the crime charged, without the need for any fresh indictment. Thus for example a defendant charged with murder may be found guilty of manslaughter, and a person charged with any indictable offence may be found not guilty of the "full" offence but guilty of an attempt to commit that offence. The House of Lords made it clear that the doctrine of *autrefois acquit* and *autrefois convict* applies to any offence which was an alternative verdict offence to the original offence of which the defendant was convicted or acquitted; thus if the defendant is acquitted of murder the defence of *autrefois acquit* will be open to him if he is charged with manslaughter or attempted murder arising out of the death of the same person. (The same would of course be true if the charge were actually murder arising out of the same facts.)

Uncertainty arises out of the rule that the doctrine also applies if the second offence is substantially the same as the first one; this must be a matter for the common sense of the court, it being quite immaterial that the second charge is founded on the same facts as the first. Thus in *R.* v. *Thomas*[5] the defendant had been found guilty of wounding his wife with intent to murder her and had been sentenced. The wife later died as a result of the injuries and the defendant was charged with murder. It was held that the plea of *autrefois convict* was not open to him.

The operation of the rule may now be illustrated generally from the facts of *Connelly* v. *Director of Public Prosecutions* itself. Connelly and three other men were charged in an indictment with murder. In a separate indictment Connelly was charged with robbery with aggravation; the separate indictment was necessary because of the then existing rule[6] that it was incorrect to charge other

---

[1] [1943] K.B. 376; [1943] 2 All E.R. 272.
[2] CHARLES, J., in *Lewis* v. *Mogan*, [1943] K.B. at p. 379; [1943] 2 All E. R. at p. 274.
[3] Criminal Appeal Act 1968, s. 2 (2): unless it orders a new trial; see p. 428, *post*.
[4] See p. 403, *ante*.
[5] [1950] 1 K.B. 26; [1949] 2 All E.R. 662.
[6] As to the present position, see p. 396, *ante*.

offences along with murder in a single indictment. Connelly was convicted of murder and sentenced; the trial judge ordered that the indictment for robbery should not be proceeded with without leave of the trial court or the Court of Criminal Appeal. Connelly appealed against his conviction of murder and the appeal was allowed[1] on the ground that the trial judge had not dealt fully and fairly with certain evidence for the defence and had exceeded the proper limits of comment in his summing-up when dealing with the defence raised to the murder charge. The court then ordered that the robbery trial should be held. When charged with robbery the defendant pleaded *autrefois acquit* (the effect of the quashing of the murder conviction being, as stated above, that the defendant was acquitted on the charge of murder). The House of Lords held that the plea failed. Clearly the second charge was not exactly the same as the first; neither was it even substantially the same; nor was robbery an alternative verdict offence to murder.[2]

Two further comments may be made on *Connelly's* case. First, much of the difficulty arose from the old rule that other offences could not be joined in the same indictment as murder; as already noted the[3] House of Lords demolished this rule and a subsequent Practice Direction completed the process. Secondly the law may develop further in the direction of admitting into English criminal law the doctrine of issue estoppel.[4]

d Demurrer, plea to the jurisdiction and pardon

All these three are extremely rare and may be mentioned briefly. By a demurrer the defendant alleges that even if all the facts alleged against him are true they do not constitute the offence charged. It is in essence an objection to the form or substance of the indictment, and is not therefore to be resolved by examination of the depositions.[5] Pleas that the court has no jurisdiction to try the offence or the defendant, or that the defendant has already received a pardon in respect of the offence in question may be raised as such, but they may also be raised on a motion to quash the indictment, or even under the cloak of a general plea of not guilty.

If any of the special pleas is raised but fails the defendant will then be arraigned in the manner described and will be called on to plead to the general issue. The trial will then proceed.

4 Motion to quash the indictment

Instead of entering any plea, general or special, the defendant may move to quash the indictment. This may be done on several grounds. If any of the rules, already described[6] as to the framing of the indictment have not been

---

[1] (1963), *The Times*, 5th April.
[2] The position presumably remains the same under the Criminal Law Act 1967.
[3] See p. 396, *ante*.
[4] See p. 474, *post*, and *Mills* v. *Cooper*, [1967] 2 Q.B. 459; [1967] 2 All E.R. 100; *R.* v. *Maskell* (1970), 54 Cr. App. Rep. 429.
[5] *R.* v. *Inner London Quarter Sessions, Ex parte Metropolitan Police Commissioner*, [1970] 2 Q.B. 80; [1969] 3 All E.R. 1537. "... I hope that now demurrer in criminal cases will be allowed to die naturally."—Lord Parker, C.J., at pp. 85 and 1541 of the respective reports.
[6] See pp. 394–398, *ante*.

followed this may be made the ground for a motion to quash; however it has already been seen that the court possesses ample power to amend the indictment and it will only be rarely that a motion to quash on this ground will succeed. It could only do so on the ground of some grave defect of substance, such as the insufficiency of the Particulars of Offence, or duplicity. An indictment may also be quashed on the ground that the offence charged in it is not one known to the law. Yet another ground is that the appropriate officer did not have jurisdiction to sign it; as has already been seen he can sign it only if certain conditions are satisfied. The most usual of these conditions is that the defendant has been committed for trial by examining justices; yet "committed" means properly committed, so that if there was some defect in the proceedings before examining justices the indictment is liable to be quashed. Thus in *R. v. Bibby*,[1] the witnesses before examining justices were examined by the chief constable from a prepared type-written statement, analogous to a proof of evidence, copies of which were handed to the magistrates and their clerk. Nothing was taken down by the magistrates in writing but the statement was checked by the clerk as the witnesses gave evidence and was ultimately signed by the witnesses. The defendants were not furnished with copies of the statements. It was held that, since there was a grave irregularity in the proceedings before examining justices, there was no lawful committal for trial and both the indictment itself and the "trial" were complete nullities.

It has been said that if the indictment is clearly bad the court not only can but must quash it and that in other cases the court may quash it if the indictment is such as to cause embarrassment to the defendants in their defence and to prejudice the fair trial of the case. The latter proposition is perhaps doubtful since the passing of the Indictments Act, with the wide and generous powers of amendment which it confers, and it is unlikely that there will now be any extension of the cases in which an indictment is liable to be quashed. Quashing does not amount to an acquittal, and the Crown is at liberty to bring a fresh indictment on the same facts; however, the reason for quashing of the indictment, for example insufficient detail in the particulars of offence, may be such that the Crown is unable to proceed further.[2] An inquisition may also be quashed on account of irregularity in the coroner's inquest, as in *R. v. Reynolds*,[3] where the coroner had had a private conversation in equivocal circumstances with a member of his jury and had also acted in his professional capacity as a solicitor in other proceedings involving the defendant.

5   Empanelling the jury: challenges

Assuming that there is a plea of not guilty to some or part of the indictment the next stage of the trial will be the swearing of the jury. The Courts Act confers on the Lord Chancellor general responsibility for the summoning of jurors.[4] From all the jurors summoned, twelve will be chosen by ballot[5] and will take

---

[1] [1936] 2 K.B. 442; [1936] 2 All E.R. 89. It will be noted that the chief constable was anticipating the procedure now allowed by the Criminal Justice Act 1967.
[2] See, for example, *R. v. Wilson, The Times,* October 15, 1962.
[3] [1945] K.B. 20.
[4] Courts Act 1971, s. 31 (1).
[5] *Ibid.,* s. 35 (1).

their place in the jury box. They must then be sworn; but before they are sworn the clerk of the court will address the defendant as follows:

> "Prisoner at the bar, the names that you are about to hear called are the names of the jurors who are to try you. If therefore you object to them or to any of them you must do so as they come to the book to be sworn and before they are sworn, and your objection shall be heard."

This is to give the defendant a right to challenge members of the jury if he so wishes. Challenges may be peremptory or for cause. A person arraigned may challenge up to seven jurors without disclosing, or even having, any cause; he will do so, as the form of the clerk's statement implies, as the juror is about to be sworn.[1] Such a challenge is called a "peremptory" challenge. Neither the prosecution nor the court has any discretion in the matter and if the defendant is denied his right of peremptory challenge the trial is a nullity.[2] Mere failure to inform him of the right will not have the same or (apparently) any effect, certainly if the defendant is represented.[3] The Crown has no right of peremptory challenge as such, although, as will be seen, the Crown has a right to "stand by" jurors which in many cases will lead to the same result. In addition to the defendant's right of peremptory challenge either side has an unlimited number of challenges for cause, either to the whole panel summoned or to an individual juror. There are certain specified causes in each case and the burden is on the party making the challenge to show such a cause. The issue is tried by the presiding judge himself and if he rules in favour of the objection being upheld that juror will stand down. The swearing of the other jurors, if there are any others to be sworn, will then continue.

As noted above the Crown has a right to make a provisional challenge in the form of "standing by" a juror. By this procedure, the juror is asked to stand down, but consideration of the cause of challenge (since a challenge made by the Crown must be for cause) is postponed. It will usually then happen that there are enough "spare" jurors for a whole jury to be assembled, however many more challenges are made, so that the trial can proceed and the cause of the Crown's challenge is never made the subject of enquiry. In effect the practice of standing by a juror gives the Crown a right of peremptory challenge. The defendant has no such right; but in an exceptional case the judge might allow a defendant to do so or even do so himself.[4]

Each member of the jury must be sworn individually;[5] there is then an opportunity given to the parties to challenge each separately. The form of the juror's oath is as follows:

> "I swear by Almighty God that I will faithfully try the several issues joined between our Sovereign Lady the Queen and the prisoner at the Bar and give a true verdict according to the evidence."[6]

The appropriate officer of the court then tells the jury of the substance of the offence to which the defendant has pleaded not guilty and informs them that it is their duty, having heard the evidence, to say whether he is guilty or not.

---

[1] Courts Act 1971, s. 35 (1).

[2] *R. v. Williams* (1925), 19 Cr. App. Rep. 67. The appellant had challenged a woman juror "because she was a woman".

[3] *R. v. Berkeley*, [1969] 2 Q.B. 446; [1969] 3 All E.R. 6.

[4] See, generally, *R. v. Chandler*, [1964] 2 Q.B. 322; [1964] 1 All E.R. 761.

[5] Courts Act 1971, s. 35 (3).

[6] *Practice Note*, [1957] 1 All E.R. 290; [1957] 1 W.L.R. 355.

F COURSE OF THE TRIAL

Prosecuting counsel starts by making an opening speech. This will be an out-line of the allegations against the defendant and of the evidence which it is proposed to call in support of the allegations. No reference should be made to any item of evidence if counsel has been informed that there is going to be an objection to the admissibility of that evidence. Such objection will be tried by the judge, in the absence of the jury, at the time in the trial when the evidence would otherwise have been called. The institution of the opening speech has been criticised[1] on the ground that counsel may make allegations which are not borne out by the evidence of his witnesses (even before they are the subject of cross-examination) yet the jury may recollect only the statements of counsel, since they came first. Only in limited circumstances has defending counsel the right to make an opening speech.[2] It is a strict rule that prosecuting counsel should limit his observations to what appears in the depositions,[3] since otherwise the present purpose of having depositions, to give the defendant fair notice of the case against him, would be nullified. The only exception arises in the case of those witnesses in respect of whom a notice of additional evidence has been served. Even this practice is not strictly required by law, but the court has an inherent discretion to prevent oppressive conduct towards the defendant[4] and it is most unlikely that a judge would allow evidence to be called which did not appear in the depositions[3] unless a notice of additional evidence, setting out a summary of that witness's evidence, had been served on the defendant.

Prosecution witnesses will then be called and will be subject to examination-in-chief by prosecuting counsel, cross-examination by defending counsel and re-examination by prosecuting counsel. In certain circumstances, however, the witness may not appear in person, but the deposition or statement taken or served before the committing justices may simply be read in the place of actual appearance. The most common example of this occurs where a conditional witness order has been made under the Criminal Procedure (Attendance of Witnesses) Act 1965, and neither side has requested the personal appearance of the witness in question. A deposition may also be read where it is proved by the oath of a credible witness that the deponent is dead, so ill as not to be able to travel, or kept out of the way by procurement of the defendant or on his behalf.[5] It must also be proved that the deposition was taken in the presence of the defendant and that he, or his counsel or solicitor, had full opportunity of cross-examining the witnesses.[5] The charge at the trial need not be the same as the charge before the justices (even assuming that a definite charge had been formulated at the time that the witness gave his evidence) although there is some

---

[1] For such criticism see Blom Cooper; *The A6 Murder*; *R. v. James Hanratty: The Semblance of Truth*, pp. 92–98.
[2] See p. 412, *post*.
[3] Including statements served under sections 1 and 2 of the Criminal Justice Act 1967.
[4] See the remarks of LORD DEVLIN, in *Connelly v. Director of Public Prosecutions*, [1964] A.C. 1254, at pp. 1346 *et seq.*; [1964] 2 All E. R. 401, at pp. 438 *et seq.*
[5] Criminal Justice Act 1925, s. 13 (1).

authority to the effect that it must be substantially the same.[1] Even if the case falls within the statute, so that the depositions can properly be read, it is still within the discretion of the trial judge as to whether he will allow the prosecution to read them; thus leave might be refused in the case of a witness who was so ill that he might never be able to attend the trial, yet whose evidence constituted the whole, or almost the whole, case for the prosecutions.[2] In such a case the defendant would in effect have no right to challenge the case against him. Again, if the defendant states at the preliminary enquiry that he will plead guilty, and conditional witness orders are made in the case of all witnesses in consequence, but at the trial the defendant changes his mind and pleads not guilty, the depositions should not be read, even though the statute strictly allows this course.[3]

> "In our view it was never contemplated by this Act, which was passed simply with the object of saving time and expense in cases where no possible injustice could be done to anybody, that it should be used to abolish in such a case as this the ordinary methods of trial by jury."[4]

Facts may also be proved by written statement, which are admissible in precisely the same circumstances as have already been discussed in connection with committal proceedings.[5] Alternatively either side may now make admissions.[6]

When all the witnesses for the prosecution have been examined, prosecuting counsel will close his case by saying "that is the case for the prosecution" or words to that effect. There may then be a submission by defending counsel that there is no case to answer as regards the whole or some part of the indictment. This is a matter for the judge to determine and, although there is no set rule, it is usually regarded as desirable that the argument on the submission should take place in the absence of the jury. Prosecuting counsel has, of course, a right to reply to defending counsel's submission. If the submission is upheld the trial will end as regards that part of the indictment at least, although the jury should be instructed to return a formal verdict of not guilty; this is analogous to the case where the defendant changes his plea to guilty in the course of the trial.[7] Even if no formal verdict is taken, the case, once withdrawn from the jury, is completely "dead" and cannot be revived by the defendant's own evidence or evidence given by a prosecution witness who is allowed to be recalled.[8] Similarly where two men are jointly charged, and a successful sub-

---

[1] See the cases cited in *Archbold*, para. 1243. In *R. v. Abbatto and Healy*, [1955] Crim. L.R. 645 the defendants were committed for trial on a charge of assault with intent to rob. Their victim then died and they were charged with murder and further committed for trial on this charge. It was held that the victim's deposition was admissible at the trial.
[2] As in *R. v. Linley*, [1959] Crim. L.R. 123.
[3] *R. v. Collins*, [1938] 3 All E.R. 130.
[4] *Ibid.*, at p. 132 *per* HUMPHREYS, J.
[5] Criminal Justice Act 1967, s. 9; see p. 382, *ante*.
[6] *Ibid.*, s. 10. In *R. v. Lewis* (1971), 55 Cr. App. Rep. 386 defending counsel admitted every allegation in the opening speech for the prosecution, whereupon the prosecution called no evidence. The Court of Appeal approved of the procedure in the particular case, but said that the procedure should only be adopted "rarely and with extreme caution".
[7] See p. 404, *ante*.
[8] *R. v. Plain*, [1967] 1 All E.R. 614; [1967] 1 W.L.R. 565.

mission is made on behalf of one of them, he is to be regarded as no longer charged during what remains of the trial.[1]

If the submission is simply rejected the trial will proceed. Even if no submission is made the judge may at any time after the close of the prosecution's case ask the jury whether they think that the prosecution case has been proved and invite them to return a verdict of not guilty if they think that it has not; the Court of Criminal Appeal has indicated that the more desirable practice may be for the judge to take the initiative and direct the jury to return a verdict of not guilty.[2] This would certainly obviate those cases where a jury has returned an unreasonable verdict of guilty and the defendant has had to appeal to the Court of Appeal to have the matter determined in his favour.

The defence case will then open, assuming that the trial is proceeding as to part or all of the indictment. Defence counsel has no right to make an opening speech to the jury unless he is calling witnesses as to fact other than the defendant (whether or not he is also calling the defendant); even then the matter is in his discretion. Witnesses for the defence are then called. If the defendant is giving evidence it is the general rule that he should give evidence before other witnesses; he must be in court, and if he heard the evidence of other witnesses before him, he might be tempted to "trim" his own evidence.[3] A witness about whose evidence there could be no controversy may of course be taken before the defendant. What evidence is called for the defence depends on the nature of the case, but it has already been seen that "evidence in support of an alibi" cannot be called, without leave, unless prior notice has been given.[4] It has however been held that the statutory definition of "evidence in support of an alibi" postulates an offence committed in a particular place at a particular time; where therefore the indictment alleged no place, for the commission of the crime, more precise than "the city of Cardiff", section 11 did not apply.[5] All defence witnesses are subject to examination-in-chief, cross-examination and re-examination in the normal way. Where there is more than one defendant cross-examination of prosecution witnesses and speeches will normally be taken in the order in which the defendants' names appear on the indictment, although there is no fixed rule on the matter. Once the case for the defence has been closed the prosecution may be allowed to call rebutting evidence, in the discretion of the judge. This is a necessary right, since apart from the "alibi defence", there is no obligation on the defendant to reveal his case until the actual presentation of it in court. However, the general rule has been established that rebutting evidence should be allowed only where evidence has been called on behalf of the defendant which could not fairly have been foreseen by the prosecution; it has even been said that such evidence should only be allowed where the defence has called evidence "which no human ingenuity

---

[1] *R. v. Meek* (1966), 110 Sol. Jo. 867.
[2] In *R. v. Young*, [1964] 2 All E.R. 480; [1964] 1 W.L.R. 717.
[3] *R. v. Smith*, [1968] 2 All E.R. 115; [1968] 1 W.L.R. 636.
[4] Criminal Justice Act 1967, s. 11, and see pp. 388–389, *ante*. The section does not apply to summary trial, but of course the defendant may give particulars voluntarily and strengthen his case thereby.
[5] *R. v. Hassan*, [1970] 1 Q.B. 423; [1970] 1 All E.R. 745. *Quaere* how far the section can apply at all to an offence of a continuing nature. As to the court's discretion see *R. v. Sullivan*, [1971] 1 Q. B. 253; [1970] 2 All E.R. 681.

can foresee".[1] This may go too far, and in one case evidence was allowed, for example, in rebuttal of a claim made by the defendant in evidence that the charge against him was false and concocted.[2] Rebutting evidence may be called at any time up to the conclusion of the summing-up and retirement of the jury and defending counsel has a right to cross-examine the witnesses called in rebuttal. Further, if evidence is called after the conclusion of the speeches, counsel may deliver supplemental speeches dealing with the new evidence.

The judge has a right to recall witnesses himself or even call witnesses whom neither side has called; he may also question witnesses to clarify matters of doubt or to probe further into matters which he thinks have not been sufficiently investigated. If the evidence called by the judge falls into the category of rebutting evidence the rules stated above apply to it and breach of them would be a matter for consideration on appeal.[3] Equally, the judge may not himself introduce evidence after the jury have retired to consider their verdict.

Closing speeches then follow. Each side may address the jury, except that where a defendant is unrepresented and either gives no evidence at all or only gives evidence himself the prosecution have no right to sum up their case. In all cases the rule is that prosecuting counsel speaks first and is then followed by counsel for the defendant.[4] The judge will then sum up and invite the jury to consider their verdict.[5] Towards or at the end of his summing-up he will direct them as to majority verdicts, saying that while the law in certain circumstances permits majority verdict the circumstances have not yet arisen and the jury should endeavour to reach a unanimous verdict.[5]

Verdict

The Criminal Justice Act 1967[6] introduced into English law the majority verdict. A verdict need not be unanimous if where there are not less than eleven jurors, ten agree on the verdict, and where there are ten, if nine agree. The court cannot accept any majority verdict unless the jury have had not less than two hours for deliberation, or such longer period as the court thinks reasonable having regard to the nature and complexity of the case,[7] nor can the court accept a majority verdict of guilty unless the foreman of the jury states in open court the number of jurors who agreed on, and dissented from, the verdict.[8] The Practice Direction[9] contains procedure whereby it is hoped to conceal the fact that an acquittal was by a majority. Majority verdicts are novel in English law,[10] and there are various precautions. When the jury first

---

[1] *R.* v. *Day*, [1940] 1 All E.R. 402, at p. 405.
[2] *R.* v. *Milliken* (1969), 53 Cr. App. Rep. 330.
[3] As in *R.* v. *Cleghorn*, [1967] 2 Q.B. 584; [1967] 1 All E.R. 996. Contrast *R.* v. *Tregear*, [1967] 2 Q.B. 574; 1 All E.R. 989.
[4] Criminal Procedure (Right of Reply) Act 1964.
[5] *Practice Direction*, [1967] 3 All E.R. 137; [1967] 1 W.L.R. 1198. Errors in the summing-up should be corrected by counsel before the jury retire: *R.* v. *Southgate*, [1963] 2 All E.R. 833; [1963] 1 W.L.R. 809.
[6] Section 13. For majority verdicts in civil cases, see p. 200, *ante*.
[7] Section 13 (3).
[8] Section 13 (2).
[9] *Supra.*
[10] Verdicts by a bare majority have been permissible in Scotland for many years. The number of jurors is fifteen.

retire, it is on the basis that they are to reach a unanimous verdict. After two hours (or the further time allowed) they will be told that they should still try to be unanimous, but that a majority verdict will be accepted. The procedure may have to be modified according to the circumstances, if there is more than one count in the indictment.[1]

The two hours include time spent back in court, when the jury were receiving further guidance.[2] To avoid difficulties arising from "travelling time" between the court and the jury-room, an ample margin (say 10 minutes) over two hours should be allowed.[3] In any event the judge is entitled to discharge the jury from giving a verdict, if they are disagreed, and need not accept a majority verdict.[4]

Section 13 applies to any verdict of a jury on any issue.

In very clear cases the jury will return a verdict without leaving the jury box, but normally they will retire to a room provided for the purpose. They are put in charge of two officers of the court called jury bailiffs who must take an oath not, without leave of the court, to allow any person to speak to the jury or to speak to them themselves without such leave, except only to ask them if they are agreed on their verdict. Once they have retired to consider their verdict the jury can separate only with leave of the court, which in turn can be given only in case of "evident necessity",[5] such as a juror being taken ill in the course of the jury's deliberations. They do not have to stay in the same jury room until they have reached a conclusion, but they must not separate, subject to the very limited exception noted above, and it is desirable if not essential for them always to be in the custody of one of the court bailiffs while, for example, staying at a hotel overnight. The jury may, of course, ask for further guidance from the judge upon any point of law or evidence arising in the case, but both the request for information and the answer to it must be given in open court; if the jury have asked for guidance in the form of a note sent to the judge, this note should be read out *verbatim* and then the answer given.[6]

Breach of this rule (however worthy the motives for the breach, as, for example, to save a child embarrassment) will almost certainly lead to the quashing of the conviction. Thus in *R. v. Davis*[7] a jury retired and after some deliberation sent a request for certain guidance to the presiding judge. He did not return to court, neither did he inform either counsel of the contents of the request, but merely sent an answer back through the medium of the clerk of the peace. This was then repeated. The Court of Criminal Appeal held that this was wholly irregular.

> "It is at the very basis of the whole of the administration of justice in this country that everything in the course of doing justice shall be done in open court, so that everybody concerned may know precisely what has taken place and what has led either to the conviction or the acquittal. . . ."[8]

---

[1] *Practice Direction*, p. 413, *ante*.
[2] *R. v. Adams*, [1968] 3 All E.R. 437; [1969] 1 W.L.R. 106.
[3] *R. v. Bateson*, [1969] 3 All E.R. 1372; *Practice Note*, [1970] 2 All E.R. 215; [1970] 1 W.L.R. 916.
[4] *R. v. Elia*, [1968] 2 All E.R. 587.
[5] *R. v. Neal*, [1949] 2 K.B. 590; [1949] 2 All E.R. 438.
[6] *R. v. Green*, [1950] 1 All E.R. 38.
[7] (1960), 44 Cr. App. Rep. 235.
[8] *R. v Davis* (*supra*), at p. 240, *per* HILBERY, J.

The matter was made worse by the fact that certain parts of the clerk's statements to the jury amounted to the introduction of fresh evidence, and, as has already been noted, no fresh evidence whatever can be introduced after the jury have retired.[1]

On appeal, the court will not permit any enquiry into what happened in the jury room, or how the jury reached their verdict.[2]

When the jury have concluded their deliberations they will return to court and one of their number, whom they have appointed foreman, will stand up and, subject to the possibility of a majority verdict, in answer to questions put by the appropriate officer of the court, deliver the verdict of the jury.[3] It has already been noted that there may be a verdict that the defendant is not guilty of the crime charged but guilty of some other, alternative, offence.[4] Theoretically it is still possible for a jury to return a "special verdict", which is in form a statement of the facts as found, leaving it to the court to decide of what offences, if any, the defendant is guilty upon those facts. However, special verdicts are now rare if not obsolete, and the Court of Criminal Appeal has said that they ought only to be found in the most exceptional circumstances.[5] Reference may, however, be made to the "special verdict" of "not guilty by reason of insanity" which may be returned under section 1 of the Criminal Procedure (Insanity) Act 1964. This is described as a "special verdict" but is, of course, of a completely different character from the special verdict discussed above. It is, in fact, a special form of acquittal.

No verdict is complete until the jury have dealt with all verdicts which may possibly be returned on the indictment, and if a jury is discharged by the judge before they have completed their verdict, that is to say before giving a verdict not only in relation to the crime charged but also as to all alternatives which are relevant in the particular case, that discharge is a complete nullity.[6]

This is important, since as has been seen[7] s. 6 (3) of the Criminal Law Act 1967 now enables a jury to find the defendant not guilty of the offence charged in the indictment, but guilty of another expressly or impliedly alleged. The judge is not bound to record the first verdict which the jury return but may ask them to reconsider it.[8] He may also do this if the verdict is ambiguous, or is one which cannot properly be returned on the indictment.

The provisions as to majority verdicts have already been discussed. If after such discussion as is practicable in the circumstances the jury still cannot reach the necessary measure of agreement the judge has no option but to discharge them. The defendant will then be remanded in custody or on bail to be tried

---

[1] The fresh evidence was also inaccurate.

[2] See among many cases *R.* v. *Thompson*, [1962] 1 All E.R. 65.

[3] Once a verdict is given in the presence and hearing of all the jury, their assent to it is conclusively presumed: *R.* v. *Roads*, [1967] 2 Q.B. 108; [1967] 2 All E.R. 84.

[4] See p. 403, *ante*. Or the defendant may be found not guilty in relation to certain items or articles named in the indictment but guilty in relation to others: *Machent* v. *Quinn*, [1970] 2 All E.R. 255.

[5] *R.* v. *Bourne* (1952), 36 Cr. App. Rep. 125. A special verdict was found in the celebrated case of *R.* v. *Dudley and Stephens* (1884), 14 Q.B.D. 273. For what was incorrectly called a "special verdict" see *R.* v. *Parker*, [1969] 2 All E.R. 15; [1969] 2 Q.B. 248, p. 395, *ante*.

[6] *R.* v. *Carter*; *R.* v. *Canavan*, [1964] 2 Q.B. 1; [1964] 1 All E.R. 187.

[7] See p. 403, *ante*.

[8] See, for example, *R.* v. *Philpot* (1912), 7 Cr. App. Rep. 140.

afresh. Theoretically this could happen several times, but if successive juries disagree the practice is for the prosecution to offer no evidence at a third trial. On a retrial, the fact that there has been a previous trial is usually irrelevant and inadmissible, but it may become necessary to refer to it, for example for the purpose of proving that the defendant or a witness made some particular statement or admission. Thus in *R. v. McGregor*[1] the defendant was charged with receiving. At an earlier, abortive, trial he had admitted possession. A police officer was allowed to give evidence of this admission.

Other circumstances in which the jury may be discharged are: (1) illness. If during the course of a criminal trial a juror falls ill he may be discharged by the judge from further service, and depending on the facts, normally will be so discharged. The judge may then discharge the whole jury, but does not have to do so; neither is discharge of the single juror fatal to the continuance of the trial, since statute now provides that when, in the course of a trial, any member of the jury dies or is discharged the trial may nevertheless continue provided that the number of jurors does not fall below nine. If, however, the charge is murder or any offence punishable by death the prosecution and every accused must consent in writing to the trial continuing, even if only one juror is discharged or dies;[2] (2) misconduct of a juror, such as holding improper conversations with a member of the public about the case or absenting himself from his colleagues at the time when the jury were in the course of retiring to consider their verdict; and (3) improper revelation to the jury of the defendant's past criminal record. In such a case the jury is frequently discharged in the defendant's own interest, although every case depends on its own facts. It is material to consider which side brought out the record and what the degree of prejudice could have been.[3]

Passing sentence

If the defendant has been found guilty on any part of the indictment the court will then proceed to sentence. There is first such an enquiry into the defendant's antecedents as normally follows a plea of guilty, as has already been described.[4] The defendant is then customarily given an opportunity of making such observations as he wishes, in addition to his counsel's speech in mitigation. It should always be made clear whether separate sentences are intended to be consecutive or concurrent.[5] In the course of this part of the trial it not infrequently happens that the defendant asks for other offences to be taken into consideration. This practice is based on convention and has no statutory foundation; yet at the same time it is extremely convenient both from the point of view of the police and of the defendant. If there are other offences which the defendant has committed but which are still untried (or unknown), then the defendant may admit them to the court of trial and ask the judge to take them into consideration when

---

[1] [1968] 1 Q.B. 371; [1967] 2 All E.R. 267.
[2] Criminal Justice Act 1965, s. 1.
[3] *R. v. Weaver and Weaver*, [1968] 1 Q.B. 353; [1967] 1 All E.R. 277. See also *R. v. Palin*, [1969] 3 All E.R. 689; [1969] 1 W.L.R. 1544.
[4] See pp. 402–403, *ante*.
[5] *Practice Direction*, [1962] 1 All E.R. 417; [1962] 1 W.L.R. 191. For difficulties which arose when this was not made clear, see the litigation in the name of *Re Hastings*: for example, that reported at [1958] 1 All E.R. 707; [1958] 1 W.L.R. 372.

sentencing him for the offence of which he has just been convicted. In practice he will probably tell the police well before the hearing that he wishes certain offences to be taken into consideration or the police may suggest the matter to him and he will then be supplied with an appropriate form of admission; however there seems to be nothing to prevent a court taking an offence into consideration even if the defendant does not either admit it or ask for it to be taken into consideration until the actual trial. The defendant should be asked in open court whether he has seen the list of his other offences, whether he now admits them and whether he desires the judge to take them into consideration. Once the defendant has served his sentence he will not, by long established custom, be prosecuted in respect of any of the offences which have been taken into consideration, although if he were prosecuted the defence of *autrefois convict* would not be open to him, there having been no trial, let alone conviction, in respect of those offences.[1] If, however, his conviction were quashed, a prosecution might be brought.

The mere fact that the defendant asks for the offence to be taken into consideration does not, of course, compel the court to do so. Certain limitations have been laid down in the cases. Broadly, the offence to be taken into consideration should be of the same character as the offence of which the defendant has been convicted; if the defendant has already been separately committed for trial in respect of the offence to be taken into consideration the judge should obtain the consent of the prosecution before doing so.[2] Even if the prosecution does consent the judge ought to consider whether the public interest requires a separate enquiry. Neither ought the court to take into consideration: (1) an offence carrying disqualification.[3] The reason is that in very many cases it will be desirable if not obligatory to disqualify the defendant, yet there can only be a disqualification on conviction, and taking other offences into consideration does not amount to a conviction in respect of them; (2) a breach of probation. This should be separately considered and a separate sentence passed in respect of it, for otherwise the original offence in respect of which the defendant was put on probation will not rank as a conviction in the future and the defendant will appear to have a better record than is in fact the case.

G SENTENCES AND ORDERS

1 Death

The death penalty was abolished for nearly all murders in 1957,[4] and finally abolished in 1965,[5] for the other murders. The provisions of the 1965 Act were expressed to be temporary and experimental, but Parliament in 1969 decided that abolition was to be permanent. Death continues to be the penalty for treason and piracy.[6]

---

[1] *R.* v. *Nicholson*, [1947] 2 All E.R. 535.
[2] *R.* v. *McLean*, [1911] 1 K.B. 332.
[3] *R.* v. *Williams*, [1962] 3 All E.R. 639; [1962] 1 W.L.R. 1268.
[4] Homicide Act 1957, ss. 5–9.
[5] Murder (Abolition of Death Penalty) Act 1965.
[6] The Home Secretary has announced his intention to abolish the death penalty for piracy. The death penalty for arson of Her Majesty's ships and dockyards was abolished by s. 11 (2) of the Criminal Damage Act 1971.

2 Imprisonment and fine

Life imprisonment is the fixed penalty for murder[1] and the maximum penalty for manslaughter[2] and a large number of other offences. It is of course rarely imposed.

In the case of a life sentence for murder, the court may declare the minimum period which in its view should elapse before the defendant is released on licence.[3] Such a recommendation is not binding on the Home Secretary who must however consult the trial judge if available and the Lord Chief Justice before permitting release on licence. It was formerly doubted whether a judge had power to recommend that a prisoner convicted of murder should never be released, but such an order was made in *R. v. Skingle and Sparrow*.[4]

Imprisonment for a specified period of years or months is also the maximum penalty for a great number of offences in English law; very often statute prescribes a fine as an additional or alternative penalty, but in any event any court may now fine for any offence except where the penalty is fixed by law.[5] A fine of a specified amount is of course the maximum penalty, on its own, for a very large number of summary offences.

A sentence of imprisonment may be imposed but suspended, i.e. ordered not to take effect immediately.[6] The sentence must not be for more than two years and the period of suspension must be between one and three years.[7] The effect of a suspended sentence is that so far as that sentence is concerned, the defendant is not liable to be imprisoned unless (i) during the period of suspension he commits another offence punishable with imprisonment, and thereafter (ii) a court orders that the sentence shall take effect.[8] A sentence of six months or less in respect of one offence must normally be suspended.[9] The court which deals with a suspended sentence after re-conviction is not bound to order it to take effect, if it thinks that it would be unjust to do so in view of all the circumstances which have arisen since the sentence was passed. These include the facts of the subsequent offence.

No person under 17 years of age may be sentenced to imprisonment by any court.[10] If an offender under that age requires custodial treatment it must be in a

---

[1] Murder (Abolition of Death Penalty) Act 1965, s. (1) (1). The Criminal Law Revision Committee is now considering the difficult question as to whether the penalty for murder should continue to be fixed or whether life imprisonment should merely be the maximum (which would have a considerable effect on the law of murder). For the position as to appeal, see p. 422, *post*.

[2] Offences against the Person Act 1861, s. 5.

[3] As to an appeal, see p. 422, *post*.

[4] *The Times*, October 16, 1971.

[5] Criminal Law Act 1967, s. 7 (3).

[6] Criminal Justice Act 1967, ss. 39–42. As to committal for sentence see p. 361, *ante*.

[7] *Ibid.*, s. 39 (1); but see note 9 below.

[8] *Ibid.*, s. 40 (1).

[9] *Ibid.*, s. 39 (3). The Criminal Justice Bill 1971 abolishes this requirement, which is generally thought to have materially increased the prison population. The reason alleged was that the courts were passing a sentence of imprisonment instead of, for example, a probation order, but suspending it even when they did not have to. When therefore, the defendant committed a further offence, the suspended sentence was brought into effect with a term for the subsequent offence added on. The Bill also reduces the maximum period of suspension from three years to two.

[10] Criminal Justice Act 1948, s. 17, as amended.

Borstal or detention centre. Further, and subject to this, a person within the age limits (15–21 years) for Borstal, can only be sentenced to imprisonment for six months or less or three years or more.[1] The object of this provision is to ensure that those eligible to go to Borstal are in fact sent there; thus it does not apply if the defendant has already served a sentence of Borstal training.

3 Borstal and detention centre

An offender who is (i) aged 15 or over but under 21 and (ii) convicted of an offence punishable with imprisonment, may be sent to Borstal.[2] The period in Borstal must normally be for a minimum period of six months and cannot exceed two years; the exact term depends on the offender's progress in Borstal and for this reason the court will simply order "Borstal training" without specifying any term. The emphasis is on training and discipline, and following release the offender is under the supervision of a probation officer for a period of up to two years, depending again on progress.

An alternative place of detention for young offenders is the detention centre itself, available for an offender who is (i) aged 14 or over but under 21; (ii) convicted of an offence punishable with imprisonment.[3] The minimum period of detention is three months and the maximum period normally six. There is again emphasis placed on training and discipline, with a period of after-care of up to twelve months.

4 Probation

Except where the sentence is fixed by law, a court may make a probation order in respect of an offender aged 17 or over where it thinks it right to do so provided that the offender himself is willing to be bound by the order.[4] This will require the offender to be under the supervision of a probation officer for between one and three years, and conditions, e.g. as to residence, may also be imposed. The object of the order is to re-establish the offender in the community with the assistance of a probation officer. Probation being instead of punishment, a fine cannot be imposed, along with probation, for the same offence.[5] An offender who fails to comply with the terms of his probation, whether by committing another offence or otherwise, is liable to be sentenced for the original offence.

5 Absolute and conditional discharge[6]

Where a court thinks it inappropriate to pass any sentence, or make a probation order, it may discharge the offender either absolutely, without any condition, or subject to the condition that he does not commit any further offence for a period,

---

[1] Criminal Justice Act 1961, s. 3.
[2] Criminal Justice Act 1948, s. 20. As to committal for sentence, see pp. 360–361, *ante*. Section 7 (1) of the Children and Young Persons Act 1969 raises the lower age limit to 17, but this provision is not yet in force.
[3] Criminal Justice Act 1961, s. 4.
[4] Criminal Justice Act 1948, s. 3, as amended by Children and Young Persons Act 1969, s. 7 (2).
[5] *R. v. Parry*, [1951] 2 K.B. 590; [1950] 2 All E.R. 1179.
[6] Criminal Justice Act 1948, s. 7 (1), as amended.

fixed by the court of between one and three years. If he commits another offence in that period he is liable to be sentenced for his original offence.

6   Compensation and restitution

An offender on being convicted of any indictable offence may be ordered to make up to £400 compensation for any loss or damage to property suffered through or by means of the offence.[1] Application must be made immediately on conviction by a party aggrieved.[2] Magistrates' courts have a similar power.[3] Where goods have been stolen and a person is convicted of any offence in relation to the theft, the court may order restoration of the actual goods or any other goods bought with the proceeds of their realisation.[4]

---

[1] Forfeiture Act 1870, as amended by the Criminal Law Act 1967.
[2] *R. v. Forest Justices, Ex parte Coppin*, [1969] 2 All E.R. 668; [1969] 1 W.L.R. 916.
[3] Magistrates' Courts Act 1952, s. 34.
[4] Theft Act 1968, s. 28 (1). Clauses 1 to 6 of the Criminal Justice Bill now provide a new code of compensation and restitution orders, substantially on the lines of the old law. The £400 limit will apply only to a compensation order made by a magistrates' court. The Bill also confers on the Crown Court power to make a criminal bankruptcy order and on any court power (i) to make a community service order, requiring the defendant to perform unpaid work in the interests of the community (ii) to defer sentence for a period up to six months for the purpose of, for example, enabling the defendant to make reparation. The latter provision vindicates the action of the trial judge in *R. v. Collins* (1969), 53 Cr. App. Rep. 385.

CHAPTER 26

Appeal Following Conviction on Indictment

A RIGHTS OF APPEAL

It is now necessary to consider the rights of appeal available to a person convicted on indictment. It must be borne in mind, as a fundamental principle, that it is the mode of trial which determines the rights of appeal, not the nature of the offence. Thus if the defendant is convicted at the Crown Court his appeal lies, if at all, to the criminal division of the Court of Appeal. It does not matter whether he was convicted of an indictable, summary or "hybrid" offence. Equally, appeal following summary conviction lies to those courts having jurisdiction over summary appeals—the Crown Court and the divisional court of the Queen's Bench Division—irrespective of the fact that the defendant was convicted of an indictable offence.

The whole law as to appeals following conviction on indictment is now to be found in the Criminal Appeal Act 1968, which consolidated the Criminal Appeal Acts of 1907, 1964 and 1966. There is no right of appeal except such as is conferred by the Act.

1 Appeal against conviction

By section 1 of the Criminal Appeal Act 1968 a person convicted on indictment may appeal to the Court of Appeal:

(*a*) against his conviction on any ground which involves a question of law alone; and

(*b*) with the leave of the Court of Appeal, against his conviction on any ground which involves a question of fact alone, or a question of mixed law and fact, or any other ground which appears to the court to be a sufficient ground of appeal.

The trial judge may also grant a certificate that the case is fit for appeal, on a question of fact or mixed law and fact; he should not give the certificate merely for the asking, but only if he is satisfied that there is a substantial point and one worthy of consideration by the Court of Appeal.[1] Where leave to appeal is required, it may be granted, in the first instance by a single judge of the court; if he refuses, the applicant may have his case considered by the Court itself.[2]

There is nothing in the Act to prevent an appeal against conviction even though the defendant pleaded guilty at his trial. However, as might be expected, there is a settled rule that an appeal in these circumstances will only be entertained if either the defendant did not appreciate the nature of the charge, or he did not intend to admit that he was guilty of it, or, on the admitted facts, he could not in point of law have been guilty of the offence to which he pleaded guilty.[3] With the more generous provision of legal aid, cases of the first and second type are likely to become increasingly rare.

One such case was *R. v. Inglcson.*[4] The defendant in that case pleaded guilty to receiving and subsequently handed to the judge a written statement which, if believed, was a complete exculpation, and concluded with the words "I am guilty of [receiving] not knowing them to have been stolen." It was held on appeal that the plea of guilty was wrongly received and that the proceedings were a nullity.

2 Appeal against sentence

The defendant may appeal against the sentence passed on his conviction, unless the sentence is one fixed by law, but only with the leave of the Court of Appeal.[5] An application for leave may be determined by a single judge of the Court of Appeal but, if he refuses leave, the appellant has a right to have his application determined by the full court.[2]

"Sentence" includes certain sentences passed by the Crown Court on defendants committed to that court for sentence, as well as sentences passed in the normal way on defendants convicted at the Crown Court.[6] There is no appeal against a sentence fixed by law (such as death for treason or life imprisonment for murder) or against a recommendation made by a trial judge that a defendant convicted of murder shall not be released before a certain number of years.[7] There may also be an appeal against an order for disqualification from driving or against a recommendation for deportation whether or not in either case there is an appeal against the sentence otherwise imposed on the defendant (since a recommendation for deportation cannot be imposed on its own).[8]

---

[1] *R. v. Eyles* (1963), 47 Cr. App. Rep. 260.

[2] Criminal Appeal Act 1968, s. 31. See also p. 430, *post.*

[3] *R. v. Forde,* [1923] 2 K.B. 400, at p. 403; *R. v. Gould,* [1968] 2 Q.B. 65; [1968] 1 All E.R. 849.

[4] [1915] 1 K.B. 512. Cf. pp. 404, 428, *ante* and *post.* See, for a further example, *R. v. Clarke,* [1972] 1 All E.R. 219 in which case the appellant had changed her plea to guilty after the trial judge had construed the defence of absence of intention as one of insanity thereby exposing the appellant, if her defence succeeded, to a finding that she was insane. The resulting conviction was quashed.

[5] Criminal Appeal Act 1968, s. 9.

[6] Criminal Appeal Act 1968, s. 10. For cases in which persons may be committed to the Crown Court for sentence see pp. 357–362, *ante.*

[7] *R. v. Aitken,* [1966] 2 All E.R. 453; [1966] 1 W.L.R. 1076.

[8] See Criminal Appeal Act 1968, s. 50 (1), defining sentence to include "any order made by a court when dealing with an offender". No appeal will lie against a "criminal bankruptcy order" (for which see p. 420(n), *ante*), but where a conviction is quashed the order will normally be rescinded.

3 Application to the Home Secretary

By section 17 (1) (a) of the 1968 Act any person convicted on indictment may apply to the Home Secretary and the Home Secretary may, even in the absence of such application, refer the whole case to the Court of Appeal, in which event the case is treated for all purposes as an appeal by the person convicted. It follows that there may be an appeal to the House of Lords.[1] Alternatively the Home Secretary may refer any point arising in the case to the Court of Appeal for consideration and the opinion of the Court on that point.[2] This may, in effect, give the defendant "two bites at the cherry" since the Home Secretary may refer a case even though there has already been an unsuccessful appeal.[3]

4 Appeal against a verdict of "not guilty by reason of insanity" or against findings of fitness and unfitness to plead.

Although the verdict of "not guilty by reason of insanity" is, in form, an acquittal, the defendant may appeal against the verdict, in effect, as if it were a conviction. The defendant may appeal, in the same way, against the finding of a jury that he is unfit to plead.[4] It had already been held[5] that the defendant has the right to appeal against a finding, on a preliminary issue, that he is fit to plead.

The powers of the Court of Appeal in dealing with appeals of this nature are dealt with below.[6]

B POWERS OF THE COURT OF APPEAL

1 Power to quash conviction

The Court may allow an appeal against conviction if they think that either:

(a) *Under all the circumstances of the case the verdict is unsafe or unsatisfactory*—This formula was substituted by the Criminal Appeal Act 1966 for the formula contained in the Criminal Appeal Act 1907: "the verdict is unreasonable or cannot be supported having regard to the evidence". Two criticisms were made of the old formula and the courts' interpretation of it. First, the two parts of the formula were always treated as synonymous, in spite of it being the apparent intention of the draftsmen of the 1907 Act by the use of the word "or", that they should mean something different. Secondly, the Court adopted what was widely considered to be a very narrow view of its powers, refusing to interfere except in cases (usually of joint trials) where there was literally no evidence

---

[1] See pp. 430–431, *post*.
[2] Act of 1968, s. 17 (1) (b). In *R. v. Bardoe*, [1969] 1 All E.R. 948; [1969] 1 W.L.R. 398 the reference was made under section 17 (1) (a) "in order that the court may review the sentence imposed". It was held that by implication that that point only was referred, and there could be no argument about the conviction.
[3] See, for example, *R. v. Hinds* (1965), *The Times*, 27th July.
[4] Criminal Appeal Act 1968, ss. 12, 15.
[5] *R. v. Podola*, [1960] 1 Q.B. 325; [1959] 3 All E.R. 418.
[6] See p. 429, *post*. By clause 28 of the Criminal Justice Bill 1971 the Court will have jurisdiction in certain circumstances to hear an appeal by the prosecution on a point of law where the defendant has been acquitted.

against the defendant yet the jury had convicted.   The attitude of the Court has been stated as follows:[1]

> "[The Court] is not here to consider whether the jury was right or wrong . . . [but] to review the proceedings below with the assistance of counsel to see if the proceedings were properly conducted and, if not, to see whether any irregularities which arose in the course of the proceedings were sufficient to render the finding of the jury unsafe or unsatisfactory. . . . If we come to the conclusion that there were such irregularities, then we quash the convictions and since there is no machinery in English law for a re-trial in such circumstances, the matter rests in that somewhat inconclusive state."

It was suggested in the first edition of this work that, in future, where, in cases of disputed identity, there is only one witness identifying the defendant, the court will say that a verdict of guilty based on such evidence is unsafe or unsatisfactory.   This suggestion appears to be supported by *R. v. Cooper*,[2] where it was said that:

> "until the passing of the Criminal Appeal Act 1966 . . . it was almost unheard of for this court to interfere in such a case.   However, now our powers are somewhat different in cases of this kind the court must in the end ask itself a subjective question, whether we are content to let the matter stand as it is, or whether there is not some lurking doubt in our minds which makes us wonder whether an injustice has been done."[3]

It may well be that such identification is correct and a guilty person escapes on appeal, but:

> ". . . We think reliance can safely be placed upon the experience and acumen of Her Majesty's judges to reduce this risk to a minimum.   The advantage to be gained from the provision we suggest, however, is that the safeguards for an innocent person, wrongly identified and convicted, are sensibly increased.   We think the country would probably be prepared to pay what we believe would be a small price for this reform.   It might operate in other cases besides those of disputed identity, e.g. some cases of alleged rape where there is substantial evidence of consent which the jury reject in favour of the woman's denial."[4]

Here, most markedly, the appellate system shows favour to the defendant; or

(b)   *The judgment of the court should be set aside on the ground of a wrong decision of any question of law*—This formula appeared in the 1907 Act and is unchanged. It covers misdirection in the summing-up either as to the law applicable or as to the facts (including failure to put the defence to the jury), wrongful rejection of a submission that there is no case to answer, wrongful admission or exclusion of evidence and defects in the indictment.   Thus if the judge fails to give the jury an appropriate warning as to corroboration in those cases where such

---

[1] Lord Widgery, C.J., giving the judgment of the Court of Appeal in *R. v. Anderson*, [1972] 1 Q.B. 304 at p. 309, [1971] 3 All E.R. 1152, at p. 1156.   For another point arising from the case see p. 526, *post*.

[2] [1969] 1 Q.B. 267; [1969] 1 All E.R. 32.

[3] Widgery, L.J. (as he then was), at pp. 271 and 34 of the respective reports.   The phrase "lurking doubt" is now much canvassed in the Court; see, e.g. *R. v. Milliken* (1969), 53 Cr. App. Rep. 330.   For another point arising from the case, see p. 413, *ante*.

[4] Report of the Interdepartmental Committee on the Court of Criminal Appeal (Donovan Committee) (Cmnd. 2755 of 1965), para. 150.

direction is required this omission will normally lead to the quashing of the conviction;[1] or

(c)   *There was a material irregularity in the course of the trial*—This formula was introduced by the 1966 Act; it replaced the words in the 1907 Act: "on any ground there was a miscarriage of justice". These latter words have been held to cover a variety of errors in the course of the trial, such as unfair conduct or undue interruption by the judge, improper disclosure to the jury of the defendant's previous record, tampering with a juror, misconduct of a juror and failure to inform an undefended person of his right to call witnesses. No doubt the new formula will cover residual cases in the same way.[2] It is not perhaps easy to see the significance of the word "material" since if the irregularity is not material the Court has another way of reflecting that fact in its order. This must now be considered.

2   Applying the proviso

On an appeal against conviction the Court may dismiss the appeal, even though of the opinion that the point raised might be decided in favour of the appellant, if it is considered that no miscarriage of justice has actually occurred.[3] In section 4 (1) of the 1907 Act the word "substantial" appeared before "miscarriage"; this seemed "devoid of practical significance"[4] and was deleted by section 4 (1) of the 1966 Act. Where the Court exercises this power it is said to "apply the proviso".[5] It appears that the proviso was intended in substitution of a general power to order a new trial; yet it is now clear that, whether or not it is regarded as desirable that the Court should have power to order a new trial, the proviso is not an adequate substitute for that power. A mass of case law has grown up around the original artless words of the 1907 Act and LORD GODDARD publicly stated that the Court finds great difficulty in applying the proviso. The test is whether a reasonable jury, after a proper summing-up, could have failed to convict the defendant;[6] the Court assumes a reasonable jury, puts itself in the place of that jury and asks itself whether the only reasonable verdict was one of guilty. If so, it applies the proviso. It can only proceed on evidence that could lawfully have come before the jury.[7]

The Court has, on occasion, applied the proviso despite a substantial misdirection in law. The test is by no means one of the degree of error. Research[8]

---

[1] *R. v. Trigg*, [1963] 1 All E.R. 490; [1963] 1 W.L.R. 305. Cp. *R. v. O'Reilly*, [1967] 2 Q.B. 722; [1967] 2 All E.R. 766; see p. 495, *post.*

[2] See *R. v. Hood*, [1968] 2 All E.R. 56; [1968] 1 W.L.R. 773, where one of the jurors knew or suspected that the defendant might have previous convictions. The Court of Appeal deprecated this but dismissed the appeal by application of the proviso (*infra*).

[3] Criminal Appeal Act 1968, s. 2 (1).

[4] Donovan Committee Report, para. 164.

[5] Because the paragraph in question of the 1968 Act (and of the 1907 Act) begins "Provided that. . . ."

[6] *Stirland* v. *Director of Public Prosecutions*, [1944] A.C. 315; [1944] 2 All E.R. 13; see also (among many cases) *R. v. Haddy*, [1944] K.B. 442; [1944] 1 All E.R. 319. For the proper attitude to application of the proviso in a murder case, see *Anderson* v. *R.*, [1972] A.C. 100; [1971] 3 All E.R. 768.

[7] *R. v. Sowden*, [1964] 3 All E.R. 770; [1964] 1 W.L.R. 1454, where the defendant wrote out, for the purpose of mitigation, a statement substantially admitting the prosecution case. The court felt unable to take this into account.

[8] Cf. Knight: *Convicting the Guilty*, [1966] Crim. L.R. 24.

has shown that in 96 cases where the Court of Criminal Appeal or the House of Lords applied the proviso 44 were cases involving substantial misdirection of the jury. The proviso has even been applied where the trial judge omitted to tell the jury that the burden of proof was on the prosecution.[1] If, however, wrongfully admitted evidence may have had a substantial effect on the jury's verdict the Court will not apply the proviso. It almost certainly will not do so where a defence was wrongly withdrawn from the jury[2] or where alibi evidence was wrongly excluded,[3] or generally, however obvious the guilt of a defendant may seem, if the Court's desire for fair treatment of defendants outweighs this consideration. It has been said that:[4]

> "We are not aware of any precedent for applying the proviso in a case where cross-examination as to character has been deliberately [and wrongly] admitted by the trial judge."

There were in fact a number of precedents and the House of Lords did apply the proviso very shortly afterwards in the same circumstances in *Stirland* v. *Director of Public Prosecutions*.[5] The fact that on a previous trial the jury disagreed is no automatic bar to application of the proviso, although no doubt a relevant factor.[6]

3 Power to substitute an alternative verdict

Where the defendant has been convicted of an offence and (1) the jury could on the same indictment have found him guilty of some other offence; and (2) it appears to the Court of Appeal that the jury must have been satisfied of the facts proving him guilty of that other offence, the Court may, instead of allowing or dismissing the appeal against conviction, substitute a verdict of guilty of that other offence and pass sentence on the defendant for it.[7] The sentence must not be greater than that passed on the defendant at the trial, and must not, of course, exceed the maximum permitted by law for the substituted offence.[8] The Court exercises this power with care, particularly in the light of (2) above, which involves some consideration of a verdict for which necessarily no reasons were given; further, it is a material, though not decisive, point against exercising the power if the jury were not given any direction as to the alternative offence.[9]

---

[1] R. v. *Sparrow* (1962), 46 Cr. App. Rep. 288, and see R. v. *Cashmore*, [1971] 2 Q.B. 572 n; [1971] 2 All E.R. 970; where the Courts-Martial Appeal Court applied the proviso despite a summing-up described as being "in many respects defective".

[2] R. v. *Badjan* (1966), 50 Cr. App. Rep. 141.

[3] R. v. *Lewis*, [1969] 2 Q.B. 1; [1969] 1 All E.R. 79; p. 388, *ante*.

[4] R. v. *Turner*, [1944] K.B. 463, at p. 471; [1944] 1 All E.R. 599, at p. 602.

[5] [1944] A.C. 315; [1944] 2 All E.R. 13.

[6] See *Customs and Excise Commissioners* v. *Harz*, [1967] 1 A.C. 760; [1967] 1 All E.R. 177, *per* LORD MORRIS OF BORTH-Y-GEST (a decision given before the introduction of majority verdicts). When the leading case of *Woolmington* v. *Director of Public Prosecutions* was before the Court of Criminal Appeal that Court applied the proviso even though the jury had disagreed at the first trial. The appellant succeeded in the House of Lords on the same point which was raised in the Court of Criminal Appeal; see p. 491, *post*.

[7] Criminal Appeal Act 1968, s. 3 (1).

[8] *Ibid.*, s. 3 (2).

[9] See, generally, R. v. *Caslin*, [1961] 1 All E.R. 246; [1961] 1 W.L.R. 59. This case was decided under the corresponding provisions of the Criminal Appeal Act 1907, but appears still to be good law.

Where the indictment contains counts for two offences (such as theft and handling) which are in the circumstances alternative to each other, and the jury
convict of one but acquit of the other, the Court cannot substitute a verdict
of guilty of the latter, even if that seems the correct verdict, since the jury
expressly acquitted. The proper course, if there is a conviction on one is for
the jury to be discharged from giving a verdict on the other whereupon the
Court of Appeal may substitute a verdict of guilty.[1] This may also be important from the point of view of a retrial.[2]

4 Appeal against sentence

On an appeal against sentence the Court may reduce the sentence or it may vary
it, by substituting one form of detention or treatment for another. The facts
of each case differ so much that it is difficult to lay down any general principle on
which the Court acts but it is commonly said that the Court will only interfere
where the sentence is "wrong in principle" and not merely on the ground that
the members of the Court themselves would have passed a different sentence.
Where the appeal is against conviction only there is no power to interfere with
the sentence in any way. Formerly the court had power to increase sentence,
but this power was taken away by section 4(2) of the 1966 Act.[3] It had some effect
as a deterrent against frivolous appeals, but was largely ineffective since in cases
where the Court was thinking of increasing sentence it felt obliged to give
the defendant legal aid; counsel would then realise what the Court had in
mind and advise the defendant to discontinue his appeal. Further, the power
undoubtedly acted as a deterrent to some meritorious appeals, since counsel
might think that the sentence was on the high side, yet not so high that the Court
was bound to interfere; in that case he did not dare to advise an appeal against
sentence in case the Court disagreed with his estimate and in fact increased the
sentence. The power was of some use in avoiding disparity of sentence between
co-defendants, but only in a very few cases.[4] In fact the Court exercised the
power to increase only very rarely, and abolition of the power will probably
make little difference. It may be noted that a variation of sentence can result in
the defendant being detained for longer than would otherwise have been the
case. Thus a hospital order under the Mental Health Act cannot be regarded
as more severe than a sentence of imprisonment[5] and a sentence of Borstal
training cannot be regarded as more severe than a sentence of eighteen months'
imprisonment.[6]

---

[1] *R. v. Melvin and Eden,* [1953] 1 Q.B. 481; [1953] 1 All E.R. 294.

[2] See pp. 428–429, *post.*

[3] Although it may do so on one count, if the conviction on another is quashed subject
to the proviso that the sentence on the indictment as a whole must not be of greater
severity than the sentence passed at the trial: Criminal Appeal Act 1968, s. 4. For difficulties which arose under the 1966 Act, see *R. v. Craig,* [1967] 1 All E.R. 1052; [1967]
1 W.L.R. 645.

[4] Thus in *R. v. Ryall; R. v. Gardiner,* [1962] Crim. L.R. 853, the appellants had been
convicted at different Assizes of "wage-snatches" committed in remarkably similar
circumstances and had been sentenced to 5 and 10 years' imprisonment respectively.
Their appeals were heard on the same day, and the court increased Ryall's sentence, and
reduced Gardiner's sentence, to 7 years.

[5] *R. v. Bennett,* [1968] 2 All E.R. 753; [1968] 1 W.L.R. 998.

[6] *R. v. Bernard,* [1969] Crim. L.R. 550.

5 Power to receive fresh evidence and to order a new trial

a *Power to receive fresh evidence*

Section 23 is complementary to sections 7 and 8 of the Act insofar as it deals with fresh evidence. It does not deal at all with the powers of the Court on the reception of fresh evidence but materially affects the conditions subject to which it can be received. The Court cannot now refuse to hear fresh evidence merely on the ground that it was available at the trial, provided that a reasonable explanation is given for failure to adduce it. The evidence must of course be admissible, and "likely to be credible"; equally the Court is under no duty to receive the evidence if it would not in any event be any ground for allowing the appeal. Subject however to these conditions, the Court *must* receive the evidence. "The normal case where fresh evidence is tendered and received under this section [23 (2)] is on a question of fact, where, for example, some eye-witness or alibi witness not previously available has later been discovered."[1] In *R. v. Lomas*[2] however the Court allowed fresh evidence of expert opinion, stating that the case depended on exceptional facts and was to be no encouragement to similar applications in the future.

b *Power to order a new trial*

The power to order a new trial, first introduced by the Criminal Appeal Act 1964, is now contained in sections 7 and 8 of the 1968 Act. Assuming that the Court receives the fresh evidence in the first place, and is then satisfied that if given at the trial it would have created a reasonable doubt in the mind of the jury it must still allow the appeal and quash the conviction but may now order a new trial if it considers that the interests of justice so require. One circumstance in which a new trial might not be ordered is where a considerable length of time has elapsed since the relevant events took place.[3] The new trial may be for the offence charged at the first trial, for any offence which is an alternative verdict offence to that offence or for any offence which was charged in the indictment at the first trial but in respect of which the jury were discharged from giving a verdict, in consequence of convicting the defendant of the first-mentioned offence.

6 Venire de novo

The appeal court has always had the power to order a *venire de novo* where proceedings in the court of trial were so defective as to amount to a nullity. To the defendant this no doubt seems very like ordering a new trial, but strictly the court is ordering not a new trial but a proper one. It has not, unfortunately, been established what degree of irregularity suffices to render proceedings a nullity; there are only particular examples in the cases of proceedings which

---

[1] *Per curiam* in *R. v. Lomas, infra.*
[2] [1969] 1 All E.R. 920; [1969] 1 W.L.R. 306.
[3] *R. v. Pedrini*, [1964] Crim. L.R. 719. See generally for the proper approach to fresh evidence *R. v. Flower*, [1966] 1 Q.B. 146; [1965] 3 All E.R. 669 and *R. v. Stafford and Luraglio* (1969), 53 Cr. App. Rep. 1. In this case the Court of Appeal indicated reluctance to hear fresh evidence if that would involve raising a line of defence wholly different from that raised at the trial. Fresh evidence may be found in additional evidence from a witness who appeared at the trial (as in *R. v. Flower*).

have been held to be a nullity. This has been held to be so where the judge at the trial was not properly qualified,[1] where the defendant specifically asked for but was denied his right of peremptory challenges,[2] or where a plea of not guilty was misheard and dealt with as a plea of guilty.[3] "To constitute a mistrial the proceedings must have been abortive from beginning to end. . . .";[4] thus there was held not to be a mistrial where the defendant was arraigned and technically put in peril on the charge, although by reason of the misconduct of the judge in procuring an acquittal against the weight of evidence he soon ceased to be in peril.[4]

7 Orders for admission to hospital; Criminal Procedure (Insanity) Act 1964 and Criminal Appeal Act 1968, ss. 12–16.

It has been noted that the Criminal Procedure (Insanity) Act 1964 created a right of appeal against a finding of "not guilty by reason of insanity" (called in the Act a "special verdict"), and against a finding of unfitness to plead. On appeal against a hospital order the Court will consider whether the order was right at the time when it was made, and will not review the applicant's subsequent progress.[5] If an appeal against the special verdict is allowed, the Court may at the same time conclude that the defendant was guilty of an offence; in that case the Court may substitute a verdict of guilty of that offence, provided it is the offence charged at the trial or an offence of which the defendant could have been found guilty by way of alternative verdict.[6] In any other case, the Court must simply substitute a verdict of acquittal, but may make an order that the defendant be admitted to hospital for observation.[7] Where the Court allows an appeal against a finding of unfitness to plead, the appellant may be tried for the offence originally charged.[8] Conversely, the defendant may have been convicted of an offence at the trial (whether or not insanity or unfitness to plead were alleged) but the Court of Appeal may be of opinion that the special verdict should have been returned or a finding of unfitness made. In this case the Court of Appeal may quash the conviction, enter a special verdict or a finding of unfitness and order the defendant to be admitted to hospital.[9]

8 Procedural powers of the Court

As noted above, some appeals to the Court may be brought without leave, but in most cases there must be an application to the Court itself for leave. The time limit for giving notice of appeal, or application for leave to appeal, is 28 days from the date of conviction or sentence. This time may be extended by the Court, except in a case involving sentence of death. Such application

---

[1] *R. v. Cronin*, [1940] 1 All E.R. 618.
[2] *R. v. Williams* (1925), 19 Cr. App. Rep. 67; see p. 409, *ante*. *Aliter* if he made no request; *ibid.*
[3] *R. v. Scothern*, [1961] Crim. L.R. 326.
[4] *R. v. Middlesex Justices, Ex parte Director of Public Prosecutions*, [1952] 2 Q.B. 758, at p. 769; [1952] 2 All E.R. 312, at p. 314, *per* LORD GODDARD, C.J.
[5] *R. v. McNaney*, [1969] 2 All E.R. 35; [1969] 1 W.L.R. 623.
[6] Criminal Appeal Act 1968, s. 13 (4).
[7] *Ibid.*, s. 14.
[8] *Ibid.*, s. 16.
[9] *Ibid.*, s. 6.

is made in the first instance to a single judge of the Court, who considers it in private.[1]   A single judge has most of the powers of a court of three judges (besides, of course, the power to grant leave); exceptionally he does not have any of the powers relating to fresh evidence.[2]   An application may of course be abandoned, and notice of abandonment can only be withdrawn if there was fraud, or mistake, or at any rate bad advice, resulting in an "unintended, ill-considered decision to abandon".[3]   Where however an application for leave to appeal was granted but, because of a postal strike, was not communicated to the applicant before he gave notice of abandonment, he was permitted to withdraw his notice.[4]   If the single judge refuses leave to appeal (or to exercise any other of his powers) the application may be considered by a court of three judges.[5]   Both the single judge and the court may grant legal aid and bail. Bail, for obvious reasons, is very rarely granted;[6] indeed almost the only cases where it will be granted are where the defendant has obtained (or does not need) leave to appeal and has a very good chance of succeeding on appeal, or where the defendant has been given a comparatively short sentence after a long and complex trial.   In the latter case he might otherwise have served much of his sentence before the appeal was heard.   Time spent on bail does not, of course, count as part of the sentence.[7]   Conversely, time spent in custody pending the determination of the appeal now counts as part of the defendant's sentence, subject to any direction to the contrary (for which reasons must be given).   No such direction may be given where the defendant obtained leave to appeal, from the Court of Appeal or the trial court, or where the case has been referred to the Court by the Home Secretary.[7]

Once an appeal has been heard and dismissed, it cannot be re-opened and the applicant's only recourse is to petition the Home Secretary (who, as seen, may refer the case to the Court).   A case may only be re-listed for further argument if there was "some procedural defect" in the hearing, such as papers being lost.[8]

C   APPEAL TO THE HOUSE OF LORDS

A further appeal lies by either prosecution or defence from the Court of Appeal (criminal division) to the House of Lords if (1) the Court of Appeal certifies

---

[1] This practice is not invariable, and some applications for leave to appeal against conviction may go direct to a court of three judges.   See the Donovan Report, paras. 229–241.

[2] Neither does the court of three judges, at the stage of application.

[3] *R. v. Sutton*, [1969] 1 All E.R. 928; [1969] 1 W.L.R. 375.

[4] *R. v. Noble*, [1971] 3 All E.R. 361; [1971] 1 W.L.R. 1772.

[5] Criminal Appeal Act 1968, s. 31 (2).   The application must normally be made to the Court within 14 days of communication of the notice of refusal by the single judge, but the Court has jurisdiction to extend the time even though the further application is not made until after the 14 days have expired: *R. v. Ward*, [1971] 3 All E.R. 619; [1971] 1 W.L.R. 1450; *R. v. Doherty*, [1971] 3 All E.R. 622; [1971] 1 W.L.R. 1454.

[6] If the appeal is dismissed, it may embarrass the court to order the defendant's return to prison.   "The court is always anxious in such a case, because although a man may have been on bail he will have had the appeal hanging over him for all this time": LORD PARKER, C.J. in *R. v. Cavendish*, [1961] 2 All E.R. 856 at p. 858; [1961] 1 W.L.R. 1083 at p. 1085.

[7] Criminal Appeal Act 1968, s. 29,

[8] *R. v. Grantham*, [1969] 2 Q.B. 574; [1969] 2 All E.R. 545; a decision of the Courts-Martial Appeal Court, but stated to apply to the Court of Appeal.

that a point of law of general public importance is involved in the decision; and (2) either the Court of Appeal or the House of Lords gives leave to appeal on the ground that the point is one which ought to be considered by the House.[1] The certificate is a necessary condition to avoid the House of Lords being inundated with hopeless applications. If the Court of Appeal is satisfied that there is a point of law of general public importance involved it will give the certificate, as it were, automatically. There will always, nevertheless, be an element of discretion as to whether an appeal is allowed to proceed, since even if the point were of general public importance it might still not be worthy of consideration by the House of Lords in the particular case; for example it might already be the subject of clear and satisfactory decisions of lower courts. This element of discretion is preserved by the requirement that there must be leave to appeal. It will be observed that only the Court of Appeal can give the certificate, and if that court refuses the certificate there can be no further proceedings.[2] On the other hand, the Court of Appeal may give a certificate and yet refuse leave, in which case a petition may be made to the House of Lords for leave to appeal, the petition being heard by the Appeals Committee of the House.

It is proper and convenient that the certificate should state what the point of law of general public importance is;[3] however, it seems likely that other points may be raised by either side once the case is before the House of Lords on the point certified.[4] However, the grant of a certificate on some point affecting the validity of the conviction does not enable the appellant to argue that the sentence is invalid.[3] The House of Lords may exercise similar powers to those of the court below. As to applying the proviso,[5] however, VISCOUNT SIMONDS said in *Jones* v. *Director of Public Prosecutions* that the House of Lords:

> "may feel some difficulty about exercising a jurisdiction which demands an examination not only of the particular question of law that is raised but of all the circumstances of the case."[6]

Notwithstanding, the House of Lords did apply the proviso in the case of *Myers* v. *Director of Public Prosecutions.*[7]

---

[1] Criminal Appeal Act 1968, s. 33. Application for leave must be made within 14 days of the Court of Appeal decision, if made to that court, or within 14 days of the Court of Appeal's refusal to grant leave if made to the House of Lords (s. 34).
[2] *Gelberg* v. *Miller*, [1961] 1 All E.R. 618 n.; [1961] 1 W.L.R. 459.
[3] *Jones* v. *Director of Public Prosecutions*, [1962] A.C. 635; [1962] 1 All E.R. 569.
[4] *A.-G. for Northern Ireland* v. *Gallagher*, [1963] A.C. 349; [1961] 3 All E.R. 299.
[5] To s. 2 (1) of the 1968 Act, see pp. 425–426, *ante*.
[6] [1962] A.C. 635, at p. 660; [1962] 1 All E.R. 569, at p. 573.
[7] [1965] A.C. 1001; [1964] 2 All E.R. 881; see p. 531 footnote 2, *post*.

CHAPTER 27

Summary Procedure

A PROCESS

The rules as to process are the same as in the case of an indictable offence, except that a summons cannot be issued merely on the ground that the defendant resides or is, or is believed to reside or be, in the county or borough in question and a warrant cannot be issued in any case where a summons has already been issued. In any event, as has already been noted,[1] a warrant cannot be issued for the arrest of an adult in the case of a summary offence, unless the offence is punishable with imprisonment or the defendant's address is "not sufficiently established" for a summons to be served on him. Even where a warrant may lawfully be issued, it is rarely thought necessary in the case of any summary offence. The position therefore is that a summons or a warrant may be issued if:

(1) the summary offence was committed or is suspected to have been committed in the county or borough;

(2) it appears to the magistrate issuing process necessary or expedient, with a view to the better administration of justice, that the person charged should be tried jointly with or in the same place as some other person who is charged with an offence and who is in custody or is to be proceeded against in the county or borough;

(3) under any enactment the magistrates' court has jurisdiction to try the offence. In this context, there should be noted section 28 of the Criminal Justice Act 1967, permitting a magistrates' court to try a number of offences provided that it has jurisdiction to try any one of them.[2]

(4) In addition, a warrant, but not a summons, may be issued if the person charged resides or is, or is believed to reside or be, in the county or borough.[3]

---

[1] See p. 376, *ante*.

[2] See p. 374, *ante*.

[3] Magistrates' Courts Act 1952, ss. 1, 3. See the rules as to offences committed on boundaries etc. which also apply here, p. 374, *ante*. It is further provided that a magistrates' court may issue process in the case of an offence committed outside England and Wales, where the offence is punishable exclusively on summary conviction, provided that the court would have jurisdiction to try the offence (by virtue of section 28 of the 1967 Act) if the offender was before it: Courts Act 1971, Schedule 8, Pt. II, para. 34 (2).

B JURISDICTION

The basic rule is that a magistrates' court may try all summary offences committed in the county or borough.[1] It will be seen at once that the jurisdiction to issue process is apparently much wider than the jurisdiction to try, since if the basic rule stood alone the court would have no jurisdiction to try those offences in respect of which it had issued process under (2) and (4) above. The difficulty is met by provisions in the Act that: where process is issued under (2) above the court shall have jurisdiction to try the offence even though it was not committed in the county or borough;[2] this is no doubt subject to the limitations laid down in *R. v. Blandford, R. v. Freestone* discussed above;[3] a warrant issued under (4) must require the person charged to be brought before a court with jurisdiction to try the offence.[1]

C THE COURSE OF THE TRIAL

I Time-limit

Unless expressly provided to the contrary a magistrates' court cannot try an information unless the information was laid within six months from the time when the offence was committed.[4] Time, therefore, runs from the time of commission of the offence, not from the time of its discovery; however, it is sufficient if the information is laid within the six months, even if the trial takes place outside that time. It is in each case a question of construction of the statute whether the offence in question is a continuing offence, that is, committed each day that the act or state of affairs in question continues, or whether it is a "once and for all" offence in that it is committed on one day and one day only. Thus in *R. v. Wimbledon Justices, Ex parte Derwent*[5] a statute made it an offence to let or offer to let a house in excess of a certain rent. The divisional court held that a person lets a house once and for all when he demises it by means of a lease and that an information laid six months after the date of the demise was out of time. Proceedings could therefore be restrained by prohibition since:

"... If in a case brought before justices it can be seen on the face of the proceedings that the offence is alleged to have been committed more than six months before the information was laid, justices have no power to enter upon the case at all, because they have no jurisdiction to sit as a court of summary jurisdiction in the case of an offence alleged to have been committed more than six months before the proceedings were instituted."[6]

Even where the offence is continuing it seems that the time limit runs from each day, so that the magistrates cannot hear any information that charges the offence as occurring more than six months before the date of the information;[7]

---

[1] See footnote 3 on p. 432, *ante*.
[2] Magistrates' Courts Act 1952, s. 2 (2) and s. 1 (2). Note again section 28 of the Criminal Justice Act 1967: see p. 374, *ante*.
[3] See p. 373, *ante*.
[4] Magistrates' Courts Act 1952, s. 104.
[5] [1953] 1 Q.B. 380; [1953] 1 All E.R. 390.
[6] [1953] 1 Q.B. 380, at p. 385; [1953] 1 All E.R. 390, at p. 391, *per* LORD GODDARD, C.J.
[7] *R. v. Chertsey Justices, Ex parte Franks*, [1961] 2 Q.B. 152; [1961] 1 All E.R. 825.

in other words the matter is to be regarded as if the defendant committed the offence once every day.

2 Number of offences

A magistrates' court must not proceed to the trial of an information which charges more than one offence.[1] This is a natural rule, since the information fulfils the same function in summary trial as the indictment in the case of trial at the Crown Court; the same considerations of, *inter alia*, fairness to the defendant, which prohibit duplicity in an indictment, also prohibit an information charging more than one offence. Thus in *Ware* v. *Fox*[2] an information charged the defendant with being concerned in the management of premises which were used for the purpose of smoking cannabis or cannabis resin or dealing in cannabis or cannabis resin. The Queen's Bench Divisional Court held that on the proper construction of the relevant statute[3] the information alleged two offences, namely managing premises used for smoking and managing premises used for dealing and was bad for duplicity. By contrast, section 134 (1) of the Road Traffic Act 1960 creates the offence of wilfully or negligently failing to comply with the conditions of a road traffic licence; it was held in *G. Newton, Ltd.* v. *Smith*[4] that the section creates one offence, namely failure to comply with the licence, whether wilful or negligent. Where an information is found to charge more than one offence the prosecutor should be called on to elect before the trial begins on which offence to proceed; if he declines to make his election the information should be dismissed.[5] It is essential that the matter should be put right at the outset, since, as will be noted below, the magistrates must state the substance of the information to the defendant and ask him to plead to it; therefore the information must be in order for a proper plea to be received, and the defendant cannot be required to plead to an information that is bad for duplicity. It is very doubtful whether this irregularity is one which can be cured by the operation of section 100 of the Magistrates' Courts Act.[6] In any event if the information is not amended:

> "If a conviction is to be drawn up, how is it to be done? The information has to be dealt with as a whole. . . . To split it into halves and say that one bit is proved and another bit is disproved involves, to my mind, an operation as impossible as a few years ago splitting the atom was thought to be."[7]

To avoid the difficulty the information itself should always be in court from the beginning of proceedings.[8]

It is however quite permissible, and indeed common, for two informations against the same defendant to be tried together, provided that he consents.[9]

---

[1] Magistrates' Courts Rules 1968, r. 12 (1).
[2] [1967] 1 All E.R. 100; [1967] 1 W.L.R. 379.
[3] Dangerous Drugs Act 1965, s. 5.
[4] [1962] 2 Q.B. 278; [1962] 2 All E.R. 19.
[5] *Edwards* v. *Jones*, [1947] K.B. 659; [1947] 1 All E.R.385;
[6] See p. 372, *ante*.
[7] [1947] K.B. 659, at p. 667; [1947] 1 All E.R. 830, at p. 834, *per* OLIVER, J.
[8] *Per* LORD PARKER, C.J. and SALMON, J. (as he then was) in *Hargreaves* v. *Alderson*, [1964] 2 Q.B. 159; [1962] 3 All E.R. 1019. See also *Garman* v. *Plaice*, [1969] 3 All E.R. 342; [1969] 1 W.L.R. 19.
[9] *Brangwynne* v. *Evans*, [1962] 1 All E.R. 446; [1962] 1 W.L.R. 267.

3 Hearing

If the defendant appears at the hearing the court must state to him the substance of the information and ask him whether he pleads guilty or not guilty.[1] In spite of these words, the same pleas as are open to a defendant charged with an indictable offence may be raised by a defendant charged with a summary offence. If the plea is one of not guilty the prosecutor may make an opening speech, and will then call his evidence. Where the prosecutor is unrepresented, it is open to the magistrates, in their discretion, to permit their clerk to examine prosecution witnesses.[2] Section 78 of the Magistrates' Courts Act, already cited,[3] will apply, and the witnesses will be subject to cross-examination and re-examination according to the circumstances of the case. At the conclusion of the evidence for the prosecution the defendant may address the court, whether or not he calls evidence; if he is calling evidence it will follow at once. The defendant may then address the court a second time but only if he himself has given evidence, another witness has been called on his behalf, and the court gives leave.[4] If the defendant addresses the court twice the prosecutor has a right to address the court a second time immediately before the defendant's second speech.[4] The court will then retire if necessary and convict the defendant or dismiss the charge.

If on the other hand the defendant pleads guilty the court may convict him without hearing evidence.[5] The wording of the sub-section shows that it is often desirable to hear some evidence, particularly where it is part of the prosecution's case that the offence was committed in circumstances of aggravation, or perhaps if a committal for sentence to the Crown Court is contemplated or if the plea of guilty tendered may be "equivocal."[6] In any event the court retains full power over the case until sentence is passed and has discretion to allow a change of plea until that time if justice so requires.[7]

Whether there is a plea of guilty or finding of guilt, there will normally be such an enquiry into the past record of the defendant as follows conviction of an indictable offence; the court may then adjourn, for not more than three weeks at a time, for enquiries to be made or for the purpose of determining the best way to deal with the case.[8] When the court resumes it need not be composed of the same magistrates; if, however, there are any newcomers the court which sentences or deals with the offender must make such enquiry into the facts and circumstances of the case as are necessary to acquaint the newcomers fully with those facts and circumstances.[9] This must be done even though the court will *ex hypothesi* have held some such enquiry before; the use of the words "the court" seems to prohibit the newcomers being given information privately before the court sits.

---

[1] He must himself be asked: *R. v. Wakefield Justices, Ex parte Butterworth*, [1970] 1 All E.R. 1181. *Quaere* whether solicitor or counsel may answer on his behalf.

[2] *Simms* v. *Moore*, [1970] 2 Q.B. 327; [1970] 3 All E.R. 1.

[3] See p. 383, *ante*.

[4] Magistrates' Courts Rules 1968, r. 14.

[5] Magistrates' Courts Act 1952, s. 13 (3).

[6] See p. 440, *post*.

[7] *S. (An Infant)* v. *Manchester City Recorder*, [1971] A.C. 481; [1969] 3 All E.R. 1230.

[8] Magistrates' Courts Act 1952, s. 14 (3).

[9] *Ibid.*, s. 98 (7). This is perhaps the nearest that English law comes to allowing special "sentencing tribunals".

D ABSENCES

1 General effects of absence[1]

It sometimes happens that one or both of the parties fails to appear at the trial or adjourned trial of the information. If the defendant does not appear the court may hear the case in his absence provided that, where a summons was issued, either, the court is satisfied that the summons was served on the defendant within what appears to be a reasonable time before the hearing, or the defendant appeared on a previous occasion to answer the information. Alternatively the court may adjourn the hearing, with or without issuing a warrant for the arrest of the defendant; but a warrant can only be issued if the court is satisfied as to the matters stated above, and if the information is substantiated on oath. There is a further restriction on the issue of a warrant: if the court adjourns the trial after hearing evidence, or convicting the defendant without hearing evidence on a plea of guilty, the court must not issue a warrant unless it thinks it undesirable, by reason of the gravity of the offence, to continue the hearing in his absence. In any event, a warrant cannot be issued unless the offence is punishable by imprisonment or unless the court, having convicted the defendant, proposes to disqualify him.

If the prosecutor fails to appear the court may dismiss the information or, if evidence has been received on a previous occasion, continue the hearing. This is one example of the importance of the stage of the trial at which the justices begin to hear evidence. Alternatively the court may adjourn the trial, but must release the defendant on bail except in eight specified circumstances, unless he cannot enter into a recognisance or find sureties.[2] If neither side appears, the court may again dismiss the information or, if evidence has been received on a previous occasion, continue the hearing; the Act says nothing about adjourning the hearing, but this seems also to be possible.

2 Pleading guilty by post: Magistrates' Courts Act 1957

This Act provided a new and convenient method whereby the defendant can plead guilty in cases where his appearance at court would be no more than a formality, if not a serious waste of time and money. The procedure laid down by the Act is generally acknowledged to have worked well and is extensively used, particularly in motoring cases; however, it has no application at all to (1) juvenile court proceedings; (2) indictable offences; (3) hybrid offences; and (4) summary offences in which the defendant can claim the right to be tried by jury. Where the Act does apply, procedure is as follows. The prosecutor will serve with the summons a notice in prescribed terms as to the effect of section 1 of the Act and a concise statement of such facts as he will place before the court if the defendant does decide to plead guilty by post. Although the Act is silent on the point it seems that it is entirely within the discretion of the prosecutor as to whether he will make use of the Act and serve the above documents with the

---

[1] Magistrates' Courts Act 1952, ss. 15–17, as amended by section 24 of Criminal Justice Act 1967.
[2] Criminal Justice Act 1967, s. 18.

summons, even on the assumption that the Act applies to the offence charged. Where, however, the prosecutor does elect to use the procedure, he must serve the documents and then inform the clerk to the justices that he has done so. It is then for the defendant or his solicitor to inform the clerk that he desires to plead guilty without appearing, if that is so, by sending, appropriately completed, the part of the notice described above. He does not, of course, have to use the procedure, and even if he does at first give notification that he is not going to appear he may change his mind and appear.

If, however, he does not appear the court may proceed to hear the case in his absence (whether or not the prosecutor is also absent) provided that it is satisfied that the notice and statement of facts were served on the defendant with the summons. Before accepting the plea of guilty[1] and convicting the defendant in his absence the court must cause to be read out aloud the defendant's notification that he is going to plead guilty, the statement of facts served on the defendant and any statement by way of mitigation which the defendant himself may have submitted. The statement of facts read out must be precisely the same as that served upon the defendant. These rules must be meticulously observed, and breach of them may be a ground for quashing the conviction by means of certiorari.

> "We all know that these matters have to be dealt with expeditiously. . . . It seems to me, however, to be quite clear that, before the magistrates can exercise jurisdiction in a case of this sort, they must strictly observe the conditions of the statute. Mere knowledge of the contents of the accused's submission, the mere reading of it themselves, is not sufficient; the submission must be read in open court."[2]

The rule that the precise statement of facts must be read out is also important, because after hearing it the magistrates may decide that the case is too grave to be dealt with in the way contemplated by the parties and may adjourn the case for the defendant to be present.

Assuming that, after hearing the notification of intention to plead guilty, the statement of facts and the submissions in mitigation, the magistrates accept the plea, they will record a conviction and (in the majority of cases to which the Act applies) impose a fine. Where they think it desirable to imprison the defendant or to impose any disqualification on him they must adjourn the hearing[3] without imposing any penalty whatever. There must then be sent to the defendant a notice stating the time and place of the adjourned hearing and the reason for the present adjournment (that is that the court is considering imprisonment or disqualification). If he chooses not to appear after receiving notice of what the court has in mind the court can proceed to disqualify him in his absence;[4] they cannot however sentence him to imprisonment or detention in a detention

---

[1] As to "acceptance" of a plea of guilty, see p. 435, *ante*; and p. 440, *post*.

[2] *R. v. Oldham Justices, Ex parte Morrissey*, [1958] 3 All E.R. 559n, at p. 560; [1959] 1 W.L.R. 58, at p. 59, *per* LORD PARKER, C.J.

[3] Under Magistrates' Courts Act 1952, s. 14: see p. 435, *ante*. This applies even if disqualification is mandatory under the "totting-up" provisions; further there may even in this case be grounds for mitigating the normal consequences of conviction, which the defendant should have the chance to state: *R. v. Llandrindod Wells Justices, Ex parte Gibson*, [1968] 2 All E.R. 20; [1968] 1 W.L.R. 598.

[4] Criminal Justice Act 1967, s. 26 (2).

centre in his absence.[1]   In such a case the proper course is to issue a warrant for the defendant's arrest.[2]

Thus a person can never be imprisoned in his absence and can only be disqualified in his absence following an adjournment for the purpose of giving him an opportunity to appear.

---

[1] Criminal Justice Act 1967, s. 26 (1).
[2] *Ibid.*, s. 24 (2).

CHAPTER 28

Appeal Following
Summary Trial

A defendant convicted by a magistrates' court may appeal either (1) to the Crown Court; or (2) by case stated to the Queen's Bench Division of the High Court and subsequently (3) to the House of Lords, in certain circumstances. Each of these will be considered in turn.

A APPEAL TO THE CROWN COURT

Where the defendant has been convicted in the magistrates' court of either a summary offence or an indictable offence tried summarily or a hybrid offence tried summarily he may appeal to the Crown Court, if he pleaded guilty against his sentence only, or if he pleaded not guilty against both conviction and sentence.[1] It will be seen that there is an express statutory prohibition against an appeal against conviction if the defendant pleaded guilty. This may be contrasted with the position following trial on indictment, where, as already noted,[2] there is nothing in the Criminal Appeal Act to prevent an appeal against conviction to the Court of Appeal even if the defendant pleaded guilty. It has been observed[2] that the judges have laid down that appeals against conviction following a plea of guilty will only be entertained by the Court of Appeal in certain exceptional circumstances; so in the case of appeals to the Crown Court also, the judges have given a construction to the statute which evades the effect of the exact words used by Parliament, but on this occasion in favour of the defendant. It has been held that to make a plea of guilty binding and effective it must be unambiguous;[3] if therefore the defendant says the actual word "guilty" but adds to it a statement which, if true, amounts to a defence to the

---

[1] Magistrates' Courts Act 1952, s. 83 (1). The section is not amended by the Courts Act 1971 save that the Crown Court is substituted for Quarter Sessions; therefore, decisions such as *R. v. Durham Quarter Sessions (infra)*, remain relevant: Courts Act 1971, s. 9 (6).
[2] See p. 422, *ante.*
[3] *R. v. Durham Quarter Sessions, Ex parte Virgo,* [1952] 2 Q.B. 1; [1952] 1 All E.R. 446; cf. *R. v Ingleson,* cited at p. 422, *ante.*

charge, or if from the circumstances it is clear that he is denying the charge but has pleaded guilty through ignorance of the law, a plea of guilty accepted in these circumstances is a nullity.[1]   The Crown Court can, therefore, hear an appeal against the "conviction" which is equally a nullity, and under powers presently to be considered can remit the case to the magistrates with an expression of opinion that a plea of not guilty ought to be entered.   Where on the other hand there has been a deliberate and unequivocal plea of guilty no appeal against conviction can be entertained.[2]

The expression "sentence" includes any order made on conviction by a magistrates' court, with certain exceptions, namely: (1) a probation order or an order for conditional discharge, although if on a later date sentence is passed in respect of the offence for which the probation order or order for conditional discharge was made, that is following "breach" of the order, there may be an appeal against that later sentence; (2) an order for the payment of costs; (3) an order for the destruction of an animal, made under the Protection of Animals Act 1911; and (4) any order, if the court has not discretion as to the making of the order or its terms, for example if the court is bound to order endorsement of a driving licence.[3]   It has already been noted[4] that there is no appeal against a committal for sentence, in the cases already discussed in which there may be such a committal, although there may be an appeal against the conviction on which the committal is based.   There is a right of appeal against an order to enter into recognisances to keep the peace or be of good behaviour.[5]

With limited exceptions only the defendant may appeal.   Procedure[6] is that an appeal must be commenced by giving notice of appeal, to the clerk of the magistrates' court, and to the other party, within 21 days after the day on which the decision of the magistrates' court was given (meaning the day on which sentence is passed if there is an adjournment of the case after conviction).   The Crown Court may extend the time, either in relation to a notice not yet given or to a notice already given but out of time.

Proceedings before the Crown Court take the form of a complete re-hearing of the case;[7] the prosecution must open the case and call its witnesses afresh and either side may introduce fresh evidence without any leave.   This is of course in sharp contrast to proceedings in the Court of Appeal.   The Crown Court may confirm, reverse or vary the decision of the magistrates' court,[8] or remit the case with an expression of their opinion;[9] as already seen this latter procedure will be appropriate where an "equivocal" plea of guilty has been entered, which in all the circumstances the Crown Court considers should have been treated as a plea of not guilty.

As regards appeals against sentence, the Crown Court may impose any

---

[1] *R. v. Blandford Justices, Ex parte G.*, [1967] 1 Q.B. 82; [1966] 1 All E.R. 1921; see p. 435, *ante*.
[2] *R. v. West Kent Quarter Sessions Appeals Committee, Ex parte Files*, [1951] 2 All E.R. 728.
[3] Magistrates' Courts Act 1952, s. 83 (2).
[4] See p. 359, *ante*.
[5] Magistrates' Courts (Appeals from Binding Over Orders) Act 1956.
[6] See generally, Crown Court Rules 1971, r. 7.
[7] Courts Act 1971, s. 9 (6).
[8] *Ibid.*, s. 9 (2) (*a*).
[9] *Ibid.*, s. 9 (2) (*b*).

sentence which the magistrates' court could have passed, whether more or less severe than that which they actually passed. The court may also do this if the appeal is against conviction only.[1] Again, there is a sharp contrast between appeals to the Crown Court and appeals to the Court of Appeal following trial on indictment, since the Court of Appeal never has had the power to interfere with the sentence in any way if the appeal is against conviction only and, in addition, cannot now increase sentence;[2] the Crown Court can do both. Finally, the Crown Court may:

> "make such other order in the matter as the court thinks just, and by such order exercise any power which the said authority might have exercised."[3]

The wording is liberal, but it was held,[4] on an almost identical provision in the previous legislation, that Quarter Sessions had no power to vary the sentence by quashing the sentence passed at the magistrates' court and committing to itself for sentence. The reason lies in the point already noted[5] that committal for sentence is not itself a sentence; if therefore magistrates elect to sit as a sentencing court instead of as a committing court Quarter Sessions could not go behind that election. Their power was to interfere with a sentence, not a decision as to whether the defendant should be committed or sentenced. This is presumably still true for the Crown Court.

If the appeal is against sentence only it may proceed on the basis of the facts relevant to sentence produced before the magistrates, if counsel for the appellant agrees to that course; there will then be no need for any evidence whatever to be called before the Crown Court. The same strictness of proof is not demanded in matters relevant to sentence as in matters relevant to conviction. In fact proceedings on an appeal against sentence normally take the same course as if the defendant had just been convicted, or had pleaded guilty, before the court.

From the Crown Court a further appeal lies by way of case stated to the Queen's Bench Division of the High Court; this will be considered below.[6]

B APPEAL BY CASE STATED TO THE QUEEN'S BENCH DIVISION FROM MAGISTRATES' COURTS AND THE CROWN COURT

1 Magistrates' Courts

Any person who was a party to proceedings before a magistrates' court or (although not a party) is aggrieved by the conviction, order, determination or other proceeding may appeal against the proceeding on the ground that it is wrong in law or in excess of jurisdiction by applying to the magistrates' court to state a case for the opinion of a divisional court of the Queen's Bench Division of

---

[1] Courts Act 1971, s. 9 (4).
[2] See p. 427, *ante.*
[3] Courts Act 1971, s. 9 (2) (*c*).
[4] In *R. v. Bullock*, [1964] 1 Q.B. 481; [1963] 3 All E.R. 506.
[5] See p. 354, *ante.*
[6] See p. 444, *post.*

the High Court.[1] Thus, either the defendant or the prosecutor in a criminal case may make application for a case to be stated. Application may also be made by a person aggrieved, but:

> "the words 'person aggrieved' do not really mean a man who is disappointed of a benefit which he might have received if some other order had been made (still less does it mean someone having a merely sympathetic interest in the proceedings). A 'person aggrieved' must be a man who has suffered a legal grievance, a man against whom a decision has been pronounced which has wrongfully deprived him of something, or wrongfully refused him something, or wrongfully affected his title to something."[2]

A party to proceedings who has succeeded in part only may appeal against the incompleteness of his success. Executors of a person who has died since the hearing of the case in the magistrates' court are "interested", at any rate if a fine has been imposed, since the money to pay this would come out of the estate of the deceased; they may accordingly bring an appeal by way of case stated.[3] If the deceased had been sentenced to imprisonment the executors appear not to be "interested".[4]

Application must be made in writing, within fourteen days after the day on which the decision of the magistrates' court was given;[5] again, if the magistrates adjourn after conviction, the day on which sentence is actually passed is the first day on which time begins to run.[5] The application should be delivered to the clerk of the magistrates' court whose decision is being questioned or sent to him by post; the names of the magistrates constituting the court do not have to be given and it is therefore immaterial that there is an error in their names.[6] Nor need the application state the point of law which it is desired to raise, although the magistrates to whom application is made may require the applicant to satisfy them that there is some point of law involved.

The magistrates may refuse to state a case only on the ground that the application is in their opinion frivolous, and may not refuse to state a case if the application is made by or under the direction of the Attorney-General, even in the unlikely event of such an application being considered frivolous.[7] On refusal the magistrates must give the applicant a certificate of refusal if he so requires; he may then apply to the High Court for an order of mandamus directing the justices to state a case.[8] On the making of the application, whether granted or refused, the applicant loses his right to appeal to the Crown Court.[8]

A "case" will normally contain a statement of the information as laid, the facts found, the contentions of the parties, the cases cited, the decision and the question or questions for the decision of the High Court. If one or other of the

---

[1] Magistrates' Courts Act 1952, s. 87 (1).

[2] *Ex parte Sidebotham* (1880), 14 Ch.D. 458, at p. 465, *per* JAMES, L.J., described as "the best definition of the expression 'aggrieved'" in *R.* v. *London Sessions, Ex parte Westminster Corporation*, [1951] 2 K.B. 508, at p. 511; [1951] 1 All E.R. 1032, at p. 1033, *per* LORD GODDARD, C.J.

[3] *Hodgson* v. *Lakeman*, [1943] K.B. 15. *Aliter* in an appeal following trial on indictment: *R.* v. *Jefferies*, [1969] 1 Q.B. 120; [1968] 3 All E.R. 238.

[4] *R.* v. *Rowe*, [1955] 1 Q.B. 573; [1955] 2 All E.R. 234.

[5] Magistrates' Courts Act 1952, s. 87 (2), (3).

[6] *R.* v. *Oxford (Bullingdon) Justices, Ex parte Bird*, [1948] 1 K.B. 100.

[7] Magistrates' Courts Act 1952, s. 87 (5), (6).

[8] *Ibid.*, s. 87 (4).

parties is contending that there was no evidence on which the magistrates could come to their decision, a statement of the evidence should be included. This form, originally settled by LORD GODDARD, C.J., should always be used.

> "I have been oppressed for a long time with the unnecessary recitals which are always put into cases, by which we are told that some person is dissatisfied with the justices' decision, and are referred to the provisions of statutes and so forth. Therefore, I have settled a form. . . ."[1]

The case may be stated by all the justices whose decision is questioned or by any two of them[2] and may be stated in relation to a number of different prosecutions, even against different defendants on different days, provided that they raise precisely the same point. Under no circumstances should the case state that the decision was that of a majority, if that was the position.[3] The case should in any event be submitted to both parties for their consideration and in the event of any difficulty it should be left to the parties themselves to produce a draft and submit it to the magistrates for their consideration.[4] If, in spite of this, a party to an appeal considers that the facts have been improperly stated in the case he may apply to the Queen's Bench Division for the case to be remitted to the justices for restatement of the facts, the application being accompanied by an affidavit setting out the facts which it is alleged should go in the case.[5]

The case should be stated within three months of the application.[6] This rule, however, is "directory and not mandatory" so that the court may hear a case stated outside the time limit if satisfied that the delay is not the fault of the appellant.[7] An application, supported by affidavit, should be made to extend the time; the parties have no power to do so merely by consent.[8] Thus in a case where, owing to the illness of a solicitor acting for the appellant, the case was not stated for seven months the court declined to hear the appeal, no application having been made earlier for an extension of time.[9]

> "I attach importance to the observance of the rules because it is highly desirable that these cases, which are of a criminal nature, should be disposed of as promptly as possible."[10]

On the hearing the court will hear and determine the questions of law arising, after argument by counsel for the parties. The court may allow argument on a point not raised in the court below or even take such a point itself,[11] provided that in each case the point is one of pure law, not requiring any evidence. The magistrates themselves may file an affidavit, setting out the grounds of the decision and any facts which they may consider to have a bearing on the

---

[1] *R.A.H. (Transporters), Ltd.* v. *Edgar: (Practice Note)* [1953] 2 All E.R. 999; [1953] 1 W.L.R. 1309.
[2] Magistrates' Courts Rules 1968, r. 66.
[3] *More O'Ferrall, Ltd.* v. *Harrow U.D.C.*, [1947] K.B. 66, at p. 70; [1946] 2 All E.R. 489, at p. 491.
[4] *Cowlishaw* v. *Chalkley*, [1955] 1 All E.R. 367 n.; [1955] 1 W.L.R. 101.
[5] *Spicer* v. *Warbey*, [1953] 1 All E.R. 284; [1953] 1 W.L.R. 334.
[6] Magistrates' Courts Rules 1968, r. 67.
[7] *Moore* v. *Hewitt*, [1947] K.B. 831; [1947] 2 All E.R. 270.
[8] *Whittingham* v. *Nattrass*, [1958] 3 All E.R. 145 n.; [1958] 1 W.L.R. 1016.
[9] *Rippington* v. *Hicks and Son (Oxford), Ltd.*, [1949] 1 All E.R. 239.
[10] *Ibid.*, at p. 240, *per* LORD GODDARD, C.J.
[11] *Whitehead* v. *Haines*, [1965] 1 Q.B. 200; [1964] 2 All E.R. 530.

issues;[1] in view of the existence of the case this procedure will rarely be appropriate. Unless misconduct is alleged there is no need for the justices to be represented by counsel. The court may reverse, affirm or amend the decision in respect of which the case has been stated, or may remit the matter to the magistrates with its opinion, or make such other order as it sees fit.[2]

2 The Crown Court

The Crown Court may also state a case for the opinion of the High Court. Either party to any order, judgment or other decision of the Crown Court, other than one relating solely to trial on indictment, may apply for a case to be stated on the ground that the decision is wrong in law or in excess of jurisdiction.[3] Thus, either party to an appeal from the magistrates' court, against conviction or sentence may apply, as (apparently) may a person sentenced at the Crown Court after committal for sentence from a magistrates' court. These provisions are in several respects an extension of the old law; however, a person aggrieved by the Crown Court's decision, but not a party, still has no right of appeal. Application should be made in writing to the appropriate officer of the Crown Court within 14 days after the decision; again, the Crown Court may only refuse to state a case if the application is considered frivolous.[4] The powers of the Queen's Bench Division appear to be the same as those exercisable on an appeal from the magistrates.

C APPEAL TO THE HOUSE OF LORDS

Finally it should be noted that an appeal to the House of Lords may be made from the divisional court of the Queen's Bench Division, subject to exactly the same conditions as those governing appeals from the Court of Appeal in the case of trial on indictment.[5] Thus there must be a certificate from the divisional court that a point of law of general public importance is involved in its decision and either the divisional court or the House of Lords must give leave to appeal on the ground that the point is one which ought to be considered by the House of Lords. In this way a summary offence may be considered by four courts; the magistrates' court, the Crown Court, the divisional court of the Queen's Bench Division and the House of Lords.

---

[1] Review of Justices' Decisions Act 1872.
[2] Summary Jurisdiction Act 1857, s. 6.
[3] Courts Act 1971, s. 10 (1)–(3). Certain decisions of the Crown Court are made final: see s. 10 (1) (b).
[4] Crown Court Rules 1971, r. 21 (1), (3).
[5] Administration of Justice Act 1960, s. 1; see pp. 430–431, *ante*.

PART VI

Outline of the Law of Evidence

SUMMARY

CHAPTER 29

What is Evidence?

A NATURE OF JUDICIAL EVIDENCE

All litigation involves the court making findings of fact and applying the law to those facts. It is sometimes stated, erroneously, that one case turned solely on its facts while another was decided on a point of law. In fact there can be no litigation, civil or criminal, which does not involve a mixture of law and fact. It is a fundamental principle of English law that the courts do not adjudicate upon hypothetical legal problems, so that a factual situation must form the basis of every case. The law of evidence is concerned with the means by which facts are presented to the court. The facts which are presented to the court as the basis of the dispute which is the subject of the litigation are termed the "facts in issue". The law of evidence does not determine which facts are facts in issue in any particular case. This question is determined by reference to the substantive law, and, in civil cases, to the pleadings. Thus in a prosecution for murder, if the accused pleads not guilty it is for the prosecution to prove the elements of that crime according to the common law definition of murder. This involves proving that the accused unlawfully killed the deceased and that he did so with malice aforethought. These facts are thus facts in issue. If the defence of insanity is raised, the accused's sanity becomes a fact in issue. These are matters of substantive law. The province of the law of evidence is the means by which these facts in issue may validly be proved. Thus Blackstone defined judicial evidence as:

> "That which demonstrates, makes clear, or ascertains the truth of the very fact or point in issue, either on the one side or on the other."[1]

It ought to be noted that the word "evidence" is variously used in two distinct senses. In its narrower, and more usual, meaning "evidence" connotes the means by which the facts in issue are proved. This is the meaning inherent in Taylor's classic definition of judicial evidence as:

> "All the legal means, exclusive of mere argument, which tend to prove or disprove any matter of fact, the truth of which is submitted to judicial investigation."[2]

---

[1] 3 Comm. 367.   [2] *A Treatise on the Law of Evidence* (12th Edn.), I, I.

The second, and wider, sense in which the word "evidence" is used is to describe those facts which may be proved, rather than the means by which they are proved. Facts may often be proved as evidence of the existence of other facts. This type of evidence is known as "circumstantial evidence".[1] For example, in a prosecution for murder a witness may testify to the fact that he sold the murder weapon to the accused. This fact is not in itself a fact in issue but it is relevant as tending to show that the accused killed the deceased, which is, of course, a fact in issue. In the above example, therefore, the word "evidence" may be used to describe both the testimony of the witness and the fact to which he testifies. Phipson's definition of judicial evidence embodies both these meanings of the word "evidence":

> "Firstly, the means, apart from argument and inference, whereby the court is informed as to the issues of fact as ascertained by the pleadings; secondly, the subject-matter of such means."[2]

This definition applies rather to civil than to criminal proceedings since only in the former are the facts in issue ascertained by reference to the pleadings, there being, of course, no pleadings in criminal cases where facts in issue are ascertained by reference to substantive law.

Thus the law of evidence deals, to a limited extent, with what facts may be proved as well as with how those facts may be proved.[3] Where the question arises as to what facts may or must be proved in any case, this question may depend upon a consideration of the law of evidence, of substantive law or of rules of procedure. For this reason there is an overlap between evidence and substantive law and between evidence and procedure. Just as substantive law may sometimes be seen to be "secreted in the interstices of procedure", so may it be secreted in the law of evidence.

1　Relationship between evidence and substantive law

As stated above the question of whether or not a fact may be proved to the court is sometimes dependent upon rules of evidence and sometimes upon rules of law. It is sometimes asserted that rules which determine what facts may be proved are not rules of evidence at all. Thus the thirteenth report of the Law Reform Committee in 1966 dealing with hearsay evidence in civil proceedings[4] stated that:

> "Questions as to *what* facts must be proved to give rise to a cause of action or to a defence thereto, or as to *what* facts may not be proved, are questions of substantive law ... even though the answer to such a question may sometimes be disguised as a rule of evidence."

Nevertheless although such rules sometimes have the effect of rules of law they are generally treated as rules of evidence. Usually it will be of purely academic interest whether a rule is treated as a rule of evidence or as a rule of law. However, the classification is important in at least two circumstances. First, in conflict of laws cases any rule which the English courts classify as a rule

---

[1] See p. 450, *post.*
[2] *Law of Evidence* (9th Edn.), p. 2.
[3] In fact the word "evidence" is sometimes used in a third sense as meaning "admissible evidence"; for example in the words "that's not evidence".
[4] Cmnd. 2964.

of evidence is applied in a case irrespective of which system of substantive law is appropriate to decide the case. For example in *Leroux* v. *Brown*,[1] a contract, valid according to the law by which it was to be construed, was held unenforceable in the English courts because of the absence of writing required under the Statute of Frauds, the requirement being treated as a matter of evidence.

The second circumstance in which the classification of a rule as a rule of evidence or a rule of law is critical occurs in the interpretation of statutes. Since courts are bound to adopt the procedure (including rules of evidence since these are procedural) obtaining at the hearing, there is a presumption that statutes concerned with procedural matters are retrospective in the sense that the statutory rule in question applies irrespective of the date of the events to which the evidence is directed. This is contrary to the general presumption against retrospective operation which applies to statutes which affect substantive law.[2]

Having illustrated that it is sometimes important to distinguish a rule of evidence from a rule of law it must, unfortunately, be stated that there is no acid test by which evidence may be distinguished from law. Estoppel, for example, is a rule of evidence which sometimes has the effect of a rule of law in that it, in effect, creates a right by preventing the other party from denying that right. The doctrine of *Central London Property Trust, Ltd.* v. *High Trees House, Ltd.*[3] is a form of estoppel and therefore a rule of evidence though it has the effect of a rule of law by creating a contractual obligation which would not otherwise exist. Presumptions are rules of evidence but they may also sometimes have the effect of a rule of law. For example there was, until 1963,[4] a rule that a husband who had sexual intercourse with his wife knowing that she had committed a matrimonial offence was thereby irrebuttably presumed to have condoned that offence. It has been established that this was a rule of evidence[5] though it had the effect of removing a right completely. In truth every presumption which is irrebuttable has the effect of a rule of law since it creates or extinguishes some right or obligation.

2 Relationship between evidence and procedure

Evidence is often regarded as a branch of procedure. The term "adjective law" is used to describe evidence and procedure and is distinct from "substantive law" which determines rights and liabilities. Since evidence is a branch of procedure it might appear that any statutory power to make rules of procedure would include a power to make rules of evidence. For this reason "evidence" as a branch of procedure is limited to its narrower meaning as governing the way in which facts may be proved rather than what facts may be proved. Thus a rule of court which provided for the admission of facts otherwise irrelevant would be *ultra vires* as being a rule of law rather than a rule of procedure. The power to make rules governing the means of proof in the Supreme Court is contained in

---

[1] (1852), 12 C.B. 801.
[2] See p. 99, *ante*: for a recent illustration of the importance of classification in the interpretation of statutes, see *Blyth* v. *Blyth*, [1966] A.C. 643; [1966] 1 All E.R. 524.
[3] [1947] K.B. 130; [1956] 1 All E.R. 256 n.
[4] Matrimonial Causes Act 1963.
[5] *Blyth* v. *Blyth* (*supra*). The Divorce Reform Act 1969 has removed the point of the case since condonation is no longer a bar to divorce.

section 99 (1) (i) of the Judicature Act 1925 and rules have been made[1] under this section.

B CLASSIFICATIONS OF JUDICIAL EVIDENCE

While it is important to characterise rules of evidence so as to distinguish them from rules of law it is less important to arrive at a subsidiary classification of the rules themselves. Nevertheless, though certain classifications are of little practical importance, certain major subdivisions of evidence cannot be ignored since the courts and even, occasionally, the legislature refer specifically to certain types of evidence; for example, hearsay. For this reason the major subdivisions of judicial evidence are set out briefly below.

1   Direct and circumstantial

Direct evidence is evidence of the facts in issue themselves; the testimony of an eye-witness or a written confession, for example. Circumstantial evidence is evidence of other facts from which a fact in issue may be inferred. For example, in a prosecution for murder the testimony of a witness who claims to have seen the killing is direct evidence since the killing of the deceased by the accused is a fact in issue. On the other hand evidence that the accused purchased a gun, that his finger-prints were found on the gun, that the bullet which caused death was fired from the same gun and that the accused had previously threatened the deceased are all items of circumstantial evidence. None of the above facts are themselves facts in issue but each supports the existence of a fact in issue; that the accused shot the deceased. It will be appreciated from the above example that circumstantial evidence is certainly no less cogent than direct evidence. Direct evidence may more easily be fabricated or inaccurate than a strong chain of circumstantial evidence. Incidentally it may be noted that the phrase "circumstantial evidence" may be used to describe either the fact which is proved or the means of its proof. Thus where a witness testifies that the accused's fingerprints were found on the murder weapon, both his testimony and the fact to which he testifies are described as circumstantial evidence.

2   Original and hearsay

This classification relates to the means of proof. Original evidence[2] is proof of a fact by "first-hand" proof. This is usually the testimony of a witness who perceived the fact with his own senses, though either a document or an object (real evidence) may constitute original evidence. For example a letter containing a threat is original evidence of the words of the threat; the production of a knife in court is original evidence of the length of the blade. Hearsay evidence is "second-hand" evidence. It consists of evidence of what someone else said or wrote as proof of the truth of what was said or written. Hearsay evidence may be oral or written. For example a policeman's notebook containing the statement of a witness to an accident is hearsay evidence of the accident. It

---

[1] The Rules of the Supreme Court (Revision) 1965 are the principal rules currently in operation. See p. 233, *ante*.

[2] It is fair to warn the student that this terminology is not universal. "Original evidence ' is described by some commentators as "direct evidence". See, for example, Nokes, *An Introduction to Evidence* (2nd Edn.), p. 10.

should be noted that evidence of what another person said or wrote is not necessarily hearsay. If it is submitted to prove not the truth of what was said or written, but merely the fact that it was said or written, it is original, not hearsay, evidence. For example the testimony of a witness that he heard X threaten Y is original evidence, since its purpose is to prove that a statement was made. On the other hand, the testimony of a witness to the effect that he heard X, immediately before being shot, shout out Y's name is hearsay, since its purpose is to prove the truth of what X stated, i.e., that Y was his murderer. The distinction between original and hearsay evidence is of great importance because hearsay evidence is generally excluded as a means of proof.[1]

3 Best and secondary

The "best evidence" rule is one of the oldest common law rules of evidence. It is self-explanatory; the best (or most direct) evidence of a fact must be adduced. Thus the best evidence of the contents or existence of a document is the production of the original; a copy is secondary evidence. The best evidence of the condition of a physical object is the production of that object to the court. The rule also operated to exclude circumstantial evidence where direct evidence was available.[2] The best evidence rule is of declining importance. It is no longer a bar to the reception of circumstantial evidence and it does not now apply to real evidence.[3] It does, however, still apply to proof of the contents of private documents although, even here, it is subject to several exceptions.[4]

4 Oral, documentary and real

This is the modern classification of means of proof. Oral evidence is the testimony of witnesses, documentary evidence the production of documents and real evidence the production of physical objects for the inspection of the court. The distinction between documentary and real evidence is important since the best evidence rule applies to the former but not to the latter. Although the distinction is generally self-evident, difficulty may arise where a physical object bears an inscription; for example, a tombstone, a car number plate or a banner. The test of whether these objects are to be treated as real or documentary evidence is the purpose for which they are produced. If they are tendered as proof of their physical existence they are real evidence while if they are submitted as evidence of the matter inscribed they are documents.

As an alternative to the production of an object in court, the judge and jury may leave the court to inspect an object or a site. Such an inspection is termed a "view" and may be classified as real evidence.[5] It is less easy to characterise the demeanour of witnesses. The court is undoubtedly entitled to have regard to the physical characteristics and demeanour of witnesses, particularly in assessing their cogency. This is usually described as real evidence though demeanour is sometimes regarded as an ancillary of oral evidence. Where the physical

---

[1] See p. 526, *post.*
[2] *Williams* v. *East India Co.* (1802), 3 East 192.
[3] *Hocking* v. *Ahlquist Brothers, Ltd.,* [1944] K.B. 120; [1943] 2 All E.R. 722; see p. 521, *post.*
[4] See p. 513, *post.*
[5] *L.G.O. Co., Ltd.* v. *Lavell,* [1901] 1 Ch. 135; *Buckingham* v. *Daily News, Ltd.,* [1956] 2 Q.B. 535; [1956] 2 All E.R. 904; see p. 521, *post.*

characteristic of a witness is a fact in issue, such as facial disfigurement, it is undoubtedly a form of real evidence.[1]

C FUNCTIONS OF JUDGE AND JURY

The respective functions of judge and jury differ irrespective of whether they are trying a civil or a criminal case. This demarcation between the function of the judge and that of the jury obtains even where there is no jury, as is the case in most civil actions at the present day. In these cases the judge discharges the functions of both judge and jury but the functions themselves remain distinct, so that different considerations must be observed by the judge according to whether he is acting *qua* judge or *qua* jury.

The general rule is that the judge decides questions of law while the jury decides questions of fact and assesses damages. Where the question is one of mixed law and fact it is for the judge to determine the point of law and for the jury to decide the facts, assuming that the judge's decision on the law does not effectively dispose of the question in issue in which event the facts must not be left to the jury. For example, where an innuendo is pleaded in the tort of defamation it is for the judge to decide whether the words are capable of bearing the defamatory meaning alleged. If he decides this question, which is a question of law, in the affirmative it is then for the jury to decide whether the words are, in fact, defamatory. However this question must be left to the jury only if the judge decides that the words are capable of bearing the alleged meaning. If he decides to the contrary he must withdraw the question from the jury and failure to do so is a ground of appeal on a point of law.[2] Since every case, civil or criminal, involves mixed law and fact it follows that the issues of fact must be withdrawn from the jury where the judge's decision on any question of law conclusively determines the case. Such a finding is sometimes made following a submission of "no case to answer" by the defence. A finding of no case to answer may be based on a point of law or on the point that there is no evidence, or insufficient evidence, of an essential fact in the case of the plaintiff or prosecution. Thus where, in a prosecution for dangerous driving, the prosecution failed to call any evidence to identify the accused as the driver of the car it was held that there was no case to answer.[3]

As well as determining questions of law and deciding whether there is evidence in support of material allegations of fact, the judge also decides all questions concerning the admissibility of evidence, even where the question of admissibility depends upon a preliminary finding of fact, such as whether an original document has been destroyed or whether a confession is voluntary.[4] Although most questions regarding the admissibility of evidence are determined by the judge in the presence of the jury, the jury in a criminal case is invariably required to retire while the judge decides on the admissibility of evidence whose admission would be highly prejudicial to the accused, such as a confession or evidence of the accused's previous convictions.

---

[1] See *Cole* v. *United Dairies (London), Ltd.*, [1941] 1 K.B. 100; [1940] 4 All E.R. 318.
[2] *Nevill* v. *Fine Arts and General Insurance Co.*, [1897] A.C. 68.
[3] *Middleton* v. *Rowlett*, [1954] 2 All E.R. 277; [1954] 1 W.L.R. 831.
[4] *Chan Wai-Keung* v. *R.*, [1967] 2 A.C. 160; [1967] 1 All E.R. 948.

Finally the judge, even when sitting with a jury, decides certain questions of fact by way of exception to the general rule that issues of fact are for the jury. It has already been noted that the judge decides questions of fact upon which the admissibility of evidence depends. In addition the judge decides other isolated issues of fact such as questions of foreign law, which must be proved as a question of fact[1] or whether a covenant in restraint of trade is reasonable.[2] Other questions of reasonableness are nowadays treated as questions of fact for the jury, such as whether the defendant in an action for negligence acted as a reasonable man.

Having dealt with these introductory matters the law of evidence may be divided into three parts: (1) what facts may be proved (relevance and admissibility); (2) on whom is the burden of proving these facts and what standard of proof is required of that party, and (3) how may these facts be proved (and how may they not be proved). The ensuing chapters deal with these questions.

---

[1] See p. 526, *post.*
[2] *Mason v. Provident Clothing and Supply Co., Ltd.,* [1913] A.C. 724, at p. 732.

CHAPTER 30

Relevance and Admissibility

A GENERAL CONDITIONS OF RELEVANCE AND ADMISSIBILITY

When discussing the relevance and admissibility of evidence, the word "evidence" is used as meaning facts, rather than the means by which facts may be proved (except in so far as facts may be proved by other facts). Thus it is very confusing to speak of hearsay evidence as being relevant or irrelevant since hearsay evidence is a means of proof. Similarly opinion evidence is neither relevant nor irrelevant; it is a means of proving facts which may in themselves either be relevant or not. Confusion arises particularly since hearsay and opinion evidence are almost always described as "inadmissible". It would be more logical to speak of hearsay and opinion as "unpermitted" means of proof, leaving admissibility to relate solely to the issue of *what* facts may be proved irrespective of *how* they may be proved.

In order to be receivable by the court evidence must be both relevant and admissible. Relevant facts form a wider category than admissible facts. All admissible facts are relevant[1] though not all relevant facts are admissible. Two classes of facts are relevant; the facts in issue and other facts from which the facts in issue may be inferred (circumstantial evidence). There is rarely any difficulty in determining whether or not a fact is or is not a fact in issue. This question is determined by reference to the substantive law and, in civil cases, to the pleadings if there are any. Difficulty is encountered, however, in determining whether a fact, not in itself in issue, is relevant as circumstantial evidence. Basically the question of whether or not one fact may be inferred from proof of another is a question of logic. Stephen defined the word "relevant" as meaning that:

"Any two facts to which it is applied are so related to each other that according to the common course of events one either taken by itself or in connection with

---

[1] It is arguable that facts upon which the admissibility of evidence depends, such as whether a document has been lost or whether a prospective witness has died, are admissible but not relevant within the general definition. It is probably better to regard such facts as indirectly relevant. See Cross, *Evidence* (3rd Edn.), p. 20, text and footnotes.

other facts proves or renders probable the past, present or future existence or non-existence of the other."[1]

Obviously there are endless combinations and permutations of facts and in each case it will be for the judge to decide whether or not one fact is logically probative of a fact in issue and therefore relevant as circumstantial evidence. Circumstantial evidence may exist prior to a fact in issue, contemporaneously with it or subsequent to it. Thus, if the speed of a vehicle at a given moment is a fact in issue, evidence may be received of the speed of the vehicle a few moments earlier.[2] Evidence is also admissible of facts which supply a motive for conduct the existence of which is in issue. Thus familiarity between a husband and another woman may be evidence in support of subsequent alleged adultery. The purchase of poison by an accused murderer[3] and the financial standing of a person accused of arson with intent to defraud an insurance company[4] have been held to be relevant evidence. These are examples of circumstantial evidence existing prior to the facts in issue. Circumstantial evidence may exist subsequent to the facts in issue. Thus a promise to marry the mother of an illegitimate child was admitted in *Lloyd* v. *Powell Duffryn Steam Coal Co., Ltd.*[5] as evidence of the paternity of the child. Similarly an illegitimate child's physical appearance or blood-group would be evidence of paternity. Evidence that a person was alive on a given day obviously proves that he was alive on an earlier day and is therefore relevant.[6] Attempts by parties to suborn witnesses to commit perjury,[7] to tamper with evidence[3] or to give a false alibi to the police[8] have all been held to be relevant to issues of guilt or liability. The third class of circumstantial evidence consists of facts contemporaneous with the facts in issue. It is on this basis that the whereabouts of an accused person at the time of the alleged crime is relevant. Similarly the fact that a man and a woman spent a night together in a hotel bedroom is evidence of adultery. Those facts which are relevant to the facts in issue on account of their proximity or contemporaneity are often denoted by the expression *res gestae*. So much evidence is received under this head that it merits separate consideration.

Res Gestae

This expression has been described as:

"A phrase adopted to provide a respectable legal cloak for a variety of cases to which no formula of precision can be applied."[9]

and as an expression which:

"like many Latin phrases, is often used to cover situations insufficiently analysed in clear English terms."[10]

---

[1] *Digest of the Law of Evidence* (12th Edn.), art. 1.
[2] *Beresford* v. *St. Albans Justices* (1905), 22 T.L.R. 1.
[3] *R.* v. *Palmer* (1856), unreported. See Stephen, *History of the Criminal Law*, III, p. 389.
[4] *R.* v. *Grant* (1865), 4 F. & F. 322.
[5] [1914] A.C. 733.
[6] *Re Watkins*, [1953] 2 All E.R. 1113; [1953] 1 W.L.R. 1323.
[7] *Moriarty* v. *London, Chatham and Dover Rail.* (1870), L.R. 5 Q.B. 314.
[8] *R.* v. *Knight*, [1966] 1 All E.R. 647; [1966] 1 W.L.R. 230.
[9] *Homes* v. *Newman*, [1931] 2 Ch. 112, at p. 120, *per* LORD TOMLIN.
[10] *Ratten* v. *R.*, [1971] 3 All E.R. 801, at p. 806; [1971] 3 W.L.R. 930, at p. 935, *per* LORD WILBERFORCE.

Nevertheless the expression is commonly used to describe facts or statements which either form part of or accompany the facts in issue. Thus the facts in issue are themselves strictly part of the *res gestae* but, since the relevance of a fact in issue is never in dispute, the question before the court is usually whether other evidence is part of the *res gestae*. The evidence alleged to form part of the *res gestae* may be either an act or a statement. In either event its admissibility depends upon its proximity, in time or in place, to a fact in issue.

The criteria for admissibility have recently been restated by the Privy Council in *Ratten* v. *R*.[1] and the speech by LORD WILBERFORCE may be taken to have settled the law for the time being:

> "The possibility of concoction, or fabrication, where it exists, is ... probably the real test which judges in fact apply. In their Lordships' opinion this should be recognised and applied directly as the relevant test: the test should not be the uncertain one whether the making of the statement was in some sense part of the event or transaction. This may often be difficult to establish: such external matters as the time which elapses between the events and the speaking of the words (or vice versa), and differences in location being relevant factors but not, taken by themselves, decisive criteria. As regards statements made after the event, it must be for the judge, by preliminary ruling, to satisfy himself that the statement was so clearly made in circumstances of spontaneity or involvement in the event that the possibility of concoction can be disregarded. Conversely, if he considers that the statement was made by way of narrative of a detached prior event so that the speaker was so disengaged from it as to be able to construct or adapt his account, he should exclude it. And the same must in principle be true of statements made before the event. The test should not be the uncertain one, whether the making of the statement should be regarded as part of the event or transaction. This may often be difficult to show. But if the drama, leading up to the climax, has commenced and assumed such intensity and pressure that the utterance can safely be regarded as a true reflection of what was unrolling or actually happening, it ought to be received. The expression *res gestae* may conveniently sum up these criteria, but the reality of them must always be kept in mind: it is this that lies behind the best reasoned of the judges' rulings."

In the instant case the evidence in question was that of a telephone operator who stated that, at about the time the deceased was shot by her husband, a woman telephoned from the deceased's premises in a hysterical state and said "Get me the police please". The defendant's version of events was that the gun had discharged by accident while he was cleaning it. Evidence of the telephone conversation was held admissible on the basis that it was a fact which showed that a telephone call was made and the mental state of the caller. However the Privy Council went on to state that even if it was hearsay evidence it was admissible as part of the *res gestae* on the basis of the principles stated above.

It is indeed where the evidence alleged to be relevant as part of the *res gestae* is a statement rather than a fact that difficulty arises. This is because a statement may be treated either as a fact in itself or as proof of another fact. In the latter case the statement is *prima facie* inadmissible hearsay. For example, the exclamation "Stop it Harry, you're frightening me" made by a victim of rape is in itself a

---

[1] [1971] 3 All E.R. 801, at p. 807; [1971] 3 W.L.R. 930, at p. 936.

relevant fact since the making of the statement tends to prove absence of consent which is a fact in issue. However it is also hearsay evidence of the identity of the assailant if the statement is reported by a third party who overheard it. Were a statement identifying the assailant made subsequently it would be inadmissible as proof of identity.[1] It is admissible in the first place only because it forms part of the *res gestae*. It is in this context that it becomes important to determine the scope of the *res gestae*, for a statement which is hearsay evidence of another fact, such as identity or the state of mind of the maker, is only admissible as proof of that fact if it forms part of the *res gestae*. This is a genuine exception to the rule against hearsay.[2]

Thus the test as to admissibility now appears to be whether the statement is "made in circumstances of spontaneity or involvement" as opposed to being made "by way of narrative of a detached prior event". The old requirement of contemporaneity having been abolished many old cases must now be regarded as incorrectly decided on their facts. In the well-known case of *R. v. Bedingfield*[1] the deceased emerged from a room with her throat cut and was heard to utter the words "See what Bedingfield has done to me"[3] following which she died. COCKBURN, C.J. held this statement inadmissible as hearsay and not forming part of the *res gestae* since "it was something stated by her after it was all over, whatever it was, and after the act was completed". Applying the criteria laid down in *Ratten v. R.* the evidence would clearly be admissible. On the same reasoning the House of Lords in *R. v. Christie*[4] refused to regard as part of the *res gestae* a statement made by a small boy which identified the accused, the statement being made some minutes after the alleged incident; the Privy Council in *Teper v. R*[5], rejected a similar statement made some twenty-five minutes after the start of a fire in respect of which the accused, who was identified by the statement, was charged with arson. However, both of these cases would appear to be clear examples of "narrative of a detached prior event" and would appear therefore to be correctly decided on their facts.

In addition to the above criteria, the statement must explain a fact in issue. Clearly a statement cannot be relevant to a fact in issue if it concerns facts other than the facts in issue. Thus in *Agassiz v. London Tramway Co., Ltd.*[6] a statement made shortly after an accident by the conductor of a tramcar to the effect that the driver had been off the line five or six times earlier in the day was held inadmissible as referring not to a fact in issue but to earlier conduct.

Evidence, in order to be receivable, must be admissible as well as relevant. Admissible evidence comprises all relevant evidence which is not subject to a

---

[1] See *R. v. Bedingfield* (1879), 14 Cox C. C. 341.
[2] See p. 534, *post*.
[3] The precise words used were not proved at the trial and slightly different words such as "See what Harry's done!" are sometimes attributed to the deceased.
[4] [1914] A.C. 545.
[5] [1952] A.C. 480; [1952] 2 All E.R. 447; compare *Davies v. Fortior, Ltd.*, [1952] 1 All E.R. 1359 where a statement made within two minutes of an accident was admitted in a civil case. In *Tickle v. Tickle*, [1968] 2 All E.R. 154; [1968] 1 W.L.R. 937, evidence was received of a statement made by a doctor concerning a patient's health, where the patient's belief in the state of his health was something "savouring of a *res*".
[6] (1873), 21 W.R. 199.

rule of exclusion. Thus relevance depends upon logic whereas admissibility is
a question of law. It follows that there are two separate bases upon which
evidence is excluded; it may be irrelevant or, alternatively, relevant but subject
to a rule of exclusion and therefore inadmissible. In practice it is common to
refer to the evidence as inadmissible in either case.

B IRRELEVANT EVIDENCE

Any fact which is not in issue and which does not tend to prove a fact in issue is
irrelevant. Having stated this fact it might be supposed that any classification of
irrelevant evidence would be superfluous. However the law regards as irrelevant various classes of facts which the layman might suppose to be relevant.
For example, the fact that a person has behaved in a certain way on a number of
previous occasions is generally irrelevant to the issue of whether he has behaved
in that way on the occasion in question though many would doubtless consider
such evidence to be valuable. Similarly the character and previous convictions
of a person accused of crime might seem to many indicative of guilt, but the law
excludes such facts as irrelevant. Consequently, in this section certain classes of
facts are examined which, although they may appear to have probative value,
are as a rule regarded as irrelevant and therefore inadmissible.

1   Res inter alios acta

One of the oldest rules of evidence is that *res inter alios acta alteri nocere non debet*
(no one should be harmed by things done between strangers). The rule is no
longer one of fundamental importance since it has been superseded by the wider
rules relating to relevance, though certain aspects of the rule still exist. For
example an admission or confession is binding only upon the maker and not
upon third parties who are implicated, although there are exceptions to this
principle.[1] Similarly conduct on the part of third persons having no interest in
the litigation is generally irrelevant. Thus in *Wright* v. *Doe* d. *Tatham*[2] the fact
that letters were written to a testator on the assumption that he was sane was
held not to be evidence of his sanity.

Nevertheless there are a number of circumstances in which the conduct or
statements of strangers to the proceedings are admitted as relevant. For example,
on a charge of handling stolen goods, the fact of the goods being stolen must
be proved; in order to prove his legitimacy a person may show that his parents
lived together as man and wife;[3] a company attempting to prove itself to be a
bank may prove that third parties treated it as a bank;[4] an admission by a predecessor in title binds his successors in title;[5] an admission by an agent may
bind his principal;[6] the conduct of a managing director may be relevant on a
charge against a limited company of conspiracy to defraud.[7] In all these

---

[1] See p. 536, *post.*
[2] (1838), 4 Bing. N.C. 489.
[3] *Doe* d. *Fleming* v. *Fleming* (1827), 4 Bing. 266.
[4] *United Dominions Trust, Ltd.* v. *Kirkwood*, [1966] 2 Q.B. 431; [1966] 1 All E.R. 968.
[5] *Woolway* v. *Rowe* (1834), 1 Ad. & El. 114.
[6] *Re Devala Provident Gold Mining Co.* (1883), 22 Ch.D. 593.
[7] *R.* v. *I.C.R. Haulage, Ltd.*, [1944] K.B. 551; [1944] 1 All E.R. 691.

circumstances, and in many others, facts are admitted which would fall within the description *res inter alios acta*. For this reason it is better to regard the operation of the rule as being confined to the few special examples given above.

2 Similar facts

As a rule evidence that a person has behaved in a certain way on other occasions is not relevant to prove that he behaved in a similar way on the occasion in question merely because of the similarity of the conduct. Such evidence is described as "similar fact" evidence and is excluded as irrelevant. The existence of this rule is recognised and illustrated in a number of leading cases. Perhaps the best-known statement of the rule is to be found in the advice of the Privy Council delivered by Lord Herschell, L.C. in *Makin v. A.-G. for New South Wales*:[1]

> "It is undoubtedly not competent for the prosecution to adduce evidence tending to show that the accused has been guilty of criminal acts other than those covered by the indictment, for the purpose of leading to the conclusion that the accused is a person likely from his criminal conduct or character to have committed the offence for which he is being tried."

The rule generally operates to exclude evidence of other conduct by the accused in criminal cases, though it is not confined to such evidence. Thus in *Harris v. Director of Public Prosecutions*[2] a policeman was indicted on eight counts of larceny from an office in a Bradford market. The counts were tried together and the eight offences were committed in a somewhat similar manner at times when the accused might have been on duty in the vicinity. Harris was acquitted on seven counts but convicted on the eighth count. His conviction was quashed on the eighth count since the summing-up had not warned the jury that what had occurred on the earlier occasions was irrelevant to the accused's guilt on the eighth count. Similarly in *R. v. Rodley*[3] a conviction of burglary (with intent to ravish) was quashed by the Court of Criminal Appeal because of the wrongful admission of evidence that the accused had entered another house by the chimney later the same night and had consensual sexual intercourse with the occupant.[4] The rule also applies in civil cases. The fact that a brewer had supplied good beer to other publicans was not evidence that he had not supplied bad beer to the defendant publican in *Holcombe v. Hewson*.[5] On the issue of whether a person has been negligent on a particular occasion evidence is not relevant either that he has or has not been negligent on other occasions, even though performing similar conduct on all the occasions in question.

It should not be supposed, however, that all similar fact evidence is irrelevant. It is not relevant merely because of its similarity to a fact in issue but, if it is otherwise logically relevant, conduct on other occasions is admissible. Thus on a charge of rape the fact that the prosecutrix has had consensual sexual intercourse with the accused on other occasions is relevant to the issue of consent and

---

[1] [1894] A.C. 57, at p. 65.
[2] [1952] A.C. 694; [1952] 1 All E.R. 1044.
[3] [1913] 3 K.B. 468.
[4] See also *Noor Mohamed v. R.*, [1949] A.C. 182; [1949] 1 All E.R. 365; *R. v. Holmes* (1871), L.R. 10 C.C.R. 334.
[5] (1810), 2 Camp. 391.

therefore admissible evidence notwithstanding that it is similar fact evidence.[1] There are various types of connection which may exist between similar fact evidence and a fact in issue other than the mere fact of similarity which, as stated above, does not make the evidence relevant. These cases are generally treated as exceptions to the rule excluding similar fact evidence and the most important of them are set out below, though many would not consider them as exceptions at all but merely as cases where the rule is inapplicable.

a System

Conduct on other occasions is treated as relevant to conduct which is in issue where, taken together, they may be said to form part of a systematic course of conduct. This principle is construed very narrowly. The mere fact that conduct is repeated on several occasions does not constitute a system. The question is one of degree. In *Harris* v. *Director of Public Prosecutions*,[2] eight offences of larceny from the same office in the same market did not constitute a system. However in *Makin* v. *A.-G. for New South Wales*[3] a system was established by the prosecution. The accused man and woman were charged with the murder of a child whose body was found in their garden. They had adopted the child on receipt of a small sum from its mother for its support. Evidence was held admissible that other children had been adopted by the accused in the same way and that their bodies had been found buried in the gardens of houses occupied by the accused. The purpose of proving a system, and thereby rendering admissible conduct on other occasions, may be to prove either the *actus reus* or the *mens rea* of a crime. Thus in *Makin's* case the similar fact evidence tended to show the unlikelihood of the death being due to natural causes and was thus evidence of an *actus reus*. A similar case is *R.* v. *Smith*,[4] the famous "brides in the bath" murder. The deceased, who had gone through a ceremony of marriage with the accused, was drowned in her bath having insured her life in favour of the accused. The death was claimed by the accused to have been caused by an attack of epilepsy. Evidence was admitted that two other women with whom Smith had gone through ceremonies of marriage had also drowned in their baths in circumstances in which the accused would gain financially by their death.

Evidence of system may also serve to prove the *mens rea* of an offence, in which case it may be doubly relevant as it also serves to rebut a defence of accident or mistake. For example in *R.* v. *Mortimer*,[5] on a charge of murdering a lady cyclist by running her down, evidence was admitted that the accused had intentionally driven his car at other lady cyclists thus proving that his conduct was intentional and not merely negligent.

b Rebutting defences

The purpose of establishing a system is to prove either *mens rea* or *actus reus*. This incidentally involves rebutting such defences as accident or mistake. Nevertheless similar fact evidence which operates to rebut a defence may be

---

[1] *R.* v. *Riley* (1887), 18 Q.B.D. 481.
[2] [1952] A.C. 694; [1952] 1 All E.R. 1044.
[3] [1894] A.C. 57.
[4] (1915), 11 Cr. App. Rep. 229.
[5] (1936), 25 Cr. App. Rep. 150.

regarded as a separate category. The evidence need not amount to a systematic course of conduct. Thus in *R. v. Armstrong*[1] the accused, a solicitor, charged with murdering his wife by arsenic poisoning, raised the defence that she had committed suicide. Evidence was admitted of a subsequent attempt by the accused to poison a rival solicitor with arsenic. Similarly in *R. v. Bond*[2] evidence that the accused, a doctor, had used instruments upon a woman to perform an abortion on an earlier occasion was admitted in order to rebut the defence that his use of similar instruments on the occasion in question was to carry out a *bona fide* examination.

c Identity

There are various ways of proving identity by circumstantial evidence. A comparison of finger-prints or handwriting is circumstantial evidence of identity. So also is the physical resemblance or blood group of an illegitimate child evidence of the identity of the father. In exceptional circumstances the conduct of a person on other occasions may identify him as the perpetrator of conduct which is a fact in issue, provided that the conduct is sufficiently idiosyncratic. In *R. v. Straffen*[3] the accused was charged with the murder of a small girl. Evidence was admitted that the accused had previously murdered two other small girls.[4] The evidence served to identify Straffen because of the peculiar similarity shared by the three murders; all three victims were young girls, all were strangled, there was no sexual assault or other apparent motive and no attempt to conceal the bodies.

d Knowledge

Similar fact evidence may support *mens rea* in a criminal case or a relevant mental element in a civil case. If a person acts in a certain way on more than one occasion this may tend to show that he knew what he was doing and was not ignorant or mistaken. For example in *R. v. Francis*[5] the accused was charged with obtaining an advance from a pawnbroker by the false pretence that a worthless ring was valuable. In order to prove knowledge of the falsity of this pretence evidence was admitted that the accused had made similar pretences to other pawnbrokers in order to obtain advances.

Certain statutes provide for the admission of evidence of conduct on the part of an accused person on other occasions. Thus section 27 (3) of the Theft Act 1968[6] provides:

> "Where a person is being proceeded against for handling stolen goods (but not for any offence other than handling stolen goods), then at any stage of the proceedings, if evidence has been given of his having or arranging to have in his possession the goods the subject of the charge, or of his undertaking or assisting in, or arranging to undertake or assist in, their retention, removal, disposal or realisation, the following evidence shall be admissible for the purpose of proving that he knew or believed the goods to be stolen goods:—

[1] [1922] 2 K.B. 555.
[2] [1906] 2 K.B. 389.
[3] [1952] 2 Q.B. 911; [1952] 2 All E.R. 657.
[4] In respect of these murders Straffen had been found unfit to plead and had been ordered to be detained in a Broadmoor institution, from which he had escaped.
[5] (1874), L.R. 2 C.C.R. 128.
[6] Replacing s. 43 (1) of the Larceny Act 1916.

(*a*) evidence that he has had in his possession, or has undertaken or assisted in the retention, removal, disposal or realisation of, stolen goods from any theft taking place not earlier than twelve months before the offence charged; and

(*b*) (provided that seven days' notice in writing has been given to him of the intention to prove the conviction) evidence that he has within the five years preceding the date of the offence charged been convicted of theft or of handling stolen goods."

Most of the cases concerning the relevance of similar fact evidence are criminal cases but the principles apply equally in civil cases. Thus similar fact evidence frequently tends to prove knowledge in cases where liability depends upon knowledge. For example the tendency of a servant to play dangerous practical jokes is admissible to show that his master was negligent in employing him.[1]

3 Character

Character is usually regarded as *res inter alios acta*. The fact that a person is of good or bad character is generally irrelevant to the issue of whether or not he has performed a certain act on the occasion in question. Consequently evidence of character is, as a rule, irrelevant and inadmissible. Nonetheless there are numerous exceptions to this rule. For example reputation, which is one facet of character, is a fact in issue in defamation; admissible similar fact evidence may demonstrate character, in the sense of disposition, directly or by implication. Thus evidence that a person has strangled two small girls is, incidentally, evidence of bad character. Before examining the exceptional circumstances in which evidence of character may be adduced it will be convenient to consider what the word "character" comprises. For the purposes of the law of evidence there are three aspects of character;—reputation, disposition and convictions. The question of which of these three aspects of character are admissible in any particular circumstance differs according to the circumstances in which a person's character is admitted in evidence.

a Character of the parties in civil cases

Character is relevant in civil cases only in very limited circumstances. The character of the parties *qua* parties (as opposed to *qua* witnesses, where different considerations apply) is generally irrelevant. Character witnesses, as such, are hardly ever encountered at civil trials, even where issues bearing upon character are involved. Thus in *A.-G.* v. *Bowman*[2] the defendant to an information for keeping false weights was not permitted to call a witness as to character because the proceedings were civil, notwithstanding that the information necessarily involved an imputation on his character.

There are, however, exceptions. In certain civil cases the character of a party is a fact in issue. In defamation, for example, the plaintiff's reputation is in issue and the plaintiff may seek to establish his good character while the defendant attempts to prove the plaintiff's bad character. The plaintiff's reputation is also relevant, in defamation, to the issue of the amount of damages recoverable by him, but evidence of the defendant in mitigation of damages is confined to

---

[1] *Hudson* v. *Ridge Manufacturing Co., Ltd.*, [1957] 2 Q.B. 348; [1957] 2 All E.R. 229; see also *Bebee* v. *Sales* (1916), 32 T.L.R. 413.

[2] (1791), 2 Bos. & P. 532.

evidence of general reputation and he cannot prove specific facts which demonstrate the plaintiff's bad character.[1]

b Character of the accused in criminal cases

The character of the accused in a criminal case is, by the nature of criminal proceedings, an important matter and, if admitted, likely to have a significant effect upon the deliberations of the average jury. Although the general rule excluding evidence of character still applies, there are several exceptions to this rule where the character of which it is sought to admit evidence is that of the accused. It must be stressed once again that, notwithstanding the rule excluding evidence of character, facts which are otherwise relevant may bear upon the character of the accused. Thus relevant similar fact evidence very often indicates the accused's disposition, which is one aspect of his character. Similarly evidence of the accused's previous convictions, which is admissible under several statutes, is evidence of another aspect of his character. However, apart from these instances, the accused's character may only be introduced in evidence by the accused himself or by the prosecution in certain well-defined circumstances.

The accused may always attempt to prove his good character. He may do this by his own testimony, by calling character witnesses or by cross-examination of prosecution witnesses. However, if the accused does try to prove his good character by any of these methods he is said to "put his character in issue". The effect is that the prosecution may then give evidence of his bad character in rebuttal.[2] Such evidence may relate to the accused's general reputation though not to any individual witness's opinion as to the accused's character.[3] It may also relate to the accused's previous convictions.[4] Consequently if the accused has a number of previous convictions he must beware of seeking to establish his good character for in so doing he may let in evidence of his convictions. There is authority for saying that the accused's character is indivisible. The effect is that if evidence is admitted of his character this evidence may relate to any aspect of his character, not merely to that segment of it which seems relevant to the offence with which he is charged. In *R. v. Winfield*[5] the accused was charged with indecent assault upon a woman. He called a witness to testify as to his good behaviour with women, whereupon the prosecution was allowed to cross-examine that witness as to a previous conviction of the accused involving dishonesty.

Apart from this common law provision there are certain statutes which enable evidence to be given of the accused's bad character (as opposed to previous convictions). The most important of these statutes, the Criminal Evidence Act 1898, is discussed below. However, attention may be drawn also to section 15 of the Prevention of Crimes Act 1871 (as amended by the Criminal Law Act

---

[1] *Plato Films, Ltd., v. Speidel*, [1961] A.C. 1090; [1961] 1 All E.R. 876. However the fact that the plaintiff has previous convictions is admissible in defamation for the purpose of mitigating damages: *Goody v. Odhams Press, Ltd.*, [1967] 1 Q.B. 333; [1966] 3 All E.R. 369.

[2] The accused does not put his character in issue by attacking the character of the prosecution witnesses; *R. v. Butterwasser*, [1948] 1 K.B. 4; [1947] 2 All E.R. 415; cf. Criminal Evidence Act 1898, s. 1 (*f*) (ii); see p. 469, *post*.

[3] *R. v. Rowton* (1865), Le. & Ca. 520.

[4] *R. v. Redd*, [1923] 1 K.B. 104.

[5] (1939), 27 Cr. App. Rep. 139; see p. 470, *post*.

1967) which provides that, in order to show intent to commit an arrestable offence on the part of a suspected person loitering in a public place:[1]

> "... It shall not be necessary to show that the person suspected was guilty of any particular act or acts tending to show his purpose or intent, and he may be convicted if from the circumstances of the case, and from his known character as proved to the justice of the peace or court before whom or which he is brought, it appears to such justice or court that his intent was to commit an arrestable offence".[2]

Finally, after conviction and before sentence it is common for the court to receive evidence of the accused's character and antecedents in order to decide upon the most appropriate sentence. This procedure is informal and the strict rules of evidence relating to means of proof are not usually observed.

c Character of third parties

Evidence of the character of persons other than the parties in civil actions and the accused in criminal cases, where those persons are not called as witnesses, is only receivable in a few special circumstances. Thus, in prosecutions for rape and similar offences evidence may be given of the bad reputation for sexual conduct of the victim.[3] Such evidence is confined, however, to general reputation and proof of specific instances is not allowed.[4]

d Character of witnesses (other than the accused in a criminal case)

Witnesses may be cross-examined as to credit in order to show that they are persons who ought not to be believed on account of their bad character. This applies notwithstanding that the witness is also a party to a civil action[5] or is the prosecutor in a criminal case.[6] Moreover a witness may be called to testify that he would not believe another witness on oath. The former may testify as to his opinion of the impugned witness's credibility or as to the latter's reputation for untruthfulness, though he may not (unless asked in cross-examination) give evidence as to particular facts or incidents upon which his opinion is based.[7] This rule does not apply, however, where the witness is the accused in a criminal case since the accused may only be cross-examined as to credit under the Criminal Evidence Act 1898.[8] While being cross-examined as to credit an opposing witness may be asked any question, even if totally irrelevant to any fact in issue, concerning his bad reputation, disposition or previous convictions. However the cross-examining party must accept the answer of the witness as final. He cannot adduce evidence to rebut it. This is a practical rule which exists in order to avoid multiplication of collateral issues. Thus in *A.-G.* v. *Hitchcock*[9] the defendant was not permitted to adduce evidence to rebut a prosecution witness's denial that the latter had been offered a bribe.

---

[1] An offence under the Vagrancy Act 1824, s. 4.
[2] See also the Official Secrets Act 1911, s. 1 (2) which is similarly phrased.
[3] *R.* v. *Clarke* (1817), 2 Stark. 241. In civil cases the bad character of a wife in actions for damage for adultery and of a daughter in seduction actions were relevant on this basis. The actions in question have now been abolished.
[4] *R.* v. *Holmes* (1871), L.R. 1 C.C.R. 334.
[5] *Hobbs* v. *Tinling & Co., Ltd.*, [1929] 2 K.B. 1.
[6] *R.* v. *Holmes,* (1871), L.R. 1 C.C.R. 334.
[7] *R.* v. *Richardson, R.* v. *Longman*, [1969] 1 Q.B. 299; [1968] 2 All E.R. 761.
[8] See p. 467, *post*.
[9] (1847), 1 Ex. 91.

Similarly the prosecutrix on a charge of rape may, if she is a witness, be asked whether she has had sexual intercourse with other men but if she denies this fact evidence cannot be given to rebut her denial.[1]

There are, however, four exceptions to this general rule against rebuttal. Thus if a witness denies a previous conviction or his own previous inconsistent statement evidence may be given, under the Criminal Procedure Act 1865, of this conviction or statement. To these statutory exceptions may be added the common law rules permitting evidence to prove bias in a witness or to prove a general reputation for untruthfulness.

4 Convictions

As a general rule evidence of a person's previous convictions is excluded as irrelevant in the same way as evidence of similar facts and of character are excluded. All are illustrations of the older general rule excluding *res inter alios acta*. Before considering in detail the exceptional circumstances in which previous convictions may be put in evidence it is necessary to consider the evidential nature of convictions and the relationship between bad character and previous convictions.

In criminal proceedings a conviction is only evidence of the fact that a person has been convicted. It is not evidence that he performed the conduct upon which his conviction is based. To quote BLACKBURN, J. (as he then was):[2]

"... A judgment of conviction on an indictment for forging a bill of exchange, though conclusive as to the prisoner being a convicted felon, is not only not conclusive, but is not even admissible evidence of the forgery in an action on the bill. ..."

This much-criticised rule may have strange effects. For example, if evidence were admissible, as relevant similar fact evidence, that a person had murdered two little girls these murders could not be proved by evidence of convictions for these murders, though they could be proved by evidence of confessions or pleas of guilty made in the course of those proceedings.[3] The fact that the person had murdered the girls would be relevant; the fact that he had been convicted of those murders would not.

However, in relation to civil proceedings, this rule[4] has been abrogated by the Civil Evidence Act 1968. That Act provides that in any civil proceedings the fact that a person has been convicted of an offence by any court in the United Kingdom, or by a court-martial there or elsewhere, shall be admissible to prove that he committed that offence, whether or not he pleaded guilty and whether or not he is a party to the civil proceedings.[5] The effect is to raise a presumption that he committed the offence, unless the contrary is proved.[6]

---

[1] *R. v. Holmes (supra).* Evidence can, of course, be given of previous acts of sexual intercourse with the accused since this is a fact relevant to the issue of consent: *R. v. Riley* (1887), 18 Q.B.D. 481.
[2] *Castrique v. Imrie* (1870), L.R. 4 H.L. 414, at p. 434.
[3] *R. v. Straffen.* [1952] 2 Q.B. 911; [1952] 2 All E R. 657.
[4] The rule was known as the Rule in *Hollington* v. *Hewthorn & Co., Ltd.,* [1943] K.B. 587; [1943] 2 All E.R. 35.
[5] Civil Evidence Act 1968, s. 11 (1). Section 12 introduced a similar rule in respect of (a) the fact that a person has been found guilty of adultery in any matrimonial proceedings; and (b) the fact that a person has been adjudged to be the father of a child in affiliation proceedings.
[6] *Ibid.,* s. 11 (2) (a).

Thus the conviction is admissible but not conclusive evidence, save in defamation actions, where proof of the conviction is expressed by the Act[1] to be conclusive.

There is an interrelationship between character and convictions. That is not to say that whenever evidence of character is admissible evidence of convictions is admissible, or *vice versa*. If the whole of a person's character is admissible this includes evidence of his previous convictions. However, if only his reputation is relevant, as in defamation for example, evidence of previous convictions is inadmissible. Conversely, convictions are not only relevant as evidence of character. A previous conviction may be an element in a criminal offence or a fact in issue in a civil case in which case it will be relevant where general bad character is irrelevant.

The circumstances in which previous convictions are receivable in evidence are now examined in relation to the persons whose convictions it is sought to prove.

a   Witnesses (other than the accused in a criminal case)

In the course of cross-examination of an opposing witness as to credit, the witness may be cross-examined as to his previous convictions. This is to show that he ought not to be believed. Consequently the conviction need not be relevant to a fact in issue. The admission of such evidence may appear to contradict the general rule that only relevant evidence is admissible. In fact it is true to say that such evidence is indirectly relevant. It is indirectly relevant to a fact in issue in that it tends to show the falsity of other relevant evidence.

If the witness denies a previous conviction, this conviction may be proved by the cross-examining party under the Criminal Procedure Act 1865, section 6. This Act, despite its misleading short title, applies to both civil and criminal proceedings, though in the latter special rules apply where the witness is the accused himself.

b   Parties in civil cases

The previous convictions of a party in a civil case can only be proved where the fact of conviction is a relevant fact[2] or where the conviction is admissible under the Civil Evidence Act 1968 as proof of a relevant fact or to discredit the testimony of the party as a witness. Thus the fact of conviction would be a fact in issue in a defamation action where the defendant alleged that the plaintiff had been convicted and sought to justify the allegation, or in an action for malicious prosecution where the defendant alleged that the plaintiff had been convicted. Similarly, where the fact of a spouse having been convicted is alleged to amount to, or be part of, a course of intolerable conduct in a divorce suit, that conviction may be proved.[3]

---

[1] Section 13 (1).

[2] *Ingram* v. *Ingram*, [1956] P. 390; [1956] 1 All E.R. 785.

[3] For convictions as evidence of bad character see *Goody* v. *Odhams Press, Ltd.*, [1967] 1 Q.B. 333; [1966] 3 All E.R. 369 in which the Court of Appeal held that previous convictions in the relevant sector of the plaintiff's life, and within such a period of time as to affect his current reputation, were admissible in mitigation of damages.

c Accused persons

The extent to which an accused person, as a witness, may be cross-examined as to his previous convictions is dealt with below. However the accused's previous convictions may sometimes be proved irrespective of whether he is a witness. For example, where the accused raises a plea of *autrefois convict* the conviction in question is relevant as a fact in issue.[1] Also, there are several statutory provisions enabling the prosecution to give evidence of the accused's previous convictions. For example the Theft Act 1968, s. 27 (3),[2] allows proof of convictions as a means of proving facts in issue. Previous convictions may also be admissible to determine the appropriate method of trial[3] or form of sentence.[4]

Finally, where the accused puts his character in issue by seeking to establish his good character, the prosecution may be allowed to prove his previous convictions as part of his bad character.[5]

Cross-examination of the accused as to his character and previous convictions is governed by the Criminal Evidence Act 1898, section 1. That Act made the accused a competent though not a compellable witness for the defence. Consequently, the accused has a choice as to whether or not to give evidence. If he does elect to give evidence the accused's position differs from that of other witnesses in that he cannot be freely cross-examined as to credit. The extent to which he can be cross-examined is governed by section 1 (f) of the 1898 Act and the judicial interpretation of this important provision.

Section 1 (f) is negative in expression. It provides that:

> "A person charged and called as a witness in pursuance of this Act shall not be asked, and if asked shall not be required to answer, any question tending to show that he has committed or been convicted of or has been charged with any offence other than that wherewith he is then charged, or is of bad character, unless—
>
> (i) the proof that he has committed or been convicted of such other offence is admissible evidence to show that he is guilty of the offence wherewith he is then charged; or
>
> (ii) he has personally or by his advocate asked questions of the witnesses for the prosecution with a view to establish his own good character, or has given evidence of his good character, or the nature or conduct of the defence is such as to involve imputations on the character of the prosecutor or the witnesses for the prosecution; or
>
> (iii) he has given evidence against any other person charged with the same offence:"

Section 1 (f) may thus be regarded as a shield against cross-examination as to character and convictions which is lost in certain circumstances. The effect of the shield of section 1 (f) being lost is that the accused may be cross-examined upon his character and previous convictions.[6] A strict interpretation of the section would suggest that the accused, if he loses the shield, may be asked

---

[1] See p. 404, *ante.*

[2] See p. 461, *ante*; see also Prevention of Crimes Act 1871, s. 15; Official Secrets Act 1911, s. 1 (2).

[3] Magistrates' Courts Act 1952, s. 25; see p. 363, *ante.*

[4] Criminal Justice Act 1967, ss. 37–42.

[5] See p. 463, *ante.*

[6] He may not, however, if he is twenty-one or over be cross-examined as to offences of which he was found guilty while under the age of fourteen: Children and Young Persons Act 1963, s. 16 (2).

questions to show that he has been charged with other offences. Were this interpretation adopted the section would operate to admit evidence of previous acquittals as well as of previous convictions. It is not presumed, however, that the framers of the 1898 Act intended to affect the general rule that all evidence must be relevant in order to be admissible. Consequently evidence that the accused has been "charged" with an offence is not generally admissible in spite of the wording of section 1 (f). This was the basis of the decision of the House of Lords in *Maxwell* v. *Director of Public Prosecutions*[1] which held that, although a doctor on a charge of manslaughter had put his character in issue, he ought not to have been cross-examined as to a similar charge upon which he had been acquitted. Furthermore "charged" is interpreted as meaning "charged in court" so that section 1 (f) cannot operate to admit evidence that an accused person has been questioned about or suspected of a criminal offence of which he has never been formally charged unless he can be proved to have committed the offence.[2]

It should be noted that the shield afforded by section 1 (f) only protects the accused from questions "tending to show" his previous convictions or bad character. The words "tending to show" were interpreted narrowly by the House of Lords in *Jones* v. *Director of Public Prosecutions*[3] as meaning "tending to reveal" or "tending to make known", with the effect that questions relating to matters which have already been revealed to the court are not excluded by section 1 (f). The facts of this somewhat unusual case were as follows. Jones was charged with murdering a young girl, a girl guide. He first advanced an admittedly false alibi and later asserted an uncorroborated alibi. His explanation as to why he had not raised this alibi earlier was that he had been in trouble with the police before and was afraid that the police would not believe his uncorroborated alibi. In fact Jones had been previously convicted of raping another girl guide at which trial he had raised an alibi, similar to the one now raised, that he had been with an unnamed prostitute. He was cross-examined concerning the remarkable similarity between the two alibis. Although the fact of his previous conviction was not brought out, the cross-examination did tend to show that he was of bad character in that he had been in trouble with the police. His appeal against conviction was dismissed, the House of Lords holding that the cross-examination did not "tend to show", in the sense of "tend to reveal", that Jones had been in trouble with the police, since he had already revealed this himself.[4] Consequently the shield of section 1 (f) did not exist.

Where the shield does exist it is lost only in the circumstances specified in section 1 (f). There are four circumstances in which the shield is lost. These are as follows:

(1) *where the fact of commission or conviction of the earlier offence is relevant similar fact evidence.* (This adds nothing to the common law since relevant simi-

---

[1] [1935] A.C. 309. LORD SANKEY, L.C. in that case recognised that questions relating to a previous charge would be admissible under s. 1 (f) if the fact of the charge being made were otherwise relevant, for example where the fact of a previous charge is a fact in issue (see *R.* v. *Waldman* (1934), 24 Cr. App. Rep. 204). A previous charge is a fact in issue where a defence is raised under s. 6 (3) of the Sexual Offences Act 1956.

[2] *Stirland* v. *Director of Public Prosecutions*, [1944] A.C. 315; [1944] 2 All E.R. 13.

[3] [1962] A.C. 635; [1962] 1 All E.R. 569.

[4] This was the *ratio* of the case since it was the basis of the speeches of the majority; LORDS SIMONDS, REID and MORRIS. LORDS DENNING and DEVLIN arrived at the same decision but dissented from the reasoning of the majority.

lar fact evidence would be admissible apart from the provisions of the 1898 Act);

(2) *where the accused tries to establish his own good character.* (This also adds nothing to the common law since the effect of the accused putting his character in issue is, as noted above, to let in evidence of his bad character including his previous convictions);

(3) *where the conduct of the defence involves imputations on the character of the prosecutor or the prosecution witnesses.* A mere denial that the testimony of the prosecution witnesses is true does not amount to an imputation upon their character,[1] though a statement that the prosecutor is such a horrible liar that even his own brother would not speak to him does amount to an imputation within section 1 (f) (ii).[2]

The cases are not entirely consistent. Thus an allegation that the prosecutor was an habitual drunkard was held in one case not to be an imputation[3] though a statement that the prosecutor was drunk, driving disgracefully and shouting abuse at other drivers was, in another case, held to be an imputation.[4] Similarly, criticism of the method of holding an identification parade has been held not to be objectionable[5] though a suggestion that the accused's confession was dictated by one policeman to another was held to amount to an imputation.[6]

Difficulty arises when the proper conduct of the defence necessitates imputations upon the prosecution. In such a case the accused appears to be faced with the invidious choice of being hindered in the conduct of his defence or rendering himself liable to cross-examination upon his character and convictions. There is some authority for saying that the accused does not abandon the shield of section 1 (f) by making an imputation of unchastity to support a defence of consent to a charge of rape.[7] However this involves reading words into section 1 (f) (ii) which are not there and there is much authority to the effect that this is not permissible.[8] This would be an unfortunate principle but for the fact that the judge has a discretion to exclude cross-examination in cases where the accused abandons the shield of section 1 (f).[9] However in the recent case of *Selvey* v. *Director of Public Prosecutions*[10] the House of Lords established that even where the proper conduct of the defence necessitates imputations on the prosecution there is no rule that the discretion should be exercised in favour of the accused.

(4) *where the accused has given evidence against a co-accused.* This exception applies only where the co-accused are charged with the same offence, not where they are indicted together for different offences.[11] The question of whether

---

[1] *R.* v. *Rouse*, [1904] 1 K.B. 184.

[2] *R.* v. *Rappolt* (1911), 6 Cr. App. Rep. 156.

[3] *R.* v. *Westfall* (1912), 7 Cr. App. Rep. 176.

[4] *R.* v. *Brown (No. 2)* (1960), 124 J.P. 391.

[5] *R.* v. *Preston*, [1909] 1 K.B. 568.

[6] *R.* v. *Clark*, [1955] 2 Q.B. 469; [1955] 3 All E.R. 29; see also *R.* v. *Dunkley,* [1927] 1 K.B. 323.

[7] *R.* v. *Turner*, [1944] K.B. 463; [1944] 1 All E.R. 599, cited with approval in *Stirland* v. *Director of Public Prosecutions*, [1944] A.C. 315; [1944] 2 All E.R. 13 and in *Selvey* v. *Director of Public Prosecutions (infra).*

[8] *R.* v. *Hudson*, [1912] 2 K.B. 464; *R.* v. *Dunkley, (supra).*

[9] *Maxwell* v. *Director of Public Prosecutions*, [1935] A.C. 309, at pp. 319, 321.

[10] [1970] A.C. 304; [1968] 2 All E.R. 497, disapproving *R.* v. *Flynn*, [1963] 1 Q.B. 729; [1961] 3 All E.R. 58.

[11] *R.* v. *Roberts*, [1936] 1 All E.R. 23.

evidence is given "against" a co-accused must be answered objectively. Thus there need be no intention on the part of the accused to give evidence adverse to his co-accused so long as the evidence has that effect.[1] Where the evidence is given against a co-accused the accused who gives the evidence renders himself liable to cross-examination under section 1 (f) (iii) by both the prosecution and his co-accused. The discretion which exists to exclude cross-examination by the prosecution does not exist to exclude cross-examination by a co-accused. There is no discretion to exclude such cross-examination.[2] The combined effect of the above rules may impede an accused in the proper conduct of his defence. If the conduct of his defence involves imputations "against" a co-accused there is no discretion to exclude cross-examination by that co-accused upon the first accused's character and convictions. The only safeguard is the power to order separate trials where the defence of one accused is likely to involve evidence against another.[3]

Where cross-examination of the accused upon his character and convictions is allowed under the 1898 Act the whole of the accused's character and convictions is admissible, not merely that part of the accused's character which appears relevant to the offence charged. The accused's character appears to be indivisible.[4] However in a case where the prosecution proposed to put in evidence convictions wholly unconnected with the offence charged the judge would presumably exercise his discretion to exclude this evidence. The prosecution may prove any conviction which the accused denies in cross-examination.[5]

C RULES OF EXCLUSION APPLICABLE TO RELEVANT FACTS

When considering rules of exclusion it is necessary to remember that the word "evidence" comprises both facts and means of proof. Consequently a rule of exclusion may exclude either facts or a particular method of proving facts. The principal rule of exclusion, the hearsay rule, falls into the latter category and, together with the rules excluding opinion and secondary evidence of documents, is dealt with below.[6] This section is confined to rules of exclusion which exclude facts. To these rules may be added the discretion of the court to exclude relevant evidence.

---

[1] *R. v. Stannard*, [1965] 2 Q.B. 1; [1964] 1 All E.R. 34; *Murdoch v. Taylor*, [1965] A.C. 574; [1965] 1 All E.R. 406.

[2] *R. v. Ellis*, [1961] 2 All E.R. 928; [1961] 1 W.L.R. 1064; *R. v. Stannard (supra)*; *Murdoch v. Taylor (supra)*.

[3] However the fact that the defence of one co-accused involves imputations on the character of another co-accused (therefore giving the latter a right to avail himself of the opportunity of cross-examining the former upon his character and convictions) does not override the principle that in most cases it is in the interests of justice that all co-accused should be tried together: *R. v. Hoggins*, [1967] 3 All E.R. 334; [1967] 1 W.L.R. 1223.

[4] *R. v. Winfield*, [1939] 4 All E.R. 164. The report of this case in 27 Cr. App. Rep. 139 suggests that the cross-examination was of a defence witness rather than of the accused himself; see p. 463, *ante*.

[5] Criminal Procedure Act 1865, s. 6.

[6] See pp. 523 *et seq.*, *post*.

1   Estoppel

Estoppel is a rule of evidence whereby a party is prohibited from asserting or denying a fact. This prohibition may arise in various ways but whenever it does arise it has the effect of rendering relevant facts inadmissible. Estoppel has sometimes been described as a rule of substantive law rather than a rule of evidence.[1]   Indeed it may have the effect of a rule of substantive law where it prevents a party from asserting or denying a fact in issue since it operates in such a case to create a right against the party estopped, by preventing him from denying that right. Nevertheless estoppel is a rule of evidence rather than a rule of substantive law, even though it may affect substantive rights and so have the same effect as a rule of law. Thus a party may waive an estoppel in his favour and, in any event, estoppel cannot be used as a cause of action but only as a defence.[2]

It is also occasionally stated that estoppel is a rule of procedure or pleading. The reason for this proposition is that an estoppel must be expressly pleaded. This is an exception to the general rule that evidence need not be pleaded.[3] Failure to plead an estoppel may operate as a waiver of the benefit of the estoppel. Nevertheless it does not follow that estoppel is a rule of pleading merely because it must be expressly pleaded. The Limitation Acts must be expressly pleaded but these cannot be said to be rules of pleading. It is best to classify estoppel as a rule of evidence to which special rules of procedure apply. Estoppels may arise in three ways; by record, by deed or by conduct. These three types of estoppel must be considered individually.

a   Estoppel by record

The oldest form of estoppel is estoppel by record, alternatively known as judgment estoppel since the record in question is almost always a court record. A matter which a party is estopped by a court record from reopening is said to be *res judicata*. The doctrine of estoppel by record is based on two well-known maxims of the common law: *interest reipublicae est ut sit finis litium* (it is in the public interest that there be an end to litigation) and *nemo debet bis vexari pro eadem causa* (no one should be in jeopardy twice on the same ground). The effect of the doctrine is that a person cannot raise an allegation which has previously been decided against him by a court of competent jurisdiction. A judgment may be assailed by an appeal, where a right of appeal exists, or by applying to have the judgment set aside where it was obtained fraudulently or collusively. Similarly an estoppel is not raised by the record of a court acting in excess of jurisdiction.[4]

Judgments in rem—For the purposes of the doctrine of estoppel by record there are two classes of judgments—judgments *in rem* and judgments *in personam*. A judgment *in rem* is a judgment which involves a determination of a person's rights or status against the whole world; a judgment *in personam* is a judgment

---

[1]   See, for example, observations of LORD WRIGHT in *Canadian and Dominion Sugar Co., Ltd. v. Canadian National (West Indies) Steamships, Ltd.*, [1947] A.C. 46, at p. 56.

[2]   *Combe* v. *Combe*, [1951] 2 K.B. 215; [1951] 1 All E.R. 767.

[3]   R.S.C., O.18, r. 7 (1); see p. 263, *ante*.

[4]   *R.* v. *Hutchings* (1881), 6 Q.B.D. 300. Nor is an estoppel raised by a dismissal which involves no adjudication on the merits of the case: *Pople* v. *Evans*, [1969] 2 Ch. 255; [1968] 2 All E.R. 743; see p. 252, *ante*.

which determines one party's right against another party to the litigation. The importance of the distinction is that a judgment *in rem* raises an estoppel against the whole world whereas a judgment *in personam* operates only against the parties to the action upon which the judgment is founded and their privies. Common examples of judgments *in rem* are orders adjudicating a person bankrupt,[1] a decree absolute of divorce or nullity,[2] a declaration of legitimacy[3] and a grant of probate.[4] Thus if a person has obtained a decree absolute of nullity neither the other spouse nor any other person can assert that the marriage is valid; if a grant of probate has been obtained no person can deny the title of the executors. Generally there is no difficulty in determining whether a judgment is a judgment *in rem*, or a judgment *in personam*, the question being determined by reference to substantive law. However difficulty may arise when an action between individuals indirectly bears upon the status of one of them. In such a case the judgment *in personam* may at first sight have the appearance of a judgment *in rem*. Thus in *B.* v. *Attorney-General*[5] a husband, N.E.B., had admitted paternity of B. in divorce proceedings brought against him by the mother, and a custody order in respect of B. was made on the basis of that admission. Several years later in proceedings for maintenance by the mother N.E.B. was held to be estopped by the earlier finding of the court from denying that B. was his son. In the present proceedings B. sought a declaration of legitimacy and alleged that N.E.B. and other persons were estopped from denying that he, B., was the legitimate son of N.E.B. WILLMER, L.J. held that they were not so estopped since the earlier judgment was a judgment *in personam* which, although it had raised an estoppel against N.E.B. in favour of the mother, did not raise an estoppel in favour of B. who was not a party to the earlier proceedings.

Judgments in personam—A judgment *in personam* is binding only on the parties to the litigation and their privies.[6] The scope of an estoppel raised by a judgment *in personam* is narrowly defined. There must be both an identity of parties and an identity of issue between the judgment alleged to give rise to the estoppel and the issue before the court. The necessity for an identity of parties is illustrated by the case of *Townsend* v. *Bishop*.[7] The owner of a car brought an action against the owner of a lorry in respect of damage to his car caused in an accident in which the car was being driven by the owner's son. In this action the court held that the accident was caused by the negligence of the car owner's son. It was held in the instant action for personal injuries brought by the car owner's son against the owner of the lorry that the former was not estopped by the judgment in the first case from denying that he had been negligent. Not only must the judgment alleged to create the estoppel have affected the same parties, it must also have affected those parties in the capacity in which they appear in the action in which the estoppel is pleaded. Thus a judgment against

---

[1] Bankruptcy Act 1914, s. 137 (2).
[2] *Salvesen* v. *Administrator of Austrian Property*, [1927] A.C. 641.
[3] Matrimonial Causes Act 1965, s. 39.
[4] *Allen* v. *Dundas* (1789), 3 Term Rep. 125.
[5] [1965] P. 278; [1965] 1 All E.R. 62.
[6] Privies are persons claiming as successors of a party. Privity may be of blood or of estate. For example an executor and an heir are both privies of a testator; an assignee of a lease is the privy of the original lessee.
[7] [1939] 1 All E.R. 805.

a person appearing in his personal capacity will not raise an estoppel against him in an action in which he subsequently appears in a representative capacity, notwithstanding that both actions arise out of the same incident.[1]

The second test to be applied in deciding whether a judgment *in personam* gives rise to an estoppel in subsequent proceedings between the same parties is whether there is an identity of issue. The same facts may give rise to several causes of action because several different rights are infringed. In order to decide whether the first case necessarily decides the issue raised in the second case, the facts upon which the judgment in the first case was based must be examined. A party cannot raise an allegation of fact which has already been determined against him even though he is pleading a different cause of action. For example, cruelty and constructive desertion were, prior to the Divorce Reform Act 1969, separate grounds for divorce but in both cases the respondent spouse's conduct had to be grave and weighty. If a cruelty petition had been dismissed because the conduct alleged to amount to cruelty was found not to be sufficiently grave and weighty, the petitioner was estopped from founding a petition for constructive desertion on the same conduct.[2] This form of estoppel is termed "issue estoppel" and may be contrasted with "cause of action estoppel". Both are forms of estoppel by record but the first is raised by the court's determination of a single issue of fact while the second is raised by the court's determination of a cause of action.[3] Issue estoppel is illustrated by the decision of STREATFIELD, J. in *Wood* v. *Luscombe*.[4] A collision occurred between two motor cycles driven by W. and L. In an action by L. against W. they were found equally to blame. A pillion passenger in the accident subsequently brought an action against L. and L. brought in W. as a third party, claiming a contribution under the Law Reform (Married Women and Tortfeasors) Act 1935. It was held that W. was estopped from denying that he and L. were equally to blame in the accident, since this issue, the issue of blame was determined by the judgment in the first action.

An estoppel is binding only on the parties to the litigation. An estoppel cannot bind the court. This principle is demonstrated clearly in matrimonial proceedings, in which the court is concerned to preserve the sanctity of marriage as well as to do justice between the parties. The mere fact that one spouse is estopped from denying a matrimonial offence such as adultery or desertion does not prevent the court from enquiring into the facts since the court must be satisfied that the marriage has broken down irretrievably before granting a decree.[5]

There is a rule that findings in criminal cases do not give rise to estoppels in civil cases, and *vice-versa*. To this rule section 13 (1) of the Civil Evidence Act

---

[1] *Marginson* v. *Blackburn B.C.*, [1939] 2 K.B. 426; [1938] 2 All E.R. 539.

[2] *Hill* v. *Hill*, [1954] P. 291; [1954] 1 All E.R. 491; *Thoday* v. *Thoday*, [1964] P. 181; [1964] 1 All E.R. 341. The Divorce Reform Act 1969 abolished cruelty and constructive desertion as grounds of divorce *per se* but they are still grounds for obtaining matrimonial orders in magistrates' courts.

[3] See *Thoday* v. *Thoday*, [1964] P. 181, at p. 196; [1964] 1 All E.R. 341, at p. 352, *per* DIPLOCK, L.J. (as he then was), where "issue estoppel" and "cause of action estoppel" are distinguished and explained.

[4] [1966] 1 Q.B. 169; [1964] 3 All E.R. 972; not following *Randolph* v. *Tuck*, [1962] 1 Q.B. 175; [1961] 1 All E.R. 814.

[5] *Harriman* v. *Harriman*, [1909] P. 123; *Winnan* v. *Winnan*, [1949] P. 174; [1948] 2 All E.R. 862.

1968 affords an isolated exception;[1] this sub-section provides, in effect, that a plaintiff in a defamation action is estopped from denying the truth of an allegation that he is guilty of an offence of which he has been convicted by a criminal court.

Criminal cases—Estoppel in criminal cases has been virtually limited to "cause of action estoppel" in the form of the plea of *autrefois acquit*.[2] This plea can be raised where the accused has previously been acquitted of the offence with which he is now charged or of an offence so similar that acquittal necessarily involves acquittal of the present charge, or where the accused was at the first trial in peril of conviction of the offence now charged. In any of these circumstances the accused cannot be tried again. The doctrine of "issue estoppel" was not, until recently, recognised in English criminal law. The reason for this is that it is, by the nature of criminal verdicts, usually impossible to isolate any one issue from the others. Thus a general verdict of "not guilty" does not make it clear which of the issues have been determined in favour of the accused. It is clear that a verdict of not guilty cannot be regarded as determining every issue of fact in favour of the accused. Nevertheless in *Connelly* v. *Director of Public Prosecutions*[3] certain members of the House of Lords recognised that issue estoppel could exist in criminal cases. LORD DEVLIN explained the distinction between issue estoppel and *autrefois acquit* as follows:[4]

> "The difference between issue estoppel and the autrefois principle is that, while the latter prevents the prosecution from impugning the validity of the verdict as a whole, the former prevents it from raising again any of the separate issues of fact which the jury have decided or are presumed to have decided, in reaching their verdict in the accused's favour."

In *Connelly's* case it was held that neither the principle of *autrefois acquit* nor issue estoppel was applicable. Connelly was charged with murder. At his trial he raised the two defences of alibi and no intent to kill but the jury returned a general verdict of guilty. This conviction was quashed on appeal on the ground of misdirection by the trial judge. Connelly was subsequently indicted for robbery in respect of the same incident. It was held by the House of Lords that, since he had never been in peril of conviction for robbery, the plea of *autrefois acquit* failed and that, since no single issue could be determined in Connelly's favour from the judgment in the first trial, issue estoppel could not arise.

b Estoppel by deed

The doctrine of estoppel by deed is a reminder of the peculiar sanctity accorded by the common law to deeds. However, equity has made such substantial inroads into the common law rules concerning the enforcement of obligations under seal that the common law doctrine of estoppel by deed is now scarcely any wider than the doctrine of estoppel by agreement discussed below.

---

[1] See p. 465, *ante*; the sub-section was passed to overrule cases in which persons convicted of crimes have brought successful defamation actions aganst persons who published statements to the effect that the convicted persons were guilty of the crimes of which they had been convicted (*Hinds* v. *Sparks*, [1964] Crim. L. R. 717; *Goody* v. *Odhams Press, Ltd.*, [1967] 1 Q.B. 333; [1966] 3 All E.R. 369).

[2] See p. 404, *ante*.

[3] [1964] A.C. 1254; [1964] 2 All E.R. 401; see p. 404, *ante*.

[4] [1964] A.C. 1254, at p. 1343; [1964] 2 All E.R. 401, at p. 436.

At common law a party to a deed is estopped from denying the truth of state-ments in the deed. A recital in a deed will raise an estoppel against the party making it. It may also raise an estoppel against other parties to the deed[1] provided that the statement is one which the parties have mutually agreed to admit as true. However, if the recital is intended to be the statement of one party only, the estoppel operates only against that party and not against other parties to the deed.[2] Apart from this limitation, a deed only raises an estoppel in an action upon the deed between the parties to the deed and their privies. In addition the doctrine of estoppel does not prevent a party from setting up any plea such as fraud, undue influence, mistake or illegality which would give him a right to rescind the deed in equity.

c Estoppel by conduct

"Where one by his words or conduct wilfully causes another to believe in the existence of a certain state of things, and induces him to act on that belief, or to alter his own previous position, the former is concluded from averring against the latter a different state of things as existing at that time."[3]

This classic statement illustrates the common law doctrine of estoppel by conduct. The conduct which gives rise to the estoppel may exist in an agree-ment, a representation or in negligence. Consequently it is usual to subdivide the doctrine of estoppel by conduct in this way.

Estoppel by agreement—If two persons enter into an agreement on the basis that a certain state of affairs exists, each of them is estopped from denying that this state of affairs does exist. Perhaps the commonest illustration of estoppel by agreement is the principle that neither a landlord nor a tenant may deny the title of the landlord since the lease is entered into on the basis that the landlord has a good title. The practical result is that the landlord cannot refuse to per-form his covenants such as repairing covenants; nor can the tenant refuse to pay rent or carry out repairs by denying the landlord's title.[4] Estoppel by agreement only lasts, however, during the existence of the agreement so that after the tenancy has expired, the tenant is no longer estopped from denying the land-lord's title.[5] Other relationships to which the doctrine of estoppel by agreement applies are those between licensor and licensee, bailor and bailee and principal and agent.

Estoppel by representation—Anyone who makes a representation of existing fact with intention that the person to whom it is made should act upon it is estopped from denying the truth of that fact, in an action by someone who has acted to his detriment upon the faith of the representation. There are many varieties of the doctrine of estoppel by representation. A typical example is agency by estoppel. A person who represents another as being his agent is estopped from denying that that person acted with his authority. Thus a husband who pays for goods ordered from tradesmen by his wife is estopped from denying that his wife has authority to pledge his credit.[6] The husband, if

---

[1] *Bowman* v. *Taylor* (1834), 2 Ad. & El. 278.
[2] *Greer* v. *Kettle*, [1938] A.C. 156; [1937] 4 All E.R. 396. Intention is ascertained by construing the deed (*ibid.*).
[3] *Pickard* v. *Sears* (1837), 6 Ad. & El. 469.
[4] *Cooke* v. *Loxley* (1792), 5 Term Rep. 4.
[5] *Harrison* v. *Wells*, [1967] 1 Q.B. 263 ; [1966] 3 All E.R. 524.
[6] *Drew* v. *Nunn* (1879), 4 Q.B.D. 661.

he wishes to terminate his wife's agency by estoppel, must expressly inform the tradesmen that she no longer has authority to pledge his credit.[1] Another form of estoppel by representation occurs where a person represents himself as a partner in a firm. He is liable as a partner to anyone who has given credit to the firm on the faith of his representation.[2]

There are, however, restrictions on the doctrine of estoppel by representation at common law. The representation must be a representation of existing fact. A representation as to the law will not raise an estoppel; nor will a representation as to future intention.[3] However, a representation as to future intention may give rise to an estoppel in equity, sometimes described as a quasi-estoppel or promissory estoppel. The doctrine of equitable or quasi-estoppel is enshrined in the judgment of DENNING, J. (as he then was) in *Central London Property Trust, Ltd.* v. *High Trees House, Ltd.*[4] where it was suggested that a representation as to future intention which is acted upon may estop the person making the representation from resiling from his representation.[5] There is, however, a basic difference between common law estoppel by representation and equitable estoppel by representation. The difference is that a person can take the benefit of an equitable estoppel only if it is just and equitable for him to do so whereas there is no such limitation on the common law doctrine of estoppel. Thus if a person agrees to accept a lesser sum in satisfaction of a contractual debt he may be estopped from suing for the balance, but only if it would be inequitable, and contrary to the justice of the case, to allow to him do so.[6] Where there is a duty to disclose facts, failure to do so amounts to a representation for the purposes of estoppel. This point is illustrated by the decision of the House of Lords in *Greenwood* v. *Martins Bank, Ltd.*[7] In that case a husband's failure to inform the bank that his wife was forging his signature on cheques was held to estop him from setting up the forgeries in an action by the bank to recover the sums paid to his wife and debited to his account.

There are two further restrictions on the doctrine of estoppel by representation which should be noted. First, estoppel is a defence and cannot be used to found a cause of action. Thus a person who makes a promise, not under seal and unsupported by consideration, to pay money to another cannot be sued by that other upon his promise on the basis that he is estopped from denying his promise. This misconceived extension of the *High Trees* principle was firmly rejected by the Court of Appeal in *Combe* v. *Combe*,[8] although the first instance judge in that case had been willing to recognise it. The second restriction is that an estoppel cannot be pleaded where to do so would give effect to something illegal, immoral or contrary to public policy. This is an extension of the general principle that an estoppel cannot bind the court. Thus an infant who represents himself as being of full age in order to obtain a loan of money is not estopped

---

[1] *Debenham* v. *Mellon* (1880), 6 App. Cas. 24.
[2] Partnership Act 1890, s. 14 (1).
[3] *Jorden* v. *Money* (1854), 5 H.L. Cas. 185.
[4] [1947] K.B. 130; [1956] 1 All E.R. 256n.
[5] See *Tool Metal Manufacturing Co., Ltd.* v. *Tungsten Electric Co., Ltd.*, [1955] 2 All E.R. 657; [1955] 1 W.L.R. 761; *Inwards* v. *Baker*, [1965] 2 Q.B. 29; [1965] 1 All E.R. 446.
[6] *D. and C. Builders, Ltd.* v. *Rees*, [1966] 2 Q.B. 617; [1965] 3 All E.R. 837.
[7] [1933] A.C. 51.
[8] [1951] 2 K.B. 215; [1951] 1 All E.R. 767.

from pleading his infancy as a defence to an action on the loan.[1] Similarly a wife who agrees not to apply to the court for maintenance is not estopped from making such an application.[2]

Estoppel by negligence—Where a person by his negligence causes another, to whom he owes a duty of care, to believe in the existence of a fact, and that other acts to his detriment upon that belief, the negligent party is estopped from denying that fact. This situation usually arises where the negligent party facilitates the commission of a fraud upon the other party. Thus in *Coventry, Sheppard & Co.* v. *Great Eastern Railway Co.*,[3] a servant of the defendant company negligently issued two delivery orders in respect of one consignment of wheat enabling a fraudulent third party to obtain two advances of money on the security of the goods. The company was held to be estopped from denying that there were two consignments. Similarly a person who carelessly draws a cheque so as to enable a fraudulent holder to fill in additional figures is liable to have his account debited with the amount paid to the rogue.[4] The scope of estoppel by negligence is not wider than the tort of negligence in that negligence can only give rise to an estoppel where a duty of care is owed by the negligent party to the person who acts to his detriment.

2 Public Policy

a State privilege

Relevant evidence must be excluded if its disclosure would be prejudicial to the interests of the State. The evidence in question is, in fact, usually documentary. Consequently in actions to which the Crown is a party the objection to production is usually taken at the stage of discovery of documents[5] although it may be taken at the trial. In actions between private persons the privilege exists and cannot be waived by any person (other than the Crown) and the objection to production is usually taken at the trial. Privilege can be claimed on behalf of the Crown for a document regardless of who has possession of the document and is not confined to documents emanating from or in the possession of a department of State. Indeed, even if neither party takes the objection, the judge must exclude evidence if it appears that its reception would be injurious to the interests of the State. The scope of State privilege is properly a matter of constitutional law rather than of evidence or procedure. Basically there are two problems: the scope of the "State interest" and the question of who is to decide whether or not the reception of evidence would be contrary to that interest. Until recently these two problems merged into one since it was accepted as being the law that the executive rather than the judiciary was the final arbiter of a claim of State privilege. The result was that the scope of the State interest was determined by the State. It is this fact which accounts for the wide variety of matters which the State interest has been held to comprise.

---

[1] *R. Leslie, Ltd.* v. *Sheill*, [1914] 3 K.B. 607; see also *Kok Hoong* v. *Leong Cheong Kweng Mines, Ltd.*, [1964] A.C. 993; [1964] 1 All E.R. 300.

[2] *Hyman* v. *Hyman*, [1929] A.C. 601; Matrimonial Proceedings and Property Act 1970, s. 13.

[3] (1883), 11 Q.B.D. 776.

[4] *London Joint Stock Bank* v. *Macmillan*, [1918] A.C. 777; the decision in this case was not based primarily upon estoppel, though the principle is similar.

[5] Crown Proceedings Act 1947, s. 28.

Thus evidence has been excluded of such diverse matters as communications between the Commander-in-Chief in India and the Indian Government,[1] a company's balance sheets in the possession of the Inland Revenue authorities,[2] medical and police reports on the condition of a prisoner alleged to have assaulted a fellow prisoner,[3] and communications between the Secretary of State for War and the Soldiers', Sailors' and Airmens' Families' Association concerning the latter's attempts to effect a reconciliation between a soldier and his wife.[4] In the two most recent of these cases, *Ellis* v. *Home Office* and *Broome* v. *Broome*, the claim of the appropriate Minister of the Crown was regarded as conclusive. This principle had been established by VISCOUNT SIMON, L.C. in the leading case of *Duncan* v. *Cammell, Laird & Co., Ltd.*[5] In that case the House of Lords upheld the refusal of the First Lord of the Admiralty to allow discovery of documents relating to the details of contruction of submarines in time of war. The Lord Chancellor, however, went further and stated, in effect, that the decision as to whether or not to exclude evidence as contrary to the public interest rested with the Minister and that the judge could not go behind the Minister's decision. There followed a line of cases in which the affidavit of the appropriate Minister, generally expressed in a common form, was accepted by the judiciary with varying degrees of reluctance as conclusive. In some of these cases the Minister's refusal to allow evidence to be adduced appeared to cause considerable hardship to litigants. In addition it was widely felt that the judiciary ought to have the power to examine the evidence in question in order to satisfy itself that its reception would, indeed, be contrary to the public interest rather than having to rely upon the Minister's assertion. The result was, in 1968, a restatement of the law by the House of Lords in *Conway* v. *Rimmer.*[6]

The speeches of the House of Lords in *Conway* v. *Rimmer* vary considerably in their respective statements of the law. However, certain basic principles emerge. First, there are documents which, because either of their contents or of the class to which they belong, are conclusively privileged from disclosure. This category would include, for example, documents containing official secrets (privileged on account of their contents) and cabinet minutes (privileged on account of the class to which they belong). In respect of such documents their lordships anticipated that no difficulty would arise and that the courts would never need to go behind the certificate of a Minister claiming privilege (though it seems implicit that a court would have power to call for such a document for examination if it chose to do so). Since *Duncan* v. *Cammell, Laird & Co., Ltd.* concerned documents in this category, the House of Lords in *Conway* v. *Rimmer* expressed the view that that case was correctly decided on its facts but distinguishable.

In relation to documents outside the limited category referred to above the court will, even in the face of a Minister's certificate claiming privilege, look

---

[1] *Chatterton* v. *Secretary of State for India*, [1895] 2 Q.B. 189.

[2] *Re Joseph Hargreaves, Ltd.*, [1900] 1 Ch. 347.

[3] *Ellis* v. *Home Office*, [1953] 2 Q.B. 135; [1953] 2 All E.R. 149.

[4] *Broome* v. *Broome*, [1955] P. 190; [1953] 1 All E.R. 201.

[5] [1942] A.C. 624; [1942] 1 All E.R. 587.

[6] [1968] A.C. 910; [1968] 1 All E.R. 874. See also *Re Grosvenor Hotel, London (No. 2)*, [1965] Ch. 1210; [1964] 3 All E.R. 354; *Wednesbury Corporation* v. *Ministry of Housing and Local Government*, [1965] 1 All E.R. 186; [1965] 1 W.L.R. 261.

at the documents and attempt to strike a balance between the public interest in maintaining confidence and the principle that the administration of justice should not be impeded by the withholding of evidence. When a Minister's certificate asserts that certain documents are of a class which ought in the public interest to be withheld from disclosure then, unless his reasons are of a kind which judicial experience is not competent to weigh, the final decision rests with the court.

In the event the House of Lords in *Conway* v. *Rimmer* did order disclosure of the documents in issue, which comprised reports concerning a probationary police constable made by a police superintendent, including a report to the Chief Constable. More recently, in *R.* v. *Lewes Justices, Ex parte Secretary of State for Home Department*[1] a claim for privilege was upheld in respect of letters passing between the Gaming Board and the Chief Constable of Sussex concerning the character and reputation of an applicant for bingo club licences on the basis that the public interest required that protection be given to persons supplying information to the Gaming Board for otherwise they might refuse to give the information requested thus hindering the Gaming Board in the proper exercise of its public duties.

It may be noted that while the application of these principles to the case of *Duncan* v. *Cammell, Laird & Co., Ltd.* would not have produced a different result, it would almost certainly have brought about a different decision in the later cases, such as *Broome* v. *Broome*[2] and *Ellis* v. *Home Office*.[3]

One final aspect of the State interest may be quoted here. The sources of information to the detection of crime are privileged from disclosure. Thus in *Marks* v. *Beyfus*,[4] a civil action based on conspiracy to prosecute the plaintiff maliciously, the Director of Public Prosecutions declined to answer questions concerning the information leading to the plaintiff's prosecution. His refusal was upheld by the Court of Appeal. Indeed the Court of Appeal went further and stated that the judge ought not to have allowed the Director to answer had he wished to do so. For this reason the exclusion must be regarded as being based on public policy rather than private privilege.

b Judicial proceedings

Judges of superior courts cannot be compelled to give evidence of what took place in the course of proceedings before them. The rationale of this rule is the need for preserving the dignity of the judiciary. The privilege does not extend to arbitrators who may be required to give evidence as to what occurred during the arbitrations. Arbitrators cannot, however, be required to give reasons for their award.[5]

The general immunity which attaches to judicial proceedings extends to prevent jurors from giving evidence which would tend to cast doubts upon their verdict. Thus jurors cannot give evidence of discussions in the jury room. Nor can a juror testify that he did not understand the evidence; nor that he intended

---

[1] [1972] 1 Q.B. 232; [1971] 2 All E.R. 1126.
[2] [1955] P. 190; [1954] 1 All E.R. 201. The basis of non-disclosure in that case was expressed to be "the morale of the forces".
[3] [1953] 2 Q.B. 135; [1953] 2 All E.R. 149.
[4] (1890), 25 Q.B.D. 494.
[5] *Buccleuch* v. *Metropolitan Board of Works* (1872), L.R. 5 H.L. 418.

to give a verdict contrary to that returned;[1] nor that the verdict was arrived at by drawing lots.[2]

c Illegally obtained evidence

An involuntary or induced confession of guilt by an accused person is inadmissible. The admissibility of confessions is dealt with in a later chapter.[3] Oddly enough there is no rule of public policy which excludes facts discovered as a result of an inadmissible confession. For example evidence may be given that stolen goods were discovered at the accused's lodgings even though the confession leading to this discovery was induced and therefore inadmissible.[4] Similarly there is no rule excluding evidence of facts discovered in consequence of illegal searches. Indeed the authorities favour the admissibility of such evidence.[5] Nonetheless the courts have occasionally excluded evidence obtained in circumstances amounting to a fundamental infringement of individual liberty.

3 Discretion to exclude relevant evidence

Apart from the positive rules of exclusion discussed above, there is an overriding judicial discretion to exclude relevant evidence. This is based upon the general desire to secure a fair trial and may thus be regarded as an aspect of public policy. The discretion is most often exercised in criminal proceedings. Thus there is a discretion to exclude relevant similar fact evidence where its prejudicial effect would outweigh its probative value.[6] Similarly the permissible scope of cross-examination of an accused person by the prosecution under the provisions of the Criminal Evidence Act 1898, section 1 (f) is within the discretion of the trial judge.[7] The discretion is not, however, confined to criminal cases. There is a discretion to allow rebutting evidence after the close of the defence evidence in both civil and criminal proceedings. The question of whether to conduct a view of the *locus in quo* is within the discretion of the trial judge.

Where a statute provides for the reception of evidence, the question of whether the judge has a discretion to exclude such evidence is primarily one of statutory interpretation. Thus if a statute provides that some fact *may* be given in evidence there is a discretion to exclude it. Conversely, where the statute is couched in mandatory terms there is no discretion to exclude the evidence rendered admissible by the statute. Thus the House of Lords has held that there is no discretion to exclude cross-examination of one accused by a co-accused under section 1 (f) (iii) of the Criminal Evidence Act 1898 even though there is a discretion to exclude cross-examination by the prosecution under the section.[8]

---

[1] *Jackson* v. *Williamson* (1788), 2 Term Rep. 281; *Boston* v. *W.S. Bagshaw & Sons*, [1966] 2 All E.R. 906; [1966] 1 W.L.R. 1135.

[2] *Owen* v. *Warburton* (1805), 1 B. & P.N.R. 326.

[3] See p. 537, *post*.

[4] *R.* v. *Gould* (1840), 9 C. & P. 364.

[5] *Elias* v. *Pasmore*, [1934] 2 K.B. 164; *Kuruma Son of Kaniu* v. *R.*, [1955] A.C. 197; [1955] 1 All E.R. 236; *Rumping* v. *Director of Public Prosecutions*, [1964] A.C. 814; [1962] 3 All E.R. 256.

[6] *Harris* v. *Director of Public Prosecutions*, [1952] A.C. 694; [1952] 1 All E.R. 1044.

[7] *Maxwell* v. *Director of Public Prosecutions*, [1935] A.C. 309, at pp. 319, 321.

[8] *Murdoch* v. *Taylor*, [1965] A.C. 574; [1965] 1 All E.R. 406; see p. 470, *ante*.

Evidence of alibi

Special mention should be made of the discretionary rule of exclusion in relation to alibi defences, introduced by section 11 of the Criminal Justice Act 1967. This section provides that on a trial on indictment the defendant shall not without leave of the court adduce evidence in support of an alibi unless within 7 days of the conclusion of the committal proceedings he gives to the prosecution notice of particulars of the alibi. The notice must contain certain prescribed particulars, so as to enable the prosecution to investigate the alleged alibi. However the rule of exclusion only operates if the defendant was informed at the preliminary investigation of his obligation to give the prescribed notice. Furthermore, notice is only required in relation to the occasion on which an offence with which he is charged is alleged to have been committed. Accordingly evidence of the accused's whereabouts on other occasions is not subject to the restriction imposed by the section, however significant that evidence may be in relation to the issues in the case. Thus if the accused is charged with a robbery which is alleged to have been committed on a Monday, and part of the prosecution case is that the accused was seen on the following Tuesday driving a van which contained the stolen goods, he may tender alibi evidence concerning his whereabouts on the Tuesday without giving the statutory notice.[1]

---

[1] *R.* v. *Lewis*, [1969] 2 Q.B. 1; [1969] 1 All E.R. 79, *per* WIDGERY, L.J. (as he then was). See also p. 412, *ante.*

CHAPTER 31

The Onus of Proof

A FACTS WHICH MAY BE ESTABLISHED BY MEANS OTHER THAN PROOF

The general rule is that a party seeking to rely upon a fact must prove its existence to the tribunal. There are, however, certain matters which do not require affirmative proof. Thus facts which are admitted in civil or criminal cases need not be proved. Similarly English courts take judicial notice of a number of matters with the result that neither party need adduce proof of these matters. Finally a fact which is presumed in favour of a party need not be proved by that party, although the presumption sometimes arises only on proof of a prior basic fact; whether or not his opponent may disprove the fact depends upon the classification of the presumption as rebuttable or irrebuttable.

1 Formal admissions

Formal admissions must be distinguished from informal admissions and confessions. An informal admission and a confession are means of proving the fact admitted or confessed. For example, if a car driver, following an accident, admits that he was driving on the wrong side of the road and that he failed to give a proper signal, this statement may be put in evidence at the trial as a means of proving the facts stated by the driver. The driver may, however, attempt to explain away his statement at the trial and may produce evidence to contradict its truth. If, on the other hand, the driver in a civil action to which he is a party formally admits in the course of the proceedings that he was driving on the wrong side of the road his opponent need not prove that fact at all; it is admitted in his favour. Thus an informal admission is a means of proving the fact admitted whereas a formal admission dispenses with the need for proving that fact.

Until recently formal admissions were not receivable in criminal cases (except, of course, for pleas of guilty, which dispense with the need for a trial). Provision for formal admissions in criminal cases, by or on behalf of either prosecution or defence, was introduced by section 10 of the Criminal Justice Act 1967. An admission may, by virtue of that section, be made either at or before the trial but, if made other than in court, must be in writing. An admission made for the purpose of proceedings relating to any matter is treated as an admission for the purpose of any subsequent criminal proceedings relating to that matter, including any appeal or retrial, but may, at any stage, be withdrawn with leave of the court.

In civil cases rules of court provide for the means by which formal admissions may be made. In the High Court the Rules of the Supreme Court provide for formal admissions at various stages of the proceedings. Thus admissions may be made on the pleadings. An admission on the pleadings may be express or implied, in some circumstances, by a failure to traverse (deny) an allegation. Alternatively an admission may be made in answer to interrogatories or to a notice to admit facts or documents or on the hearing of the summons for directions.[1] Finally admissions may be made during the course of the trial. Counsel or solicitors acting as advocates have a general authority to make admissions binding upon their clients.[2]

2 Judicial notice

There are certain facts of which the court recognises the existence, in civil and criminal cases alike, without the need for proof. Such facts are said to be judicially noticed. The rationale of the principle of judicial notice is that there are matters which are so notorious that it would be pedantic to require proof of them. Certain matters must, by statute, be judicially noticed. These include the authenticity of signatures on certain public or official documents[3] and the contents of every Act of Parliament passed after 1850 unless the contrary is provided by the Act.[4] Apart from these statutory provisions it is impossible to classify satisfactorily the innumerable facts of which the courts take judicial notice. The issue depends to a certain extent upon the degree of notoriety of the fact in question. Thus judicial notice has been taken of the fact that a fortnight is an impossibly short period of human gestation[5] though not that 360 days is an impossibly long period.[6] Judicial notice has been taken of such widely divergent matters as the fact that camels are domestic animals,[7] that the value of money has declined since 1189,[8] that the streets of London are full of traffic,[9] that Great Britain is at war[10] and that many motorists prefer not to mix lubricating oils in the engines of their cars.[11]

In many cases the court will take judicial notice of a fact without inquiry.

---

1 See pp. 267, 282, 284, 291, *ante*.
2 *Swinfen* v. *Lord Chelmsford* (1860), 5 H. & N. 890.
3 Evidence Act 1845, s. 2; Bankruptcy Act 1914, s. 142.
4 Interpretation Act 1889, s. 9. By clause 3 (2) of the European Communities Bill currently before Parliament: "Judicial notice shall be taken of the Treaties, of the Official Journal of the Communities and of any decision of, or expression of opinion by, the European Court on any such questions as aforesaid; and the Official Journal shall be admissible as evidence of any instrument or other act thereby communicated of any of the Communities or of any Community institution."
5 *R.* v. *Luffe* (1807), 8 East 193.
6 *Preston-Jones* v. *Preston-Jones*, [1951] A.C. 391; [1951] 1 All E.R. 124.
7 *McQuaker* v. *Goddard*, [1940] 1 K.B. 687; [1940] 1 All E.R. 471.
8 *Bryant* v. *Foot* (1868), L.R. 3 Q.B. 497.
9 *Dennis* v. *White & Co.*, [1916] 2 K.B. 1.
10 *Re a Petition of Right*, [1915] 3 K.B. 643.
11 *Petrofina (Gt. Britain), Ltd.* v. *Martin*, [1966] Ch. 146, at p. 190; [1966] 1 All E.R. 126, at p. 144, *per* DIPLOCK, L.J. (as he then was).

Nevertheless in some cases the judge will consult sources to which it is proper for him to refer before deciding whether to take judicial notice of a particular fact. These sources are examined for reference rather than as evidence and it is for this reason that the fact ascertained is regarded as judicially noticed rather than proved. For example, the court takes judicial notice of the meaning of ordinary English words but the judge may still wish to consult a dictionary for reference. In *McQuaker* v. *Goddard*[1] the trial judge took judicial notice of the fact that a camel is a domestic animal only after consulting reference books and hearing witnesses. Similarly, although the courts take judicial notice of the sovereignty of a foreign State, the certificate of the appropriate Secretary of State is conclusive in cases of uncertainty.[2] In such cases the dividing line between judicial notice and proof is sometimes a very thin one.

It is sometimes said that the courts take judicial notice of the law of England. This is merely an alternative method of saying that law need not be proved. Actually certain rules of law must be proved. Private Acts of Parliament, certain Statutory Instruments and any custom not settled by judicial decision must be proved. Apart from these exceptions law need not be proved. However this principle only extends to English law and, in the House of Lords, to the law of Scotland and Ireland. Foreign law is, paradoxically, a question of fact and must be proved as such although it is a question of fact to be decided by the judge not by the jury.[3]

3 Presumptions

In certain circumstances the court presumes a fact in favour of a party who is thereby relieved of the burden of proving it. In a few of these cases the law provides that the party against whom the fact is presumed cannot deny its existence. The presumption is then said to be irrebuttable. However, in most cases the presumption is rebuttable. Consequently the effect of a presumption is usually to shift a burden of proof from the party in whose favour the presumption is raised to his opponent. It would be possible to consider presumptions as one aspect of the burden of proof but, since the burden of proof is a wider topic much of which is unconnected with presumptions and since not all presumptions shift the burden of proof, it is more convenient to deal with presumptions separately.

Presumptions may take two forms: direct and inferential, the latter being of greater practical importance. A direct presumption is a presumption which arises without proof of a basic fact. Direct presumptions are really rules of law which determine where the general burden of proof shall lie. The best known direct presumptions are the presumption of innocence and the presumption of sanity. An accused person is presumed innocent until the prosecution has proved his guilt beyond reasonable doubt. Similarly, every person is presumed

---

[1] *McQuaker* v. *Goddard*, [1940] 1 K.B. 687; [1940] 1 All E.R. 471.
[2] *Duff Development Co.* v. *Government of Kelantan*, [1924] A.C. 797.
[3] Administration of Justice Act 1920, s. 15; Judicature Act 1925, s. 102. By clause 3 (1) of the European Communities Bill: "For the purposes of all legal proceedings any question as to the meaning or effect of any of the Treaties, or as to the validity, meaning or effect of any Community instrument, shall be treated as a question of law and, if not referred to the European Court, be for determination as such in accordance with the principles laid down by and any relevant decision of the European Court.

sane until the contrary is proven. It will be appreciated that since these two presumptions arise without the need for proving any preliminary basic fact they do not shift a burden of proof; they merely determine where the burden shall lie in the first place. Inferential presumptions, on the other hand, have the effect of shifting a burden of proof from the party who proves the basic fact upon which the presumption depends to the party against whom the presumption is raised. A typical example is the presumption of legitimacy. It is for the person who alleges that he is legitimate to prove his legitimacy. There is, however, a presumption of legitimacy in favour of a person who was born or conceived in lawful wedlock unless his conception must have occurred while his parents were separated by court order. The result is that if the party seeking to prove his legitimacy can prove the basic fact of birth or conception in lawful wedlock the presumption arises in his favour and a burden of proof is cast upon his opponent to prove illegitimacy. However, while almost all inferential presumptions merely have the effect of shifting a burden of proof, certain inferential presumptions are irrebuttable[1] with the effect that proof of the basic fact amounts to proof of the fact presumed. In such a case the presumption does not merely affect the burden of proof; it dispenses with the need for proof completely.

Various classifications of presumptions have been attempted.[2] Although none of them is wholly satisfactory, the orthodox classification into irrebuttable presumptions of law, rebuttable presumptions of law and rebuttable presumptions of fact is the classification most widely adopted.

a Irrebuttable presumptions of law

Irrebuttable presumptions of law, sometimes described as conclusive presumptions, are not really presumptions but are rather rules of substantive law couched in presumptive terms. For example section 40 of the Children and Young Persons Act 1933[3] provides that "it shall be conclusively presumed that no child under the age of ten years can be guilty of any offence". Since the presumption is irrebuttable it is really a rule of law to the effect that a child under the age of ten cannot commit a crime. This is not a rule of evidence at all and the allusion to "presumption" in the section is misleading. There are several rules of law customarily expressed in the form of presumptions. For example, a boy under the age of fourteen years is presumed to be incapable of committing an offence involving sexual potency as principal offender. Similarly, where two or more persons have died in circumstances rendering it uncertain which of them survived the other, such deaths shall (subject to any order of the court), for all purposes affecting the title to property, be presumed to have occurred in order of seniority, and accordingly the younger shall be deemed to have survived the elder.[4] This latter "presumption" differs from the other examples in that it depends upon proof of the basic fact of uncertainty in the order of deaths. It is, nonetheless, rather a rule of substantive law than a rule of evidence.

---

[1] For example, the presumption of death in order of seniority contained in s. 184 of the Law of Property Act 1925 (*infra*).

[2] The best known unorthodox classification is that suggested by LORD DENNING in (1945), 61 L.Q.R. 379. It has not been generally adopted.

[3] As amended by the Children and Young Persons Act 1963.

[4] Law of Property Act 1925, s. 184.

b   Rebuttable presumptions of law

A rebuttable presumption of law is a rule of law compelling the court to infer the existence of the fact presumed.   The direct presumptions of innocence and sanity mentioned above are rebuttable presumptions of law.   Most rebuttable presumptions of law, however, depend upon proof of a basic fact.   The presumption of legitimacy is an example.   There are virtually innumerable other examples, some of the best known of which are the presumption of death from seven years' absence unheard of,[1] the presumption that a document proved or purporting to be not less than twenty years old and produced from proper custody has been duly executed,[2] the presumption that alterations to a deed have been made before execution and that alterations to a will have been made after execution,[3] the presumption that official acts have been duly performed[4] (*omnia praesumuntur rite esse acta*) and the equitable presumption that property purchased by a parent in his child's name constitutes a gift rather than the creation of a trust.[5]   In all of these cases the court is bound, on proof of the basic fact, to give effect to the presumption and infer the existence of the fact presumed.   The effect of this is to cast the burden of disproving the existence of the fact presumed upon the party against whom the presumption is raised.

c   Rebuttable presumptions of fact

Presumptions of fact are merely specific and frequently recurring instances of the operation of circumstantial evidence.   The nature of circumstantial evidence is that it consists of facts from which other facts may be presumed to exist.   The basic difference between a presumption of fact and a presumption of law is that in the case of the former there is no rule of law which compels the court to apply the presumption whereas in the latter case the court not only may, but must, apply the presumption.

The variety of presumptions of fact is infinite but certain examples are noteworthy on account of the frequency of their recurrence.   The presumption of continuance, for example, may arise in various forms.   Thus if a car is being driven by a certain person immediately after an incident it may be inferred that the same person was driving at the time of the incident.[6]   Similarly the fact of a

---

[1] This presumption, though basically a common law presumption, has been codified with variations in several statutes, notably the Matrimonial Causes Act 1965, s. 14 (3); see also Offences Against the Person Act 1861, s. 57.   Moreover, the presumption cannot be raised in order to fix the precise date of death for succession purposes: *Re Phenés Trusts* (1870), L.R. 5 Ch. 139.   Consequently there is very little of the original common law presumption left in operation.

[2] Evidence Act 1938, s. 4.

[3] *Doe d. Tatum* v. *Catamore* (1851), 16 Q.B. 745.

[4] There are innumerable variations of this presumption, examples are: that a marriage has been duly celebrated; that a licence has been duly granted; that a public officer has been duly appointed and that a public seal is authentic.   However in *Scott* v. *Baker*, [1969] 1 Q.B. 659; [1968] 2 All E.R. 993, one of the numerous "breathalyser" cases, the Queen's Bench Divisional Court refused to extend the presumption so as to presume, in the absence of any evidence, that a breath test device used by the police was "a device of a type approved for the purpose of such a test by the Secretary of State" (Road Safety Act 1967, s. 7 (1)).

[5] This is termed the "presumption of advancement": *Shephard* v. *Cartwright*, [1955] A.C. 431; [1954] 3 All E.R. 649.   It applies also to purchases made by a husband in his wife's name though it is nowadays easily rebutted.

[6] *Beresford* v. *St. Albans Justices* (1905), 22 T.L.R. 1.

person being alive may be presumed from the fact of his being alive and healthy at an earlier date.[1] It must be stressed, however, that continuance is a presumption of fact not a presumption of law so that the court is not bound to presume a person to be alive from the fact of his being known to be alive at an antecedent date.[2] Other examples of presumptions of fact are the presumption of guilty knowledge raised by the fact of possession of recently stolen goods,[3] the presumption that, where a person conceals evidence, that evidence would be to his disadvantage if produced (*omnia praesumuntur contra spoliatorem*)[4] and the presumption that a person intends the natural consequences of his acts.[5] The latter presumption has often been treated as a presumption of law and, occasionally, as an irrebuttable presumption of law.[6] That it is, in criminal proceedings, a rebuttable presumption of fact is now laid down by section 8 of the Criminal Justice Act 1967.

It must once again be stressed that the operation of a presumption (other than an irrebuttable presumption of law) is not conclusive of liability; the person against whom the presumption is invoked may well be able to rebut it by his evidence. An interesting illustration of this is the case of *Moore v. Maxwells of Emsworth, Ltd.*[7] In that case the driver of a lorry towing a trailer discovered that the tail light of the trailer had failed. Accordingly he stopped and, while he was attempting to repair the fuse, another vehicle ran into the unlit trailer. The court found as a fact that the lorry driver had taken all reasonable steps to avoid creating or prolonging the danger presented by the stationary unlit vehicle so that, although the presence of an unlit vehicle on the road gave rise to a presumption of negligence, that presumption had been rebutted by the evidence, with the result that the action by the owner of the other vehicle failed. A difficult academic question is whether rebuttable presumptions affect only the onus of proof or whether they are of some evidential weight in themselves. It will be appreciated that a presumption which is of no weight in itself, but which merely determines the onus of proof, ceases to have any effect when evidence one way or the other has been adduced because the court will then decide upon the evidence (unless it finds the evidence so finely balanced that it is not satisfied either way, in which event the party on whom the burden of proof lies will fail). This view was expressed recently by LORD REID when explaining the effect of the presumption of legitimacy.[8]

> " . . . the presumption of legitimacy now merely determines the onus of proof. Once evidence has been led it must be weighed without using the presumption as a make-weight in the scale for legitimacy. So even weak evidence against legitimacy must prevail if there is not other evidence to counterbalance it. The presumption

---

[1] *Chard* v. *Chard*, [1956] P. 259; [1955] 3 All E.R. 721.
[2] *R.* v. *Lumley* (1869), L.R. 1 C.C.R. 196.
[3] *R.* v. *Langmead* (1864), 9 Cox 464.
[4] *Armory* v. *Delamirie* (1721), 1 Swa. 505; *Moriarty* v. *London, Chatham and Dover Railway* (1870), L.R. 5 Q.B. 314.
[5] *Hosegood* v. *Hosegood* (1950), 66 T.L.R. (pt. 1) 735; *R.* v. *Steane*, [1947] K.B. 997; [1947] 1 All E.R. 813.
[6] See the notorious case of *Director of Public Prosecutions* v. *Smith*, [1961] A.C. 290; [1960] 3 All E.R. 161.
[7] [1968] 2 All E.R. 779; [1968] 1 W.L.R. 1077.
[8] *S.* v. *McC.*; *W.* v. *W.*, [1972] A.C. 24, at p. 41; [1970] 3 All E.R. 107, at p. 109.

will only come in at that stage in the very rare case of the evidence being so evenly balanced that the court is unable to reach a decision on it. I cannot recollect ever having seen or heard a case of any kind where the court could not reach a decision on the evidence before it."

Despite this, REES, J. in *T.* (*H.*) v. *T.* (*H.*),[1] while expressly applying LORD REID's dictum, founded his decision on the presumption, being unable to accept the evidence of either the husband or the wife as constituting proof even on a balance of probabilities; accordingly the presumption of legitimacy prevailed.

In *Stupple* v. *Royal Insurance Co., Ltd.*[2] the Court of Appeal was called upon to consider the effect in a civil case of a conviction admissible by virtue of Section 11 of the Civil Evidence Act 1968;[3] unfortunately the Court failed to lay down any principle as to whether the conviction merely operated to shift the onus of proof on to the party denying the correctness of the conviction or whether the conviction was of weight in itself. LORD DENNING, M.R. regarded the conviction as entitled to great weight; however BUCKLEY, L.J. regarded it as being of no weight and WINN, L.J. expressed no opinion.

B THE BURDEN OF PROOF

1 Nature and incidence of the burden of proof

Basically the expression "burden of proof" is simple to define. It means the obligation of proving a fact or facts. Nonetheless much recondite learning has been expended in tracing the different senses in which the expression has been used.[4] The expression has been used in at least three different senses; first to connote a party's general obligation to prove his case ("general burden"), secondly to connote a party's specific obligation to prove any individual issue or fact relevant to that issue ("specific burden") and thirdly to connote the obligation of adducing evidence in support of a disputed fact ("evidential burden"). The difference between the general, specific and evidential burdens may be illustrated by a hypothetical action for negligence. The general burden of proving negligence on the part of the defendant rests on the plaintiff. In addition the burden is on the plaintiff of proving specific acts on the part of the defendant which are alleged to amount to negligence, such as driving too fast, failing to observe traffic signals or failing to keep his vehicle properly maintained. Finally the plaintiff has the burden of adducing evidence in support of each of these facts. If the defendant in the same action alleges contributory negligence on the part of the plaintiff it is for the defendant to discharge the specific burden of proving fault on the part of the plaintiff and also to adduce evidence in support of his allegation. Similarly, in a prosecution for murder the general burden of proving guilt is upon the prosecution, the specific burden of proving the elements of the crime, that the defendant's unlawful act done with malice aforethought caused the death of the victim, death occurring within a year and a day, is on the prosecution but the specific burden of proving insanity, for example, rests on the accused. It will be apparent from these illustrations

---

[1] [1971] 1 All E.R. 590; [1971] 1 W.L.R. 429.
[2] [1971] 1 Q.B. 50 [1970] 3 All E.R. 230.
[3] See p. 465, *ante*.
[4] See, for example, Cross, *Evidence* (3rd Edn.), pp. 67–77.

that the general burden is composed of a number of specific burdens and that the question of which specific burdens go to make up the general burden is to be determined by reference to substantive law. For this reason the general burden and specific burdens are collectively referred to as the "legal burden of proof". It will be equally apparent that not every specific burden is imposed upon the party having the general burden. Thus the specific burden of proving insanity in a criminal case is on the accused though the general burden of proving guilt is on the prosecution.

It might be supposed that the evidential burden would always follow the legal burden. This is usually, though not invariably, the case. For example, in a prosecution for murder the burden of negativing provocation is on the prosecution but the jury need not be directed to consider provocation unless there is some evidence of provocation. This evidence may be found in the testimony of the prosecution witnesses but if it is not the accused must adduce some evidence in support of a plea of provocation. In other words the accused has the evidential burden.[1] Similar considerations arise where the accused pleads self-defence[2] or non-insane automatism[3] in a criminal case.

It is frequently asserted that a specific burden of proof or an evidential burden may shift during the course of proceedings. Thus the orthodox view of the effect of raising a presumption of law is that it shifts the burden of proof on to the party against whom the presumption operates. For example if a person claiming an interest in property under a settlement asserts that he is legitimate, he has the specific burden of proving his legitimacy. If he can prove that he was born or conceived in lawful wedlock the presumption of legitimacy applies and the court must then infer that he is legitimate unless an opponent can rebut the presumption by proving that the claimant is not the child of both spouses and, therefore, illegitimate. In such a case it is usually stated that the presumption operates to shift the burden of proof. In fact, if the case is inspected closely, it appears that although the party denying the claimant's legitimacy has *a* specific burden of proof it is not the *same* specific burden as the claimant had. The true position is that because one party has discharged his specific burden of proof a different burden has been cast on his opponent. The late Professor Nokes explained this extremely clearly in the following words:[4]

"The prosecutor or plaintiff has one burden, that is, the obligation to prove one set of facts; while the accused or the defendant may have another burden, that is, an obligation to adduce evidence of different facts, such as payment of a debt, or other matters in disproof of the opposing evidence. The shifting of the burden means that A. lays down his load and B. picks up another load. But A. never tosses his load to B., and B. never tosses it back to A. What shifts is the obligation; but it is an obligation to prove different facts."

Thus it appears that while a party cannot shift his burden of proof, if he discharges his burden of proof, for example by proving facts which give rise to a presumption in his favour, the effect may be to impose upon his opponent a different burden—the burden of proving facts to negative the legal effect of the

---

[1] *Mancini* v. *Director of Public Prosecutions*, [1942] A.C. 1; [1941] 3 All E.R. 272.

[2] *R.* v. *Lobell*, [1957] 1 Q.B. 547; [1957] 1 All E.R. 734.

[3] *Hill* v. *Baxter*, [1958] 1 Q.B. 277; [1958] 1 All E.R. 193; see also *Bratty* v. *A.-G. for Northern Ireland*, [1963] A.C. 386; [1961] 3 All E.R. 523.

[4] *An Introduction to Evidence* (4th Edn.), p. 480.

facts proved by the first party. A good illustration of the operation of this principle is the effect of the maxim *res ipsa loquitur* (the thing speaks for itself). *Prima facie* a person alleging negligence must prove the acts alleged to constitute negligence on the part of the defendant. However if he can prove that something under the management or control of the defendant has caused damage, that there is no explanation as to how the accident occurred[1] and that the accident is such as would not in the ordinary course of things have occurred without negligence the court must presume negligence. The maxim, which is in effect a presumption of law, has been applied to a variety of situations. The effect of the plaintiff invoking the maxim is to place upon the defendant a burden which he may discharge by proving either that he used all reasonable care or that the accident occurred in a manner which does not connote negligence on his part.[2]

2 The burden of proof in civil cases

In civil cases the general burden of proof is upon the party who would fail if no evidence at all were adduced. This party also has the right to begin. The effect of this rule is that the general burden, and also the right to begin, are upon the plaintiff if the burden of proving any single issue of fact is upon him or if damages are unliquidated. *Prima facie* the burden of proving every fact which he alleges is upon the plaintiff but in practice many of these facts will be admitted by the defendant in which case they need not be proved.

The incidence of particular burdens of proof in civil cases depends upon substantive law and upon the pleadings in a case tried with pleadings. Thus the plaintiff must prove every fact which is an essential element in his cause of action. In addition the plaintiff must prove any positive allegation to rebut a defence or to show an exception to the defence pleaded. In terms of the pleadings the plaintiff must prove every fact in his statement of claim (unless, of course, the fact in question is judicially noticed, admitted or presumed in the plaintiff's favour) and every positive allegation in a reply served by him. Thus in a libel action the plaintiff must prove publication and, if the defendant pleads qualified privilege, malice. Similarly in an action for breach of contract where the defence of frustration is pleaded the plaintiff must prove a breach of contract and also negligence if he alleges that to negative the defence of frustration.[3] The defendant has the burden of proving any particular defence which he raises. If his defence to an allegation made by the plaintiff is a mere traverse or denial the effect is simply to put that fact in issue leaving the burden of proving that fact upon the plaintiff. If, however, the defendant raises positive allegations in his defence or confesses and avoids one of the plaintiff's allegations, then the burden is upon the defendant to prove the fact alleged or matter in avoidance. Thus if the defendant in a libel action merely denies publication he assumes no particular burden of proof. However, if he alleges qualified privilege, justification, fair comment or unintentional defamation the burden of proving these

---

[1] The doctrine depends upon the absence of explanation: *Barkway* v. *South Wales Transport Co., Ltd.,* [1950] A.C. 185; [1950] 1 All E.R. 392.

[2] *Barkway* v. *South Wales Transport Co., Ltd.* (*supra*); *Moore* v. *R. Fox & Sons,* [1956] 1 Q.B. 596; [1956] 1 All E.R. 182; cf. *Lloyde* v. *West Midlands Gas Board,* [1971] 2 All E.R. 1240; [1971] 1 W.L.R. 749.

[3] *Joseph Constantine Steamship Line, Ltd.* v. *Imperial Smelting Corporation, Ltd.,* [1942] A.C. 154; [1941] 2 All E.R. 165.

positive allegations is upon him. It follows that in civil cases the particular burdens may be distributed between the parties although the general burden almost always rests upon the plaintiff.

A particular burden is no less upon a party because his allegation is negative rather than positive in character. Thus in an action for malicious prosecution it is for the plaintiff to allege and prove that the defendant had no reasonable and probable cause for the prosecution.[1] Similarly, where the statutory defence of unintentional defamation is raised it is for the defendant to show absence of malice.[2] It follows that a party gains no advantage by couching a positive allegation in negative terms. Thus whether a landlord alleges that the tenant "did not repair" the premises in question or whether he alleges that the tenant "let the house become dilapidated" the burden of proving this fact is upon the landlord.[3]

Finally it may be observed that where the admissibility of evidence is in issue the party who alleges that an item of evidence is admissible bears the burden of proving this fact. For example, a party who wishes to put in secondary evidence of a private document must account for the absence of the original; a party seeking to prove a dying declaration must prove that the declarant is dead together with the other conditions of admissibility of such declarations.[4]

3 The burden of proof in criminal cases

In criminal proceedings the combined effect of the presumption of innocence and the absence of formal admissions is that the general burden of proving guilt is upon the prosecution. Consequently the prosecution always has the right to begin except where the accused raises a special plea in bar such as *autrefois acquit*.

In addition to the general burden of proving guilt the prosecution must also discharge the particular burden of proving every element in the crime charged; this includes (subject to the exceptions noted below) the burden of disproving all defences of which there is some evidence. The number of specific burdens which combine to make up the general burden in criminal proceedings is ascertained by reference to the substantive criminal law. The leading case on the subject of the burden of proof in criminal proceedings is *Woolmington* v. *Director of Public Prosecutions*.[5] The accused, charged with murdering his wife, claimed that the killing was an accident. The trial judge in his summing-up directed the jury that if the Crown proved that the accused killed the deceased the burden rested on the accused to prove provocation or accident. The conviction was quashed in the House of Lords on the ground of this misdirection. In the hallowed words of LORD SANKEY, L.C.:[6]

---

1 *Abrath* v. *North Eastern Rail., Co.* (1883), 11 Q.B.D. 440.
2 Defamation Act 1952, s. 4.
3 *Seward* v. *Leggatt* (1836), 7 C. & P. 613.
4 See p. 539, *post.*
5 [1935] A.C. 462. For a recent reaffirmation of this principle see *R.* v. *Bone,* [1968] 2 All E.R. 644; [1968] 1 W.L.R. 583 in which the defendant's conviction was quashed because of the trial judge's failure to direct that, in relation to the defence of duress, it was for the prosecution to disprove that defence rather than for the defendant to prove it.
6 [1935] A.C. 462, at p. 481.

"Throughout the web of the English criminal law one golden thread is always to be seen, that it is the duty of the prosecution to prove the prisoner's guilt, subject to ... the defence of insanity and subject also to any statutory exception."

Nevertheless a legal burden is sometimes cast on the defence in criminal cases. Basically there are few situations in which a legal (as opposed to an evidential) burden of proof is on the defence.

(1)　The burden of proving insanity is on the defence where this issue is raised at the instance of the defence. This may be seen as the effect of the direct presumption of sanity.[1]　Similarly the burden of proving unfitness to plead[2] or diminished responsibility[3] is upon the accused where either of these issues is raised at the instance of the defence.[4]

(2)　Several statutory provisions impose a specific burden upon the defence. The statutory defence of diminished responsibility has already been mentioned. To this may be added certain statutes which impose a burden on the accused only after the prosecution has proved particular facts.[5]　For example, section 1 (3) of the Road Safety Act 1967 provides that, on a prosecution for being in charge of a motor vehicle on a road or other public place having consumed alcohol in such a quantity that the proportion thereof in his blood exceeds the prescribed limit, a person shall not be convicted if he proves that there was no likelihood of his driving it so long as there was any probability of his having alcohol in his blood in a proportion exceeding the prescribed limit.

(3)　As stated above, the burden of proving a special plea in bar is upon the accused.

(4)　Where a presumption is raised by the prosecution it is for the defence to rebut the presumption. For example there is a presumption of guilty knowledge from the fact of possession of recently stolen property. Thus if the prosecution establishes possession of recently stolen property on the part of the accused the evidential burden is on the latter to provide an explanation.[6]

In addition to the exceptional circumstances noted above in which a legal burden of proof is imposed upon the defence there are many cases in which an evidential burden is cast upon the defence. This arises principally where the burden is upon the prosecution of proving a negative averment. Thus in a case such as *Woolmington*'s case, although the legal burden of disproving provocation or accident is upon the prosecution, there is a burden upon the defence to adduce some evidence in support of these defences if such evidence has not been given during the course of the prosecution case. This is a common-sense rule for otherwise the prosecution would be faced with the intolerable burden of disproving every conceivable defence no matter how fanciful. An extension of this principle is the rule that the burden is upon the accused to prove a fact which

---

[1] *M'Naughton's Case* (1843), 10 Cl. & Fin. 200.
[2] *R. v. Podola*, [1960] 1 Q.B. 325; [1959] 3 All E.R. 418.
[3] Homicide Act 1957, s. 2 (2); *R. v. Dunbar*, [1958] 1 Q.B. 1; [1957] 2 All E.R. 737.
[4] Where insanity, diminished responsibility or unfitness to plead is raised at the instance of the prosecution the burden of proof is presumably on the prosecution. Section 6 of the Criminal Procedure (Insanity) Act 1964 permits the prosecution to allege insanity where the accused raises the issue of diminished responsibility and *vice-versa*.
[5] Other statutes which impose a specific burden on the accused are: Libel Act 1843, s. 6; Prevention of Corruption Act 1916, s. 2.
[6] *R. v. Hepworth and Fearnley*, [1955] 2 Q.B. 600; [1955] 2 All E.R. 918.

is peculiarly within his own knowledge. In *R. v. Turner*[1] the accused was charged under a statute which made it an offence to be in possession of hares without legal authority. The statute contained some ten exceptions making possession of hares legal. It was held that the Crown did not have to prove that none of these exceptions applied in the case of the accused. The principle in *R. v. Turner* has been applied so as to place the burden upon the defence of proving possession of a driving licence,[2] a certificate of insurance[3] and a licence to sell sugar.[4] It appears that this burden is evidential rather than legal unless arising under a statute, when it is a question of interpretation.[5]

C THE STANDARD OF PROOF

1 The two standards of proof

Once it is determined on whom the burden of proof rests the question arises as to what standard of proof that party must satisfy in order to discharge his burden. If the burden in question is merely an evidential burden the question of standard of proof does not really arise since the burden is, by definition, discharged merely by adducing an item of credible evidence. Where the burden is a legal burden the traditional view of English law is that there are two alternative standards of proof; proof beyond reasonable doubt, which is the appropriate standard in criminal cases, and proof on a balance of probabilities, which is the standard in civil cases. In fact the modern view is that these two standards are not perhaps as radically different as they are often stated to be. Thus, it has been stated, whether the case is civil or criminal, the judge or juror is primarily concerned with deciding whether or not he is satisfied that the case is made out. Where the allegation in question is of a grave or serious nature it will naturally require a higher degree of proof to satisfy him. Nevertheless, although it is certainly true that the degree of proof required varies with the gravity of the allegation in both civil and criminal proceedings, it can probably not be maintained that there is no practical difference between proof on a balance of probabilities and proof beyond reasonable doubt. Many cases must arise where the reasonable juror would feel that an allegation of fact was more likely than not to be true but would not be prepared to say that he felt sure that it was true.

Consequently the traditional view that there are two standards of proof still obtains. There are, however, within these two standards varying degrees of proof which differ according to the gravity of the allegation of fact which is to be proved. This principle was very clearly explained in the judgment of DENNING, L.J. (as he then was) in *Bater* v. *Bater*:[6]

"The difference of opinion which has been evoked about the standard of proof in recent years may well turn out to be more a matter of words than anything else. It

---

[1] (1816), 5 M. & S. 206.
[2] *John* v. *Humphreys*, [1955] 1 All E.R. 793; [1955] 1 W.L.R. 325.
[3] *Williams* v. *Russell* (1933), 149 L.T. 190.
[4] *R. v. Oliver*, [1944] K.B. 68; [1943] 2 All E.R. 800.
[5] See *R. v. Spurge*, [1961] 2 Q.B. 205; [1961] 2 All E.R. 688. Compare *R. v. Ewens*, [1966] 2 All E.R. 470. [1967] 1 Q.B. 322;
[6] [1951] P. 35, at p. 37; [1950] 2 All E.R. 458, at p. 459; approved in *Hornal* v. *Neuberger Products, Ltd.*, [1957] 1 Q.B. 247; [1956] 3 All E.R. 970, and in *Blyth* v. *Blyth*, [1966] A.C. 643; [1966] 1 All E.R. 524.

is of course true that by our law a higher standard of proof is required in criminal cases than in civil cases. But this is subject to the qualification that there is no absolute standard in either case. In criminal cases the charge must be proved beyond reasonable doubt, but there may be degrees of proof within that standard. . . . A civil court, when considering a charge of fraud, will naturally require for itself a higher degree of probability than that which it would require when asking if negligence is established. It does not adopt so high a degree as a criminal court, even when it is considering a charge of a criminal nature; but still it does require a degree of probability which is commensurate with the occasion."

2 The standard of proof in civil cases

The standard of proof applicable in civil cases is proof on a balance of probabilities. This standard applies, as a general rule, whether the burden of proof to be discharged is the general burden or a particular burden. It also applies where the allegation to be proved is of a criminal charge. There are old authorities to the effect that an allegation of crime, even if made in a civil case, had to be proved beyond reasonable doubt. These authorities have now been discredited and the present law is that an allegation of a criminal offence made in the course of civil proceedings need only be proved on a preponderance of probability, although, of course, the degree of probability will be higher in the case of such an allegation. The leading modern authority is *Hornal* v. *Neuberger Products, Ltd.*[1] in which case the Court of Appeal upheld an award of damages for fraud made by a county court judge who had expressly stated that he was satisfied on a balance of probabilities that the false statement had been made as alleged but that he was not satisfied beyond reasonable doubt. The reasoning of the Court of Appeal has been applied to an allegation of unlawful killing.[2] On the same basis it was thought until recently that an allegation of a matrimonial offence made in matrimonial proceedings had to be proved beyond reasonable doubt. This view of the law was based on the quasi-criminal nature of matrimonial offences, notably adultery.[3] However, since it is now established that criminal allegations made in civil proceedings need only be proved on a balance of probabilities, it is understandable, as laid down by the House of Lords in *Blyth* v. *Blyth*[4] that the same civil standard applies in matrimonial proceedings which are, after all, civil not criminal proceedings.

There remain, after *Hornal* v. *Neuberger Products, Ltd.* and *Blyth* v. *Blyth*, very few instances in which an allegation of fact made in civil proceedings must be proved beyond reasonable doubt. It is now enacted that the presumption of legitimacy can be rebutted by proof on a balance of probabilities that the child is in fact illegitimate.[5] The standard of proof of contempt of court is beyond reasonable doubt, since contempt is quasi-criminal in nature.[6] The recent case

---

[1] [1957] 1 Q.B. 247; [1956] 3 All E.R. 970.
[2] *Re Dellow's Will Trusts*, [1964] 1 All E.R. 771; [1964] 1 W.L.R. 451.
[3] The leading authorities in support of the old view are: *Ginesi* v. *Ginesi*, [1948] P. 179; [1948] 1 All E.R. 373; *Preston-Jones* v. *Preston-Jones*, [1951] A.C. 391; [1951] 1 All E.R. 124.
[4] [1966] A.C. 643; [1966] 1 All E.R. 524.
[5] Family Law Reform Act 1969, s. 26; at common law proof beyond reasonable doubt was required: *Preston-Jones* v. *Preston-Jones (supra)*.
[6] *Re Bramblevale, Ltd.*, [1970] Ch. 128; [1969] 3 All E.R. 1062.

of *Judd* v. *Minister of Pensions and National Insurance*[1] furnishes another illustration. These cases are, however, exceptional.

3 The standard of proof in criminal cases

Proof beyond reasonable doubt is generally described as the criminal standard of proof. However it is the standard appropriate in criminal proceedings only where the burden of proof is upon the prosecution. It is trite law that the prosecution must prove the guilt of the accused beyond reasonable doubt. The words "beyond reasonable doubt" in this context have been subjected to considerable judicial analysis. In *Miller* v. *Minister of Pensions*,[2] DENNING, J. (as he then was) observed that

> "Proof beyond a reasonable doubt does not mean proof beyond the shadow of a doubt. . . . If the evidence is so strong against a man as to leave only a remote possibility in his favour, which can be dismissed with the sentence 'of course it is possible but not in the least probable' the case is proved beyond reasonable doubt, but nothing short of that will suffice."

Several attempts have been made to change the hallowed formula "beyond reasonable doubt". LORD GODDARD, C.J. in *R.* v. *Summers*[3] deprecated these words and suggested that an appropriate direction to the jury be that they should "feel sure" that the accused is guilty, an alternative which LORD GODDARD reiterated in *R.* v. *Hepworth and Fearnley*[4] in which case he suggested, as a further alternative, "completely satisfied". Nevertheless it is fair to say that the phrase "beyond reasonable doubt" is still regarded as the safest method of describing the prosecution burden in a direction to the jury.

In the few cases in which the burden of proving a fact is upon the defence in a criminal case the appropriate standard of proof is proof on a balance of probabilities—the civil standard.[5]

D CORROBORATION

As a general rule English law does not require corroboration or confirmative evidence. No doubt a jury may in practice be impressed with the cogency of several items of evidence tendered in support of the same fact but, as a matter of law, any party may discharge his burden of proof by adducing one item of evidence. Nevertheless there are exceptional circumstances in which corroboration is required either as a matter of practice or, by statute, as a matter of law. The distinction is important because where corroboration is required by statute the court cannot act on uncorroborated evidence whereas where corroboration

---

[1] [1966] 2 Q.B. 580; [1965] 3 All E.R. 642. The case turned on the construction of article 4 of the Royal Warrant 1949, which expressly provides that the Minister cannot disallow a claim by a member of the armed forces to a disablement award unless satisfied beyond reasonable doubt that the claimant's injury was not due to, or aggravated by, war service.

[2] [1947] 2 All E.R. 372. [3] [1952] 1 All E.R. 1059.

[4] [1955] 2 Q.B. 600; [1955] 2 All E.R. 918.

[5] *R.* v. *Carr-Briant*, [1943] K.B. 607 (Prevention of Corruption Act 1916, s. 2); *Sodeman* v. *R.*, [1936] 2 All E.R. 1138 (insanity); *R.* v. *Dunbar*, [1958] 1 Q.B. 1; [1957] 2 All E.R. 737 (diminished responsibility); *R.* v. *Podola*, [1960] 1 Q.B. 325; [1959] 3 All E.R. 418 (unfitness to plead).

is required only as a matter of practice the court can act on uncorroborated evidence, though it will do so only with hesitation and only after warning the jury, if there is one, of the danger of so doing. The principal circumstances in which corroboration is required, either as a matter of practice, or by statute, are discussed below.[1]

1   Cases in which corroboration is required by statute

a   Perjury

Section 13 of the Perjury Act 1911 provides that a person cannot be convicted of perjury solely upon the evidence of one witness as to the falsity of any statement alleged to be false. The origin of this rule[2] is somewhat obscure but is usually attributed to the undesirability of matching "oath against oath". There is no limitation on the form which the corroborative evidence may take. A second witness is sufficient but not essential and the court may act on documentary evidence or on the fact that the accused has frequently repeated statements contradicting the impugned statement. The mere fact that the accused has made inconsistent statements is not, however, sufficient.

b   Affiliation

The Affiliation Proceedings Act 1957, section 4 provides that an affiliation order may be made against the putative father if the evidence of the mother be corroborated in some material particular to the satisfaction of the justices. Affiliation proceedings are also unusual in that the mother must herself give evidence. The usual form which the corroborative evidence takes is evidence of acts of sexual intercourse between the parties during the time when the child must have been conceived. Likewise evidence of acts of familiarity has been held to amount to corroboration even where these acts took place at a time prior to conception.[3] Mere evidence of opportunity, unsupported by evidence of affection, is, however, insufficient.[4] Where the corroborative evidence consists of letters written by the father to the mother the handwriting may be proved by the mother, notwithstanding that it is her testimony which the letters corroborate.[5]

---

[1] The list is not exhaustive; see *Gallie* v. *Lee*, [1969] 2 Ch. 17, at p. 38; [1969] 1 All E.R. 1062, at p. 1079, *per* RUSSELL, L.J. The evidence (Further Amendment) Act 1869 made corroboration essential of a plaintiff's testimony in actions for breach of promise of marriage. Corroboration was often found in such matters as letters from the defendant, admissions, gifts and conduct consistent with impending matrimony. Since the action for breach of promise has been abolished by the Law Reform (Miscellaneous Provisions) Act 1970 the authorities are of purely academic interest.

[2] The statutory provision merely codifies the common law: *R.* v. *Muscot* (1813), 10 Mod. Rep. 192.

[3] *Moore* v. *Hewitt*, [1947] K.B. 831; [1947] 2 All E.R. 270.

[4] *Burbury* v. *Jackson*, [1917] 1 K.B. 16.

[5] *Jeffery* v. *Johnson*, [1952] 2 Q.B. 8; [1952] 1 All E.R. 450; overruling *Moore* v. *Hewitt* (*supra*) on this point.

c Procuration of women

Several sections of the Sexual Offences Act 1956,[1] which punish various forms of procuration of women, provide that a person shall not be convicted on the evidence of one witness only, unless the witness is corroborated in some material particular by evidence implicating the accused. Since the witness in question is usually the victim herself it will be appreciated that the need for corroboration stems from the fact that the witness whose evidence requires corroboration has a motive to misrepresent. The same principle underlies the need for corroboration in affiliation proceedings and (formerly) breach of promise actions. In addition the allegation in question in such cases is easy to make but generally, by its nature, difficult to refute. Once again no particular form of corroboration is prescribed but there is an express provision that the corroborative evidence must implicate the accused. This is a principle which applies generally to corroborative evidence in criminal proceedings.

d Unsworn evidence of children

A child of tender years who can understand the duty of telling the truth but who does not understand the nature of an oath may give unsworn evidence in a criminal case. This provision is contained in section 38 of the Children and Young Persons Act 1933. However, because of the inherent possibility of such evidence being unreliable, the same section also provides that the accused cannot be convicted unless the child's evidence is corroborated by some other material evidence implicating the accused. Once again the corroborative evidence must implicate the accused. The unsworn evidence of another child cannot amount to corroboration[2] and it is doubtful whether the sworn evidence of another child is sufficient either.[3]

e Exceeding a speed limit

A person charged with driving a motor vehicle at a speed greater than the maximum allowed shall not be convicted solely on the evidence of one witness to the effect that in his opinion the person charged was driving the vehicle at such greater speed. This is provided by section 4 (2) of the Road Traffic Act 1960. It should be noted that it is only the opinion of a witness which requires corroboration. Evidence other than an opinion does not require corroboration under the section. Consequently, the recording of a mechanical device such as a speedometer, being a statement of fact rather than an opinion, does not require corroboration.[4]

---

[1] Section 2 (procuring a woman by threats or intimidation to have unlawful sexual intercourse); s. 3 (procuring a woman by false pretences); s. 4 (administering drugs to obtain or facilitate intercourse); s. 22 (causing the prostitution of a woman) and s. 23 (procuration of a female infant).

[2] *R. v. Manser* (1934), 25 Cr. App. Rep. 18.

[3] *R. v. E.*, [1964] 1 All E.R. 205 n.; [1964] 1 W.L.R. 671, cited in *R. v. Hester* (1972), *The Times*, April 22nd in which the authorities were reviewed.

[4] *Nicholas v. Penny*, [1950] 2 K.B. 466; *sub nom. Penny v. Nicholas*, [1950] 2 All E.R. 89.

In all the above cases corroboration is essential. The effect is that the absence of corroborative evidence is fatal to the claim or prosecution. In addition to these statutory cases there are several cases in which corroboration is desirable though not, as a matter of law, essential. In these cases, which are discussed below, the lack of corroboration is not necessarily fatal though the judge must warn the jury, if there is one, of the absence of corroboration and of the danger of acting on uncorroborated evidence. In addition the judge must explain what evidence is capable of amounting to corroboration and also the general nature of corroborative evidence.[1]

2   Cases in which corroboration is required as a matter of practice

a   Accomplices

It is now settled that the trial judge must warn the jury of the danger of convicting the accused on the uncorroborated testimony of an accomplice. This was finally established by the House of Lords in the leading case of *Davies* v. *Director of Public Prosecutions*[2] in which case it was established that this, although a rule of practice, now has the force of a rule of law. The effect is that where the judge fails to warn the jury the accused's conviction will be quashed, even if in fact there is ample corroborative evidence, unless the appellate court can apply the proviso to section 2 (1) of the Criminal Appeal Act 1968.[3] The rationale of the rule is presumably the likely tendency of accomplices to try to shift the blame on to one another.

Davies's case is also a leading authority on the question of who is an accomplice. LORD SIMONDS, L.C. classified accomplices as (1) participants in the crime alleged, whatever the degree of participation, (2) receivers of stolen goods in relation to those who are alleged to have stolen those goods; and (3) parties to another crime alleged to have been committed by the accused of which "similar fact" evidence would be admissible. The facts of *Davies*'s case were that the accused was charged with murder by stabbing the deceased, a member of a rival gang. The witness whose testimony was in question was a member of the same gang as the accused and had joined in an assault on the deceased but had not been party to the stabbing and was not aware that the accused had a knife. It was held that the witness was not an accomplice so that the rule requiring corroboration did not apply. The speech of LORD SIMONDS in *Davies*'s case clearly indicated that a person indicted jointly with the accused and giving evidence against him is not to be regarded as an accomplice. Nevertheless it has been held that there is a rule of practice (though not of law) that the trial judge should give the jury a similar warning in respect of the evidence of a co-accused.

One accomplice's testimony cannot be corroborated by the testimony of another accomplice[4] of the accused for obvious reasons. Apart from this there is no particular restriction on the form which the corroborative evidence may take. It must, however, implicate the accused.[5]

---

[1]   *R.* v. *Goddard*, [1962] 3 All E.R. 582; [1962] 1 W.L.R. 1282.
[2]   [1954] A.C. 378; [1954] 1 All E.R. 507.
[3]   See p. 425, *ante*.
[4]   *R.* v. *Prater*, [1960] 2 Q.B. 464; [1960] 1 All E.R. 298. However, the testimony of one co-accused against another co-accused may be corroborated by the former's wife: *R.* v. *Allen*; *R.* v. *Evans*, [1965] 2 Q.B. 295; [1964] 3 All E.R. 401.
[5]   *R.* v. *Baskerville*, [1916] 2 K.B. 658.

b Sexual offences

It has already been noted that in the case of certain offences under the Sexual Offences Act 1956 corroboration is essential. In other cases involving prosecution for sexual offences corroboration is required as a matter of practice although it is not essential. The obvious underlying reasons are the inherent likelihood of the victim's testimony being exaggerated or fanciful coupled with the difficulty of refuting the victim's allegations.

The corroborative evidence must support the allegations of the complainant in some material particular and must implicate the accused. It follows that the distressed condition of the victim shortly after the alleged offence is not sufficient corroboration because it does not implicate the accused. However, evidence of the complainant's distressed condition coupled with evidence that the accused was seen with the complainant shortly before or after the incident is sufficient.[1] Evidence of a complaint made by the victim of a sexual offence shortly after the offence is admissible evidence but is not capable of amounting to corroboration because it is not independent of the complainant's testimony and a person cannot corroborate his own testimony.[2] Nevertheless evidence of a complaint is valuable because, although it is not corroboration, it does tend to show consistency on the part of the complainant and hence the likelihood of the complainant's story being true. It is sometimes said that a complaint "corroborates the complainant's credibility"[3] but the phrase is probably meaningless.

c Matrimonial causes

It is a rule of practice, though not a rule of law, that testimony alleging a matrimonial offence should be corroborated. The rule applies whether the testimony is that of the petitioner, of the respondent or of an accomplice to the matrimonial offence.[4] The court will, however, act on uncorroborated evidence if satisfied that it is reliable, especially in undefended suits.

d Sworn evidence of children

It will be recalled that the unsworn testimony of a child in criminal proceedings must, by statute, be corroborated. Where a child gives sworn evidence, as he can do in any case provided he can comprehend the nature of an oath, the jury should be warned of the risk of acting on the uncorroborated evidence of the child. Virtually all of the authorities are criminal cases though the same rule presumably applies in a civil case. Nevertheless a jury can act on the uncorroborated evidence of a child if satisfied that it is true. The sworn evidence of one child can be corroborated by the sworn evidence of another child but not by the unsworn evidence of another child.[5]

---

[1] *R. v. Redpath* (1962), 46 Cr. App. Rep. 319; *R. v. Knight*, [1966] 1 All E.R. 647; [1966] 1 W.L.R. 230.

[2] *R. v. Whitehead*, [1929] 1 K.B. 99; *R. v. Christie*, [1914] A.C. 545. Complaints are admissible only for the purpose of showing consistency (unless forming part of the *res gestae*) and only if made by the victim of a sexual assault, male or female, as soon after the incident as may be reasonably expected. In addition the complaint must have been made voluntarily and not in answer to a leading question: *R. v. Whitehead (supra).*

[3] *R. v. Osborne*, [1905] 1 K.B. 551, at p. 561.

[4] *Statham v. Statham*, [1929] P. 131; *Galler v. Galler*, [1954] P. 252; [1954] 1 All E.R. 536; *Alli v. Alli*, [1965] 3 All E.R. 480.

[5] *R. v. Hester* (1972), *The Times*, April 22nd, disapproving *R. v. Campbell*, [1956] 2 Q.B. 432; [1956] 2 All E.R. 272.

3   The nature of corroboration

The first requirement of corroboration is that it must consist of admissible evidence. Irrelevant or otherwise inadmissible evidence, such as conduct on other occasions showing criminal disposition, does not become admissible merely because it appears to be corroborative.

Generally there is no prescribed form which corroborative evidence must take. Certain minor statutory provisions expressly require two or more credible witnesses[1] but, in the absence of such express stipulation, corroboration need not involve a second witness.

There are, however, two conditions which corroborative evidence must satisfy. First it must be independent of the evidence to be corroborated; secondly it must, in a criminal case, implicate the accused. The rule against self-corroboration is of fairly recent origin, not being finally established until the case of *R. v. Lillyman*[2] in 1896. However it is now well settled that corroborative evidence "must be extraneous to the witness who is to be corroborated".[3] It is for this reason that the complaint of a victim of a sexual offence made soon after the offence, although admissible to show consistency, is not capable of amounting to corroboration of the victim's testimony. A document may amount to corroboration even though its authenticity is proved by the witness whose testimony it corroborates.[4] This does not, of course, amount to self-corroboration since the corroborative evidence exists in the contents of the document not in the witness's testimony as to its authenticity.

The second condition for the sufficiency of corroborative evidence is that in a criminal case it must implicate the accused. For this reason the distressed condition of the victim of an assault shortly after the assault, although relevant, is not corroboration of testimony identifying the accused as the assailant. However, evidence of distressed condition shortly after the accused was seen with the victim may amount to corroboration.[5]

Corroboration frequently exists in the conduct of the person against whom it will operate. This is generally the accused in a criminal case but may be, for example, the putative father in affiliation proceedings. The fact that the accused ran away,[5] gave a false alibi[6] or behaved on previous occasions in the manner now alleged[7] may corroborate the testimony against him. However it is important to bear in mind that irrelevant evidence does not become relevant merely because of its value as corroboration. Consequently irrelevant "similar fact" evidence cannot amount to corroboration. For the same reason the silence of an accused person or his failure to give evidence at his trial cannot amount to corroboration of testimony against him.[8]

---

[1] Examples are: Places of Religious Worship Act 1912; Representation of the People Act 1949, s. 146 (5).

[2] [1896] 2 Q.B. 167.

[3] *R. v. Whitehead*, [1929] 1 K.B. 99, at p. 102, *per* LORD HEWART, C.J. See also s. 6 (4) of the Civil Evidence Act 1968, which provides that the previous statement of a witness admitted under the provisions of that Act shall not amount to corroboration of the evidence of that witness.

[4] *Jeffrey v. Johnson*, [1952] 2 Q.B. 8; [1952] 1 All E.R. 450.

[5] *R. v. Knight*, [1966] 1 All E.R. 647; [1966] 1 W.L.R. 230.

[6] *Credland v. Knowler* (1951), 35 Cr. App. Rep. 48.

[7] *R. v. Hartley*, [1941] 1 K.B. 5; *R. v. Sims*, [1946] K.B. 531; [1946] 1 All E.R. 697.

[8] *R. v. Whitehead*, [1929] 1 K.B. 99; *R. v. Jackson*, [1953] 1 All E.R. 872; [1953] 1 W.L.R. 591.

CHAPTER 32

The Means of Proof

Having decided what facts may be proved, upon whom the onus of proving those facts lies and the nature of this burden the question arises as to how these facts are to be proved. Assuming that the fact in question is not admitted, judicially noticed or presumed in favour of the party who would otherwise have to prove it there are three ways in which a fact may be proved: (1) by the testimony of witnesses; (2) by documentary evidence; (3) by "real" evidence. Each of these means of proof is considered in detail below.

A WITNESSES

1 Competence and compellability

The general rule is that all persons are both competent and compellable as witnesses in judicial proceedings. The attendance of witnesses in magistrates' courts is compelled by summons or warrant. In criminal trials at the Crown Court attendance is compelled by witness order or witness summons, failure to comply with either of which is punishable as a contempt of the trial court.[1] Attendance in the High Court is compelled by subpoena failure to comply with which is a contempt of court.

In civil cases the court can neither compel a party to call any witness nor call a witness itself. In criminal proceedings and in proceedings for contempt of court,[2] however, the court may, of its own volition, call any witness without the consent of the parties.

There are several exceptions to the general rule, stated above, that all persons are both competent and compellable as witnesses. The most important of these exceptions are set out below. Before considering these exceptions, however, it is important to note that the compellability of a witness is a separate matter from any privilege which that witness may validly claim in respect of any fact as to which it is sought to elicit his testimony. Thus a witness does not cease to be compellable merely because he may claim privilege from answering any specific question or for the contents of a document.

---

[1] Criminal Procedure (Attendance of Witnesses) Act 1965; see p. 390, *ante*.
[2] *Yianni v. Yianni*, [1966] 1 All E.R. 230; [1966] 1 W.L.R. 120.

a Children

Infancy, in the legal sense, is not a disability for the purposes of competence as a witness. On the other hand young children may be incompetent to give evidence simply because of immaturity. The rule is that a child may only give sworn evidence if he appears, on examination by the court, to be able to appreciate the nature and consequences of an oath or "to entertain of the danger and impiety of falsehood" as was said in an early case.[1]

At common law a child's inability to appreciate the nature and consequences of an oath would prevent him from giving evidence in either civil or criminal proceedings. There is a statutory exception to this rule applicable only to criminal cases. This is now contained in section 38 of the Children and Young Persons Act 1933 which provides that a child who does not understand the nature of an oath may give unsworn testimony in criminal proceedings if "in the opinion of the court, he is possessed of sufficient intelligence to justify the reception of the evidence, and understands the duty of speaking the truth". As a safeguard the section goes on to provide that the unsworn evidence of a child given on behalf of the prosecution must be corroborated. The trial judge may determine the competence of a child to give sworn or unsworn evidence by a preliminary examination of the child known as *voir dire*.

If a child is competent in accordance with the above rules he is also compellable. To this rule, however, there is an exception created by the Children and Young Persons Act 1963, section 27. This section provides that, subject to certain exceptions, a child should not be called as a witness for the prosecution in proceedings before examining justices enquiring into a sexual offence but, instead, a written statement of the child's evidence shall be admissible in evidence of any matter of which the child's oral testimony would be admissible. The purpose of the section is to spare children the strain and embarrassment of repeating at the preliminary investigation and again at the trial details of sexual offences. However, either the prosecution or the defence may, notwithstanding this provision, require the attendance of the child at the preliminary investigation.[2]

b Mentally defective persons

The mere fact of mental illness does not render a person incompetent as a witness. However, as in the case of children, the disability will render him incompetent if he is intellectually incapable of understanding the nature of an oath. The derangement may be intermittent in which case the witness is competent during lucid intervals.[3] Even if a person is found by the judge to be competent as a witness it is open to the opposing side to cross-examine the witness as to his credibility and, indeed, to call a separate witness as to his credibility.[4]

c Accused persons in criminal cases

The general rule is that accused persons are not competent witnesses for the prosecution in criminal cases. This rule is of practical importance where there are two or more persons tried together. The effect is that neither co-accused

---

[1] *R. v. Brasier* (1799), 1 Leach 199.
[2] Children and Young Persons Act 1963, s. 27 (2) (a), (b).
[3] *R. v. Hill* (1851), 2 Den. 254.
[4] *Toohey* v. *Metropolitan Police Commissioner*, [1965] A.C. 595; [1965] 1 All E.R. 506.

may give evidence for the prosecution against the other, although each may, of course, give evidence on his own behalf which may support the prosecution case incidentally. If the prosecution wishes to make use of the evidence of one participant in a crime against any other participant in the same crime the solution is not to indict them together for there is no rule that an accomplice is not competent for the prosecution. Alternatively if one co-accused decides to turn "Queen's evidence" the prosecution may decide to offer no evidence against him in which event he will be formally acquitted and thereby become a competent witness against the other co-accused. The same effect may be achieved by the filing of a *nolle prosequi* in respect of one accused person or by one accused pleading guilty.[1]

There is one minor exception to the rule that an accused person is not competent for the prosecution. This occurs in prosecutions for public nuisance under the Evidence Act 1877. Proceedings under this Act are criminal in form although the obligations enforced are civil in character. In these proceedings an accused person is both competent and compellable for the prosecution.

It is only since the Criminal Evidence Act 1898 that an accused person has been a competent defence witness at his own trial. Where there are co-accused each is competent but not compellable on behalf of the other. Although neither is competent for the prosecution against the other, either may give evidence against the other on his own behalf. In addition the Criminal Evidence Act 1898, section 1 (h) expressly preserves the right which an accused person had prior to 1898 to make an unsworn statement from the dock upon which he cannot be cross-examined. This is a right which is not frequently exercised because the fact that a person was unwilling to take the oath and to submit himself to cross-examination no doubt greatly diminishes the credence which the jury is likely to accord to his statement. Moreover the unsworn statement of one co-accused is not evidence against another because of the immunity from cross-examination. The prosecution may not comment upon the failure of an accused person to give evidence, or to give sworn evidence, although the judge may do so.[2]

It should be noted finally that none of the above rules apply to the parties in civil cases, so that one party may be compelled to give evidence on behalf of his opponent.

d Spouses

At common law spouses were incompetent to give evidence either for or against one another in both civil and criminal cases. In civil cases the Evidence (Amendment) Act 1853 rendered the husbands and wives of parties both competent and compellable so that there are now no special rules applying to spouses in civil cases. In criminal cases, however, the situation is more complicated. The general rule in criminal cases is that the spouse of the accused is competent, but not compellable, for the defence and is incompetent for the prosecution.[3] There are several important exceptions to this rule. Most of these exceptions have the

---

[1] *R. v. Payne*, [1950] 1 All E.R. 102. If one accused has pleaded guilty and is to be called as a prosecution witness he should be sentenced at once.

[2] *R. v. Rhodes*, [1899] 1 Q.B. 77.

[3] Where the marriage has been dissolved or, being voidable, annulled a former spouse remains incompetent to give evidence for the prosecution as to matters occurring during

effect of making the accused's spouse a competent witness for the prosecution
though a very few render the accused's spouse compellable for the prosecution
or the defence.

The accused's spouse is a competent witness for the prosecution in those
cases listed in the schedule to the Criminal Evidence Act 1898 as amended.[1]
This schedule has been much amended and the main offences now comprised
are bigamy, child destruction, various offences against children under the
Children and Young Persons Act 1933, and the Indecency with Children Act
1960, and offences against the property of a spouse. In addition section 39 of the
Sexual Offences Act 1956, renders the accused's spouse competent, though not
compellable, for the prosecution in cases involving charges of almost every
offence contained in that Act while section 30 of the Theft Act 1968 renders
a spouse competent as a witness against the other spouse in proceedings brought
by the former and in proceedings brought by a third person for an offence in
relation to the person or property of the accused's spouse.

Section 39 of the Sexual Offences Act expressly provides that nothing in that
section shall make a spouse compellable to give evidence and that the prosecution must not comment upon the failure of any spouse to do so. The Criminal
Evidence Act 1898, which made spouses competent witnesses in criminal
proceedings, contains no such express provision but in *Leach* v. *R.*[2] the House of
Lords held that the 1898 Act did not make a spouse compellable as a witness.

In prosecutions for the various forms of public nuisance set out in the
Evidence Act 1877, a spouse is (as, indeed, is the accused) a compellable witness.
Apart from this peculiar statutory provision there are certain cases where, at
common law, one spouse may be compelled to give evidence in the course of a
prosecution against the other. The most important of these cases is a prosecution arising out of a charge of personal violence by one spouse against the other.
Thus in *R.* v. *Lapworth*[3] the wife of the accused was held by the Court of
Criminal Appeal to be a compellable witness against her husband who was
indicted for an attempt to murder by strangling and causing her grievous
bodily harm. The same principle has been applied in a case where the husband
was accused of attempted murder of his wife by poisoning.[4] It is uncertain
whether one spouse is compellable as a witness against the other on a charge of
treason.

e   Miscellaneous

The Sovereign is not a compellable witness; nor are foreign Sovereigns,
ambassadors, High Commissioners and various grades of diplomatic staff.
Finally, in any legal proceedings to which a bank is not a party a banker or bank
officer cannot be compelled either to produce any banker's book the contents of

---

the subsistence of the marriage: *R.* v. *Algar*, [1954] 1 Q.B. 279; [1953] 2 All E.R. 1381.
It is interesting to observe that marital privilege cannot be claimed in respect of communications made during the marriage where the marriage has been terminated: *Shenton*
v. *Tyler*, [1939] Ch. 620; [1939] 1 All E.R. 827. The comparison of these two cases is
even more interesting in that the cases turn on two identically worded, albeit different,
statutory provisions (Evidence Amendment Act 1853, s. 3 and Criminal Evidence Act
1898, s. 1 (*d*)).

[1] Criminal Evidence Act 1898, s. 4 (1).

[2] [1912] A.C. 1305.   [3] [1931] 1 K.B. 117.

[4] *R.* v. *Verolla*, [1963] 1 Q.B. 285; [1962] 2 All E.R. 426.

which can be proved by secondary evidence, or to prove any matter therein recorded.[1]

2   Oaths, affirmations and unsworn evidence

a   Oaths

The general rule is that all witnesses must give evidence on oath.   Any person having authority to hear evidence has power to administer an oath[2] but the oath is generally administered by the clerk of the court or other court official.   The usual form of oath differs slightly between criminal and civil proceedings. In civil proceedings it runs thus:

> "I swear by Almighty God that the evidence which I shall give shall be the truth, the whole truth, and nothing but the truth."[3]

The witness holds the New Testament uplifted in his hand.[4]   This form of oath is appropriate only to members of the Christian and Jewish faiths.   Any person who objects to take the usual oath may take any form of oath, according to his religious belief, which he declares to be binding on his conscience.

The form of oath for use in juvenile courts and by children and young persons in other courts begins with the words "I promise before Almighty God" instead of "I swear by Almighty God that".[5]

b   Affirmations

As an alternative to an oath there are three types of case in which a witness may solemnly affirm.   First, persons whose religious belief precludes the swearing of oaths, such as Quakers, may affirm.   Secondly, persons who have no religious belief may affirm.[6]   Finally a witness may be required to affirm, under the Oaths Act 1961, if he has a religious belief but it is not reasonably practicable to administer an oath appropriate to that belief.[7]   Since the 1961 Act the only circumstance in which a person could not be required either to swear an oath or to affirm would arise where a prospective witness had a religious belief but refused to state the form of oath binding on him.   In such a case the witness would presumably be incompetent to give evidence, though he would be in contempt of court.[8]

It would be wholly incorrect to classify evidence given on affirmation as unsworn evidence since an affirmation is equivalent to an oath and a false statement on affirmation amounts to perjury.[9]

---

[1] Bankers' Books Evidence Act 1879, s. 6.
[2] Evidence Act 1851, s. 16.
[3] Oaths Act 1909, s. 2.
[4] Members of the Jewish faith are sworn on the Old Testament.
[5] Children and Young Persons Act 1963, s. 28.
[6] Oaths Act 1888; until 1869 persons without religious belief were incompetent as witnesses.
[7] As, for example, where the book upon which the witness wishes to swear is not available. The Oaths Act 1961, was passed to nullify the effect of *R. v. Pritam Singh*, [1958] 1 All E.R. 199; [1958] 1 W.L.R. 143 where a witness in these circumstances was incompetent to give evidence.
[8] *Nash v. Ali Khan* (1892), 8 T.L.R. 444.
[9] Oaths Act 1888, s. 1; Perjury Act 1911, s. 15 (2).

c   Unsworn evidence

In a few clearly-defined circumstances a witness may give unsworn evidence. Thus an accused person may make an unsworn statement in a criminal case, and young children in criminal cases who cannot understand the nature and consequences of an oath but who can appreciate the duty of telling the truth may give unsworn evidence.[1] However, there is an important difference between these instances in that the accused cannot be cross-examined on his unsworn statement whereas a child can be cross-examined. In addition to the accused and young children, persons called simply to produce a document and advocates may give unsworn evidence in any proceedings.

3   The examination of witnesses

Two basic rules exist in relation to the giving of testimony by a witness. The first is that the testimony should be given orally and in open court. There are, however, on the grounds of expedience, numerous exceptions to this rule. Thus there are many provisions enabling evidence to be taken before trial. Rules of court frequently provide for evidence to be given by affidavit.[2] The evidence of witnesses who are ill or abroad and will thus be unable to attend at the trial may be taken before a special examiner or by a foreign court or judge by letters of request. Depositions taken in the presence of the accused at a preliminary investigation may be read as evidence at the accused's trial if the witness's attendance has not been required or he is proved by the oath of a credible witness to be dead, insane, too ill to travel or kept out of the way by or on behalf of the accused.[3] To these should be added the important provisions of sections 2 and 9 of the Criminal Justice Act 1967 providing, subject to conditions, for proof by written statement in criminal proceedings[4] and of section 2 of the Civil Evidence Act 1968 relating to proof by out-of-court statement in civil proceedings.[5] In addition there are certain circumstances in which legal proceedings need not take place in open court. Matters involving national security, children or evidence of sexual capacity in nullity proceedings are, by various statutes, heard *in camera.*

The second basic rule relating to the testimony of witnesses is that it must be confined to facts which the witness personally perceived. This rule operates to exclude opinions and hearsay as means of proof. The numerous exceptions to this rule are discussed below.[6]

Where a witness does give evidence at the trial, there are three stages to his examination; examination-in-chief, cross-examination and re-examination. The two latter stages need not always take place and re-examination is, by definition, only possible where there has been cross-examination.

a   Examination-in-chief

This is the first stage in the examination of a witness and is carried out by the party calling the witness, generally through solicitor or counsel. There are a

---

[1] Children and Young Persons Act 1933, s. 38; see p. 502, *ante.*
[2] Answers to interrogatories, for example; see p. 282, *ante.*
[3] Criminal Justice Act 1925, s. 13 (3).
[4] See pp. 381, 411, *ante.*
[5] See p. 533, *post.*
[6] See p. 534, *post.*

number of rigid rules which must be observed in examination-in-chief. Leading questions may not be asked. A leading question is a question framed in such a way as to suggest the answer desired. "Did you then see the accused attack the deceased?" is an extreme example. It is sometimes said that any question which can be answered with a simple "yes" or "no" is a leading question. This is often, though not invariably, true. There are certain instances in which leading questions may be asked. Thus a witness is frequently led upon the introductory part of his testimony. "Are you John Smith?" is a leading question of a type which is very commonly put.

It follows from the prohibition against leading questions that a party cannot cross-examine his own witness. No doubt counsel is frequently annoyed by the failure of a witness to give the answer desired, particularly if the witness has previously given the desired answer in a deposition or proof. Nevertheless a witness cannot be questioned by the party calling him upon a previous inconsistent statement. There is, however, one important exception to this rule: where the judge gives leave to treat a witness as "hostile" the party calling the witness may cross-examine him upon his previous inconsistent statement. Cross examination of a hostile witness is limited to putting to him a previous inconsistent statement. His credit may not be impeached by general questions about his character or convictions.[1] If the witness denies his previous statement, this statement may be put in evidence. In criminal cases the statement is only evidence of the inconsistency of the witness; it is not evidence of the truth of the earlier statement.[2] However in civil proceedings the statement, and any statement put in evidence to rebut it, is admissible as evidence of any fact stated therein of which direct oral evidence by the maker would be admissible.[3] Above all it must be remembered that an unfavourable witness is not necessarily a hostile witness. In order to be classified as hostile the witness must do more than fail to match up to his deposition or proof. He must exhibit some hostility or animosity to the party calling him. It would seem to follow that there is no way in which a party may discredit the testimony of a witness called by him who is unfavourable but not hostile. In fact this may be done by calling another witness whose testimony contradicts that of the first witness. A written statement of a witness, admissible by virtue of section 2 of the Civil Evidence Act 1968, cannot, subject to minor exceptions, be put in before the conclusion of that witness's evidence-in-chief. It cannot therefore be used as an indirect means of discrediting one's own witness.[4]

b Cross-examination

Following examination-in-chief the witness may be cross-examined by or on behalf of the opposing party or parties. Cross-examination may comprise a far wider range of questions than examination-in-chief. In addition leading questions may be put to the witness. There are three possible lines of cross-examination. First a witness may be cross-examined as to the facts in issue. The object

---

[1] Criminal Procedure Act 1865, s. 3.
[2] The jury must be directed to this effect: *R. v. Golder*, [1960] 3 All E.R. 457; [1960] 1 W.L.R. 1169.
[3] Civil Evidence Act 1968, s. 3 (1).
[4] *Ibid.*, s. 2 (2).

of this line of questioning is to establish information concerning the facts in issue that is favourable to the cross-examining party. The object of the two remaining lines of questioning is to discredit the witness. This is achieved by cross-examination as to credit or credibility.

A witness (other than the accused in a criminal case) may be asked questions whose purpose is to discredit him by showing that he is a person who ought not to be believed. Almost any question may be put extending to such matters as the witness's character, convictions, general reputation or unchastity. However, insofar as the question relates solely to the witness's credit and not to a relevant fact, the witness's answer is final and evidence cannot be called to rebut it. This is a rule of commonsense to avoid evidence being given upon a multiplicity of collateral issues in the light of which the facts in issue might become obscured. It has been noted in an earlier chapter, however, that there are four types of answer which may be rebutted; denials of a previous inconsistent statement, a previous conviction, bias or a general reputation for untruthfulness.[1] Since a witness's answer upon a collateral issue is generally final it is important to distinguish a collateral issue from a fact in issue. Thus in *R. v. Holmes*[2] the prosecutrix in a prosecution for a sexual offence denied consensual intercourse with men other than the accused. It was held that her denial was final and could not be rebutted. Conversely in *R. v. Riley*[3] evidence was admitted to rebut the denial of the prosecutrix of past acts of intercourse with the accused since these acts were relevant to the issue of consent.

It is important to note that, whereas cross-examination as to credit is aimed at the character of the witness, cross-examination as to credibility is directed at some physical or mental attribute on the part of the witness which is likely to affect the credibility of his testimony. Thus questions to impeach credibility may relate to such matters as the witness's hearing, memory or eyesight. Whereas the answer to a question going to the witness's credit is generally final, evidence may be called to impeach the credibility of a witness. Consequently a witness who denies deafness or short-sightedness is liable to have his denial rebutted by affirmative evidence. This principle emerges from the decision of the House of Lords in *Toohey* v. *Metropolitan Police Commissioner*.[4] In that case the chief prosecution witness, who was the victim of an alleged assault by the appellant, was examined shortly after the alleged assault by a police surgeon. The police surgeon was permitted to give evidence as to the witness's appearance and condition but the trial judge did not allow him to advance his medical opinion, based on examination, to the effect that the witness was prone to hysteria. This hysteria would certainly have an effect upon the credibility of the witness and for this reason the House of Lords, allowing the appeal, stated that evidence of it ought to have been admitted.

c Re-examination

Following cross-examination a witness may be re-examined by the party calling him. The object of re-examination is to reinstate any part of the witness's

---

[1] See p. 465, *ante*.
[2] (1871), L.R. 1 C.C.R. 334.   [3] (1887), 18 Q.B.D. 481.
[4] [1965] A.C. 595; [1965] 1 All E.R. 506; overruling *R. v. Gunewardene*, [1951] 2 K.B. 600; [1951] 2 All E.R. 290.

testimony which has been shaken in cross-examination. As in examination-in-chief leading questions may not be asked. Furthermore a party cannot use re-examination as an opportunity for raising matters which he omitted to raise in examination-in-chief unless the form of the cross-examination necessitates this.

4 Privilege

Privilege is a rule of evidence whereby a witness may be justified in refusing to answer a question or produce a document or a party may refuse to produce a document or answer an interrogatory. There are only a limited number of occasions of privilege and the courts are slow to recognise any new occasion of privilege. Privilege as a rule of evidence must be carefully distinguished from privilege in the law of defamation. The mere fact that words are spoken on an occasion of qualified privilege in the law of defamation does not mean that a witness may refuse to disclose in evidence what was said. Privilege is sometimes said to be public or private. In this section, however, only the occasions of private privilege are examined. Public or Crown privilege is one aspect of the principle whereby evidence may be excluded on the basis of public policy and has been considered in the context of rules of exclusion of facts. In addition there are certain basic differences between private privilege and Crown privilege which render it somewhat confusing to classify them as separate aspects of the same principle. In the first place private privilege attaches to the person claiming the privilege rather than to the evidence in respect of which it is claimed. Thus a third party may always give evidence of a fact notwithstanding that a party to the action could claim privilege from disclosing that fact. In *Calcraft* v. *Guest*,[1] for example, the Court of Appeal allowed copies of witnesses' proofs and notes on evidence to be proved notwithstanding that the plaintiff could claim privilege from producing the originals. In *Rumping* v. *Director of Public Prosecutions*[2] a third party was able to disclose a confidential letter written by the defendant to his wife, notwithstanding that his wife could have claimed privilege from disclosure if she has been in possession of the letter.

It follows from the above statement that secondary evidence may be given of a fact where private privilege could be claimed in respect of primary evidence of that fact. This is not so in the case of Crown privilege where secondary evidence as well as primary evidence is excluded. Finally a person may always waive his private privilege whereas only the Crown may waive a claim to Crown privilege. Indeed the court may refuse to admit evidence whose disclosure would be prejudicial to the State though no formal claim to privilege has been made.[3]

The following are the existing occasions of private privilege.

a Incrimination

No person may be compelled to answer any question the answer to which would tend to incriminate himself or, in civil proceedings only, his spouse[4] An

---

[1] [1898] 1 Q.B. 759.
[2] [1964] A.C. 814; [1962] 3 All E.R. 256.
[3] *Duncan* v. *Cammell Laird & Co., Ltd.*, [1942] A.C. 624; [1942] 1 All E.R. 587; see p. 477, ante.
[4] Civil Evidence Act 1968, s. 14 (1) (*b*).

answer is regarded as incriminating if it would expose the deponent to any criminal charge. The fact that a person swears that his answer would be incriminating is not conclusive. If the privilege is claimed for a document the court may inspect the document in order to determine whether its contents are incriminating. Where privilege is claimed for an oral answer the judge must decide from the surrounding circumstances whether there is a real danger of incrimination. If there is no real and appreciable danger the claim to privilege will not be upheld even if there is a remote possibility of criminal sanctions. Thus in *R. v. Boyes*[1] a witness who had been handed a royal pardon was obliged to answer a question although there remained a possibility of his being impeached, because a pardon cannot be pleaded as a defence to an impeachment. Nevertheless a claim to privilege is not defeated merely because prosecution for the offence in question is very rare.[2]

In criminal proceedings the privilege extends to answers which would tend to expose the deponent to forfeiture, including forfeiture of a lease.[3] It does not, however, extend to answers which would expose the deponent to other civil liability such as an action for debt.[4]

There are a number of statutory exceptions to the rule that a person cannot be required to incriminate himself. The most important exceptions occur in the case of the accused at a criminal trial. Section 1 (e) of the Criminal Evidence Act 1898 provides that the accused may be asked any question in cross-examination notwithstanding that it would tend to incriminate him as to the offence charged. The considerations which apply where the answer would tend to incriminate the accused as to other offences are contained in section 1 (f) of the 1898 Act and have already been considered.[5] Several other statutes,[6] concerned chiefly with the examination of debtors, create exceptions to the general rule, but the statute concerned generally provides that the answer may not be used in subsequent criminal proceedings.

b Marital privilege

There are two heads of privilege which have their origin in the confidential relationship between spouses. By virtue of section 16 of the Civil Evidence Act 1968, they apply only in criminal proceedings.

Communications between spouses—The Evidence (Amendment) Act 1853, section 3 and Criminal Evidence Act 1898, section 1 (d) provide that no spouse may be compelled to disclose communications made to him or her by the other spouse during the marriage. The privilege has been somewhat narrowly

---

[1] (1861), 1 B. & S. 311.
[2] *Triplex Safety Glass Co., Ltd.* v. *Lancegaye Safety Glass* (1934), *Ltd.*, [1939] 2 K.B. 395; [1939] 2 All E.R. 613.
[3] *Earl of Mexborough* v. *Whitwood Urban District Council*, [1897] 2 Q.B. 111. The Civil Evidence Act 1968, s. 14 (1) (a), abolished this rule in relation to civil proceedings. Section 16 (5) of the same Act abolished the rule whereby a witness in proceedings instituted in consequence of adultery could decline to answer any question tending to show that he or she had been guilty of adultery.
[4] *Blunt* v. *Park Lane Hotel, Ltd.*, [1942] 2 K.B. 253; [1942] 2 All E.R. 187 see also *Nast* v. *Nast*, [1972] 1 All E.R. 1171; [1972] 2 W.L.R. 901.
[5] See p. 467, *ante.*
[6] Examples are: Bankruptcy Act 1914, s. 15; Companies Act 1948, s. 270; Theft Act 1968, s. 31 (1); Criminal Damage Act 1971, s. 9.

construed. Thus the privilege does not outlast the marriage in question. After the termination of the marriage either spouse may be compelled to disclose communications in respect of which privilege could have been claimed during the marriage.[1] In addition the spouse to whom the communication was made may waive the privilege against the wishes of the other spouse.[2] Finally the privilege is lost if a third party can prove the contents of the communication in question.[3]

Marital intercourse—At common law neither spouse could give evidence of access or non-access to or by the other spouse since this might tend to bastardise a child and was thus contrary to public "decency, morality, and policy". This rule, known as the rule in *Russell* v. *Russell*,[4] was a rule of public policy rather than an occasion of privilege, since neither spouse could waive the privilege. The rule was abrogated in 1949 and a new privilege created which is now embodied in section 43 (1) of the Matrimonial Causes Act 1965. This section provides, in effect, that each spouse is competent but not compellable to give evidence that marital intercourse did or did not take place between them. It is uncertain whether the privilege is extinguished by the death of one of the spouses or by divorce, though it is certain that a third party may give evidence of, for example, the fact that the husband was living apart from the wife at the time of conception. Consequently the privilege is probably no wider than the privilege which attaches to communications between spouses. In any event, as stated above, it now exists only in criminal proceedings so that its application is likely to be a rare occurrence.

c Legal professional privilege

The legal profession is unique in at least one respect. This is that legal professional communications attract evidential privilege. This privilege does not exist in respect of communications made in pursuance of other relationships of an apparently equally confidential nature. Thus there is no privilege for communications between doctor and patient,[5] priest and penitent,[6] banker and customer[7] or journalist and informant.[8] It should be noted, however, that the law does respect the confidential nature of these relationships in that it may, in appropriate circumstances, restrain a party from making public that which was divulged in confidence. This is a principle of public policy and it is only displaced by the stronger principle of public policy that requires full disclosure in judicial proceedings. The result is that the courts might compel a person to disclose in evidence in judicial proceedings that which they would restrain him from disclosing anywhere else.[9]

There are two separate heads of legal professional privilege.

---

[1] *Shenton* v. *Tyler*, [1939] Ch. 620; [1938] 4 All E.R. 501.
[2] *H. M. Advocate* v. *H.D.*, 1953 S.C. (J.) 65.
[3] *Rumping* v. *Director of Public Prosecutions*, [1964] A.C. 814; [1962] 3 All E.R. 256.
[4] [1924] A.C. 687; the rule is considerably older than this case.
[5] *R.* v. *Kingston* (1776), 20 State Tr. 355; *R.* v. *Gibbons* (1823), 1 C. & P. 97.
[6] *Wheeler* v. *Le Marchant* (1881), 17 Ch. D. 675, at p. 681.
[7] Bankers' Books Evidence Act 1879, s. 7.
[8] *A.-G.* v. *Clough*, [1963] 1 Q.B. 773; [1963] 1 All E.R. 420; *A.-G.* v. *Foster*: *A.-G.* v. *Mulholland*, [1963] 2 Q.B. 477; [1963] 1 All E.R. 767. The privilege does, however, extend to the relationship between a party and his foreign legal advisers: *Re Duncan, Garfield* v. *Fry*, [1968] P. 306; [1968] 2 All E.R. 395.
[9] See *R.* v. *Statutory Visitors to St. Lawrence's Hospital*, [1953] 2 All E.R. 766; [1953] 1

Communications between solicitor and client—Oral and written communications between solicitor and client are privileged provided they were made in confidence and for the purpose of obtaining or giving legal advice. The rationale of this privilege is that the client may be able to make a full and frank disclosure of his affairs to his solicitor. Provided the communication is a professional and not a merely social or business one there is no requirement that any litigation be pending or anticipated. The privilege does not depend upon a retainer and exists even if there is no retainer or if the retainer has terminated.[1] The privilege is that of the client, not of the solicitor, so that only the client can waive it. Apart from this the privilege is lost in respect of a confidential professional communication only if it was made in furtherance of a fraudulent or criminal purpose, for example seeking advice upon the commission of a crime or fraud.[2]

Communications made in pursuance of litigation—Communications, generally written, made in pursuance of litigation that is pending or anticipated are privileged from disclosure in that or any other litigation. This head of privilege is wider than the first head in that it is not confined to the solicitor-client relationship. It extends to communications between, for example, counsel and solicitor, an insured person and his insurance company, solicitor and prospective witness and, in proceedings under the Patents Act 1949, to communications between a party and his patent agent.[3] In a recent case[4] the privilege was held to justify the defendants' refusal to disclose a statement made by the plaintiff to the defendants' insurers; the statement had been made shortly after the accident in respect of which the plaintiff's action was brought. It is, however, limited in that the communication must be referable to litigation pending or anticipated. Thus in *Wheeler* v. *Le Marchant*[5] certain reports from a surveyor to the defendant's solicitor were held not to attract privilege since, although they were prepared in respect of property which was the subject matter of the litigation, no litigation was pending or anticipated when the reports were made.

It should be noted, finally, that legal professional privilege can only be claimed by a party or a witness. Thus if the other party to litigation has secondary evidence of a confidential professional communication there is no way to prevent him from giving this evidence.[6]

d Title deeds

An ancient instance of private privilege is the privilege whereby a witness may refuse to produce deeds or documents of title. The common law basis of the rule is the sanctity of an Englishman's property in land, although the privilege is not confined to documents of title to land. If it would also tend to prove the title of his opponent, where that title is in issue, the privilege is lost.[7] By virtue

---

W.L.R. 1158; *Duchess of Argyll* v. *Duke of Argyll*, [1965] 1 All E.R. 611; [1965] 2 W.L.R. 790; *(P. A.) Thomas & Co.* v. *Mould*, [1968] 2 Q.B. 913; [1968] 1 All E.R. 963.

[1] *Calcraft* v. *Guest*, [1898] 1 Q.B. 759, at p. 761; *Minter* v. *Priest*, [1930] A.C. 558.

[2] *R.* v. *Cox and Railton* (1884), 14 Q.B.D. 153. See *Butler* v. *Board of Trade*, [1971] Ch. 680; [1970] 3 All E.R. 593 and *Crescent Farm (Sidcup) Sports, Ltd.* v. *Sterling Offices, Ltd.*, [1971] 3 All E.R. 1192; [1972] 2 W.L.R. 91, where the authorities are reviewed.

[3] Civil Evidence Act 1968, s. 15.

[4] *Britten* v. *F. H. Pilcher & Sons*, [1969] 1 All E.R. 491.

[5] (1881), 17 Ch.D. 675.

[6] *Calcraft* v. *Guest*, [1898] 1 Q.B. 759.

[7] *Morris* v. *Edwards* (1890), L.R. 15 A.C. 309.

of the Civil Evidence Act 1968, s. 16 (1) (*b*) the privilege now extends only to criminal proceedings.

B DOCUMENTARY EVIDENCE

A party who wishes to rely upon the contents of a document[1] as a means of proving a fact has to prove two separate matters. First he must prove what the document in question contains. This must usually be done by producing the document itself. His second obligation is to prove that the document upon which he relies is authentic or has been duly executed. These matters must be dealt with separately.

1 Proof of the contents of a document

a Application of the "best evidence" rule

One of the fundamental rules of evidence at common law was the best evidence rule. The rule is self-explanatory, its effect being that a fact could only be proved by the best, or most cogent, evidence available. The rule has long ceased to be a basic rule of evidence and its operation is now primarily confined to documentary evidence. In this sphere the basic rule is still that the contents of a document may be proved only by production of the original, although there are now many exceptions to this rule. The rule is well illustrated by the case of *Macdonnell* v. *Evans*.[2] One of the plaintiff's witnesses was asked in cross-examination whether a letter of his, which defendant's counsel produced, was written in answer to another letter charging the witness with forgery. The question was disallowed by the Court of Common Pleas since it purported to prove the contents of that letter without producing the original. The best evidence rule was recently applied in respect of tape recordings. In *R.* v. *Stevenson*[3] the trial judge rejected tape recordings on the ground that there was clear evidence that some interference with the tapes might have taken place with the result that it was likely that the proffered evidence was not the original or best evidence.

There may be a number of originals of one document. Thus where an agreement is drawn up in two identical documents, each of which is executed by both parties, both documents are duplicate originals.[4] Similarly the top and carbon "copies" of an unsigned document are all originals. On the other hand where a document, such as a letter, is signed and despatched an unsigned carbon is regarded as a copy not as a duplicate original. Also a deed and a counterpart,

---

[1] The word "document" probably comprises any form of permanent record of a fact and includes, for example, tape recordings; see *R.* v. *Maqsud Ali*, [1966] 1 Q.B. 688; [1965] 2 All E.R. 464. The Civil Evidence Act 1968, s. 10 (1) defines a document, for the purposes of Part I of that Act, as including, in addition to a document in writing "(*a*) any map, plan, graph or drawing; (*b*) any photograph; (*c*) any disc, tape, sound track or other device in which sounds or other data (not being visual images) are embodied so as to be capable (with or without the aid of some other equipment) of being reproduced therefrom; and (*d*) any film, negative, tape or other device in which one or more visual images are embodied so as to be capable (as aforesaid) of being reproduced therefrom".

[2] (1852), 11 C.B. 930.

[3] [1971] 1 All E.R. 678; [1971] 1 W.L.R. 1.

[4] *Forbes* v. *Samuel*, [1913] 3 K.B. 706.

each of which is executed by only one party to the transaction, are not duplicate originals; each is a separate original and neither is regarded as a duplicate of the other.

b Exceptions

Having stated the general rule that the original of a document must be put in evidence, it is necessary to examine the existing exceptions to the rule. These exceptions are very wide in scope and largely nullify the effect of the rule. Where one of these exceptions can be shown to apply, secondary evidence of the contents of the document may be given. Where secondary evidence of a document is admissible in this way there is no prescribed form which this secondary evidence must take. There are no degrees of secondary evidence. Consequently a photographic copy, strange as it may seem, is not, in theory at least, preferable to oral testimony as to the contents of the document in question[1] though a photographic copy is undoubtedly more cogent than oral testimony. The principal circumstances in which secondary evidence of a document may be given are as follows.

(1) Where a party has, in civil proceedings, failed to comply with a notice to produce a document, the party serving the notice may put a copy in evidence. In addition the party failing to comply with the notice cannot himself rely upon the original. Express notices to produce are now comparatively rare in civil proceedings in the High Court because the present Rules of the Supreme Court[2] provide that a party serving a list of documents in his custody, possession or power on another party is deemed to have been served by that other party with a notice to produce at the trial the documents specified in the list. Notwithstanding the fact that the party served with the notice may claim privilege from production of the original, his opponent may make use of a copy thus nullifying the privilege.[3]

A notice to produce is not required where the document in question is itself a notice, such as a notice to quit, a notice of intended prosecution or, indeed, a notice to produce.[4]

(2) Where the original is in the possession of a third party who may justifiably decline to produce it, a copy is admissible. This situation may arise where the third party is out of the jurisdiction and cannot be served with a *subpoena duces tecum*. This principle does not apply, however, where the third party has not been served with a subpoena or has unlawfully failed to obey a subpoena.[5] In such a case the remedy is to institute proceedings to have the witness committed for contempt of court.

(3) Where the original has been lost or destroyed, its production is excused. This principle is based, as is the one above, on expedience since it would be pedantic to require a party to do the impossible. Adequate proof must be tendered that the document has, in fact, been lost or destroyed.

(4) A copy may be admitted where production of the original would be physically impossible or, at least, highly inconvenient. Thus inscriptions on walls or

---

[1] *Brown* v. *Woodman* (1834), 6 C. & P. 206.
[2] See p. 291, *ante*.
[3] See p. 509, *ante*.
[4] *R.* v. *Turner*, [1910] 1 K.B. 346.
[5] *R.* v. *Llanfaethly (Inhabitants)* (1853), 2 E. & B. 940.

tombstones are commonly proved by oral testimony though a tombstone has been produced in the House of Lords.[1] On the same basis the copy of a notice was admitted where the original was required by statute to remain affixed to a factory wall in *Owner* v. *Bee Hive Spinning Co., Ltd.*[2]

(5) Where the document is a public document, special rules apply. A public document has been defined as "a document that is made for the purpose of the public making use of it, and being able to refer to it".[3] The distinguishing feature of a public document is often its authentication by a public officer. Public registers, court records and Parliamentary records are typical classes of public documents. The best evidence rule does not apply to public documents. Consequently the contents of a public document may always be proved by secondary evidence. However, in the case of public documents the appropriate form of secondary evidence required to constitute proof is usually prescribed by statute. Thus the statement that there are no degrees of secondary evidence is not accurate in relation to public documents.

Judicial notice is taken of the contents of certain public documents such as Public Acts of Parliament. Old Private Acts, Statutory Instruments and other Parliamentary documents are proved by production of the Queen's Printer's copy. The contents of public registers are proved by certified or office copies. Thus a birth, death or marriage is proved by a certificate of entry in the appropriate register.[4] The method of proving judgments and convictions varies according to the court in question. House of Lords judgments are proved by production of an officially printed copy of the Journal of the House. Judgments of the Supreme Court may be proved by production of an office copy[5] and those of the county court by certified copy of the registrar's book.[6] There are numerous statutory provisions governing the methods by which a conviction may be proved, proof generally being by a certified copy of the court record signed by the clerk or other officer having custody of the record.[7] By section 111 (1) of the Road Traffic Act 1960 a motor vehicle licence endorsed with particulars of a conviction is *prima facie* evidence of that conviction.

(6) Bankers' books do not come within the definition of public documents. Nevertheless, for the purpose of saving the time of banks and their staff, the Bankers' Books Evidence Act 1879, sections 3 to 5, provide that an examined copy of any entry in a bankers' book kept in the ordinary course of business shall be received in all legal proceedings as *prima facie* evidence of such entry.

(7) Any document admissible by virtue of section 2, 4 or 5 of the Civil Evidence Act 1968 may be proved by the production of a copy of that document authenticated in such manner as the court may approve.[8]

2 Proof of execution of private documents

This section is concerned with the methods by which a party may prove the validity or due execution of a private document. No question of proof of

---

[1] *Boosey* v. *Davidson* (1849), 13 Q.B. 257, at p. 265.
[2] [1914] 1 K.B. 108.
[3] *Sturla* v. *Freccia* (1880), 5 App. Cas. 623, at p. 643, *per* LORD BLACKBURN.
[4] Births and Deaths Registration Act 1953, s. 34; Marriage Act 1949, s. 65.
[5] R.S.C. (Revision) 1965, O. 38, r. 10.
[6] County Courts Act 1959, s. 26.
[7] Evidence Act 1851, s. 13; see also Civil Evidence Act 1968, s. 11 (4).
[8] Civil Evidence Act 1968, s. 6 (1).

execution arises in connection with public documents since the statutes which enable the contents of public documents to be proved by means of copies also provide that the mere production of the appropriately sealed or certified copy shall be sufficient proof of execution.[1] This is an illustration of the presumption of regularity, *omnia praesumuntur rite esse acta*.[2] Nevertheless the presumption is always rebuttable and the validity or due execution of a public document may be impeached.

In civil cases it is often not necessary for a party to prove the execution of documents in his possession since, unless authenticity is in issue, they will usually be formally admitted by his opponent. Indeed it is usual in civil cases to have an "agreed bundle" of documents for use in the course of the trial. Admission is made in answer to a notice to admit the documents in question, express or implied.[3] If a private document is not admitted in civil or criminal proceedings it must be formally proved. There are three methods of proving documents: by proof of handwriting, by proof of attestation and by presumption.

a Proof of handwriting

Probably the commonest method of proving the validity or execution of a private document is by identification of the handwriting. Handwriting is a matter which may be proved by ordinary or by expert witnesses. The usual method of proving handwriting is by calling the writer as a witness or, if he is already a witness, putting the document to him in the witness box. Alternatively a witness who saw the document written or is familiar with the handwriting of the writer by reason of their family or business connection may identify the handwriting in the document in question. The least common, and probably least cogent, method of proving handwriting is by comparison of the document in question with an authenticated specimen of the handwriting of the person who is alleged to be the author of that document. The comparison may be made by the judge or jury[4] or by an ordinary witness but is usually made by an expert witness—a graphologist.[5]

b Proof of attestation

Attestation is the signature of a document by a person who is not a party to the document as a witness to the signature of one of the parties. The principal classes of documents which require attestation under the modern law are wills and codicils.[6] If it is necessary to prove the execution of a will one of the attesting witnesses must be called to prove attestation. Only if none of the attesting witnesses can be called may attestation be proved by proof of the handwriting of one of them. Certain other documents by law require attestation[7] while many others are, as a matter of practice, needlessly attested. In the case of these other

---

[1] Evidence Act 1845, s. 1; Evidence Act 1851, s. 14.
[2] See p. 486, *ante*.
[3] R.S.C. (Revision) 1965, O. 27, rr. 4, 5; see p. 291, *ante*.
[4] Criminal Procedure Act 1865, s. 8.
[5] *R. v. Silverlock*, [1894] 2 Q.B. 766.
[6] Wills Act 1837, s. 9.
[7] Examples are: chattel mortgages (Bills of Sale (1878) Amendment Act 1882, s. 10), deeds under the seal of a corporation (Law of Property Act 1925, s. 74).

documents the attesting witness may be called though this is not essential, as it is in the case of wills, and the handwriting of such a witness may be proved.[1]

c Proof by presumption

In any proceedings, civil or criminal, there is a presumption, now contained in section 4 of the Evidence Act 1938, that a document which is not less than twenty years old is validly executed. The document must appear to be duly executed and must be produced from proper custody. This means that the document must have been produced from a place in which it might properly be expected to be kept, such as a deed box, bank or solicitor's office. For the purpose of determining the age of a document there is a presumption, which is rebuttable, that the document was executed on the date it bears.

There are certain other presumptions which apply in relation both to the contents and to the due execution of documents. Thus parties to a conveyance are presumed to be of full age.[2] Alterations in a deed are presumed to have been made before execution; alterations in a will are presumed to have been made after execution.

Before leaving the subject of the execution of documents it is necessary to refer briefly to the Stamp Act 1891. This Act, as amended, creates obligations to stamp certain classes of documents either with a fixed stamp or, in some cases, with an *ad valorem* stamp. One of the methods of enforcing the obligation to pay stamp duty is to prohibit the use in evidence of unstamped documents which ought to be stamped. Stamp objections are taken by the court,[3] not by counsel, in civil proceedings and are not taken at all in criminal proceedings. Stamping must generally take place on or before execution, though many documents may be stamped late on payment of the unpaid duty and prescribed penalties.[4]

3 Extrinsic evidence in relation to documents: the parol evidence rule

Where a transaction is recorded in a document extrinsic evidence is inadmissible as a substitute for that document, to vary or contradict the terms of the document or to interpret the document. This rule is often described as the "parol evidence" rule. The rule is a rule of exclusion, though it is difficult to classify it with other exclusionary rules of evidence. The reason for this difficulty is that the first aspect of the rule primarily excludes extrinsic evidence as a means of proof whereas the second and third parts of the rule exclude facts. In addition the second and third parts of the rule, which together exclude evidence adduced to vary, contradict or interpret a document, are best regarded as rules of substantive law rather than rules of evidence. This, coupled with the highly technical and complex rules of construction which are involved, render it undesirable to examine the parol evidence rule in any detail in a general work of this nature. Consequently only the barest outline of the three aspects of the parol evidence rule appears below.[5]

---

[1] Evidence Act 1938, s. 3.
[2] Law of Property Act 1925, s. 15.
[3] Stamp Act 1891, s. 14.
[4] *Ibid.*, ss. 14 (1), 15.
[5] For a more detailed discussion of the rule reference should be made to Cross, *Evidence* (3rd Edn.) p. 508; Nokes, *An Introduction to Evidence* (4th Edn.), p. 239.

a Extrinsic evidence in substitution for documents

The first aspect of the parol evidence rule excludes parol evidence as a means of proving the contents of a document or as a substitute for a document. Parol evidence is any evidence, oral or written, which is extrinsic to the document the contents of which it is sought to prove. It will be readily appreciated that this aspect of the parol evidence rule is largely co-extensive with the best evidence rule in relation to documents. The latter rule has already been discussed and the several exceptions which have been noted may also be classified as exceptions to the parol evidence rule.[1] However, the parol evidence rule is somewhat wider than the best evidence rule in this respect. Thus certain rules of substantive or procedural law require some transactions either to be recorded[2] in or evidenced[3] by writing. In these cases the transactions are either void or unenforceable by action at common law in the absence of writing. There are certain exceptional cases, even where the need for writing arises by statute, in which parol evidence is admissible. Thus in actions for specific performance of contracts for the sale of interests in land, parol evidence may be admitted to prove the contract in question[4] or to prove a sufficient act of part performance. Similarly extrinsic evidence may be admitted to connect two or more documents in order to show that the transaction in question was contained in more than one document.[5] These are further exceptions to the parol evidence rule.

Even where there is no substantive rule of law or procedure requiring a memorandum in writing to prove a transaction, the parol evidence rule applies to cases where the parties have chosen to record their transactions in a document.

b Extrinsic evidence to vary or contradict the contents of a document

This aspect of the parol evidence rule is entirely different from the best evidence rule in relation to documents. This aspect of the rule applies where a party wishes to adduce extrinsic evidence, not as an alternative means of proving the contents of a document, but in order to contradict or vary the express terms of the document. The general rule, which is probably based simply on commercial expedience, prohibits such evidence and applies to any written transaction whether or not it is required by law to be in writing. In *Angell* v. *Duke*[6] the defendant agreed in writing to let a house to the plaintiff together with the furniture in the house. The plaintiff sought to adduce evidence that the defendant had orally agreed to supply additional furniture but this evidence was excluded since it would contradict the written agreement which referred only to furniture already in the house. Similarly in *Henderson* v. *Arthur*[7] evidence was excluded of the prior agreement of the lessor to accept rent in arrears where the lease itself provided for the payment of rent in advance.

There are, however, a number of important exceptions to this principle. First, it is permissible to adduce evidence to prove the nature of a written transaction. Thus an apparent sale may be shown, in fact, to be a mortgage;[8]

---

[1] See p. 514, *ante*.
[2] For example, Wills Act 1837; Law of Property Act 1925, s. 52.
[3] For example: Statute of Frauds 1677, s. 4; Law of Property Act 1925, s. 40.
[4] *Chaproniere* v. *Lambert*, [1917] 2 Ch. 356.
[5] *Pearce* v. *Gardner*, [1897] 1 Q.B. 688; compare *Boydell* v. *Drummond* (1809), 11 East 142.
[6] (1875), 32 L.T. 320.
[7] [1907] 1 K.B. 10.
[8] *Re Duke of Marlborough*, [1894] 2 Ch. 133.

an apparent gift may be shown, in fact, to amount to the creation of a trust. Similarly evidence may be adduced to supplement the terms of a written transaction. For example, in *Re Huxtable*[1] a testator bequeathed £4,000 to a beneficiary "for charitable purposes agreed between us". Extrinsic evidence was admitted to show what these purposes were. It may be noted, however, that supplementary terms cannot contradict the terms they are admitted to supplement. Thus in *Re Huxtable*, while evidence was admitted to identify the charitable purposes referred to in the will, evidence was not admitted of a prior agreement that only the income of the bequest, and not the capital, was to be devoted to these purposes since this would have contradicted the terms of the bequest. The supplemental term may take the form of a collateral warranty which may be defined as a separate promise which is understood to form part of the consideration for entering into the main contract. Thus in *De Lassalle* v. *Guildford*[2] the plaintiff refused to execute a lease unless the defendant landlord warranted that the drains were in good order. A verbal warranty was given and the lease consequently executed. Although the lease contained no provision as to the drains it was held by the Court of Appeal that the plaintiff could sue for breach of warranty.

Finally, evidence may also be admissible of a subsequent variation or discharge of a written agreement. This variation or discharge may be oral notwithstanding that the original agreement was in writing or even under seal.[3] Where the original agreement is required by law to be evidenced in writing evidence of a verbal discharge of this agreement is admissible[4] though evidence of a verbal variation is not.[5]

c Extrinsic evidence as an aid to interpretation

The construction of documents is far too wide a topic to be considered even in outline in a general work of this nature. Many of the rules concerning the interpretation of statutes discussed elsewhere in this book[6] apply equally to the construction of deeds and documents. The basic rule, common to the interpretation of both statutes and documents, is that the intention of the draftsman is to be ascertained from the words used, not from extrinsic evidence. This rule excluding extrinsic facts as an aid to interpretation is in character a rule of evidence, though the topic of construction of documents has become so specialised as to become in effect a branch of substantive law. Stated simply, the rule, which is generally classified as the third aspect of the parol evidence rule, is that extrinsic facts may not be proved in order to ascertain the intention of the writer of a document in construing that document. There are several exceptions to this rule of exclusion. The exceptions fall into two classes. The first category of cases in which extrinsic evidence is admitted comprises those cases where extrinsic evidence is admitted to show the meaning of the words used. The

---

[1] [1902] 2 Ch. 793.
[2] [1901] 2 K.B. 215.
[3] This is a rule of equity: *Berry* v. *Berry*, [1929] 2 K.B. 316.
[4] *Morris* v. *Baron & Co.*, [1918] A.C. 1.
[5] *Goss* v. *Nugent* (1833), 5 B. & Ad. 58.
[6] See pp. 102 *et seq, ante.*

second category of exceptions comprises those cases where, having ascertained the meaning of the words used, equivocation results and it is necessary to resort to extrinsic evidence in order to determine which of alternative results the writer intended. The process of ascertaining the meaning of words used in a document is properly called "interpretation"; the process of determining the legal effect of the words is properly called "construction", though the two words are frequently used in the alternative to describe the same process.

In most of the cases in which extrinsic evidence has been admitted, it has been admitted as an aid to interpretation rather than as an aid to construction. The reason for this is that parties to an agreement frequently use words which bear a meaning to them, or to persons in their trade or locality, which is not a meaning in common usage. In these cases it is clearly essential to have regard to extrinsic facts to ascertain the meaning of the words used. These facts may consist of the parties' previous agreements or dealings or a customary trade or local usage. Thus in *Kell* v. *Charmer*[1] evidence was admitted of the marking practice of jewellers in order to ascertain that a legacy of "the sum of i.x.x." meant £100 and that "the sum of o.x.x." was £200. Similarly in *Smith* v. *Wilson*[2] the Court of King's Bench was prepared to admit evidence of a local custom to the effect that, in counting rabbits, a hundred consisted of six score so that the figure 10,000 in fact meant 12,000 in the lease in question.

There have been comparatively few cases in which extrinsic evidence has been admitted as an aid to construction, as opposed to interpretation. Most of these cases have turned on the construction of wills which is an extreme-ly specialised subject. Where a document, having been interpreted, discloses an ambiguity, extrinsic evidence of the intention of the writer may be admitted in order to resolve the ambiguity. The ambiguity may be patent, such as would arise if the same property were made the subject of bequests to dif-ferent persons in a will, but is generally latent. Thus in *Doe d. Gord* v. *Needs*[3] a testator devised property to "George Gord the son of Gord". There were in existence two George Gords, one the son of G. Gord, the other the son of J. Gord. Evidence was admitted of the testator's statements of intention to show that the bequest was intended for the son of G. Gord. An odd illustration of this principle is contained in *Re Jackson*.[4] In that case a testatrix left property to her "nephew" Arthur Murphy. Since she had two legitimate nephews of that name extrinsic evidence was admitted to show that the intended beneficiary was, in fact, an illegitimate nephew also named Arthur Murphy. The striking feature of *Re Jackson* is that had there been but one legitimate Arthur Murphy he would have benefited to the exclusion of the intended beneficiary since there is a strict rule of construction that words of relationship exclude illegitimates. This occurred in *Re Fish*[5] where a bequest to a "niece" E.W. was construed as a bequest to a legitimate niece of that description even though there was adequate extrinsic evidence to show that an illegitimate "niece" E.W. was, in fact, in-tended.

---

[1] (1856), 23 Beav. 195.
[2] (1832), 3 B. & Ad. 728.
[3] (1836), 2 M. & W. 129.
[4] [1933] Ch. 237.
[5] [1894] 2 Ch. 83.

C REAL EVIDENCE

The principal methods of proof—the testimony of witnesses and documentary evidence—have been considered. The third and final means of proof is real evidence. Real evidence has been defined as "material objects, other than documents, produced for the inspection of the court".[1] This definition is open to criticism on more than one ground. The physical appearance of a party is not commonly described as a "material object" and yet is classifiable as real evidence. A "view" is not "produced" and yet most commentators regard a view as one type of real evidence. Finally a document may be classified as real evidence if it is tendered as proof of something other than its contents.

The basic difference between real evidence and the more common methods of proof is that where the evidence is real evidence the fact which it is sought to prove is actually perceived by the court. There are at least three types of real evidence. The first, and most common, type of real evidence consists of material objects produced for the inspection of the court. In the course of proceedings they are referred to as "exhibits". Commonly encountered exhibits are weapons, clothing, goods alleged to have been stolen and samples. In *Line* v. *Taylor*[2] a dog was produced in court at Hertford Assizes and the jury, from the expression of the dog's eyes and other indications, concluded that it was not of a vicious disposition.

The second type of real evidence consists of the physical appearance of persons. A person's wounds or disfigurement are frequently inspected by the court particularly where such evidence is relevant to the assessment of damages in a personal injuries action.[3] The appearance of a person may also be relevant to the issue of identity. Thus a child's physical resemblance to his putative father may be evidence in affiliation proceedings though it is very weak evidence of paternity.[4] The demeanour of a witness in the witness-box is classified by some commentators as real evidence on the basis that it is a fact of indirect relevance in that it affects testimony. The alternative view is that the demeanour of a witness merely affects cogency and is not evidence at all.

Finally, it is usual to classify a view as real evidence since the fact which it is sought to prove is actually perceived by the court. A view is an inspection outside the court of a place or object where the physical characteristics of that place or object are relevant facts. Thus in *Buckingham* v. *Daily News, Ltd.*[5] the Court of Appeal held that an inspection by the trial judge of the working of a machine did form part of the evidence.

It should be noted that the best evidence rule has no application to real evidence. Even if an object could very easily be brought into court there is no obligation to do so and the fact of its physical characteristics may be proved by testimony or documentary evidence such as a photograph.[6] Since, it will be

---

[1] Phipson, *Real Evidence* (1920), 29 Yale L.J. 705, at p. 717.

[2] (1862), 3 F. & F. 731.

[3] *Cole* v. *United Dairies (London), Ltd.*, [1941] 1 K.B. 100; [1940] 4 All E.R. 318.

[4] *Slingsby* v. *A.-G.* (1916), 33 T.L.R. 120.

[5] [1956] 2 Q.B. 534; [1956] 2 All E.R. 904. There is nothing improper in a judge going to examine the *locus in quo* for himself, unaccompanied by the parties though this is not, strictly, a "view": *Salsbury* v. *Woodland*, [1970] 1 Q.B. 324; [1969] 3 All E.R. 863.

[6] *Hocking* v. *Ahlquist Brothers, Ltd.*, [1944] K.B. 120; [1943] All E.R. 722.

recalled, the best evidence rule does apply to documentary evidence it is important to distinguish documentary evidence from real evidence. A document is regarded as documentary evidence if it is tendered as a means of proving a fact to which the contents of the document relate. On the other hand a document is real evidence if it is adduced simply to prove its physical characteristics. Thus a tombstone is real evidence if tendered as proof of its height, weight or other physical characteristic. It is a document, however, if its inscription is adduced as evidence of, for example, the date of a person's death. On the same basis a coffin plate[1] and a ring[2] have been treated as documents whereas a banner[3] and a driving-licence[4] have been regarded as objects.

---

[1] *R. v. Hinley* (1843), 1 Cox C.C. 12.
[2] *R. v. Farr* (1864), 4 F. & F. 336.
[3] *R. v. Hunt* (1820), 3 B. & Ald. 566. The basis of this decision is questionable since the inscriptions on the banners in question seem to have been relevant.
[4] *Martin* v. *White*, [1910] 1 K.B. 665.

CHAPTER 33

Means of Proof which are Generally Inadmissible

It has already been noted that the word "evidence" is used alternatively to describe facts and the means of proving facts. Consequently evidentiary rules of exclusion may exclude facts altogether or, alternatively, may exclude a particular method of proof. The principal rules of exclusion of facts were considered in chapter 30. This chapter is concerned with the rules excluding certain methods of proving facts. In the preceding chapter it was noted that secondary evidence of the contents of a private document is, subject to several exceptions, inadmissible. There are two other inadmissible methods of proving facts; by opinion and by hearsay evidence. A witness's testimony must relate to a fact which he has directly perceived. It cannot relate to his opinion as to the existence of a fact which it is required to prove nor can it relate to a third person's assertion of the existence of that fact. These two rules of exclusion, together with the various exceptions to them, must be examined in detail.

A OPINIONS

The general rule is that a witness may testify only as to facts which he has directly perceived. He may not state a belief in facts which is based on anything but direct perception. This is the rule excluding proof by opinion. The rationale of this rule of exclusion is that it is the function of the tribunal, not of the witnesses, to draw conclusions from the facts proved.[1] The function of witnesses, and indeed of any method of proof, is simply to place those facts before the court.

It is essential to distinguish opinion as a means of proof from opinion as a fact in itself. Where a person's opinion is, in itself, a relevant fact there is no rule excluding proof of that opinion. Opinion, in the sense of belief in a fact, is a fact in issue in several different types of action. Thus in defamation actions where the defence of fair comment is raised the defendant's opinion is relevant.

---

[1] See *North Cheshire and Manchester Brewery Co., Ltd.* v. *Manchester Brewery Co., Ltd.*, [1899] A.C. 43.

Similarly in an action based on malicious prosecution the defendant's opinion as to whether there was a reasonable ground for the prosecution is a fact in issue. A dying declaration by a victim of homicide is only admissible if the declarant was in settled hopeless expectation of death,[1] which involves evidence of the deceased's belief or opinion. On a prosecution for having unlawful sexual intercourse with a girl under the age of sixteen the accused's opinion that the girl was over sixteen is an element in a defence to that crime.[2]

Thus evidence of an opinion is not excluded where the opinion is, in itself, a fact in issue. In addition, where opinion is tendered as a means of proving some independent fact there are a number of circumstances in which the opinion is admissible despite the general rule of exclusion. These exceptions fall into two categories according to whether the opinion tendered is that of an ordinary witness or of an "expert".

1   The opinions of ordinary witnesses

The general rule excluding the opinion of an ordinary witness as a means of proof has already been noted. It is, however, often difficult to distinguish opinion from testimony based upon perception. A person's opinion is his belief in the existence of a fact. That belief may be based upon perception, impression or inference and there are many cases in which the witness himself would not be able to identify the basis of his belief. No difficulty arises where the fact to which the witness is testifying is clearly inferential and incapable of perception, such as negligence or cruelty. In these cases the witness's evidence is clearly based upon opinion. Difficulty does arise, however, where the witness testifies as to a fact which he has perceived. Thus if a witness testified that a vehicle was, at a given moment, mobile rather than stationary no one would doubt that the witness was testifying as to his direct perception of a fact. On the other hand if a witness testified as to the speed at which the vehicle was moving it is generally accepted that the witness would be giving an opinion. Yet there is no theoretical distinction between the fact of whether a vehicle was moving at a given moment and the fact of the speed at which it was moving at that moment. Speed is not an inference of fact; it is a direct fact capable of precise measurement and perception. Nevertheless it is not capable of precise perception by an ordinary witness. Thus a witness who testifies as to the speed of a vehicle is testifying as to his impression of that fact rather than his precise perception of it. Herein lies the distinction between fact and opinion. A belief based on inference or impression is an opinion; a belief based on direct perception of a fact capable of precise perception is not an opinion and the statement of a witness as to that belief is testimony relating to facts.

Opinion evidence is admissible where the fact to which the witness's testimony relates is incapable of precise perception by an ordinary witness. In these cases a witness may relate his belief based on impression, which is an opinion. Thus opinion evidence is admissible on matters such as the speed of vehicles,[3] the

---

[1] See p. 539, *post*.

[2] Sexual Offences Act 1956, s. 6 (3).

[3] Though, as a safeguard, a person cannot be convicted of speeding on the uncorroborated opinion of one witness as to his speed: Road Traffic Act 1960, s. 4 (2). See *Nicholas* v. *Penny*, [1950] 2 K.B. 466; *sub. nom. Penny* v. *Nicholas*, [1950] 2 All E.R. 89; see p. 497, *ante*.

value of common objects,[1] the identification of handwriting, the identification of a person or an object[2] or a person's age. Age is not usually proved by opinion because direct evidence such as a birth certificate is generally available. Indeed where precise age is a fact in issue, as for example where infancy is raised as a defence to an action based on contract, age cannot be proved by opinion.[3]

Although an opinion based upon impression is sometimes admissible the opinion of an ordinary witness based upon inference is not. For this reason a witness would never be allowed to give his opinion as to whether a car driver was negligent, whether a husband was cruel towards his wife or whether the use of a trade name was calculated to deceive.[4] For the same reason sanity and insanity are not matters upon which an ordinary (as opposed to an expert) witness may testify.[5] Sanity is a question of mixed law and fact and, insofar as it is a question of fact, it depends upon inferences of fact rather than upon direct perception or impression. Drunkenness, on the other hand, is solely a question of fact. It is uncertain whether it is an inference of fact or a fact in itself capable of perception. If drunkenness is an inference of fact logic would suggest that an ordinary witness should not be permitted to testify that a person appeared to be drunk so that his testimony should be confined to his perception of direct facts such as unsteady gait, incoherent speech or alcoholic breath leaving the court to draw the inference of drunkenness from these facts. Nevertheless, in practice, there is no doubt that an ordinary witness is sometimes permitted to give his opinion to the effect that a person was drunk.

2 The opinions of expert witnesses

The rule excluding proof by opinion is subject to an important exception in favour of the opinions of persons whom the court accepts as expert witnesses. The circumstances in which the opinions of experts are admissible are wider in scope than the circumstances, mentioned above, in which the opinions of ordinary witnesses are admissible. The basic distinction is that, whereas an ordinary witness can only give an opinion based upon impression, an expert witness's opinion may be based either upon impression or upon inference. Thus the expert witness is permitted to draw an inference from facts whereas the ordinary witness is not, though the court is in no way bound to accept that inference.

It is for the judge to decide both the question of whether a witness is qualified to give an expert opinion and the question of whether the fact to which his opinion relates is a matter which permits of expertise. There is no particular standard which an expert witness must satisfy. Usually he will be professionally qualified or experienced but in *R. v. Silverlock*[6] a solicitor was permitted to give expert evidence on the subject of handwriting comparison although his expertise was only acquired through his own private study over a period of some ten years. However the qualifications and expertise of an expert witness may always be challenged by cross-examination.

[1] *R. v. Beckett* (1913), 8 Cr. App. Rep. 204.
[2] *Fryer v. Gathercole* (1849), 4 Exch. 262.
[3] *Haines v. Guthrie* (1884), 13 Q.B.D. 818.
[4] *North Cheshire and Manchester Brewery Co., Ltd. v. Manchester Brewery Co., Ltd.*, [1899] A.C. 83.
[5] *Wright v. Doe* d. *Tatham* (1838), 4 Bing N.C. 489.   [6] [1894] 2 Q.B. 766.

The second point upon which the judge must satisfy himself is that the fact which the witness's opinion is tendered to prove is something which may be the subject of expertise.   Thus expert evidence will not be admitted to the effect that a party was negligent[1] or that a publication tends to deprave or corrupt,[2] although in *Director of Public Prosecutions* v. *A. and B. C. Chewing Gum, Ltd.*[3] the Queen's Bench Divisional Court stated that on a prosecution under section 1 of the 1959 Act the evidence of child psychiatrists should be admitted on the question of the possible effects that a particular publication might have upon a child.   This case was, however, in *R.* v. *Anderson*[4] regarded as exceptional, the principle being confirmed that expert evidence is not admissible on the issue of whether or not a publication is obscene, the question of obscenity being entirely one for the jury, though expert evidence is admissible on the issue whether, if the article is found to be obscene, its publication is justified as being for the public good "on the ground that it is in the interests of science, literature, art or learning, or of other objects of general concern."[5]   Expert opinion is limited to matters involving specialist knowledge.   In some of these matters the opinion of an ordinary witness is also admissible, though possibly less cogent.   Handwriting, intoxication and value are examples of subjects upon which either expert or ordinary opinion is admissible.   Subjects such as sanity, banking practice, fingerprints, ballistics, shipping, trade customs and foreign law are a few of those upon which expert opinion has been received.   Many of the cases on this topic have turned upon proof of foreign law.   There is a presumption that foreign law is the same as English law, the effect of which is that any party who alleges that a rule of foreign law is different from the corresponding rule of English law has the specific burden of proving that fact.   Proof is almost always by the opinion of an expert witness.   In *Bristow* v. *Sequeville*[6] it was suggested that only a practitioner could be an expert upon foreign law and the evidence of a jurisconsult was rejected on the basis that he was not a competent expert.   This principle is almost certainly too narrow, for non-practising lawyers,[7] teachers of law[8] and even persons without legal qualification[9] have been permitted to voice an opinion upon the subject of foreign law.

B HEARSAY

1 The rule against hearsay

a Nature of hearsay evidence

The rule against hearsay is probably the best known and certainly the most important evidentiary rule of exclusion.   Expressed simply, hearsay is that which

---

[1] *R.* v. *Davies*, [1962] 3 All E.R. 97; [1962] 1 W.L.R. 1111.
[2] Obscene Publications Act 1959, s. 1;   *R.* v. *Penguin Books, Ltd.*, [1961] Crim. L.R. 176.
[3] [1968] 1 Q.B. 159; [1967] 2 All E.R. 504.
[4] [1972] 1 Q.B. 304; [1971] 3 All E.R. 1152—the notorious "*Oz*" prosecution.
[5] Obscene Publications Act 1959, s. 4 (1); s. 4 (2) expressly provides for the opinions of experts to be admitted either to establish or negative the defence under s. 4 (1).
[6] (1850), 5 Exch. 275.
[7] *Barford* v. *Barford*, [1918] P. 140.
[8] *Brailey* v. *Rhodesia Consolidated, Ltd.*, [1910] 2 Ch. 95.
[9] *De Beeche* v. *South American Stores etc., Ltd.*, [1935] A.C. 148.   The witness, a banker, was an expert on foreign banking law.

another person was heard to say. This would be a totally inadequate and misleading statement of the hearsay rule, however, for two basic reasons.

First, the rule against hearsay is not confined to oral statements. A document may be inadmissible by reason of the hearsay rule. Thus a birth certificate is hearsay evidence of a date of birth, although it is in fact admissible as an exception to the hearsay rule. There is, in addition, authority for the proposition that conduct may be hearsay. For example, if in answer to a question, a person shook his head, evidence of this conduct would be inadmissible since it is equivalent to the person uttering the word "no". Similarly the fact that a person pointed at another is hearsay evidence of identification of that other person.[1] These are, however, exceptional circumstances and it is probably accurate to regard conduct as hearsay only when the conduct can be described as a means of expressing a fact as an alternative to expressing it in words. This is illustrated by the well-known case of *Wright* v. *Doe* d. *Tatham*[2] in which three letters written to a testator on the assumption that he was sane were held by the House of Lords to be inadmissible evidence of his sanity since they infringed both the rule excluding proof by opinion and the rule excluding proof by hearsay. Thus the conduct of the writers of the letters in treating the testator as sane was treated as hearsay on the basis that it amounted to an assertion of sanity.

The paragraph above illustrates that hearsay evidence is not confined to oral or even to oral and written statements. On the other hand not every oral or written statement made by a person other than the witness testifying is hearsay evidence. It must be remembered that the rule against hearsay is only a rule excluding a means of proof; it is not a rule excluding facts. Consequently evidence of an oral or written statement only infringes the hearsay rule if that statement is tendered as a means of proving the truth of the matter stated. Where the statement is tendered as a fact rather than as a means of proving a fact it is not hearsay. Some authors describe statements which are facts as "admissible hearsay" as opposed to "inadmissible hearsay" which, they say, consists of statements tendered as a means of proving other facts. There is no objection to this terminology except that statements which were admitted pursuant to one of the many exceptions to the hearsay rule would be difficult to classify. Consequently it is probably safest to treat statements which are not tendered as a means of proof not as being hearsay at all.

The distinction between statements as facts and statements as proof was clearly defined in the advice of the Judicial Committee of the Privy Council in *Subramaniam* v. *Public Prosecutor*:[3]

> "Evidence of a statement made to a witness by a person who is not himself called as a witness may or may not be hearsay. It is hearsay and inadmissible when the object of the evidence is to establish the truth of what is contained in the statement. It is not hearsay and is admissible when it is proposed to establish by the evidence, not the truth of the statement, but the fact that it was made."

The case itself illustrates this point very clearly. The appellant, on a charge of unlawful possession of firearms, set up the defence of duress. At his trial he was not allowed to testify to threats which Malayan terrorists had allegedly

---

[1] See *Chandra Sekera* v. *R.*, [1937] A.C. 220 (Signs made by a dying woman).
[2] (1838), 4 Bing N.C. 489.
[3] [1956] 1 W.L.R. 965, at p. 969.

made to him, the trial judge regarding these threats as hearsay. The Privy Council advised that this was wrong since the threats were original evidence of the fact of duress and should have been admitted. Since it is of vital importance to be able to recognise whether a statement is or is not hearsay it will be convenient to classify the situations in which a statement is original as opposed to hearsay evidence.

(1) Statements by a person as to his present health, feelings or state of mind are original evidence. Thus in *Gilbey* v. *Great Western Railway Co.*[1] COZENS-HARDY, M.R. observed that:

> "Statements made by a workman to his wife of his sensations at the time, about the pains in his side, or head, or what not, whether the statements were made by groans, or by actions, or were verbal statements, would be admissible to prove those sensations."

Nevertheless the Master of the Rolls excluded evidence of the workman's statements as to the cause of these feelings since this was hearsay evidence of the accident in question.

(2) The making of a statement is, in certain cases, a fact in issue. Obvious examples occur in the torts of libel, slander and malicious falsehood where, in each case, the plaintiff must prove publication of a statement concerning himself or his property. Indeed if the plaintiff were prevented from adducing such evidence these causes of action could not exist. There are numerous other types of action in which the statement is in itself a fact in issue. In actions in contract an offer, acceptance, waiver, repudiation or release may all be facts in issue and will usually consist of assertions by one of the parties.

(3) In many other cases oral or written statements, though not themselves facts in issue, may constitute circumstantial evidence of facts in issue. Thus evidence would undoubtedly be admissible that a person was speaking incoherently or singing if his sobriety, or even his sanity, were a fact in issue. It is on this basis that the evidence of the threats ought to have been admitted in *Subramaniam* v. *Public Prosecutor*[2] since they amounted to facts from which duress, which was a fact in issue, might be inferred. Similarly a male person under the age of twenty-four charged with unlawful sexual intercourse with a girl under the age of sixteen[3] may testify to the fact that the girl told him she was over sixteen since this fact tends to support his belief in her age, that belief being a fact in issue.

(4) Where conduct is relevant, accompanying statements may explain or identify the nature of the conduct. Thus delivery of a chattel is equally consistent with the transaction being a bailment or a gift in which event words accompanying the delivery and explaining the nature of the transaction would be admissible.[4] Such statements often form part of the *res gestae*[5] in which event it is unnecessary to decide whether they constitute hearsay or not since, even if they do, they are admissible as an exception to the rule against hearsay.

(5) In a few cases the previous statements of a witness may be put in evidence. There is a common law rule excluding such evidence, sometimes known as the rule against narrative. There are, however, exceptions to the rule against

---

[1] (1910), 102 L.T. 202.   [2] [1956] 1 W.L.R. 965.
[3] Sexual Offences Act 1956, s. 6.
[4] See *Hayslep* v. *Gymer* (1834), 1 Ad. & El. 162.
[5] See p. 455, *ante*.

narrative. First, as has already been noted,[1] in criminal cases evidence is admissible of the complaint of a victim of a sexual assault. The admissibility of such complaints in no way infringes the hearsay rule because the complaint is, strictly speaking, not evidence of the truth of the content of the complaint but only of the consistency of the complainant. Nonetheless it is questionable whether the average jury is able to distinguish the fact of the complaint from its content. Secondly, any opposing witness or a party's own hostile witness may be cross-examined upon his previous inconsistent statement in both civil and criminal cases. If the witness denies the previous statement it may be put in evidence.[2] Finally, in civil proceedings a witness's previous statement is admissible under section 2 of the Civil Evidence Act 1968 and, when admitted, constitutes evidence of any fact stated therein. However, section 2 (2) provides that the statement of a person whom a party has called or intends to call as a witness may not be given in evidence without the leave of the court and, generally, may not be given in evidence even then before the close of the witness's examination-in-chief. Thus the main use of such statements will be in re-examination to bolster the evidence of a witness who has been cross-examined upon, for example, a previous inconsistent statement.

(6) A witness may refer to a document in order to "refresh his memory", although he cannot read from a prepared statement. The distinction is often artificial because a witness is frequently allowed to testify to matters concerning which he could not possibly have any personal recollection, simply because he has before him a written record of the matter to which he may refer. There are limits, however, on the use of documents to refresh the witness's memory. The document must have been compiled by the witness contemporaneously with, or at least very shortly after, the matter recorded. Thus a document such as a ship's log, a diary and a policeman's notebook have been used to refresh memory though the witness's proof before trial is not a valid aid to recollection. Indeed in criminal cases the evidence of police officers is invariably given by reference to notebooks, the accuracy of the notes often being the subject of vigorous cross-examination on behalf of defendants. The opposite party has a right to inspect the document and to cross-examine the witness upon its contents. In addition the judge and jury may inspect the document for the purpose of assessing the witness's credibility.[3] In a criminal case the document does not constitute evidence of the facts recorded; however in civil proceedings any statement made in a document by a person who uses that document to refresh his memory is admissible as evidence of any fact stated therein of which direct oral evidence would be admissible.[4]

b Formulation of the hearsay rule

Having illustrated that evidence of what another person said or wrote on a previous occasion is not always hearsay evidence it is possible to attempt a

---

[1] See p. 499, footnote 2, *ante.*

[2] Criminal Procedure Act 1865, ss. 3–5; in civil proceedings such a statement is evidence of any fact stated therein of which direct oral evidence would be admissible (Civil Evidence Act 1968, s. 3 (1)) but in criminal cases it merely shows inconsistency and is not evidence of the truth of any fact contained in the statement.

[3] *R. v. Bass,* [1953] 1 Q.B. 680; [1953] 1 All E.R. 1064.

[4] Civil Evidence Act 1968, s. 3 (2).

formulation or definition of the hearsay rule.　Perhaps the most comprehensive formulation of the hearsay rule is that which has been suggested by Professor Rupert Cross:[1]

> "Express or implied assertions of persons other than the witness who is testifying and assertions in documents produced to the court when no witness is testifying are inadmissible as evidence of the truth of that which was asserted."

Numerous other formulations of the rule have been attempted but many of these are open to criticism.　Phipson's exposition of the rule runs as follows:[2]

> "Oral or written statements made by persons who are not parties and are not called as witnesses are inadmissible to prove the truth of the matters stated."

This statement brings out the basic point that a statement is only hearsay when it is adduced to prove the truth of the matter stated but it is open to criticism on other grounds.　First, it has been noted that conduct may amount to hearsay so that the rule is not limited to "oral or written statements". Secondly, there is no rule that a witness may testify as to what another said merely because that other is a party or is called as a witness.　It is true that a witness's testimony as to what he himself said or wrote on a previous occasion is not hearsay but it is clear that, for example, a prosecution witness's testimony concerning statements made to him by the accused would be hearsay if adduced as evidence of their truth.　Other commentators suggest that hearsay is limited to "out of court" assertions[3] but this ignores the fact that a statement may be excluded as hearsay even though it was made on oath at a former trial.[4]

In the context of civil proceedings the hearsay rule now has a statutory definition; section 1 (1) of the Civil Evidence Act 1968 in effect defines hearsay as:

> "in any civil proceedings a statement[5] other than one made by a person while giving oral evidence in those proceedings . . . as evidence of any fact stated therein."

In fact this definition would comprise not only statements made by a person other than the witness testifying but also previous statements made by the witness himself.　At common law previous statements of the witness testifying are not within the hearsay rule; in fact such statements remain admissible in civil proceedings by virtue of the provisions of the 1968 Act to at least the extent to which they were admissible prior to the Act.　Thus the 1968 Act has in no way enlarged the hearsay rule; nevertheless it should be pointed out that to this extent the substance of section 1 (1), set out above, does not set out (nor of course was it intended so to do) a true definition of the hearsay rule.　It merely classifies the statements to which Part I of the 1968 applies and, as noted above, these statements include, as well as hearsay, previous statements of the witness who is testifying.

---

[1] Cross, *Evidence* (3rd Edn.), p. 387.
[2] Phipson, *Law of Evidence* (9th Edn.), p. 221.
[3] See, for example, Nokes, *An Introduction to Evidence* (4th Edn.), p. 271.
[4] *R. v. Eriswell (Inhabitants)* (1790), 3 Term Rep. 707.
[5] "'Statement' includes any representation of fact, whether made in words or otherwise": Civil Evidence Act 1968, s. 10 (1).

Arguments for the retention of the hearsay rule

The principal arguments in favour of the retention of the hearsay rule are as follows.

(1) *Unreliability*—One of the main arguments in favour of the rule excluding hearsay is that the evidence is unreliable due to the possibility of inaccurate repetition or fabrication. This argument has some force in relation to the repetition of oral statements since it is no doubt possible that the witness who testifies as to what he heard another say may have misheard or misunderstood, though the possibility of fabrication is no greater than the possibility which exists in relation to documentary evidence. Assuming that the authenticity of a document can be proved the fact that the writer is not called as a witness can scarcely be said to diminish the accuracy of the facts recorded in the document. Indeed the hearsay rule sometimes operates to exclude a document the accuracy and reliability of which are unimpeachable. Perhaps the most striking recent illustration of the capricious operation of the hearsay rule is to be found in the case of *Myers v. Director of Public Prosecutions*.[1] Myers was charged with various offences in relation to stolen cars. The prosecution case was that Myers would buy wrecked cars with their log books and would then disguise stolen cars so as to conform with the details contained in the log books of the wrecked cars. For this purpose he transferred small plates containing the engine and chassis numbers from the wrecked cars to the stolen cars. The trial judge allowed the admission in evidence of a car manufacturer's records which contained, in relation to each car manufactured, the engine and chassis number and also the cylinder block number which was indelibly stamped on the engine. These records showed that the cylinder block numbers of the cars in question belonged to the stolen cars. The House of Lords held that these records were hearsay evidence and should not have been admitted. None of the majority of their Lordships (LORD REID, LORD MORRIS OF BORTH-Y-GEST and LORD HODSON) doubted the accuracy or reliability of the manufacturer's records but all thought it beyond the judicial function to create a new exception to the hearsay rule merely on the ground of expedience. LORD PEARCE and LORD DONOVAN, however, dissented on this point. LORD DONOVAN expressed his reason as follows:[2]

> "The common law is moulded by the judges, and it is still their province to adapt it from time to time so as to make it serve the interests of those it binds. Particularly is this so in the field of procedural law. Here the question posed is—'Shall the courts admit as evidence of a particular fact authentic and reliable records by which alone the fact may be satisfactorily proved?' I think the courts themselves are able to give an affirmative answer to that question."

Following this decision the Criminal Evidence Act 1965 was passed to provide for the reception of trade or business records in criminal proceedings thus nullifying the effect of *Myers*'s case. Nevertheless the case illustrates that hearsay evidence is by no means necessarily unreliable.

---

[1] [1965] A.C. 1001; [1964] 2 All E.R. 881.
[2] [1965] A.C. 1001, at p. 1047; [1964] 2 All E.R. 881, at p. 902. In fact the conviction was upheld by the application of the proviso to s. 4 (1) of the Criminal Appeal Act 1907 (now s. 2 (1) of the Criminal Appeal Act 1968); see p. 425, *ante*.

(2) *Hearsay evidence is unsworn and not subject to cross-examination*—The second main reason advanced for the retention of the hearsay rule is that the statement in question is not made on oath and the person against whom the evidence is given has no opportunity of cross-examining the maker. The absence of an oath is not a cogent reason because some evidence may be unsworn and, in any case, the fact that the statement was made on oath would not be a ground for excepting it from the operation of the rule.[1] The lack of opportunity for cross-examination is a real objection to the reception of hearsay evidence but it is arguable that this should affect the cogency of the evidence rather than its admissibility.

(3) *Best evidence rule*—It is doubtful whether there is any historical connection between the hearsay rule and the best evidence rule though the latter is sometimes advanced as a reason for the existence of the former. In any event hearsay evidence is excluded even though original evidence is not available because, for example, the maker of the statement is dead or cannot be found.

d   Arguments for the abolition of the hearsay rule

The Law Reform Committee Thirteenth Report (Hearsay Evidence in Civil Proceedings)[2] specified five disadvantages of the rule against hearsay.

(1) Injustice is caused where a witness who could prove a fact in issue is dead or unavailable to be called.

(2) The rule adds to the cost of proving facts in issue which are not really in dispute.

(3) The rule adds greatly to the technicality of the law of evidence because of its numerous exceptions.

(4) The court is deprived of material which would be of value in ascertaining the truth.

(5) The rule often confuses witnesses and prevents them from telling their story in the witness box in the natural way. A casual visitor to the criminal courts will often hear questions put by prosecuting counsel to a police officer in the following form: "Did you make certain inquiries?" the affirmative answer being followed by "As a result of these inquiries what did you do?" By these means counsel is able to elicit that which he could not ask directly—the substance of the answers given by some third party to the witness. Such is the capricious operation of the rule against hearsay.

2   The hearsay rule in civil proceedings

The hearsay rule, as formulated above, applies (subject to the exceptions noted below) in all criminal proceedings. In relation to civil proceedings, however, a very substantial inroad into the hearsay rule was made by the Civil Evidence Act 1968.

a   The distinction between first-hand and second-hand hearsay

As a preliminary to examining the provisions of the Civil Evidence Act 1968, it is essential to clarify the distinction between first-hand and second-hand (or

---

[1] *R. v. Eriswell (Inhabitants)* (1790), 3 Term Rep. 707.
[2] Cmnd. 2964 of 1966. Part I of the Civil Evidence Act 1968 was based upon recommendations contained in this Report.

"double") hearsay; at common law the distinction was of little importance but under the 1968 Act, as will appear, it is paramount. The distinction is essentially a simple one and can best be explained by reference to the definition of hearsay contained in section 1 (1) of the 1968 Act:

> "a statement other than one made by a person while giving oral evidence in those proceedings . . . as evidence of any fact stated therein."

If the maker of the statement in question had personal knowledge of the facts contained in his statement, the statement is first-hand hearsay. If, on the other hand, the maker of the statement did not have personal knowledge of the facts stated, so that his evidence of those facts would be hearsay, evidence of the contents of his statement (assuming, of course, that he is not the person giving that evidence) is second-hand hearsay. This may be illustrated by the following example. A foreman makes out an accident report and sends it to his employers; the employers seek to put the report in as evidence of the circumstances of the accident. If the foreman saw the accident the report is first-hand hearsay; if, however, the foreman did not see the accident but simply took down statements made to him by other employees who did see the accident, the report is second-hand hearsay.

b Admissibility of first-hand hearsay

Section 2 (1) of the 1968 Act provides:

> "In any civil proceedings a statement made, whether orally or in a document or otherwise, by any person, whether called as a witness in those proceedings or not, shall, subject to this section and to rules of court, be admissible as evidence of any fact stated therein of which direct oral evidence by him would be admissible."

This sub-section has the effect of rendering first-hand hearsay admissible in civil proceedings and is, therefore, the most far-reaching provision in the 1968 Act. Where the statement was made otherwise than in a document no evidence other than direct oral evidence by the maker or any person who heard or otherwise perceived it being made is admissible for the purpose of proving it, unless the statement was made by a person while giving oral evidence in some other legal proceedings (whether civil or criminal) in which event it may be proved in any manner authorised by the court.[1]

In estimating the weight to be attached to a statement admitted under this section the court must have regard to all the circumstances from which any inference can reasonably be drawn as to the accuracy or otherwise of the statement and, in particular, to the question whether or not the statement was made contemporaneously with the occurrence or existence of the facts stated, and to the question whether or not the maker of the statement had any incentive to conceal or misrepresent the facts.[2] Furthermore where the maker is not called as a witness, any evidence which would have been admissible for the purpose of

---

[1] Act of 1968, s. 2 (3); cf. R.S.C. O.38, r. 28 as to the means by which a party may obtain directions. Where the statement is contained in a document it may, subject to any rules of court, be proved by the production of that document or (whether or not that document is still in existence) by the production of a copy, authenticated in such manner as the court may approve; *ibid.*, s. 6 (1).

[2] *Ibid.*, s. 6 (3).

destroying or supporting his credibility, including a previous inconsistent statement (which is then evidence of the facts therein stated), if he had been called as a witness, is admissible in his absence.[1]

The admissibility of statements under section 2 is expressly made subject to Rules of Court. In the Supreme Court the relevant Rules are R.S.C., O. 38, rr. 20–33. These Rules contain detailed procedural requirements with which a party must comply in order to avail himself of section 2 of the Act.[2] Nevertheless there is a discretionary power to allow a party to adduce a statement in evidence notwithstanding that he has failed either to serve the requisite notice or to comply with a counter-notice.

c   Admissibility of second-hand hearsay

The Civil Evidence Act 1968 abrogated the hearsay rule in civil proceedings only in relation to first-hand hearsay. Second-hand hearsay remains, *prima facie*, inadmissible. Sections 4 and 5 of the Act do, in fact, permit second-hand hearsay evidence in certain circumstances. However, these sections are best regarded as special exceptions to the hearsay rule and are hereinafter dealt with accordingly in that context.

3   Exceptions to the rule against hearsay

Of all the arguments against the retention of the hearsay rule, however, surely the most forceful is the existence of so many exceptions formulated by the judiciary and, in more modern times, by Parliament. These exceptions, of which there are probably more than seventy, have little in common. Some are based on the fact that the maker of the statement is deposing to a fact to his own disadvantage, others on the basis that the declarant is dead (though death alone is not a ground for receiving hearsay evidence) while many appear to be based almost solely on expedience. They now apply principally in criminal proceedings, their application to civil proceedings being superseded by section 2 of the Civil Evidence Act 1968 except where the statement in question is second-hand hearsay, in which event it will be admissible only if falling within one of the prescribed exceptions.

a   Statements forming part of the res gestae

The general nature of *res gestae* has already been considered in connection with relevance.[3] The traditional view of English law is that a statement admitted as part of the *res gestae* was not hearsay evidence because it did not constitute proof of the truth of the matter stated.[4] However the modern tendency is to regard the admission of such statements as a genuine exception to the hearsay rule.[5] No doubt there are many statements admitted as part of the *res gestae* which do not infringe the hearsay rule because the statement is admitted to

---

[1] Act of 1968, s. 7 (1), (3). The admissibility of such evidence is subject to compliance with certain procedural requirements; see R.S.C., O. 38, rr. 30, 31.

[2] See p. 291, *ante* for details of the procedure.

[3] See p. 455, *ante*.

[4] See *R. v. Christie*, [1914] A.C. 545, at p. 553, *per* LORD ATKINSON.

[5] See *Teper v. R.*, [1952] A.C. 480; [1952] 2 All E.R. 447; *Ratten v. R.*, [1971] 3 All E.R. 801; [1971] 3 W.L.R. 930; Cross, *Evidence* (3rd Edn.), p. 459.

prove something other than the truth of the matter stated. On the other hand there are certainly many cases in which statements have been admitted when the only purpose for their admission has been to provide proof of the matter stated.[1]

b Informal admissions

It was observed in an earlier chapter[2] that self-serving statements made by parties to litigation on a previous occasion are not usually admissible. On the other hand evidence is admissible of the earlier statement of a party where that statement is adverse to the interest of the maker. Since the earlier statement is usually proved by a person other than the maker it is hearsay, but admitted as an exception to the hearsay rule. In civil proceedings the statement will usually be admissible under section 2 of the Civil Evidence Act 1968, but, where it is not, the 1968 Act expressly provides for the retention of the common law rule that it may be received as an admission.[3] Such statements are described as informal admissions and it is important to distinguish them from formal admissions. The latter dispense with the need for proof and can only be made in the course of proceedings.[4] Informal admissions do not dispense with the need for proof; they are one means of proof. Consequently it is always open to a party to attempt to explain away or qualify his own informal admission. The informal admission of an accused person is described as a confession when made to a person in authority, such as a police officer. Confessions are dealt with separately because their reception is subject to additional conditions. The rationale of this exception to the hearsay rule is simply the intrinsic unlikelihood of a person making a statement against his own interest unless that statement were true.

An informal admission may take many forms. It may be made orally or in writing and may be express or implied. It also appears that, in certain circumstances, mere passive conduct or silence may amount to an admission. The leading authority for this proposition is the decision of the Court of Appeal in *Bessela* v. *Stern*.[5] In this action for breach of promise of marriage the plaintiff was proved to have said to the defendant—"You always promised to marry me, and you don't keep your word." The defendant did not answer and it was held that his silence corroborated the plaintiff's testimony. It was stressed in *Bessela* v. *Stern*, however, that the defendant's silence only amounted to an admission because in the circumstances he might have been expected to deny the allegation.[6] It is uncertain how far this principle applies in criminal cases. Clearly the conduct of an accused person may amount to an admission; so may silence coupled with demeanour.[7] Nevertheless a mere failure to say anything at all, even in the face of a positive allegation where a denial might be

---

[1] See, for examples: R. v. *Foster* (1834), 6 C. & P. 325; *The Schwalbe* (1861), 4 L.T. 160; *Davies* v. *Fortior, Ltd.*, [1952] 1 All E.R. 1359.

[2] See p. 500, *ante*.

[3] Civil Evidence Act 1968, s. 9 (2) (*a*).

[4] See p. 482, *ante*.

[5] (1877), 2 C.P.D. 265.

[6] Compare *Wiedemann* v. *Walpole*, [1891] 2 Q.B. 534 where the facts were similar except that the plaintiff's allegation was contained in a letter to the defendant. The Court of Appeal held that the failure of the defendant to send a letter of denial did not constitute an admission of a promise to marry.

[7] R. v. *Christie*, [1914] A.C. 545.

expected, can probably not constitute an admission.[1]   For the same reason the failure of an accused person to give evidence at his trial is not evidence against him.[2]   Nevertheless the judge may comment upon the failure of the accused to give evidence on his own behalf.[3]

It may be noted, finally, that an admission is generally evidence only against the maker and not against a third party even though he is implicated by the admission.   This is very important in criminal cases where a statement by one accused person admitting guilty conduct on the part of himself and his co-accused is not evidence against the latter.   Similarly, in divorce proceedings a decree may be granted against A on the ground of irretrievable breakdown, based upon his adultery with B while B may be found not to have committed adultery with A.   This odd result can, and often does, occur because the admission by A is not evidence against B and there might be insufficient evidence, apart from the admission, to warrant a finding of adultery.[4]   There are certain exceptional cases in which the out of court admission of one party is evidence against another.   These exceptions are based either upon agency or upon privity between the parties.   An admission made by an agent acting on behalf of his principal binds the latter in accordance with the general law of agency.   Similarly the admission of a predecessor in title binds a party provided that the admission was made in relation to the title.[5]

"Without prejudice" communications

Where a communication is made as part of a *bona fide* attempt to effect a compromise or settlement of a civil dispute, that communication is said to be made "without prejudice".   This is so that parties and their advisers may freely attempt to settle their disputes out of court without fear that any admission of liability they may make will be used against them.   A solicitor making such an offer by letter will usually mark the letter with the words "without prejudice".   However, it is the nature of the communication, not its description, which is the basis of the privilege.   Thus a communication may be impliedly without prejudice.   *Mutatis mutandis* a party cannot magically clothe his written or oral statements with immunity simply by expressing them to be without prejudice.   For example a libel or a threat would be actionable notwithstanding that the letter containing it were headed "without prejudice".[6]   The privilege attaches to oral or written communications provided they were made in the course of an attempt to compromise a dispute.   The communication in question is often a letter between solicitors or between insurance companies but extends to communications between spouses before a probation officer or marriage guidance counsellor.[7]

The rule extends, however, only to communications made in an attempt to

---

[1] *R.* v. *Whitehead*, [1929] 1 K.B. 99;   *Hall* v. *R.*, [1971] 1 All E.R. 322;   [1971] 1 W.L.R. 298.
[2] *R.* v. *Naylor*, [1933] 1 K.B. 685.
[3] *R.* v. *Littleboy*, [1934] 2 K.B. 408.
[4] *Rutherford* v. *Richardson*, [1923] A.C. 1, at p. 6.
[5] *Woolway* v. *Rowe* (1834), 1 Ad. & El. 114.
[6] *Kurtz & Co.* v. *Spence & Sons* (1887), 58 L.T. 438.
[7] *Mole* v. *Mole*, [1951] P. 21;   [1950] 2 All E.R. 328;   *Theodoropoulas* v. *Theodoropoulas*, [1964] P. 311;   [1963] 2 All E.R. 772.

compromise. Where the negotiations actually result in a contractual settlement, the documents containing the terms thereof may be put in evidence notwithstanding that one or more of them was originally expressed to be "without prejudice".[1]

c Confessions

The distinction between admissions in criminal cases and confessions is largely one of terminology. In this section the word "confession" is used to denote a statement made by a person charged with a crime which tends to prove any element in the prosecution case. It is customarily used to describe a statement made to a policeman or other person in authority, though its admissibility is in no way dependent on this.

The burden is on the prosecution to prove that a confession was voluntary. This involves proving that the confession was not induced by a threat or promise of a temporal nature made by a person in authority. Not every threat or promise will tender a confession, inadmissible. There are two types of inducement which will not vitiate a confession:

(1) *An inducement of a spiritual as opposed to a temporal nature* Many confessions have been admitted in evidence even though the maker was prompted by religious or moral exhortation such as "Don't run your soul into more sin, but tell the truth"[2] or "Be sure to tell the truth".[3] The dividing line between temporal and spiritual inducement is, however, indistinct. Thus "you had better tell the truth"[4] is an inducement which has been sufficient to exclude a subsequent confession whereas "you had better, as good boys, tell the truth" has been held to be innocuous.[5]

It was formerly thought that an inducement was of no effect unless bearing directly upon the proceedings so that a collateral inducement, such as on offer to allow the prisoner to see his wife, was unobjectionable.[6] However, this principle was discredited by the House of Lords in the recent case of *Customs and Excise Commissioners* v. *Harz*[7] and it now seems that there is no distinction between a direct and a collateral inducement.

(2) *An inducement by a person not in authority*—The inducement will only affect the admissibility of a confession if made by a person in authority or, at least, a person whom the prisoner believes to be a person in authority.[8] The person concerned is usually a policeman but may be a magistrate, prison officer, private prosecutor, employer or even the prisoner's father. The authority which he must be shown to possess, or appear to possess, is the authority to carry out the threat or fulfil the promise.

Judges' Rules. At this stage it is necessary to note the substance and effect of the Judges' Rules. These rules have been drawn up by the judges of the Queen's

---

[1] *Tomlin* v. *Standard Telephones and Cables, Ltd.*, [1969] 3 All E.R. 201; [1969] 1 W.L.R. 1378.
[2] *R.* v. *Sleeman* (1853), 6 Cox C.C. 245.
[3] *R.* v. *Court* (1836), 7 C. & P. 486.
[4] *R.* v. *Jarvis* (1867), L.R. 1 C.C.R. 96.
[5] *R.* v. *Reeve* (1872), L.R. 1 C.C.R. 362.
[6] *R.* v. *Lloyd* (1834), 6 C. & P. 393; see *Sparks* v. *R.*, [1964] A.C. 964; [1964] 1 All E.R. 727.
[7] [1967] 1 A.C. 760; [1967] 1 All E.R. 177.
[8] See *Deokinanan* v. *R.*, [1969] 1 A.C. 20; [1968] 2 All E.R. 346.

Bench Division for the guidance of the police in questioning suspects and charging persons in custody. The latest set of rules are the Judges' Rules 1964.[1] These rules are only guides for the police; they do not have the force of law. The most important of the rules are those which relate to cautions. The 1964 rules provide for two cautions. A person must be given the "usual caution" when a police officer who has evidence which would afford reasonable grounds for suspecting that person wishes to question him. The usual caution runs: "You are not obliged to say anything unless you wish to do so but what you say may be put into writing and given in evidence." Whether or not the usual caution has been previously administered a person must receive the "formal caution" when he is formally charged or informed that he may be prosecuted. The formal caution is: "Do you wish to say anything? You are not obliged to say anything unless you wish to do so, but whatever you say will be taken down in writing and may be given in evidence." The words "against you" used to be added to the above version of the formal caution but were deleted by the Judges' Rules 1912. This formal caution may be compared with the statutory caution which is administered by examining justices to the accused at a preliminary investigation.[2] An accused person should not normally be questioned after he has been charged but if he is so questioned, for example in order to clarify an ambiguity, he must be cautioned a third time.

Should the accused wish to make a written statement after caution he must first be given the opportunity of writing this statement himself. It he cannot or does not wish to write it himself a police officer may offer to write it for him and the accused must certify that the statement as written is true.

Failure to comply with the Judges' Rules does not necessarily render a confession to the police inadmissible,[3] unless it is shown that the confession was not made voluntarily. Thus in *R. v. Prager*[4] a confession made as a result of prolonged interrogation was held to have been rightly admitted despite a failure to caution until a late stage of the interrogation.

A confession, in the same way as an admission, if admissible, is evidence only against the maker, not against a third person such as an accomplice or a co-accused.

d   Statements of persons since deceased

It is on the ground of expedience that certain statements are admissible in evidence when the maker can be proved to be dead. It would, nevertheless, be wrong to suppose that the hearsay rule has no application in relation to the statements of persons since deceased. The fact that the maker of a statement has died does not necessarily mean that a witness may report the statement even though there may be no other means of proving the fact contained in the statement. No statement is admissible solely on the ground that the maker is dead. Nevertheless several exceptions to the hearsay rule operate only where the maker of the statement is dead. The most important of these exceptions are set out below.

---

[1] Home Office Circular No. 31, 1964, Appendix A; *Practice Note*, [1964] 1 All E.R. 237; [1964] 1 W.L.R. 152.
[2] Magistrates' Courts Rules 1968, r. 4 (7); see p. 384, *ante*.
[3] See, for example, *R. v. Voisin*, [1918] 1 K.B. 581; *R. v. Mills and Lemon*, [1947] K.B. 297; [1946] 2 All E.R. 776.
[4] [1972] 1 All E.R. 1114; [1972] 1 W.L.R. 260.

Dying declarations—On a charge of murder or manslaughter an oral or written statement made by the deceased concerning his injury is admissible provided that it can be proved that he was, at the time of making the statement, in settled hopeless expectation of death and would have been a competent witness had he lived. Such a statement is termed a "dying declaration". Dying declarations are admissible only on charges of murder or manslaughter. There is no logical reason for excluding dying declarations in other proceedings but there is clear authority against this.[1] The rationale of this exception to the hearsay rule is that dying declarations are made:

> "when every motive to falsehood is silenced, and the mind is induced by the most powerful considerations to speak the truth; a situation so solemn and so awful is considered by law as creating an obligation equal to that which is imposed by a positive oath administered in a court of justice."[2]

For this reason in *R. v. Pike*[3] the court refused to admit a statement made by a four-year-old child on the basis that the declarant would not have been capable of appreciating the awfulness of her future state.

Apart from the condition that the declarant would have been competent as a witness had he lived the main condition for the admissibility of dying declarations is that the declarant must have been in "settled hopeless expectation" of death. The test is purely subjective. Thus it is not sufficient that the declarant was, in fact, certainly about to die if he was not appreciative of this fact. It was for this reason that the statement of the deceased in *R. v. Bedingfield*[4] could not be admitted under this exception since, although her throat was cut from ear to ear, there was no evidence that she was conscious of her impending death. On the other hand if the declarant was in settled hopeless expectation of death a statement will be admissible even though death does not immediately occur.[5]

As a rule it is the prosecution who seek to adduce evidence of dying declarations since their value often lies in the fact that they identify the accused with the death. However in *R. v. Scaife*[6] a dying declaration was admitted in favour of the accused since the deceased had said "I don't think he would have struck me if I had not provoked him".

Declarations against interest—A statement is admissible if it is against the pecuniary or proprietary interest of the deceased. The rationale of the admission of such statements is that a person would be unlikely to make a statement against his interest unless it were true. Nevertheless such statements are only admissible if the maker can be proved to be dead. It may seem logical to suppose that a person still living would be just as unlikely to have made an untrue statement against his own interest. Such statements are not, however, admissible unless they fall within the definition of admissions or confessions or, of course, are admissible under the provisions of the Civil Evidence Act 1968.

Apart from the death of the declarant the principal condition for the admissibility of declarations against interest is that the declaration be against the

[1] *R. v. Mead* (1824), 2 B. & C. 605.
[2] *R. v. Woodcock* (1789), 1 Leach 500, *per* EYRE, C.B.
[3] (1829), 3 C. & P. 598.
[4] (1879), 14 Cox C.C. 341; see p. 457, *ante*.
[5] *R. v. Perry*, [1909] 2 K.B. 697.
[6] (1836), 2 Lew. C.C. 150.

pecuniary or proprietary interest of the deceased. It is generally accepted that the deceased must have known, at the time of making the statement, that it was against his interest[1] and must also have had personal knowledge of the facts stated.[2] No interest other than a pecuniary or proprietary interest will suffice. Thus in *Ward* v. *H.S. Pitt & Co.*[3] the Court of Appeal held that an admission of paternity made by a deceased putative father was not admissible as a declaration against interest merely because it might involve possible future liability for the maintenance of the child.[4] On the other hand a pecuniary interest is something less than a pecuniary obligation. In *Coward* v. *Motor Insurers' Bureau*[5] the Court of Appeal admitted proof of oral declarations by the deceased to the effect that he had gratuitously promised to pay money in return for lifts to work. Notwithstanding the fact that there was no contractual or other legal obligation to pay the money the statements were against the deceased's pecuniary interest and therefore admissible.

If a statement is admitted as being against the pecuniary or proprietary interest of the deceased it constitutes proof of any collateral fact contained in the statement. Indeed the purpose for which it sought to adduce proof of the statement is often in order to prove some collateral fact. *Higham* v. *Ridgway*[6] affords a good illustration of this. In this leading case an entry in the books of a deceased male midwife was admitted in evidence because it acknowledged receipt of his fee, a receipt being a declaration against pecuniary interest. This entry was admitted, however, as evidence of the date of the child's birth which was the fact which it was sought to prove.

Declarations in the course of duty—Written or oral statements made by a deceased person in pursuance of a duty to record acts performed by him are admissible as an exception to the hearsay rule. However this exception is of very little importance since, in so far as it applied to civil proceedings, it was effectively abolished by section 1 of the Civil Evidence Act 1968.[7] Thus it can now only apply in criminal cases and the Criminal Evidence Act 1965[8] is framed sufficiently widely to incorporate most declarations within the common law exception. Nevertheless it is possible to envisage statements which would fall outside the provisions of the 1965 Act but which might be admissible in criminal proceedings by virtue of the common law rule as declarations made in the course of duty. The conditions for the admissibility of these declarations are extremely restrictive. Apart from the death of the declarant, which is an essential condition,[9] there must have been a duty both to act and to record, the record must have been made contemporaneously with the act and the deceased must have had no motive to misrepresent the facts recorded.[10]

---

[1] *Tucker* v. *Oldbury U.C.*, [1912] 2 K.B. 317.

[2] *Lloyd* v. *Powell Duffryn Steam Coal Co.*, [1914] A.C. 733.

[3] [1913] 2 K.B. 130.

[4] But see the judgment of WILLMER, L.J. in *B.* v. *A.-G.*, [1965] P. 278; [1965] 1 All E.R. 62.

[5] [1963] 1 Q.B. 259; [1962] 1 All E.R. 531.

[6] (1808), 10 East 109.

[7] Nevertheless any statement which would have been admissible in civil proceedings by virtue of this exception will now be admissible under section 2 of the 1968 Act.

[8] See p. 544, *post*.

[9] This was established in *Price* v. *Torrington* (1703), 1 Salk. 285.

[10] *The Henry Coxon* (1878), 3 P.D. 156.

Declarations concerning pedigree—A peculiar exception to the hearsay rule operates to admit declarations of deceased persons concerning the pedigree of their relatives where this is the subject of proceedings. The rationale of this exception is somewhat obscure but appears to be based principally on the personal knowledge possessed by the declarant. Oddly enough, this exception to the hearsay rule was expressly preserved by the Civil Evidence Act 1968.[1] Nevertheless the mere possession of personal knowledge is insufficient. The declarant must have been a relative, either by blood or marriage, of the person whose pedigree is the subject of the proceedings. Thus is *Johnson* v. *Lawson*[2] the Court of Common Pleas rejected the declaration of a family housekeeper though she had known the family for twenty-four years. At common law a bastard was regarded as having no relatives but in more recent times the courts have extended this exception to the hearsay rule so as to admit declarations by the mother[3] of an illegitimate child though it is uncertain whether the declaration of a putative father is admissible.[4]

The exception is limited to pedigree cases, that is to say cases in which the relationship by blood or marriage between two or more persons is in issue. The issue of pedigree generally arises in proceedings involving legitimacy or succession to property. One further condition for the admissibility of pedigree declarations must be mentioned. The declaration must have been made *ante litem motam* (before any dispute has arisen). The obvious reason for this restriction is that a statement made in the course of a dispute may be biased.[5]

Declarations as to public or general rights—A very old exception to the hearsay rule, the basis of which is simple expedience, admits declarations of deceased persons of competent knowledge as to the reputed existence of public or general rights. As with pedigree declarations, this exception to the hearsay rule was expressly preserved, in relation to civil proceedings, by the Civil Evidence Act 1968.[6] A public right is a right enjoyed by every member of the public, such as the right to use a highway. A general right is a right possessed by a class of persons, such as the inhabitants of a parish. Rights of common and customary manorial rights are typical general rights. Since a customary right must be proved to be of immemorial antiquity it is common for a customary right to be proved by evidence of reputation which frequently involves the admission of the declaration of a deceased person.[7] Such declarations may take any form but are generally documentary.

This exception to the hearsay rule bears a certain affinity to the foregoing exception concerning pedigree declarations. As is the case with pedigree declarations a declaration as to public or general rights must have been made *ante litem motam*. If a general right is alleged the declaration must have been made by a person with competent knowledge of the reputed right. Where the

---

[1] Section 9 (3), (4) (*b*).
[2] (1824), 2 Bing. 86.
[3] *Re Jenion*, [1952] Ch. 454; [1952] 1 All E.R. 1228.
[4] *B.* v. *A.-G.*, [1965] P. 278; [1965] 1 All E.R. 62.
[5] *Butler* v. *Mountgarrett* (1859), 7 H.C. Cas. 633.
[6] Section 9 (3), (4) (*c*).
[7] *Weeks* v. *Sparke* (1813), 1 M. & S. 679. The declaration must be confined to reputation. A declaration relating to a specific fact such as the siting of a boundary is not within the exception: *Mercer* v. *Denne*, [1905] 2 Ch. 538.

alleged right is a public right any member of the public may be a competent declarant. On the other hand where a general right is alleged it seems that the declarant must have been a member of the class of persons for whose benefit the right is alleged to exist. It was for this reason that the declarations of deceased officers of the Crown were not admitted in one case[1] to prove whether the city of Chester was within the county of Cheshire.

e   Statements in public documents

Mention has already been made of public documents for the purpose of noting that the best evidence rule does not apply in relation to public documents so that they may be proved by copies.[2] It will be recalled that a public document is "a document that is made for the purpose of the public making use of it, and being able to refer to it".[3] Where a public document, or a copy, is admitted in evidence as a means of proving a fact stated in the document, the admission of the document clearly constitutes an exception to the hearsay rule. The basis of this exception is the intrinsic unlikelihood of inaccuracy in a document prepared by public officers. There are many classes of public documents of which the following may be mentioned by way of illustration: public statutes,[4] registers of births, marriages and deaths, parish registers, reports of official inquiries, ordnance survey maps and the London Gazette.

Strictly speaking, a document is only a public document if made in the performance of a legal duty to record. On this basis the courts have from time to time rejected documents such as the results of private surveys, the register of attendances at a work-house and non-parochial records of births, marriages and deaths kept by nonconformist ministers. Nevertheless the modern tendency is to treat analogous documents such as these as if they were public documents. Thus certificates of various kinds such as a bishop's certificate upon an ecclesiastical matter are generally admitted as proof of the fact certified. Similarly there are now numerous statutes which provide for proof by documents which are not, in the strictest sense, public documents. For example, the registration of a company may be proved by the certificate of the Registrar of Companies;[5] a conviction may be proved by the certificate of the clerk of the court;[6] the name of the driver and the ownership of a vehicle may, subject to certain conditions, be proved by a constable's certificate of statements made to him.[7] This exception to the hearsay rule was expressly preserved by the Civil Evidence Act 1968.[8] In this connection reference may once again be made to section 3 of the Bankers' Books Evidence Act 1879, which provides that a copy of any entry in a bankers' book shall be received as *prima facie* evidence of such entry and of the matters, transactions and accounts therein recorded.[9]

---

[1] *Rogers* v. *Wood* (1831), 2 B. & Ad. 245; cf. *Knight* v. *David*, [1971] 3 All E.R. 1066; [1971] 1 W.L.R. 1671.
[2] See p. 515, *ante*.
[3] *Sturla* v. *Freccia* (1880), 5 App. Cas. 623, at p. 643, *per* LORD BLACKBURN.
[4] Since judicial notice is taken of public statutes the question is purely academic; see p. 483, *ante*.
[5] Companies Act 1948, s. 15.
[6] Evidence Act 1851, s. 14; Criminal Procedure Act 1865, s. 6.
[7] Criminal Justice Act 1948, s. 41; see also Road Traffic Act 1960, s. 242; Road Traffic Act 1962, s. 2 (1).
[8] Section 9 (2).
[9] See p. 515, *ante*.

f Documentary records under the Civil Evidence Act 1968, ss. 4 and 5

Section 4 of the 1968 Act provides for the admissibility of certain documentary records as evidence of any fact stated therein of which direct oral evidence would be admissible. The conditions for the admissibility of such documents are as follows.

(1) The document must be, or form part of, a record compiled by a person acting under a duty.[1]

(2) It must have been compiled from information which was supplied[2] by a person (whether acting under a duty or not) who had, or may reasonably be supposed to have had, personal knowledge of the matters dealt with in that information and which, if not supplied by that person to the compiler of the record directly, was supplied by him to the compiler of the record indirectly through one or more intermediaries each acting under a duty.

It will be appreciated that if the person having personal knowledge of the information supplied is called as a witness, the document is not hearsay at all, while if the compiler is called as a witness the document is first-hand hearsay and therefore admissible in any event under section 2 of the 1968 Act. Where, however, neither the supplier nor the compiler is called, the document is second-hand hearsay and admissible only if it satisfies the conditions of section 4, set out above.

Prior to the enactment of section 4 of the 1968 Act a similar exception to the hearsay rule in civil proceedings existed under the Evidence Act 1938 (which was repealed when section 4 came into operation). The 1938 Act contained certain restrictions on admissibility which are not reproduced in the present enactment. Thus the original document had to be in existence and it had to be authenticated by the maker; neither of these requirements exists under the 1968 Act. Furthermore, under the 1938 Act the statement was inadmissible if made by an interested person whereas under the 1968 Act the statement of an interested party is not *ipso facto* excluded. However it is provided by section 6 (3) that in estimating the weight to be attached to a statement admissible under section 4 the court must have regard to all the circumstances from which any inference can reasonably be drawn as to the accuracy or otherwise of the statement and, in particular, to the question whether or not the person who originally supplied the information from which the record was compiled did so contemporaneously with the occurrence or existence of the facts dealt with in that information, and to the question whether or not that person, or any person concerned with compiling or keeping the record, had any incentive to conceal or misrepresent the facts.

Any evidence which, if the person supplying the information had been called as a witness, would be admissible for the purpose of destroying or supporting

---

[1] References to a person acting under a duty include a reference to a person acting in the course of any trade, business, profession or other occupation in which he is engaged or employed or for the purposes of any paid or unpaid office held by him (s. 4 (3)).

[2] In *Barkway* v. *South Wales Transport Co., Ltd.*, [1950] A.C. 185; [1950] 1 All E.R. 392 (a decision on the Evidence Act 1938) a shorthand writer's transcript of evidence was held inadmissible on the ground that it was not "supplied" to him.

his credibility, including a previous inconsistent statement (which is then evidence of the truth of any fact stated therein) is admissible in his absence.[1]

Section 4 renders admissible a great variety of reports and records including such documents as accident reports, medical reports, police notebooks, manufacturers' records, invoices and estimates. As a sign, perhaps, of the times specific provision was made by section 5 of the 1968 Act for the admissibility of statements contained in documents produced by computers.[2] Such statements are admissible of any fact stated therein of which direct oral evidence would be admissible, subject to the conditions set out in the section. The principal conditions are: that the computer producing the record must have been used regularly to store or process information for the purpose of any activities regularly carried on, over the period during which the record was produced, by any body or individual; that over that period the computer was regularly supplied in the ordinary course of these activities with information of the kind contained in the statement or of the kind from which the information therein is derived (the information contained in the statement must either reproduce or be derived from information supplied to the computer in the ordinary course of those activities); that throughout the material time the computer was operating properly or, if it was not, that this did not affect the production of the document or the accuracy of its contents.[3]

As with statements admissible under section 2 of the 1968 Act, the procedure which must be followed by a party wishing to put in evidence a document under section 4 or 5 of the Act is laid down by Rules of Court made pursuant to section 8.[4]

g   Trade or business records under the Criminal Evidence Act 1965

The most significant limitation of the Civil Evidence Act 1968 is that it applies only in civil proceedings. The need for a corresponding measure in the context of criminal proceedings was indicated by the decision of the House of Lords in *Myers* v. *Director of Public Prosecutions*.[5] The point at issue in this case was the admissibility of car manufacturers' records as a means of identifying disguised stolen cars. There could be no doubt as to the accuracy of the records. Notwithstanding, the House of Lords rejected these records as being hearsay and not within any recognised exception to the hearsay rule. The immediate result of *Myers* v. *Director of Public Prosecutions* was the passing of the Criminal Evidence Act 1965. This Act provides for the admission in evidence in criminal proceedings of certain trade or business records where direct oral evidence of the fact recorded would be admissible. The two basic conditions for admissibility are set out in section 1 (1) of the Act: (a) the document must be, or form part of, a trade or business record compiled in the course of that trade or business from information supplied by persons having personal knowledge of the matters recorded; and (b) the person who supplied the information must be dead,

---

[1] Civil Evidence Act 1968, s. 7. Admissibility is, however, subject to compliance with certain procedural requirements; see R.S.C. O. 38, rr. 30, 31.
[2] A "computer" means any device for storing and processing information: s. 5 (6).
[3] S. 5 (2); see s. 6 (3) (c) as to factors affecting the weight to be attached to a statement admissible under section 5.
[4] See p. 291, *ante*.
[5] [1965] A.C. 1001; [1964] 2 All E.R. 881; see p. 531, *ante*.

beyond the seas, unfit by reason of his bodily or mental condition to attend, or cannot be identified or found or cannot be expected (having regard to the time which has elapsed and to all the circumstances) to have any recollection of the information which he supplied.

It will be appreciated from the above that the Criminal Evidence Act 1965 is far narrower in scope than section 4 of the Civil Evidence Act 1968.   Thus the 1965 Act is restricted to trade or business records;[1]   the 1968 Act is not restricted to any particular class of documents.   Furthermore, under the 1965 Act the document is admissible only in the absence of the person who supplied the information recorded (though if called as a witness he could, no doubt, refer to the document at common law in order to refresh his memory); if the supplier of the information is called as a witness in civil proceedings the document may still be put in evidence under section 4 of the 1968 Act, but only with leave of the court.[2]

---

[1] See *R. v. Gwilliam*, [1968] 3 All E.R. 821; [1968] 1 W.L.R. 1839.
[2] Civil Evidence Act 1968, s. 4 (2) (a).

Index